From Stress to Success DVD from Trivium Test Prep

Dear Customer,

Thank you for purchasing from Cirrus Test Prep! Whether you're looking to join the military, get into college, or advance your career, we're honored to be a part of your journey.

To show our appreciation (and to help you relieve a little of that test-prep stress), we're offering a **FREE *Praxis Chemistry Essential Test Tips DVD**** by Cirrus Test Prep. Our DVD includes 35 test preparation strategies that will help keep you calm and collected before and during your big exam. All we ask is that you email us your feedback and describe your experience with our product. Amazing, awful, or just so-so: we want to hear what you have to say!

To receive your **FREE *Praxis Chemistry Essential Test Tips DVD***, please email us at 5star@cirrustestprep.com. Include "Free 5 Star" in the subject line and the following information in your email:

1. The title of the product you purchased.
2. Your rating from 1 – 5 (with 5 being the best).
3. Your feedback about the product, including how our materials helped you meet your goals and ways in which we can improve our products.
4. Your full name and shipping address so we can send your **FREE *Praxis Chemistry Essential Test Tips DVD***.

If you have any questions or concerns please feel free to contact us directly at 5star@cirrustestprep.com.

Thank you, and good luck with your studies!

* Please note that the free DVD is not included with this book. To receive the free DVD, please follow the instructions above.

Praxis II Chemistry 5245 Study Guide

Test Prep and Practice Questions for the Praxis Chemistry Content Knowledge (5245) Exam

Copyright © 2018 by Cirrus Test Prep

ALL RIGHTS RESERVED. By purchase of this book, you have been licensed one copy for personal use only. No part of this work may be reproduced, redistributed, or used in any form or by any means without prior written permission of the publisher and copyright owner.

Cirrus Test Prep is not affiliated with or endorsed by any testing organization and does not own or claim ownership of any trademarks, specifically for the Praxis Chemistry: Content Knowledge (5245) exam. All test names (and their acronyms) are trademarks of their respective owners. This study guide is for general information only and does not claim endorsement by any third party.

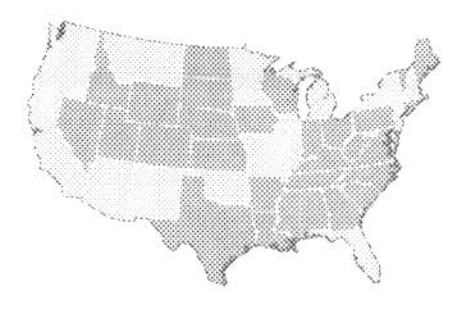

Table of Contents

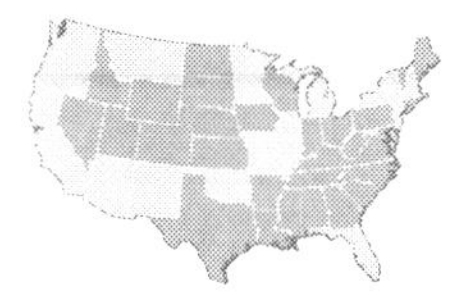

Introduction

Congratulations on choosing to take the Praxis Chemistry: Content Knowledge (5245) Test! By purchasing this book, you've taken the first step toward becoming a chemistry teacher.

This guide will provide you with a detailed overview of the Praxis Chemistry test, so you know exactly what to expect on test day. We'll take you through all the concepts covered on the test and give you the opportunity to test your knowledge with practice questions. Even if it's been a while since you last took a major exam, don't worry; we'll make sure you're more than ready!

What is the Praxis Chemistry (5245) Test?

The Praxis Chemistry test measures aptitude in chemistry for teacher candidates looking to certify as chemistry teachers. This test must be taken *in addition to* the assessments in reading, writing, mathematics, and professional knowledge required in your particular state. The Praxis Chemistry test does not replace these other exams.

What's on the Praxis Chemistry (5245) Test?

The Praxis Chemistry test gauges college-level content knowledge in chemistry, as well as the necessary skills for chemistry. Candidates are expected to demonstrate thorough and extensive conceptual knowledge in principles of matter and energy, atomic and nuclear structures, chemical composition and nomenclature, chemical reactions, and solutions and solubility. You will also be expected to demonstrate mastery of key skills related to scientific inquiry. The content is divided into seven categories.

You will have two hours and thirty minutes to answer 125 selected-response questions.

What's on the Praxis Chemistry: Content Knowledge (5245) Test?	
Content Category	**Objectives**
I. Basic Principles of Matter and Energy; Thermodynamics 17 questions	1. Organization of matter 2. Particulate structure of matter 3. Differences between chemical and physical properties and chemical and physical changes 4. Conservation of energy and the conservation of matter in chemical processes 5. Different forms of energy 6. Temperature, thermal energy, and heat capacity 7. Concepts and calculations involving phase transitions between various states of matter 8. Kinetic molecular theory and ideal gas laws 9. Energetics of chemical reactions 10. Relation of laws of thermodynamics to chemical reactions and phase changes
II. Atomic and Nuclear Structure 15 questions	1. Current model of atomic structure 2. Electron configuration of the elements 3. Radioactivity 4. Relationship between electron absorption and emission and electron energy levels
III. Nomenclature; Chemical Composition; Bonding and Structure 19 questions	1. Systematic names and formulas of simple inorganic compounds 2. Names of common organic compounds 3. Mole concept 4. Common properties of bonds 5. Types of bonds (ionic, covalent, metallic) 6. Structural formulas and molecular geometry 7. Polar and nonpolar molecules 8. Intermolecular interactions 9. Relationship between bonding and structure and physical properties

Content Category	Objectives
IV. Chemical Reactions; Periodicity 25 questions	1. Periodic table 2. Periodic trends in the elements 3. Balancing chemical equations 4. Stoichiometric calculations 5. Products of simple reaction types 6. Chemical kinetics 7. Chemical reaction equilibrium 8. Oxidation-reduction reactions 9. Biochemical compounds 10. Common organic compounds
V. Solutions and Solubility; Acid-Base Chemistry 19 questions	1. Solution terminology and calculations 2. Solubility and dissolution rate 3. Solution phenomena based on colligative properties 4. Equilibrium in ionic solutions 5. Acids and bases 6. pH scale 7. Acid-base titrations 8. Equilibrium relations in acid-base chemistry
VI. Scientific Inquiry and Social Perspectives of Science 15 questions	1. Processes involved in scientific inquiry 2. Experimental design 3. Nature of scientific knowledge 4. Major historical developments and figures in chemistry 5. Impact of chemistry and technology on society and the environment 6. Applications of chemistry in daily life 7. Pros and cons of different types of energy production
VII. Scientific Procedures and Techniques 15 questions	1. Collection, evaluation, manipulation, interpretation, and reporting of data 2. Units of measurement, notation systems, conversions, and chemistry-related mathematics 3. Basic error analysis 4. Proper preparation, use, storage, and disposal of materials 5. Proper preparation, use, maintenance, and calibration of laboratory equipment 6. High school chemistry lab safety procedures and precautions

Category I assesses your understanding of matter and energy as well as the basic principles and methods of thermodynamics. You must demonstrate mastery of the organization and processes of matter and identify different forms of energy. You also must be able to explain how chemical processes impact the conservation of energy and matter. In addition, you must be able to conduct calculations involving temperature and phase transitions, and explain the kinetic molecular theory and the ideal gas laws. Finally, you must show you understand how chemical reactions work, the difference between endothermic and exothermic reactions, and how the laws of thermodynamics relate to these reactions.

Category II assesses your understanding of the structure of atoms and electron configurations. You should be able to properly describe the current atomic model and explain the electron configuration of the elements based on the periodic table. You should also be able to demonstrate understanding of radioactivity, including decay processes and nuclear reactions, and the absorption and emission spectra of electrons and how they relate to frequency and wavelength.

Category III assesses your understanding of nomenclature, bonding, and structure. You should be able to name basic inorganic compounds (along with the chemical formulas) and common organic compounds. You also should be able to define and apply the mole concept. In terms of bonding, you must be able to identify types of bonds and their common properties. You should be able to describe different structural formulas, including their molecular geometry, and explain how both structure and bonding correlate with physical properties. Finally, you should be able to differentiate between polar and nonpolar molecules and explain different types of intermolecular interactions.

Category IV assesses your understanding of periodicity and chemical reactions. In terms of the first, you must demonstrate mastery of the periodic table, including its basis, its general layout, and trends in the physical and chemical properties of the elements (e.g. atomic/ionic radius, electron affinity, chemical reactivity, etc.). You must also show that you can interpret and solve equations and calculations related to chemical reactions. This means balancing chemical equations, including those involving oxidation-reduction; completing stoichiometric calculations; applying chemical kinetics; and determining oxidation states. Finally, you must demonstrate your understanding of biochemistry and organic chemistry.

Category V assesses your understanding of solubility and acids and bases. In addressing solubility, you must be able to use proper terminology and conduct accurate calculations. You must also understand the different factors that can affect a substance's solubility and dissolution rate and the various phenomena that can occur based on the colligative properties of a substance. Furthermore, you must be able to identify certain acids and bases, as well as their properties, and demonstrate mastery of the pH scale. Finally, you must understand the equilibrium relationships in acid-base chemistry and be able to complete calculations involving acid-base titrations.

Categories VI and VII emphasize the process of doing science. The material addresses formulating and investigating scientific questions; it also approaches experiment design and implementation, from proper handling of data to mastery of key equipment. Additionally, Category VI assesses your understanding of chemistry in a broader historical and current social context, with a particular focus on current methods of energy production.

HOW IS THE PRAXIS CHEMISTRY (5245) TEST SCORED?

Your scores on your Praxis Chemistry test will become available online on a predetermined release date ten to eleven days after the close of your testing window. For more information, check https://www.ets.org/praxis. Your scores will be available for one year after your test date. In order to have your scores sent to a particular institution, you must make a request when you register for the exam. You can select up to four institutions to receive your scores.

Each multiple-choice question is worth one raw point. The total number of questions you answer correctly is added up to obtain your raw score, which is then converted to a number on a scale of 100 – 300. The passing score is determined by each state and can be found here: https://www.ets.org/praxis/states.

There will be some questions on the test that are not scored; however you will not know which ones these are. Praxis uses these to test out new questions for future exams.

There is no guess penalty on the Praxis, so you should always guess if you do not know the answer to a question.

HOW IS THE PRAXIS CHEMISTRY (5245) TEST ADMINISTERED?

The Praxis Chemistry Test is a computer-based test offered in pre-determined testing windows at a range of universities and testing centers. Check out https://www.ets.org/praxis/ for more information.

You will need to print your registration ticket from your online account and bring it, along with your identification, to the testing site on test day. You will not need a calculator for the test and will be provided with the periodic table and other information during the test. No pens, pencils, erasers, printed or written materials, electronic devices, or calculators are allowed. You also may not bring any kind of bag or wear headwear (unless for religious purposes). You may take the test once every twenty-one days.

About Cirrus Test Prep

Cirrus Test Prep study guides are designed by current and former educators and are tailored to meet your needs as an incoming educator. Our guides offer all of the resources necessary to help you pass teacher certification tests across the nation.

Cirrus clouds are graceful, wispy clouds characterized by their high altitude. Just like cirrus clouds, Cirrus Test Prep's goal is to help educators "aim high" when it comes to obtaining their teacher certification and entering the classroom.

About This Guide

This guide will help you master the most important test topics and also develop critical test-taking skills. We have built features into our books to prepare you for your tests and increase your score. Along with a detailed summary of the test's format, content, and scoring, we offer an in-depth overview of the content knowledge required to pass the test. Our sidebars provide interesting information, highlight key concepts, and review content so that you can solidify your understanding of the exam's concepts. Test your knowledge with sample questions and detailed answer explanations in the text that help you think through the problems on the exam and practice questions that reflect the content and format of the Praxis Chemistry test. We're pleased you've chosen Cirrus to be a part of your professional journey!

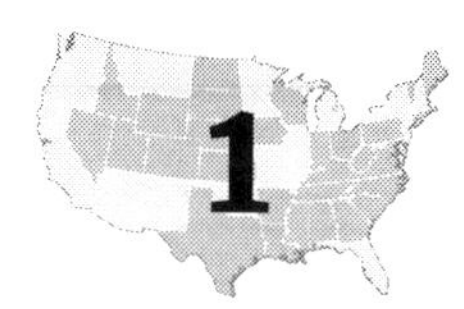

Basic Principles of Matter

Matter is the physical foundation for all the processes in the universe. **Matter**, by definition, is anything that has mass and occupies space. Soil, trees, water, engines, all living beings, and even the air that surrounds us are examples of matter.

The Particulate Structure of Matter

All matter is composed of **atoms**. Atom, in turn, are made up of subatomic particles. **Protons**, which are positive, and **neutrons**, which are neutral, form the nucleus of the atom. Negative particles called **electrons** orbit the nucleus.

A neutral atom will have an equal number of protons and electrons. When a neutral atom loses or gains electrons, it gains or loses charge accordingly, forming an **ion**. An ion with more protons than electrons has a positive charge and is called a **cation**. An ion with more electrons than protons has a negative charge and is considered an **anion**.

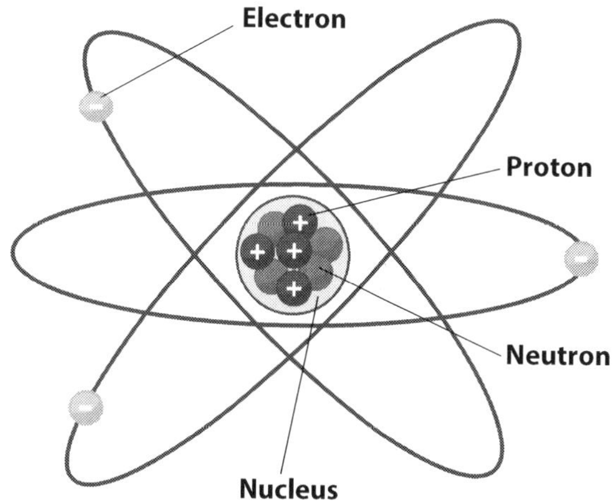

Figure 1.1. Structure of an Atom

For example, the element nitrogen has seven protons and seven electrons (and so has an atomic number of 7 in the periodic table). A neutral nitrogen atom is represented as N. However, if there are seven protons and eight electrons instead, it is called an anion form of nitrogen and has a charge of –1. This nitrogen anion with a charge of –1 is represented as N^-.

All atoms with the same number of protons are the same **element** and cannot be further reduced to a simpler substance by chemical processes. The number of protons in an atom is that atom's **atomic number**. A **molecule** is formed when two or more atoms combine chemically.

SAMPLE QUESTIONS

1) **What is the charge of an atom with five protons and seven electrons?**

A. 12

B. −12

C. 2

D. −2

Answers:

D. **Correct.** There are five protons and seven electrons in the atom. The total charge of an atom is calculated by the difference of the number of protons and electrons. Subtracting the number of electrons from the number of protons results in −2 (total charge of atom $= 5 - 7 = -2$).

2) **If an atom has seventeen protons and sixteen electrons, it is**

A. a cation.

B. an anion.

C. neutral.

D. a molecule.

Answers:

A. **Correct.** The charge of an atom is found by subtracting the number of electrons from the number of protons. This atom has seventeen protons and sixteen electrons. Since $17 - 16 = +1$, a positive number, this atom has a positive charge and is therefore a cation.

B. Incorrect. The atom has a positive charge as it has more protons than electrons. Therefore, it cannot be an anion.

C. Incorrect. The atom has a positive charge; it is not neutral.

D. Incorrect. A molecule is composed of two or more atoms.

STATES OF MATTER

Matter can exist in a solid, liquid, gas, or plasma state. The state of a substance is determined by the various properties of the matter, and is largely dependent on the forces holding the atoms or molecules together.

In **solids**, the atoms or molecules are packed close together. The force that holds the particles together is strong, providing very little freedom for movement. Particles in solids have thermal energy associated with them, which leads to the vibration of the particles. However, because the atoms are packed very close to each other, the movement caused by vibration is negligible and does not force the molecules to move apart. As a result, solids are rigid and have a definite shape and volume.

HELPFUL HINT

Important properties of solids include solubility, conductivity, melting point, and density.

Solids can be categorized as **crystalline solids**, in which the positions of the atoms or molecules are fixed on a lattice, or **amorphous solids**, in which atoms or molecules are randomly arranged. Crystalline solids can further be categorized as either molecular, network, metallic, or ionic solids.

- Molecular solids are composed of discrete molecules held together by weak intermolecular forces.
- Network solids are composed of atoms held together by covalent bonds.
- Ionic solids are composed of cations and anions held together by ionic bonds.
- Metallic solids are composed of metal atoms bound together by metallic bonds.

In a **liquid** state, particles are not tightly bound and take the shape of the container used to keep them. They still have a definite volume and can flow and change shape depending on the shape of the container.

Two special properties of liquids are surface tension and viscosity. **Surface tension** is the force of attraction by the particles at the surface by the bulk of the liquid, which results in minimum surface area. This property is the reason water forms drops that are spherical in shape. **Viscosity** is the internal resistance that inhibits the flow of liquids.

In a **gas** state of matter, the force between the particles is weak (compared to solids and liquids). Due to this weak force of attraction, the gaseous form of matter does not have a defined shape or volume. Instead, a gas will expand to take the shape of the closed container in which it is stored. The properties of gas—such as pressure, volume, and temperature—are interrelated and discussed in greater detail in a later section.

Table 1.1. States of Matter

	Solid	Liquid	Gas
Volume	Definite volume	Definite volume	Volume of container
Shape	Definite shape	Takes shape of container	Expands to take shape of closed container
Particle Arrangement	Close together	Random but still close	Random and far apart

Table 1.1. States of Matter (continued)

	Solid	Liquid	Gas
Interparticle Interaction	Extremely strong	Strong	Extremely weak
Particle Movement	Extremely slow (vibration)	Moderate	Fast
Example	Ice, wood, iron rod	Water, chlorine	Water vapor, oxygen

Finally, **plasma** can be defined as ionized gas, where electrons become free from the atoms or molecules, allowing the electrons and positive ions to coexist. Plasma can occur either in partially ionized or fully ionized form.

Plasma is produced by subjecting gases to a strong electromagnetic field. Unlike the solid, liquid, and gas phases, plasma does not exist naturally under normal conditions, but it can be generated artificially from neutral gases. Plasmas can be categorized as artificially produced (plasma display TV screens), terrestrial (lightning, polar winds), and space and astrophysical (sun and stars, solar winds). Plasmas occur in auroras, lightning, and flames.

SAMPLE QUESTION

3) **Which of the following is true of plasma?**

A. It has molecules that are closely packed together.

B. It can only be artificially produced in a laboratory setting.

C. It is an ionized gas.

D. It has fixed volume and shape.

Answers:

A. Incorrect. The molecules of solids are closely packed together.

B. Incorrect. Plasma is produced in natural settings such as stars and lightning.

C. Correct. Plasma is an ionized gas.

D. Incorrect. Solids have fixed volume and shape.

Special Properties of Water

In general, particles in a solid are closer to each other than the particles in liquid. However, there is an exception to this rule. In ice, the solid form of water, the molecules are farther apart than the molecules in water's liquid form. Because of this unique property, ice is less dense than water and will float instead of sinking.

Ice has hydrogen bonding among its molecules and an open structure with empty space between the molecules. The structure breaks down as ice melts, and molecules fill up the empty space. As a result, ice takes up more space than the water formed when it melts; this is unlike the behavior of other solids, which increase in volume on melting. Likewise, the hydrogen bonding of the liquid structure expands when water freezes, while most liquids contract on freezing.

The rigid hydrogen bonded structure remains present until 4°C. In the temperature range from 0°C to 4°C, the density of water increases because molecules free themselves and occupy less space. At temperatures above 4°C, the molecules move apart and density falls.

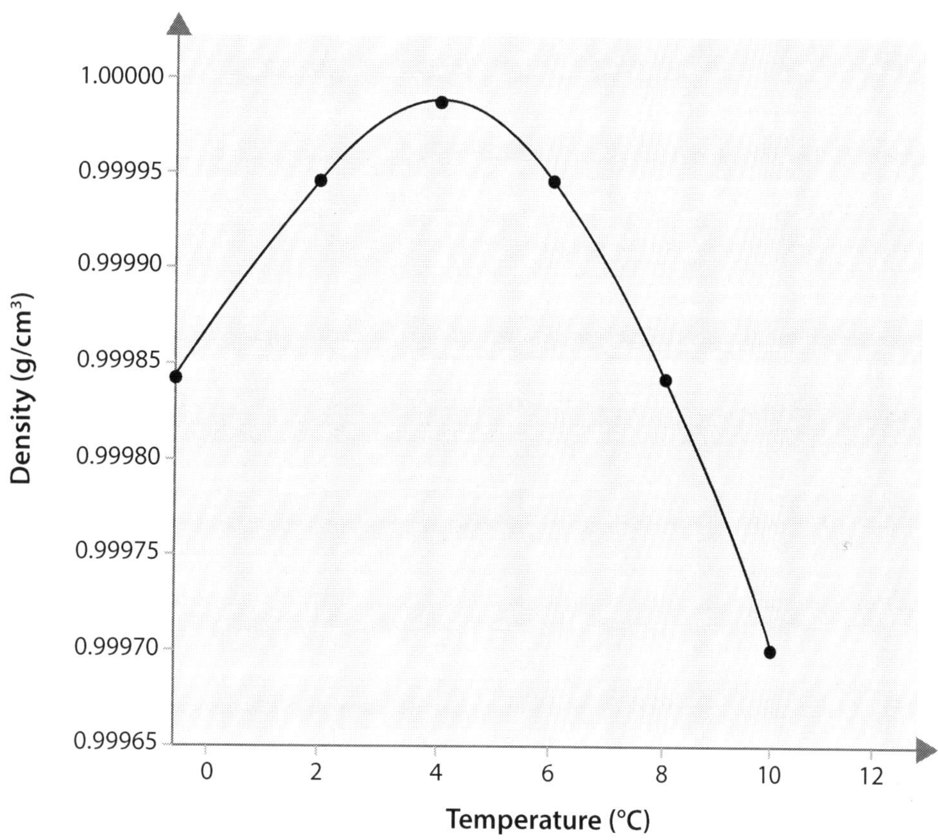

Figure 1.2. Density versus Temperature Plot for Water

Water has a number of other properties that make it unique. It has unusually high boiling and freezing points and a high heat capacity, meaning it takes a great deal of energy to change temperature or state. This property makes it ideal for supporting life in a wide variety of climates, and explains why water exists naturally on Earth in all three states.

In addition, water molecules are **cohesive**, meaning they are attracted to each other, and **adhesive**, meaning they are attracted to other substances. Cohesion is responsible for water's high surface tension, which is caused by the attraction of water molecules on the surface of a liquid. Adhesion is the property behind

capillary action, the process by which water climbs against gravity in narrow spaces such as glass tubes and plant xylem.

SAMPLE QUESTION

4) **Which of the following is true of solid water?**

A. The molecules in solid water are more closely packed together than the molecules in liquid water.

B. Water remains solid at all temperatures below 4°C.

C. The density of solid water is less than the density of liquid water.

D. Molecules of solid water have a large amount of kinetic energy.

Answers:

A. Incorrect. Unlike solids, molecules are not closely packed together in ice.

B. Incorrect. Water is at its most dense at 4°C, but it only freezes to become a solid at 0°C.

C. Correct. This is called the anomalous behavior of water, and because it has less density than water, ice floats on water.

D. Incorrect. Although the molecules are not tightly packed, they do not possess high kinetic energy and are at fixed positions.

Classifying Matter

There are two kinds of matter on the macroscopic scale: pure substances and mixtures. These can further be divided into subcategories: mixtures can be homogeneous or heterogeneous, and pure substances can be elements or compounds.

A **pure substance** has a constant composition with fixed chemical as well as physical properties. A pure substance cannot be broken down further by physical processes. There are two categories of pure substances: elements and compounds.

An **element**, as discussed in the previous section, can be defined as a pure substance composed of one type of atom that cannot be further reduced to a simpler substance by chemical means. A **compound** can be defined as a pure substance composed of two or more elements combined in fixed proportion that can be broken down into simpler matter chemically but not physically.

HELPFUL HINT

All compounds are molecules but not all molecules are compounds.

- examples of elements: lead (Pb), copper (Cu), gold (Au)
- examples of compounds: water (H_2O), salt (NaCl)

A **mixture** is a physical combination of two or more pure substances (elements or compounds) mixed together in any ratio. Different combination ratios of substances (1:2 versus 1:1 versus 1:3) result in a mixture with different properties and compositions. Also, each component involved in the mixture retains its original characteristics. The ease or difficulty of separating the substances in a mixture depends on their properties, such as solubility, particle size, electrical charge, and density. Mixtures can be separated by processes such as filtration, evaporation, chromatography, and distillation.

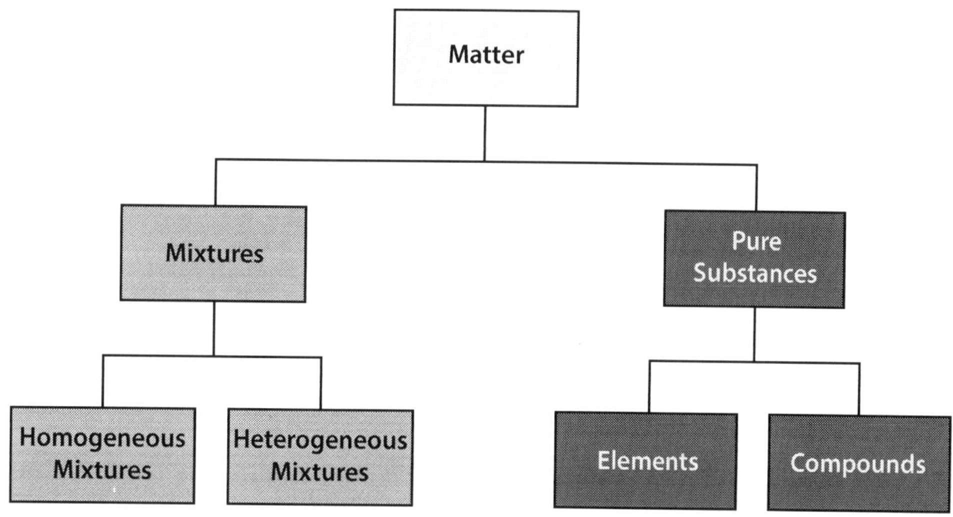

Figure 1.3. Classification of Matter

Some examples of mixtures include:

- alloy mixtures: brass (zinc and copper), cupronickel (copper and nickel)
- food mixtures: tea, lemonade
- other mixtures: air, smog

Mixtures are further classified into homogeneous and heterogeneous mixtures. **Homogeneous mixtures** have the following characteristics:

- uniform composition, that is, uniform properties and appearance throughout
- uniform distribution of different components of the mixture, making it difficult to see them
- can be separated using chromatography and distillation techniques
- can also be called solutions, if they have certain characteristics
- can be solid, liquid, or gas

Examples of homogeneous mixtures include air (a gaseous solution), salt dissolved in water (a liquid solution), and brass (a solid solution).

Heterogeneous mixtures have the following characteristics:

- nonuniform composition, that is, different properties and appearance throughout
- different components of the mixture are separated into regions with different properties, making those different components visible
- substances present in the mixture do not lose their properties
- easy to separate using the physical properties of different parts of the mixture
- can be emulsions (liquid-liquid), suspensions (solid-liquid), or aerosols (solid-gas)

Examples of heterogeneous mixtures include soda (a liquid solution), and oil and vinegar dressing (an emulsion).

A **solution** is a homogeneous mixture with a certain set of properties. It has small particle size and uniform distribution of molecules or ions, which makes it difficult to see different parts of the solution. The solute can pass through the filter paper, which implies the solution cannot be separated by filtration. (For instance, sugar in a water solution—sugar as solute and water as solvent—cannot be separated by filter paper. Nothing will settle on the filter paper; instead the entire solution will pass through.) There is no scattering when light passes through a solution. Also, components present in the solution cannot be separated by filtration or centrifugation, but they can be separated using techniques like distillation.

> HELPFUL HINT
>
> Two or more substances combined chemically in fixed ratio → compound
>
> Two or more substances combined physically in any ratio → mixture

A **suspension** is a heterogeneous mixture. Unlike a solution, particle size is not very small, and it is easy to see different parts of the suspension as the distribution is nonuniform. Suspensions can be separated by filtration—particles can pass through the filter paper. (For instance, if sand mixed with water is made to pass through filter paper, sand will deposit on the filter paper and not pass through it.) If a suspension can stand for a while, then the particles settle and separate out.

SAMPLE QUESTION

5) **Which of the following statements about classifying matter is true?**

A. All pure substances are atoms.

B. All atoms are molecules.

C. All molecules are compounds.

D. All compounds are molecules.

Answers:

A. Incorrect. Pure substances can be atoms or molecules.

B. Incorrect. Atoms make up molecules.

C. Incorrect. O_2 is an example of a molecule that is not a compound.

D. Correct. This is true—all compounds are also molecules.

PHYSICAL AND CHEMICAL PROPERTIES OF MATTER

One of the important ways of classifying matter is based upon its set of physical and chemical properties. A **physical property** of a substance can be measured or observed without changing its composition or changing the chemical nature of the substance. Examples of the physical properties of substances include:

- color
- odor
- density
- hardness
- melting point
- boiling point
- refractive index
- ionization energy
- atomic radius
- ductility
- malleability
- allotropes

Physical properties can help categorize matter in different ways. For example, metals and nonmetals can be grouped based on the physical properties they exhibit. Metals are malleable and ductile, whereas nonmetals do not exhibit these physical properties. However, even though all metals might exhibit a certain set of physical properties, they can be further categorized by other properties such as melting point, density, and so on.

Physical properties can be classified as intensive and extensive properties. **Intensive properties** of a substance are not dependent on the size or mass of the sample and cannot be determined by simply looking at the substance. Intensive properties of a substance do not change unless the substance itself is changed. Examples of intensive properties of a substance include boiling point, melting point, density, temperature, and pressure.

Extensive properties of a substance are dependent on the amount of matter present in each sample. Examples of extensive properties of a substance include mass and volume.

Chemical properties of a substance can only be determined by changes in the chemical identity of the substance. Chemical properties describe how a substance will change when it reacts with other substances. For example, properties like flammability, heat of combustion, enthalpy of formation, toxicity, oxidation states, and so on, are all associated with chemical changes in the substance.

SAMPLE QUESTION

6) **Which of the following describes a physical change?**

A. Water becomes ice.

B. Batter is baked into a cake.

C. A firecracker explodes.

D. Neutralizing an acid with a base.

Answers:

A. Correct. When water changes form, it does not change the chemical composition of the substance. Once water becomes ice, the ice can easily turn back into water.

B. Incorrect. During a chemical change, the chemical composition of the substance changes and cannot be reversed. Baking a cake is an example of a chemical change.

C. Incorrect. Setting off fireworks causes a chemical change.

D. Incorrect. Neutralizing an acid with a base is a chemical change.

The Periodic Table

Elements are arranged in the **periodic table** by increasing atomic number. Each block on the table includes an element's atomic number and the one or two letters that represent the element. The table also includes an element's **mass number**, the sum of its protons and neutrons. Atoms of the same element may have different numbers of neutrons, resulting in **isotopes**. Oxygen, for example, has three stable isotopes: oxygen-16, oxygen-17, and oxygen-18 (the attached number is the isotope's mass number). On the periodic table, an element's mass number is a weighted average of the element's most common isotopes.

HELPFUL HINT

The superscript on an element symbol is its mass number, and the subscript is its atomic number. Subtracting the bottom number from the top gives the number of neutrons in the atom.

$^{18}_{8}O$

protons + neutrons = 18

protons = 8

neutrons = 10

The rows of the periodic table are called **periods**, and the vertical columns are called **groups**. Each group contains elements with similar chemical properties, and the groups are labeled 1 – 18 from left to right.

The majority of the elements in the periodic table are metals. **Metals** have the following properties:

- They are ductile and malleable.
- They conduct electricity.

Atomic Number / Symbol / Name / Atomic Mass

1	2	3	4	5	6	7	8	9	10	11	12	13	14	15	16	17	18
1 H Hydrogen 1.008																	2 He Helium 4.0026
3 Li Lithium 6.941	4 Be Beryllium 9.0122											5 B Boron 10.81	6 C Carbon 12.011	7 N Nitrogen 14.007	8 O Oxygen 15.999	9 F Fluorine 18.998	10 Ne Neon 20.180
11 Na Sodium 22.990	12 Mg Magnesium 24.305											13 Al Aluminum 26.982	14 Si Silicon 28.085	15 P Phosphorus 30.974	16 S Sulfur 32.06	17 Cl Chlorine 35.45	18 Ar Argon 39.948
19 K Potassium 39.098	20 Ca Calcium 40.078	21 Sc Scandium 44.956	22 Ti Titanium 47.867	23 V Vanadium 50.942	24 Cr Chromium 51.996	25 Mn Maganese 54.938	26 Fe Iron 55.845	27 Co Cobalt 58.933	28 Ni Nickel 58.963	29 Cu Copper 63.546	30 Zn Zinc 65.38	31 Ga Gallium 69.723	32 Ge Germanium 72.64	33 Es Arsenic 74.922	34 Se Selenium 78.971	35 Br Bromine 79.904	36 Kr Krypton 83.798
37 Rb Rubidium 85.468	38 Sr Strontium 87.62	39 Y Yttrium 88.906	40 Zr Zirconium 91.224	41 Nb Niobium 92.906	42 Mo Molybdenum 254	43 Tc Technetium 98	44 Ru Ruthenium 101.07	45 Rh Rhodium 102.91	46 Pd Palladium 106.42	47 Ag Silver 107.87	48 Cd Cadmium 112.41	49 In Indium 114.82	50 Sn Tin 118.71	51 Sb Antimony 121.76	52 Te Tellurium 127.60	53 I Iodine 126.90	54 Xe Xenon 121.29
55 Cs Caesium 132.91	56 Ba Barium 137.33	57-71	72 Hf Hafnium 178.49	73 Ta Tantalum 183.84	74 W Tungsten 183.84	75 Re Rhenium 186.21	76 Os Osmium 190.23	77 Ir Iridium 192.22	78 Pt Platinum 195.08	79 Au Gold 196.97	80 Hg Mercury 200.59	81 Tl Thallium 204.38	82 Pb Lead 207.2	83 Bi Bismuth 208.98	84 Po Polonium 209	85 At Astatine 210	86 Rn Radon 222
87 Fr Francium 223.020	88 Ra Radium 226	89-103	104 Rf Rutherfordium 267	105 Db Dubnium 268	106 Sg Seaborgium 271	107 Bh Bohrium 272	108 Hs Hassium 277	109 Mt Meitnerium 276	110 Ds Darmstadtium 281	111 Rg Roentgenium 280	112 Cn Copernicium 285	113 Uut Ununtrium Unknown	114 Fl Flerovium 254	115 Uup Ununpentium Unknown	116 Lv Livermorium 291	117 Uus Ununseptium Unknown	118 Uuo Ununoctium Unknown

Lanthanide	57 La Lanthanium 138.905	58 Ce Cerium 140.12	59 Pr Praseodymium 140.91	60 Nd Neodymium 144.24	61 Pm Promethium 144.913	62 Sm Samarium 150.36	63 Eu Europium 151.96	64 Gd Gadolinium 157.25	65 Tb Terbium 158.93	66 Dy Dysprosium 152.50	67 Ho Holmium 154.930	68 Er Erbium 167.259	69 Tm Thulium 168.934	70 Yb Ytterbium 173.065	71 Lu Lutetium 174.967
Actinide	89 Ac Actinium 227.028	90 Th Thorium 232.038	91 Pa Protactinuim 231.036	92 U Uranium 238.029	93 Np Neptunium 237.048	94 Pu Plutonium 244.064	95 Am Americium 243.061	96 Cm Curium 247.070	97 Bk Berkelium 247.070	98 Cf Californium 251.080	99 Es Einsteinium 254	100 Fm Fermium 257.095	101 Md Mendelevium 258.1	102 No Nobelium 259.101	103 Lr Lawrencium 262

Alkaline Metal | Alkaline Earth Metals | Transition Metal | Basic Metal | Metalloid | Nonmetal | Halogen | Noble Gas | Lanthanide | Actinide

Figure 1.4. The Periodic Table

- They can form alloys.
- They are thermally conductive.
- They are hard, opaque, and shiny.
- With the exception of mercury, they are solids.

Solid metals usually consist of tightly packed atoms, resulting in fairly high densities. Metals begin on the left side of the periodic table and span across the middle of the table, almost all the way to the right side. Examples of metals include gold (Au), tin (Sn), and lead (Pb).

Nonmetals are elements that do not conduct electricity and tend to be more volatile than metals. They can be solids, liquids, or gases. The nonmetals are located on the right side of the periodic table. Examples of nonmetals include sulfur (S), hydrogen (H), and oxygen (O).

Metalloids, or semimetals, are elements that possess both metal and nonmetal characteristics. For example, some metalloids are shiny but do not conduct electricity well. Many metalloids are semiconductors. Metalloids are located between the metals and nonmetals on the periodic table. Some examples of metalloids are boron (B), silicon (Si), and arsenic (As).

The groups are discussed in more detail in Chapter 3.

SAMPLE QUESTIONS

7) **Which of the following is the correct symbol for the isotope of boron that contains 6 neutrons?**

A. $^{5}_{6}B$

B. $^{11}_{5}B$

C. $^{11}_{6}B$

D. $^{6}_{0}B$

Answer:

B. Correct. The periodic table shows that boron has 5 protons, giving it an atomic number of 5. With 6 neutrons, it will then have a mass number of 6 + 5 = 11. The atomic number (5) is written as the subscript, and the mass number (11) is written as the superscript.

8) **Bismuth is a**

A. metal.

B. nonmetal.

C. metalloid.

D. transition element.

Answer:

A. **Correct.** Bismuth is a metal.

GASES

KINETIC MOLECULAR THEORY

The **kinetic molecular theory** of gases is used to describe the macroscopic properties of a gas (such as pressure and temperature) based on the behavior of its microscopic components (i.e., atoms). This theory explains why the temperature, pressure, volume, and number of moles of gas are all related, and can be used to predict the behavior of gases.

The kinetic molecular theory describes the behavior of an **ideal gas**, which is a theoretical model of a gas with the following assumptions:

- The gas particles exert no attractive forces on each other or the surroundings; that is, gas particles do not attract or repel each other.
- Compared to the volume of the container, the volume occupied by individual particles is negligible.
- Molecules of a gas are in a constant state of random motion, and they travel in a straight line until they collide.
- Molecules only interact in collisions, and these collisions do not change the average kinetic energy of the molecules.
- The average kinetic energy of molecules of gas is directly proportional to absolute temperature, meaning all gases have the same average kinetic energy at the same temperature.

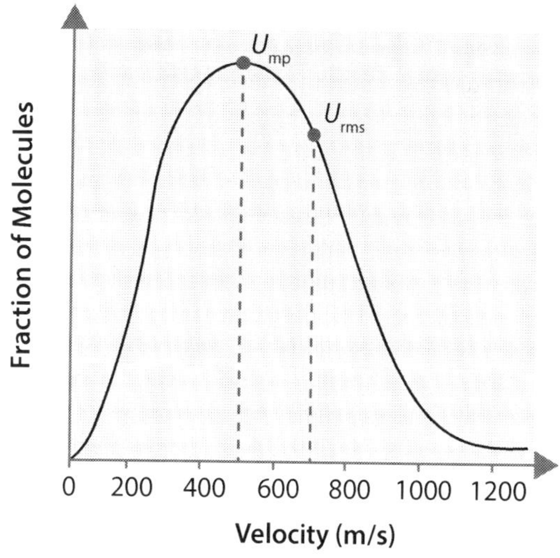

Figure 1.5. Molecular Speed Distribution

Although the molecules in a gas have a constant average kinetic energy, each molecule moves at a different (and changing) speed. The speed of molecules in a gas is shown on a molecular speed distribution curve. The peak of the curve shows the most probable speed of the molecules (u_{mp}). The curve will also show the **root-mean-square speed** (u_{rms}), which is the speed of a molecule with the same kinetic energy as the entire sample's average kinetic energy. The shape of the curve depends on the substance and the sample's temperature.

SAMPLE QUESTION

9) **Kinetic molecular theory includes all of the following assumptions EXCEPT**

A. Gas molecules neither attract nor repel each other.

B. All molecules in a gas move with a uniform velocity.

C. The kinetic energy of gas molecules is proportional to temperature.

D. Gas molecules occupy a negligible amount of space in their container.

Answer:

B. Correct. The molecules in a gas do not all have the same velocity. The speed of individual particles varies and is clustered around the speed that corresponds to the molecules' average kinetic energy.

Gas Laws

The kinetic molecular theory can be used to explain many properties of gases, including the relationship between pressure, temperature, volume, and amount of a substance. These relationships are described in the gas laws.

HELPFUL HINT

The gas laws describe the behavior of all gases, regardless of their chemical composition.

Kinetic molecular theory assumes that average kinetic energy of gas particles is dependent on the temperature of the gas. At constant volume, an increase in the temperature leads to more forceful and frequent collisions between the molecules, and thus creates a higher pressure. This relationship is described in **Amonton's law**:

$$\frac{P_1}{T_1} = \frac{P_2}{T_2}$$

where P_1 is initial pressure, P_2 is final pressure, T_1 is initial temperature, and T_2 is final temperature.

When temperature is increased and pressure is held constant, the volume of the gas will expand. The extra space will prevent the number of collisions between molecules from increasing due to their higher average kinetic energy. This relationship is described in **Charles's law**:

$$\frac{V_1}{T_1} = \frac{V_2}{T_2}$$

where V_1 is initial volume, V_2 is final volume, T_1 is initial temperature, and T_2 is final temperature.

When the volume of the gas is decreased without changing the temperature, the particles of the gas are compressed, resulting in more collisions among the gas particles. This, in turn, increases the pressure of the gas. This relationship is described in **Boyle's law**:

$$P_1V_1 = P_2V_2$$

where V_1 is initial volume, V_2 is final volume, P_1 is initial pressure, and P_2 is final pressure.

Avogadro's law is derived from the observation that equal volumes of gases at the same temperature and pressure will have the same number of molecules. Accordingly, increasing the number of moles of a gas will increase its volume:

$$V = kn$$

where V is volume, k is a constant, and n is the number of moles.

HELPFUL HINT

1 atmosphere = 101,325 Pa

1 bar = 100 kPa = 100,000 Pa

Dalton's law of partial pressures states that the total pressure of the gas mixture is equal to the sum of the partial pressures of the individual gases. Dalton's law can be written as:

$$P_t = P_1 + P_2 + P_3 + \dots.$$

where P_t is the total pressure and P_n is the partial pressure of each gas.

Combining Amonton's, Charles's, Boyle's, and Avogadro's laws gives the **ideal gas law**:

$$PV = nRT$$

where P is pressure, V is volume, T is temperature, R is the gas constant, and n is the number of moles.

The variables in the ideal gas law can be expressed in different combinations of units, and the value of R will depend on the units used in the equation (as shown in Table 1.2).

Table 1.2 The Gas Constant

Value of R	Units
8.314	$\frac{J}{K \cdot mol}$
	$\frac{m^3 \cdot Pa}{K \cdot mol}$
	$\frac{L\,kPa}{K^{-1} \cdot mol^{-1}}$
	$\frac{cm^3\,MPa}{K^{-1} \cdot mol^{-1}}$
	$\frac{cm^3\,bar}{K^{-1} \cdot mol^{-1}}$
8.314×10^{-6}	$\frac{m^3\,MPa}{K^{-1} \cdot mol^{-1}}$
8.314×10^{-5}	$\frac{m^3\,bar}{K^{-1} \cdot mol^{-1}}$
8.314×10^{-2}	$\frac{L\,bar}{K^{-1} \cdot mol^{-1}}$
83.14	$\frac{cm^3\,bar}{K^{-1} \cdot mol^{-1}}$

Table 1.2 The Gas Constant (continued)

Value of R	**Units**
8.314×10^3	$\frac{\text{cm}^3\,\text{kPa}}{\text{K}^{-1}\cdot\text{mol}^{-1}}$
8.314×10^6	$\frac{\text{cm}^3\,\text{Pa}}{\text{K}^{-1}\cdot\text{mol}^{-1}}$
1.987×10^{-3}	$\frac{\text{kcal}}{\text{K}^{-1}\cdot\text{mol}^{-1}}$
8.206×10^{-5}	$\frac{\text{m}^3\,\text{atm}}{\text{K}^{-1}\cdot\text{mol}^{-1}}$
8.206×10^{-2}	$\frac{\text{L atm}}{\text{K}^{-1}\cdot\text{mol}^{-1}}$
82.06	$\frac{\text{cm}^3\,\text{atm}}{\text{K}^{-1}\cdot\text{mol}^{-1}}$

SAMPLE QUESTIONS

10) **What is the final volume of a sample of gas with an initial volume of 4 L and an initial temperature of 28°C if the temperature is raised to 305.15 K?**

Answer:

$V_1 = 4\text{ L}$	Define the initial volume of the system.
$T_1 = 28°\text{C} = 28 + 273 = 301\text{ K}$	Define the initial temperature.
$T_2 = 32°\text{C} = 32 + 273 = 305\text{ K}$	Define the final temperature.
$\frac{V_1}{T_1} = \frac{V_2}{T_2}$ $V_2 = \frac{V_1 T_2}{T_1}$ $= \frac{(4\text{ L})(305\text{ K})}{301\text{ K}}$ $= \mathbf{4.05\text{ L}}$	The final volume can be calculated using Charles's law.

11) **What is the volume of 3 moles of O_2 at 25°C if it has a pressure of 1 atm?**

Answer:

Use the ideal gas law.

$PV = nRT$

$P = \frac{nRT}{V}$

$= \frac{(3\text{ mol})(8.206 \times 10^{-5}\text{ L atm K}^{-1}\text{ mol}^{-1})(605.15\text{ K})}{4\text{ L}} = \mathbf{0.37\text{ m}^3}$

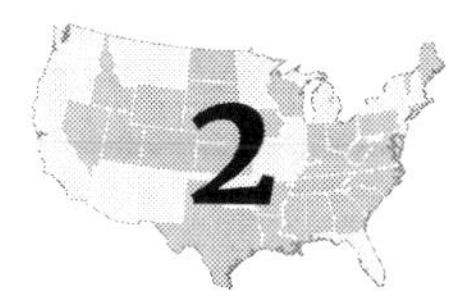

Atomic and Nuclear Structure

THE EVOLUTION OF THE ATOMIC MODEL

Understanding of the atom has developed and improved over the course of many centuries. With each new discovery about the structure of the atom, a new atomic model was developed. That model, in turn, was tested and improved upon. The current model of atomic structure incorporates many of the features of previous models.

The first model of the atom was based on philosophical ideas that can be traced to ancient Greek and Indian cultures. The Indian sage Acharya Kanada (b. 600 BCE) first postulated the idea of a particle that was indivisible, and referred to it as a *parmanu* or *anu*. Democritus (460 – 370 BCE) theorized that objects can be divided into smaller pieces until a point is reached where the object cannot be divided any further. This led to his conclusion that all matter is made up of particles that cannot be broken apart; these particles are called **atoms**, derived from the Greek word *atomos*, meaning indivisible. Democritus had no experimental evidence to support his claims, but scientists have worked since then to better understand the structure of matter and the atom.

Table 2.1. Evolution of the Atomic Model

Model	Shape	Description
John Dalton 1803		Stated that atoms are indivisible, atoms belonging to same element are identical, and atoms combine in whole number ratios to form compounds.

Table 2.1. Evolution of the Atomic Model (continued)

Model	Shape	Description
J.J. Thomson 1904		Confirmed the existence of electrons with the cathode ray experiment.
Ernest Rutherford 1911		Showed that the atom includes a positively charged core at the center—the nucleus—with the gold foil experiment.
Niels Bohr (also called the Rutherford-Bohr model) 1913		Proposed that electrons orbit the nucleus in specific energy levels.
Erwin Schrödinger (Quantum Mechanical Model) 1926		Showed that electrons move in orbitals and not in defined paths.

Dalton's Model of the Atom

John Dalton's (1766 – 1844) atomic model expanded on Democritus's idea that the atom is indivisible. According to his model, atoms belonging to the same element have the same mass, whereas atoms of different elements have different masses. The main postulates of Dalton's atomic theory are:

- All matter is made up of indivisible, minute particles called atoms.
- Atoms belonging to a single element are identical and have the same size and mass; atoms belonging to different elements have different sizes, masses, and properties.
- When atoms belonging to different elements combine in whole number ratios, compounds are formed. The types of atoms in a given compound are always the same.
- Atoms are neither created nor destroyed in a chemical reaction; they are only reorganized. Additionally, atoms of one element cannot be changed into atoms of another element.

Dalton's theory addressed several important laws that had previously been established. His theory explained the law of conservation of mass (that matter cannot be created or destroyed) and the law of definite proportions (that the relative numbers of different kinds of atoms is constant in a compound). Despite this success, Dalton's model had a number of problems:

- The theory did not explain why atoms belonging to different elements had different sizes and masses.
- The theory did not explain what types of forces hold the atoms together.
- The theory did not explain how atoms belonging to different elements combined to form compounds.
- The theory did not explain the law of gaseous volume, which states that the ratio between the volumes of reactant gases and the gaseous products in a reaction can be expressed in simple whole numbers.

SAMPLE QUESTION

1) **Which of the following was NOT explained by Dalton's model of the atom?**

   A. the law of conservation of mass

   B. the law of definite proportions

   C. the law of multiple proportions

   D. the law of gaseous volume

Answers:

A. Incorrect. Dalton's theory proposed that atoms are neither created nor destroyed during reactions, but instead are reorganized.

B. Incorrect. Dalton's theory proposed that atoms of different elements combine in whole number ratios to create compounds.

C. Incorrect. Dalton's theory explained the law of multiple proportions, which applies the law of definite proportions to different compounds composed of the same elements.

D. Correct. Dalton's law did not explain the law of gaseous volume, which states that the ratio between the volumes of reactant gases and the gaseous products in a reaction can be expressed in simple whole numbers. His theory only addressed the ratio of elements in a compound.

THOMSON'S MODEL OF THE ATOM

In 1897, J.J. Thomson (1856 – 1940) discovered the existence of electrons while examining the properties of **cathode rays**, which are produced when a high voltage is applied to electrodes in a vacuum tube. Thomson found that these particles could be deflected by a negatively charged plate, and thus were negatively charged. He also found that changing the material of the cathode did not change the properties of the resulting cathode ray. He proposed that cathode rays were composed of a stream of negatively charged particles that became known as electrons. Further experimentation by Thomson determined an electron's charge-to-mass ratio to be 1.76×10^8 coulombs per gram.

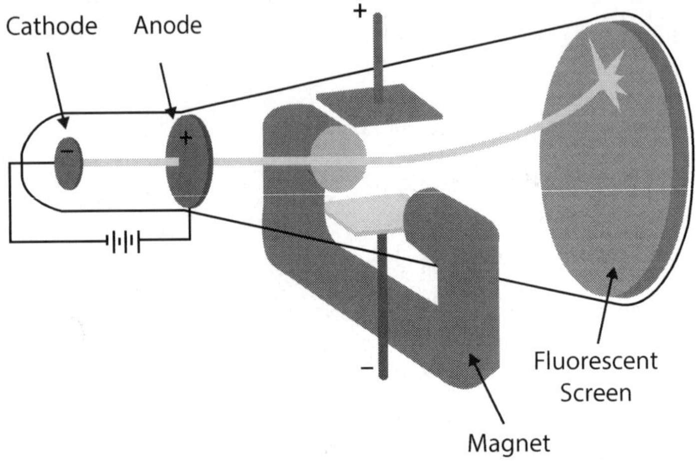

Figure 2.1. Cathode Ray Experiment

Thomson incorporated the electron into a new model of the atom. He proposed that the atom had a spherical shape with a uniformly distributed positive charge. The electrons, which made up only a small portion of the atom's mass, were uniformly embedded in the positive mass. This would provide a stable arrangement in which the negative charges canceled out the positive charges. This model is also called the **plum pudding model**.

Figure 2.2. Plum Pudding Model

SAMPLE QUESTION

2) **Which of the following statements about J.J. Thomson's cathode ray experiment is NOT true?**

   A. Cathode rays were negatively charged.

   B. Changing the material of the cathode changed the properties of the resulting cathode ray.

   C. Cathode rays are produced by applying a high voltage to electrodes in a vacuum.

   D. The particles in the cathode ray could be deflected by a negatively charged plate.

Answers:

A. Incorrect. Cathode rays, composed of electrons, are negatively charged.

B. Correct. Changing the material of the cathode did not change the properties of the resulting cathode ray.

C. Incorrect. Cathode rays are produced by applying a high voltage to electrodes in a vacuum.

D. Incorrect. The negatively charged particles were deflected by a negatively charged plate.

RUTHERFORD'S MODEL OF THE ATOM

Ernest Rutherford (1871 – 1937) built on Thomson's model of the atom by introducing the concept of the nucleus. During his gold foil experiment, he observed that positively charged alpha particles fired through gold foil did not always follow a straight path, as they would have if Thomson's model was accurate. Instead, a small number of particles were deflected at large angles, including back in the direction they were originally traveling. If Thomson's model had been accurate, all the alpha particles would have passed straight through the foil because the charge of that atom was balanced throughout. As Rutherford described in his experiment, "It was almost as incredible as if you fired a 15-inch shell at a piece of tissue paper and it came back and hit you." This suggested there was a very dense region in the atom.

> **HELPFUL HINT**
>
> Rutherford used different types of foils like lead, aluminum, and iron; however, his experiment with gold foil is most widely discussed.

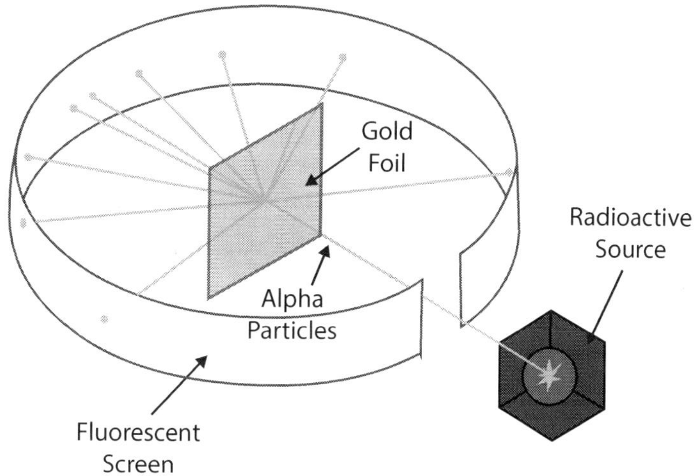

Figure 2.3. Gold Foil Experiment

From this experiment, Rutherford concluded that an atom is not just empty space with electrons distributed inside it. Instead, an atom has a positively charged nucleus that contains most of its mass. Because so few alpha particles bounced back, he also concluded that the positively charged nucleus of the atom was tiny compared to the size of the entire atom.

Rutherford's atomic model includes the following:

- An atom consists of a nucleus, which is a densely concentrated mass that exists in an extremely small region and has a positive charge.
- Electrons surround and move around the nucleus at high speed, in circular paths called orbits.
- Strong electrostatic forces hold the nucleus and electrons together.

There were limitations to Rutherford's model. According to the laws of physics, when a body moves in an orbit at constant speed, it is accelerating. An electron accelerating in an orbit would constantly emit radiation (Maxwell's electromagnetic theory) and hence would lose energy and eventually collide with the nucleus. It would take just 10^{-8} seconds for electrons to collapse into the nucleus. Because this does not happen, the stability of the atom described by Rutherford's model was questioned. Rutherford's model also does not explain the arrangement of electrons around the nucleus and the energies associated with them.

HELPFUL HINT

The radius of an atom is 10^{-10} m, and the radius of its nucleus is just 10^{-15} m.

SAMPLE QUESTION

3) **Which of the following statements about Ernest Rutherford's gold foil experiment is NOT true?**

A. The alpha particles shot at the gold foil did not always follow a straight path.

B. A few alpha particles were deflected at large angles, including straight back.

C. The alpha particles took a straight path but were occasionally deflected.

D. The alpha particles took a parabolic path.

Answers:

A. Incorrect. Some of the particles were deflected or even directed back in the direction they were originally traveling.

B. Incorrect. Some of the particles were deflected or even directed back in the direction they were originally traveling.

C. Incorrect. Most of the particles took a straight path but some were occasionally deflected.

D. Correct. None of the alpha particles took a parabolic path.

BOHR'S MODEL OF THE ATOM

Niels Bohr (1885 – 1962) addressed the problem of stability in Rutherford's model by proposing that electrons did not simply orbit the nucleus in circular paths. Instead, electrons could only exist in certain orbits that have a specific energy state; electrons in that state would not lose energy, and thus would not collide with the nucleus.

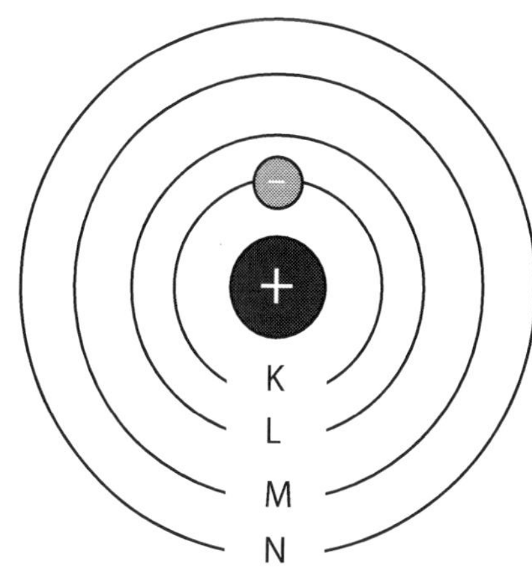

Figure 2.4. The Bohr Model of the Atom

Bohr based his model on his observations of the **line spectrum** of hydrogen. When a high voltage is applied to a gas, it emits a characteristic color, which can then be broken down into a spectrum showing its component wavelengths. Hydrogen has a simple line spectrum that includes only four wavelengths of visible light. Bohr proposed that hydrogen's line spectrum resulted from the emission of discrete amounts of energy that were released when electrons moved from a high to a low energy orbit.

According to the Bohr model, electrons must gain or lose energy in specific amounts (or quanta) called **photons** in order to move between orbits. The energy of a photon is given by the equation $E = h\nu$ where h = Planck's proportionality constant (6.626×10^{-34} joule-sec.) and v is the frequency of the radiation. Electrons in the lowest energy orbit are in their **ground state**. When they absorb a photon, they are **excited** and "jump" to a higher energy orbit. Conversely, when electrons "fall" to a lower energy orbit, they release a photon and emit electromagnetic radiation at a wavelength inversely proportional to the energy released.

> **HELPFUL HINT**
>
> Electromagnetic radiation absorbs and releases energy in small "packets" called **quanta**. Thus, a change in energy is not continuous (like a ramp), but instead occurs in discrete bursts (like stairs).

Bohr's model was able to explain the stability of the atom that Rutherford's model could not. However, just like other models of the atom, Bohr's model had some limitations:

- The model was based on experiments with the hydrogen atom and did not explain the behavior of atoms with more than one electron.
- The model did not explain why electrons did not simply fall into the nucleus.
- The model was two dimensional and suggested that electrons move in defined circular paths, which later models would show was not accurate.

SAMPLE QUESTION

4) **Which of the following questions did Bohr's model of the atom NOT answer?**

A. Why do electrons not fall into the nucleus?

B. Why does hydrogen have a distinctive line spectrum?

C. Why do electrons emit energy with discrete wavelengths when going from a higher energy level to a lower energy level?

D. Why do different elements produce different line spectra?

Answers:

A. **Correct.** The model did not explain what prevented the electrons from falling into the nucleus.

B. Incorrect. Bohr proposed that electrons in a hydrogen atom "falling" to a lower energy level emit electromagnetic radiation with a discrete wavelength that is dependent on the spacing of energy levels in hydrogen. These wavelengths are responsible for hydrogen's line spectrum.

C. Incorrect. Bohr proposed that electrons release discrete packets of energy called photons that have a discrete wavelength inversely proportional to the energy they release.

D. Incorrect. In Bohr's model, each element has a unique spacing of energy levels, resulting in emission spectra that can be likened to a fingerprint since a characteristic emission spectrum is obtained for each type of element.

The Quantum Mechanical Model of the Atom

Probability Densities and Orbitals

The discovery that matter can act like a wave led to the next step in the development of the atomic model. According to Werner Heisenberg's (1901 – 1976) **uncertainty principle**, the wave-like nature of electrons means that it is impossible to know both an electron's momentum (i.e., its velocity) and its position at the same time. While its momentum may be known with greater accuracy, it is at the expense of its location and vice versa. Thus, it is only possible to find the *probability* that an electron will be found in a specific position, not its exact location.

HELPFUL HINT

The uncertainly principle applies to all matter. However, the magnitude of the uncertainty is inconsequential compared to the size of everyday objects, which is why their momentum and location can be found using the equations in Newtonian mechanics.

The probability that an electron will be in a given location is found using Erwin Schrödinger's (1887 – 1961) **wave functions**, which are denoted with the

Greek letter psi, Ψ, (the functions themselves are complex and will not be covered here). The value Ψ^2, called the **probability** or **electron density**, represents the probability that an electron will be found at any given location. The collection of wave functions for an atom yields a set of **orbitals**, which are the areas around the nucleus where an electron is most likely to be found.

This quantum mechanical model of the atom corrected the Bohr model by explaining that electrons do not orbit the nucleus. Instead of following a set circular trajectory, electrons exist in "clouds" around the nucleus.

SAMPLE QUESTION

5) **According to the uncertainty principle, what properties of an electron can never be known at the same time?**

A. momentum and velocity

B. velocity and position

C. momentum and wavelength

D. wavelength and velocity

Answers:

A. Incorrect. Because the mass of an electron is known, it is possible to calculate its velocity from its momentum ($p = mv$).

B. **Correct.** Because the magnitude of the uncertainty is large compared to the size of an electron, it is only possible to know either the momentum (which gives velocity) or position of an electron, not both.

C. Incorrect. The uncertainly principle does not address an electron's wavelength, which can be found using the DeBroglie equation.

D. Incorrect. The uncertainly principle does not address an electron's wavelength, which can be found using the DeBroglie equation.

QUANTUM NUMBERS

Schrödinger's wave functions result in three quantum numbers that describe the position and shape of an orbital. Another quantum number is used to describe the rotation of an electron around its axis, resulting in four total quantum numbers for each electron in an atom:

- n: principal quantum number
- l: azimuthal or orbital angular momentum quantum number
- m_l: magnetic quantum number
- m_s: spin magnetic quantum number

The **principal quantum number** (n) describes the energy level of an orbital. It has positive integer values (1, 2, 3, ...), with increasing numbers that denote an increase in the orbital's energy. Larger numbers also describe larger orbitals in which electrons spend more time farther away from the nucleus. All the orbitals with the same principal quantum number are called a **shell**.

The secondary quantum number, called the **azimuthal quantum number** (l), gives the shape of the orbital. It can have values from zero to (n – 1), but each numerical value is usually described using letters as shown in Table 2.2. As with the principal quantum number, the energy of orbitals increases as the secondary quantum number increases. All of the orbitals that share a primary and secondary quantum number (n and l) are called **subshells**.

Table 2.2. Secondary Quantum Number Notation

Azimuthal Quantum Number	Letter Notation
0	*s*
1	*p*
2	*d*
3	*f*
4	*g*

The **magnetic quantum number** (m_l) describes the orientation of the orbitals around the nucleus. Its value ranges from $-l$ to $+l$ (including zero). The relationship between the first three quantum numbers is shown in Table 2.3.

Table 2.3. The First Three Quantum Numbers

Principal quantum number, *n* *shell*	Azimuthal quantum number, *l* *subshell*		Magnetic quantum number, m_l *orientation*	Number of orbitals in subshell	Number of orbitals in shell
1	0	1*s*	0	1	1
2	0	2*s*	0	1	4
	1	2*p*	–1, 0, 1	3	
3	0	3*s*	0	1	9
	1	3*p*	–1, 0, 1	3	
	2	3*d*	–2, –1, 0, 1, 2	5	
4	0	4*s*	0	1	16
	1	4*p*	–1, 0, 1	3	
	2	4*d*	–2, –1, 0, 1, 2	5	
	3	4*f*	–3, –2, –1, 0, 1, 2, 3	7	

Each electron in an atom rotates on its axis, producing the final quantum number—the **spin magnetic quantum number** (m_s). Electrons can **spin** in one of two opposite directions, yielding two possible values for m_s: $+\frac{1}{2}$ and $-\frac{1}{2}$.

For atoms containing more than one electron, the energy of an orbital depends on both its principal and azimuthal quantum numbers (*n* and *l*). Because inner electrons **screen**, or shield, outer electrons from the attraction of the nucleus, orbitals within a shell do not all have the same energy. The energy of orbitals in a shell increases with l: $s < p < d < f$. The energy of the 2*p* orbital, for example, is greater than the energy of the 2*s* orbital. In other words, an *s*-orbital electron is more tightly bound to the nucleus than a *p*-orbital electron. As discussed above, each orbital within a subshell is **degenerate**, meaning it has the same energy.

HELPFUL HINT

In a hydrogen atom, which has only one electron, the energy level of an orbital depends only on its principal quantum number, *n*:

$1s < 2s = 2p < 3s = 3p = 3d < 4s = 4p = 4d = 4f$

SAMPLE QUESTION

6) **Which set of the following quantum numbers is correct?**

A. $n = 4, l = 3, m_l = 3, m_s = +\frac{1}{2}$

B. $n = 1, l = 1, m_l = 1, m_s = +\frac{1}{2}$

C. $n = 3, l = 1, m_l = 2, m_s = -\frac{1}{2}$

D. $n = 2, l = 1, m_l = 1, m_s = 0$

Answer:

A. $n = 4, l = 3, m_l = 3, m_s = +\frac{1}{2}$

B. l must be at least one less than n

C. m_l ranges from $+l$ to $-l$

D. m_s must be $+\frac{1}{2}$ or $-\frac{1}{2}$

Orbital Shapes

The shape of orbitals is determined using electron densities, which use the wave function to show the likelihood that an electron will be found in a specific position. The dots on the electron density distribution represent the probability of finding an electron in that region. To approximate the shape of the orbital, **boundary surface diagrams** are drawn to enclose a certain percentage of the probability density.

HELPFUL HINT

All orbitals except the *s*-orbital have an electron density of zero at the nucleus. An area where the electron density is zero is called a node.

The shape of the **s-orbital** is a sphere, implying that the probability of finding an electron at a certain distance in all directions is equal. It has $n - 1$ nodes where n is the principal quantum number. As the value of n increases, the size of the s-orbital increases.

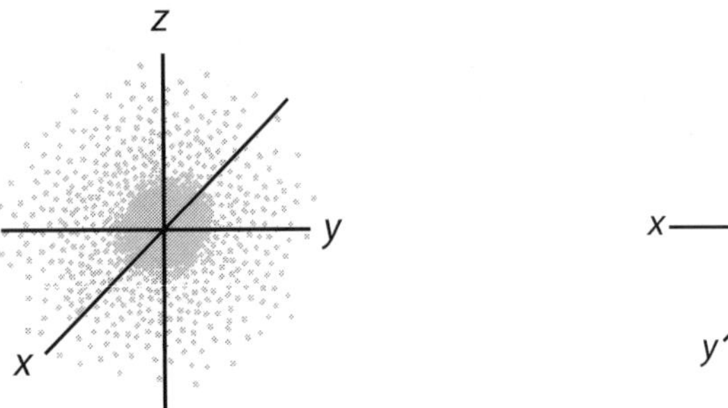

Figure 2.5. Electron-Density Distribution

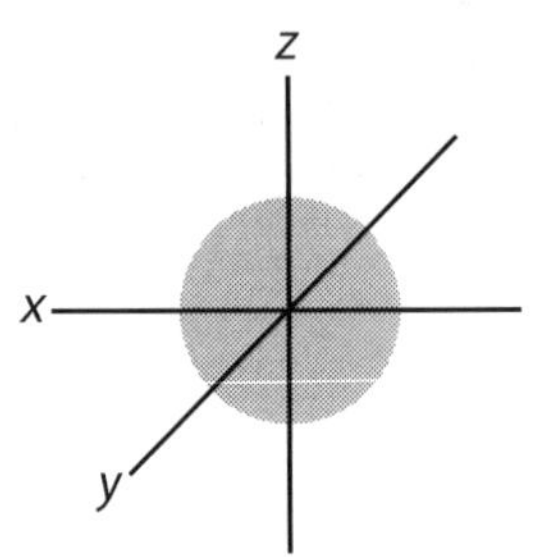

Figure 2.6. *s*-orbital

Each ***p*-orbital** has two lobes with a radial node at the nucleus (represented as the origin on the diagrams below). Each shell has three p-orbitals (for the magnetic quantum numbers –1, 0, 1) that have the same shape, energy, and size. It has $n - 1$ total nodes ($n - 2$ radial and 1 angular). The only difference between the orbitals is their orientation, and the orbitals are named by the axis with which they align: $2p_x$, $2p_y$, and $2p_z$. As with the s-orbital, the energy and size of these orbitals increase with increasing values of n.

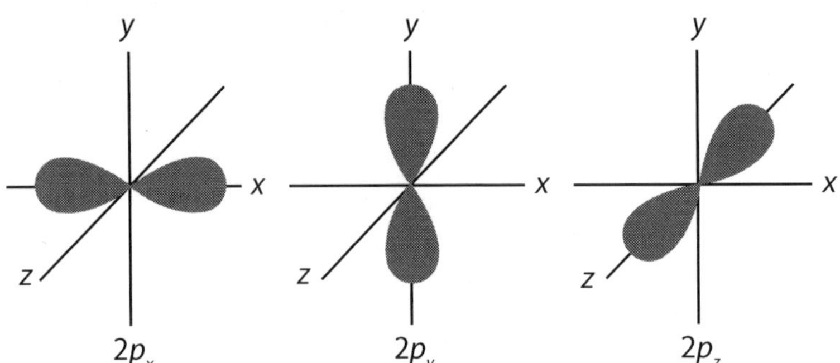

Figure 2.7. *p*-orbital

The five ***d*-orbitals** (for the magnetic quantum numbers –2, –1, 0, 1, 2) have two different shapes. Four of the orbitals have four lobes that meet at the nucleus. The fifth orbital has two lobes surrounded by a donut shape at the nucleus. The orbitals are written as d_{xy}, d_{yz}, d_{xz}, d_{x2-y2}, and d_{z2}. As with the other shells, the orbital's energy and size increase with each increase in n. It has a total of $n - 1$ nodes ($n - 3$ radial and 2 angular).

The shape of the seven ***f*-orbitals** is too complex to be covered here, but each orbital has a different number and orientation of lobes and donuts. Like the d-orbitals, the f-orbitals in a shell have the same energy and size, both of which increase with each increase in n.

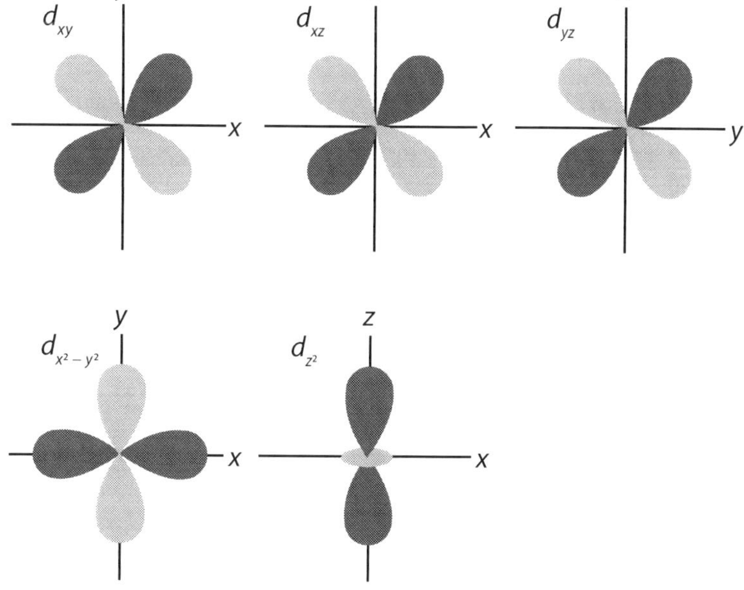

Figure 2.8. *d*-orbital

SAMPLE QUESTION

7) **How many nodes does a 2*p* orbital have?**

A. 0

B. 1

C. 2

D. 3

Answer:

B. Correct. The total number of nodes for *p*-orbitals is one less than its principal quantum number *n*.

ELECTRON CONFIGURATION

Electron configuration describes the way in which electrons in an atom are arranged in orbitals. It is written in the form nl^x, where n is the principal quantum number, l is the azimuthal quantum number, and x is the number of electrons in the orbital. The electron configuration for hydrogen, for example, is written as $1s^1$ because its one electron occupies the 1*s* orbital.

Hydrogen

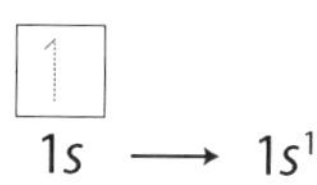

Figure 2.9. Orbital Diagram and Electron Configuration for Hydrogen

An atom's electron configuration can be shown visually using an **orbital diagram**, which includes a box for each orbital and half-arrows representing electrons. The arrows point up or down to indicate spin.

The **Pauli exclusion principle** states that no electrons in an atom may have the same four quantum numbers. In practice, this means that orbitals can hold a maximum of two electrons, and that those two electrons will have opposite spins. Thus, an *s*-shell will hold only 2 electrons. A *p*-shell, which has three orbitals, will hold 6 electrons, the *d*-shell will hold 10, and the *f*-shell will hold 14.

Table 2.4. Electron Configuration and Orbital Diagrams for the Four Subshells

Subshell	Electron Configuration When Full	Orbital Diagram When Full
s	ns^2	[↿⇂]
d	nd^6	[↿⇂][↿⇂][↿⇂]
p	np^{10}	[↿⇂][↿⇂][↿⇂][↿⇂][↿⇂]
f	nf^{14}	[↿⇂][↿⇂][↿⇂][↿⇂][↿⇂][↿⇂][↿⇂]

According to the **aufbau principle**, electrons fill the orbital with the lowest available energy. Because of screening, however, the energy of orbitals does not simply increase with each shell. Instead, orbitals increase in energy as shown in Figure 2.10. All degenerate orbitals within a subshell must be filled before electrons will begin to fill the next orbital.

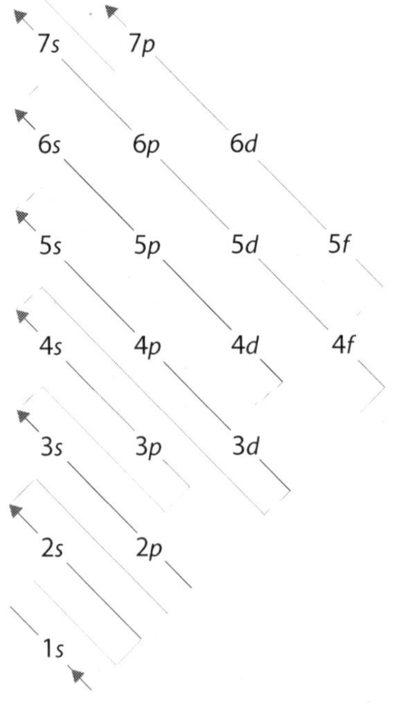

increasing energy

1s 2s 2p 3s 3p 4s 3d 4p 5s 4d 5p 6s . . .

Figure 2.10. Orbital Energy Levels

Hund's rule of maximum multiplicity states that when orbitals of equal energy (i.e., degenerate orbitals), are available, electrons first occupy all the orbitals singly before pairing up. Electrons repel each other if they are present in the same subshell with parallel spin, so the repulsion has to be minimized by placing electrons as far apart as possible.

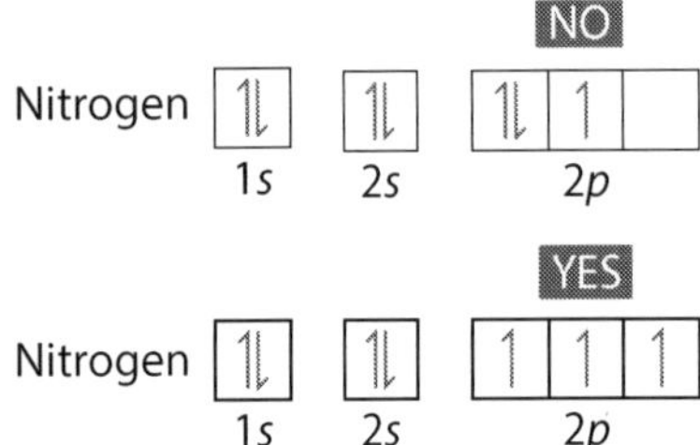

Figure 2.11. Hund's Rule

> **HELPFUL HINT**
>
> In a condensed electron configuration, core electrons are replaced with a corresponding noble gas to shorten the notation.
>
> Tin: $[1s^2 2s^2 2p^6 3s^2 3p^6 4s^2 3d^{10} 4p^6] 5s^2 4d^{10} 5p^2 \rightarrow$ $[Kr] 5s^2 4d^{10} 5p^2$

Using these rules, it is possible to find electron configurations for all the elements. Consider a sulfur atom, which has sixteen electrons. Starting with 1*s*, electrons fill orbitals following the pattern shown in Figure 2.10: $1s^2\ 2s^2\ 2p^6\ 3s^2$. In the last subshell, 3*p*, two orbitals contain only one electron each (both with the same spin), in accordance with Hund's rule.

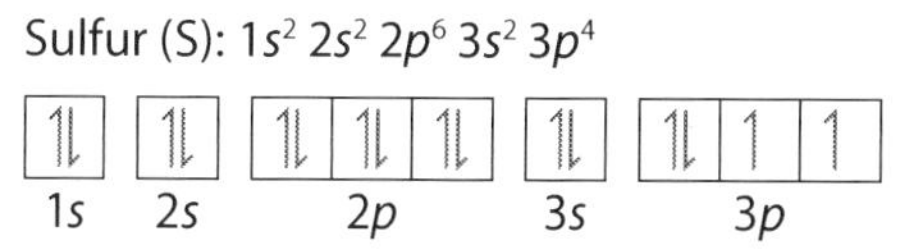

Figure 2.12. Electron Configuration of Sulfur

The electrons in the outermost shell of an atom are the **valence electrons**. In sulfur, shown at left, the six electrons in the $n = 3$ shell (3*s* and 3*p*) are the valence electrons. Atoms are most stable when they have a configuration of ns^2np^6—8 total electrons—in their outer shell. Atoms that are close to having a complete valence shell are extremely reactive: atoms with one extra electron will lose it easily, and atoms that need only one atom to complete their shell will gain it easily. Atoms with full valence shells (the noble gases) are inert. Electrons that are not in the valence shell are the **core electrons**.

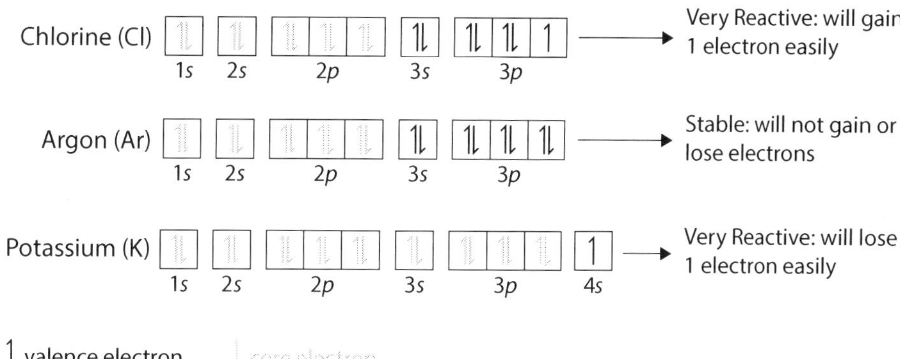

Figure 2.13. Valence Electrons

SAMPLE QUESTIONS

8) **Which of the following electron configurations does NOT follow the aufbau principle?**

A. $1s^2\ 2s^2\ 2p^6\ 3s^1$

B. $1s^2\ 2s^2\ 2p^6\ 3s^2$

C. $1s^1\ 2s^2\ 2p^6\ 3s^1$

D. $1s^2\ 2s^2\ 2p^6\ 3s^2\ 3p^1$

Answer:

C. Correct. $1s^1\ 2s^2\ 2p^6\ 3s^1$

The 1*s* orbital is not completely filled.

9) **Which of the following is the correct electron configuration for phosphorus (P)?**

A. $1s^2\ 2s^2\ 2p^6\ 3s^2\ 3p^2$

B. $1s^2\ 2s^2\ 2p^6\ 3s^2\ 3p^4$

C. $1s^1\ 2s^2\ 2p^6\ 3s^2\ 3p^4$

D. $1s^2\ 2s^2\ 2p^6\ 3s^2\ 3p^3$

Answers:

A. Incorrect. This configuration has the wrong number of electrons.

B. Incorrect. This configuration has the wrong number of electrons.

C. Incorrect. This configuration has a half-filled 1*s* orbital.

D. Correct. This configuration has the correct number of electrons in the correct orbitals.

Electron Configuration and the Periodic Table

The periodic table is arranged in order of increasing atomic number, meaning the table is organized by the number of electrons in an atom. This arrangement makes it possible to easily identify the number of valence electrons in each element, as shown in Figure 2.14. All the elements in a group have the same number of valence electrons, with the number of the period corresponding to the principal quantum number of the valence shell.

HELPFUL HINT

Reading the periodic table from left to right and top to bottom gives the order in which orbitals are filled: 1*s*, 2*s*, 2*p*, 3*s*, 3*p*, 4*s*, 3*d*, 4*p*, and so on.

Because valence electrons determine the reactivity of elements, the members of a group on the table all share similar properties. Group 1 (IA) contains the **alkali metals**, which create alkaline aqueous solutions. Group 2 (IIA) contains the **alkali earth metals**, which are extracted from minerals and create alkaline solutions. Both groups contain very reactive metals and, as such, the metals are found only in compounds in nature, not in their free metallic forms.

Groups 13 (IIIA) through 17 (VIIA) do not have special names, but they do contain the most abundant elements in the earth's crust and atmosphere. Groups 14 (IVA), 15 (VA), and 16 (VIA) each begin with at least one nonmetal, include a metalloid, and end with a metal. Group 17 (VIIA) contains the **halogens**, which are highly reactive. The word *halogen* comes from two Greek words: *hals* (salt) and *genes* (forming). The halogen elements all form salts upon reacting with metals. Group 18 (VIIIA) contains the **noble gases**, which are the least reactive elements.

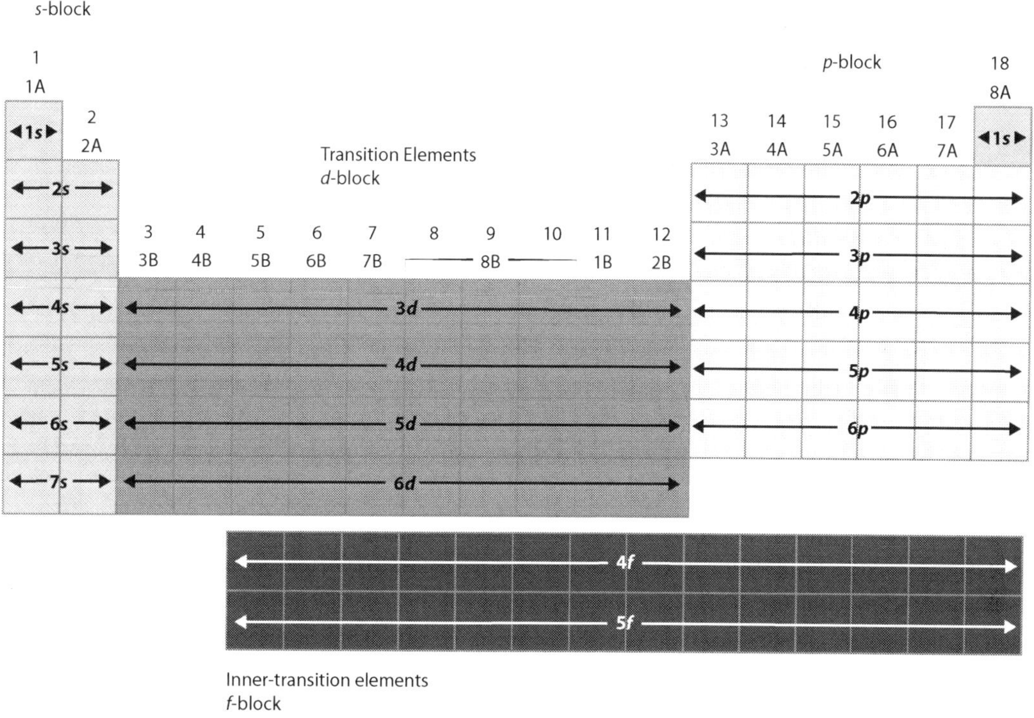

Figure 2.14. Valence Electron Configuration in the Periodic Table

The two rows at the bottom of the periodic table contain the **lanthanides** and **actinides**. They are separated to keep the periodic table from becoming too wide. Their location in the periodic table is indicated by the two blocks below Scandium (Sc) and Yttrium (Y).

HELPFUL HINT

While the number of valence electrons typically increases sequentially across a period, there are some exceptions to this in the *d*- and *f*-blocks. These exceptions occur because of the significant increase in stability for an element with a half-filled valence shell.

SAMPLE QUESTION

10) Which of the following groups are included in the *f*-block elements?

A. alkali metals

B. alkaline earth metals

C. halogens

D. lanthanides

Answers:

A. Incorrect. The alkali metals are group 1, which is in the *s*-block.

B. Incorrect. The alkaline earth metals are group 2, which is in the *s*-block.

C. Incorrect. The halogens are group 17, which is in the *p*-block.

D. **Correct.** The lanthanides are in the *f*-block because they all contain partially filled *f*-orbitals.

Periodic Properties of Elements

The elements in the periodic table are arranged in order of increasing atomic number because of the **law of chemical periodicity**, which states that the properties of the elements are periodic and predictable when they're arranged in order of increasing atomic number. Because of this law, the periodic table shows trends across groups and periods for a number of important properties, including atomic radii, ionic radii, ionization energy, electron affinity, and electronegativity.

> HELPFUL HINT
>
> left to right → electron added to same valence shell → atomic radii decrease
>
> top to bottom → electron added to a different shell → atomic radii increase

Atomic radius is a measure of the size of an atom from the nucleus to the boundary of the surrounding electron cloud. In the periodic table, the atomic radii increase going down a group as more electrons are added. It decreases going across a period from left to right as the attraction between the nucleus and the increasing number of electrons grows stronger.

The trend for the ionic radii is the same as that for the atomic radii. Positive and negative ions of elements in the same group increase in size down a group. The cation radius of an element is smaller than the anion radius of the element because a cation can hold the electron cloud of the atom more tightly.

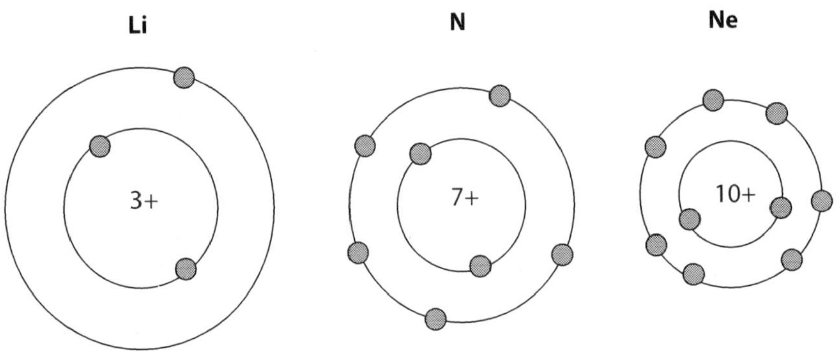

Figure 2.15. Atomic Radii Left to Right Within a Period

The **ionization energy** of an element is the energy required to remove an electron from an atom of the element in the gas phase. The more energy that is required to remove the electron, the greater the ionization energy. Ionization energies tend to decrease down a group and increase across a period. When moving down a group, the atoms become larger and the valence electrons are farther away from the nucleus, making it easier to remove electrons. However, when moving across a period, the atoms have more protons, which more strongly attract the electrons to the nucleus and make it harder to remove an electron.

The **electron affinity** of an element is the change in energy when a –1 ion is formed; it indicates the attraction an atom has for an electron. Atoms with a negative electron affinity value have a higher electron affinity than atoms with a positive value. This is because atoms that become more stable with the addition of an electron decrease in potential energy, resulting in a negative value. When atoms become less stable with the addition of an electron, the potential energy increases, resulting in a more positive electron affinity value. The electron affinity tends to increase across a period, with the halogens having the largest electron affinity.

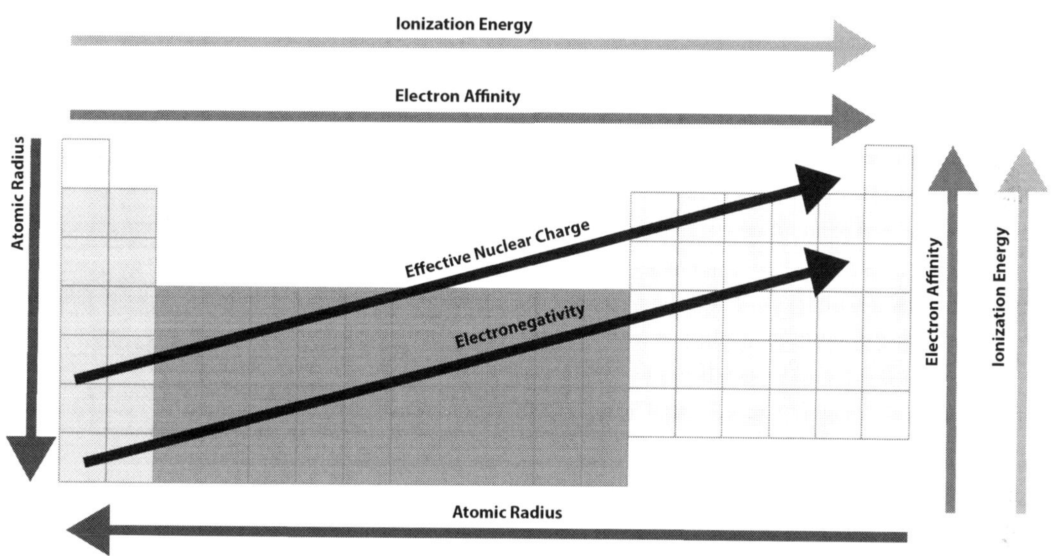

Figure 2.16. Trends of the Periodic Table

The **electronegativity** of an element is the ability of an atom in a covalent bond to attract the shared electrons. On the periodic table, the electronegativity increases diagonally upward and to the right. That is, electronegativity increases across a period because of a stronger attraction for electrons as the nuclear charge increases; it decreases down a group because of the increased distance between the nucleus and the valence electron shell.

Effective nuclear charge (Z_{eff}) is the net positive charge experienced by an electron in a multi-electron atom. It is described by the equation

$$Z_{eff} = Z - S$$

HELPFUL HINT

While they are mostly inert, the noble gases Krypton and Xenon can be made to react with highly electronegative atoms, so both elements have an electronegativity value.

where Z_{eff} is the effective nuclear charge, Z is the number of protons, and S is the screening constant. The value of S is close to the number of core electrons, whose charge shields valance electrons from the nucleus. Effective nuclear charge increases from left to right across periods as the number of protons increases, but the number of core electrons remains constant.

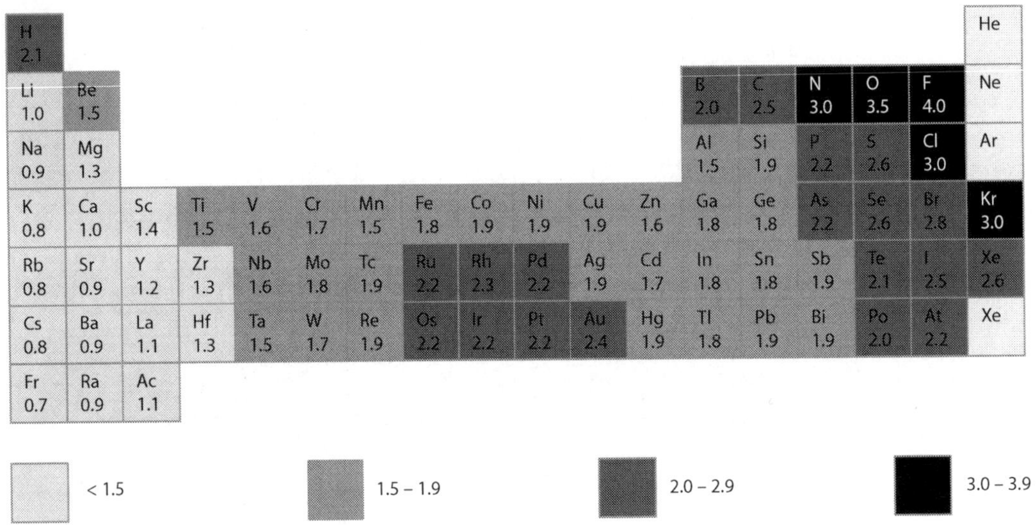

Figure 2.17. Electronegativity

SAMPLE QUESTIONS

11) Arrange the following elements in order of increasing ionization energy: Al, S, Na, and Mg.

A. Mg < Na < S < Al

B. Na < Mg < Al < S

C. Na < Al < Mg < S

D. Al < Na < Mg < S

Answer:

B. Correct. Na < Mg < Al < S

The ionization energy of elements increases across a period (row).

12) Arrange the following elements in order of increasing electronegativity: C, F, N, and O.

A. C < N < O < F

B. F < N < O < C

C. F < O < N < C

D. C < N < F < O

Answer:

A. Correct. C < N < O < F

Electronegativity increases across a period (row).

NUCLEAR CHEMISTRY

RADIOACTIVITY

In a chemical reaction, such as combustion or acid-base neutralization, it is only the number of electrons in an atom that changes—the nucleus remains unaffected. Conversely, in a **nuclear reaction**, changes occur in an atom's nucleus, affecting the number of protons, neutrons, or both. In a nuclear reaction, unstable atoms called **radioisotopes** spontaneously emit particles and energy.

HELPFUL HINT

A **nuclide** is a nucleus that contains a specific number of protons and neutrons.

Table 2.5. Particles and Emissions in Nuclear Reactions

Proton	${}^{1}_{1}p$
Neutron	${}^{1}_{0}n$
Electron	${}^{0}_{-1}e$
Alpha particle	${}^{4}_{2}\alpha$
Beta particle	${}^{0}_{-1}\beta$
Gamma particle	${}^{0}_{0}\gamma$
Positron	${}^{0}_{1}e$

In **alpha decay**, atoms emit **alpha (α) particles**, which contain two protons and two neutrons. Alpha particles are written as ${}^{4}_{2}\alpha$ or ${}^{4}_{2}He$ because they are identical to a helium nucleus. They have a high ionization power (100 times higher than beta particles and 10,000 times higher than gamma radiation), meaning they have the potential to cause severe damage to biological tissue. However, their penetrating power is low: they can only travel a few centimeters through the air, and they cannot penetrate even thin surfaces.

HELPFUL HINT

A **radioactive series** is a sequence of nuclear reactions that create a stable nucleus from a previously unstable one. There are three naturally occurring radioactive sequences: thorium-232 to lead-208, uranium-235 to lead-207, and uranium-238 to lead-206.

Alpha decay can be described using a **nuclear equation**, which includes the element symbols of each atom or particle along with their atomic and mass numbers.

In a nuclear equation, the number of neutrons and protons must balance on each side. To balance a nuclear reaction or find a missing part of the equation, make sure that the sum of the top numbers is equal and that the sum of the bottom numbers is equal.

The equation below shows the decay of radium-226 to create radon and an alpha particle. Note that the top and bottom numbers balance:

$$^{226}_{88}Ra \rightarrow ^{222}_{86}Ra + ^{4}_{2}\alpha$$

$$226 = 222 + 4$$

$$88 = 86 + 2$$

Beta decay releases **beta (β) particles**, which have the charge of an electron but can be thought of as fast-moving electrons emitted by the nucleus. Beta particles are written as $^{0}_{-1}e$ or $^{0}_{-1}\beta$ or , so the resulting element will have a higher atomic number. They have a low ionization power (about 1/100th the power of an alpha particle), but are highly penetrative (100 times more than alpha particles). The nuclear equation below shows the decay of carbon-14 to nitrogen-14:

$$^{14}_{6}C \rightarrow ^{14}_{7}N + ^{0}_{-1}\beta$$

Gamma (γ) radiation consists of high-energy, short wavelength photons that are often released with other radioactive particles during decay. They are written as $^{0}_{0}\gamma$ and do not change the number of protons or neutrons in the atom. Their penetrating power is greater than alpha and beta particles, but their ionization power is much lower.

HELPFUL HINT

When positrons collide with electrons, they create gamma rays: $^{0}_{1}e + ^{0}_{-1}e \rightarrow ^{0}_{0}\gamma$

A **positron** has a charge of +1 and the same mass as an electron, so it is written as $^{0}_{1}e$. The nuclear equation below shows the decay of sodium-22, which produces a neon atom.

$$^{22}_{11}Na \rightarrow ^{22}_{10}Ne + ^{0}_{1}e$$

Electrons themselves can also be taken into the nucleus during **electron capture**. The equation below shows the decay of beryllium to produce lithium caused by electron capture; note that the electron appears on the left side of the equation.

$$^{7}_{4}Be + ^{0}_{-1}e \rightarrow ^{7}_{3}Li$$

The type of radioactive decay an element undergoes is determined by the ratio of neutrons to protons in its nucleus. Because neutrons are needed to counteract the attraction between protons, larger atoms require more neutrons. The optimum neutron to proton ratio lies in the **belt of stability** shown in Figure 2.18. An element's position relative to the belt determines its radioactivity:

- Elements above the belt will experience beta decay and move closer to the belt by increasing their number of protons.

- Elements below the belt will undergo either positron emission or electron capture; they move closer to the belt by decreasing their number of protons.
- Nuclei with more than 84 protons will undergo alpha decay, which moves them closer to the belt by decreasing the numbers of both protons and neutrons.

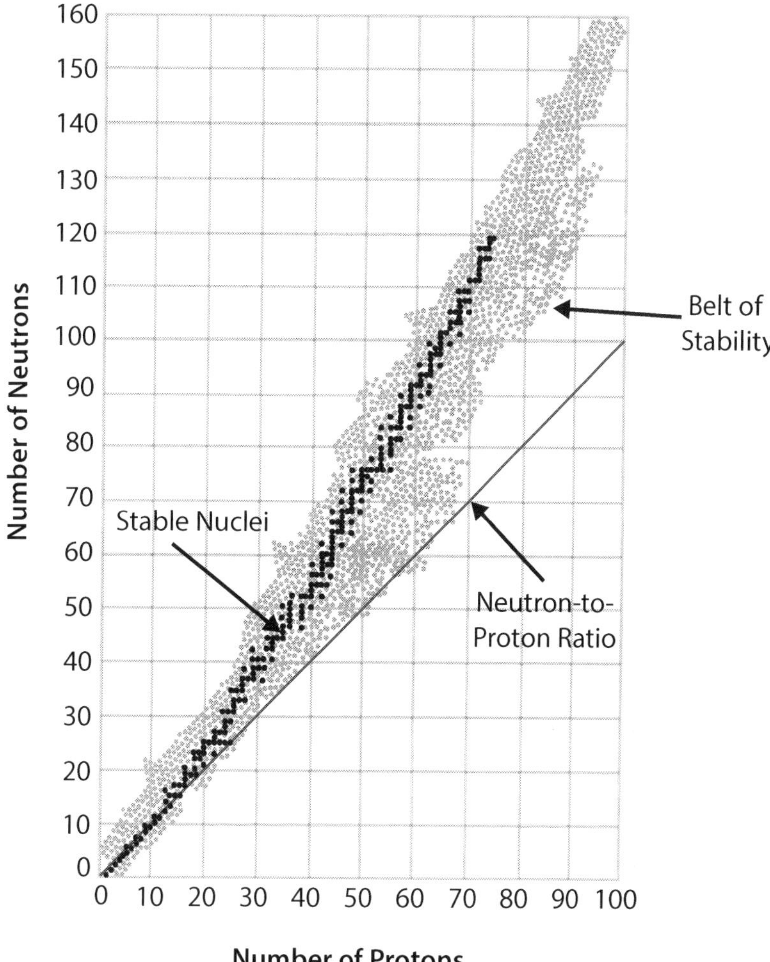

Figure 2.18. Belt of Stability

SAMPLE QUESTIONS

13) **What type of particle is released when thorium-232 undergoes decay to form radon-228?**

A. alpha particle

B. beta particle

C. gamma particle

D. positron

Answer:

A. Correct. Write the nuclear equation and set up two equations to find the missing values:

$^{232}_{90}\text{Th} \rightarrow {}^{228}_{88}\text{Ra} + {}^{a}_{b}X$

$232 = 228 + a$

$a = 4$

$90 = 88 + b$

$b = 2$

The decay releases an **alpha particle**:

$^{232}_{90}\text{Th} \rightarrow {}^{228}_{88}\text{Ra} + {}^{4}_{2}\alpha$

14) **What type of particle is released when cesium-137 undergoes decay to form barium-137?**

A. alpha particle

B. beta particle

C. gamma particle

D. positron

Answer:

B. Correct. Write the nuclear equation and set up two equations to find the missing values:

$^{137}_{55}\text{Cs} \rightarrow {}^{137}_{56}\text{Ba} + {}^{a}_{b}X$

$137 = 137 + a$

$a = 0$

$55 = 56 + b$

$b = -1$

The decay releases a **beta particle**:

$^{137}_{55}\text{Cs} \rightarrow {}^{137}_{56}\text{Ba} + {}^{0}_{-1}\beta$

Half-Life

The time it takes for substances to decay varies widely—some radioisotopes decay completely in only a few seconds, while others decay over millions of years. The time it takes for half of a radioactive sample to decay is that substance's **half-life** (h or $t_{\frac{1}{2}}$). The equation for half-life is written as

$$A = A_0\left(\frac{1}{2}\right)^{\frac{t}{h}}$$

where A is the final amount, A_0 is the initial amount, t is the time, and h is the half-life.

Half-life is also described using the first-order rate constant, k:

$$\ln\frac{N_t}{N_0} = -kt$$

where N_t is the remaining number of nuclei, N_0 is the original number of nuclei, k is the **decay constant**, and t is time.

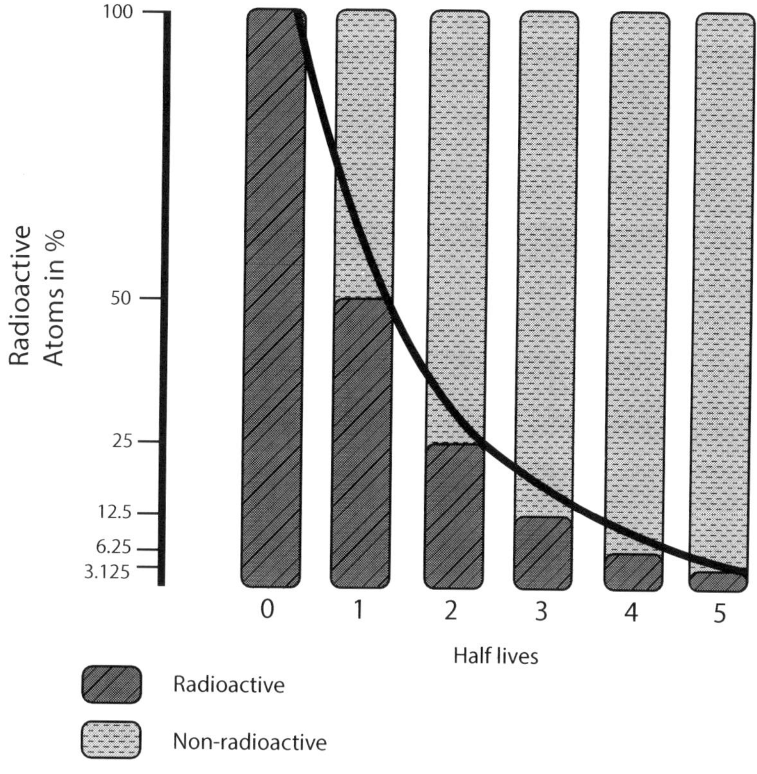

Figure 2.19. Half-Life Decay

Half-life and the decay constant are related by the equation

$$k = \frac{0.693}{t_{\frac{1}{2}}}$$

SAMPLE QUESTION

15) What is the half-life of uranium-235 if $k = 1.65 \times 10^{-10}$ yr^{-1}?

A. 1.65×10^{9} years

B. 8.25×10^{10} years

C. 4.20×10^{9} years

D. 4.50×10^{10} years

Answer:

C. Correct. Use the equation for the decay constant.

$$t_{\frac{1}{2}} = \frac{0.693}{k} = \frac{0.693}{1.65 \times 10^{-10}\text{ yr}^{-1}} = \mathbf{4.20 \times 10^{9}\ years}$$

Nuclear Energy of an Atom

Nuclear fission occurs when a nucleus splits into two or more light nuclei after being bombarded by particles such as protons, neutrons, or alpha particles. Fission occurs to heavy nuclei with atomic numbers greater than 230. For example, when uranium is bombarded with low energy thermal neutrons, it splits into two smaller nuclei and releases neutrons:

$$^{1}_{0}n + ^{235}_{92}U \rightarrow ^{141}_{56}Ba + ^{92}_{36}Kr + 3\,^{1}_{0}n$$

The neutrons released during fission can in turn lead to more fission reactions, ultimately setting off a series of nuclear fission reactions called a **chain reaction**. When the chain reaction is **uncontrolled**, it is self-sustaining and gives off energy at a rapidly increasing rate. If the reaction is **controlled** so that only a single neutron emitted during fission leads to another fission, the fission rate stays constant and energy is steadily released. Nuclear fission is used in atomic bombs and to power nuclear power plants.

Nuclear fusion happens when two or more light nuclei fuse to form a single heavy nucleus. Below is an example of the fusion of hydrogen nuclei into helium nuclei, a process that is believed to power most stars:

$$^{1}_{1}H + ^{1}_{1}H \rightarrow ^{2}_{1}H + ^{0}_{1}e$$

$$^{2}_{1}H + ^{2}_{1}H \rightarrow ^{3}_{2}He + ^{1}_{0}n$$

$$^{2}_{1}H + ^{2}_{1}H \rightarrow ^{3}_{1}H + ^{1}_{1}H$$

These reactions only occur under extremely high heat and pressure. Such conditions have been created in thermonuclear (or hydrogen) bombs, but nuclear fusion is not currently used for other purposes.

SAMPLE QUESTION

16) Which of the following is an example of nuclear fission?

A. $^{2}_{1}H + ^{3}_{1}H \rightarrow 2 + ^{1}_{0}n$

B. $4\,^{1}_{1}H \rightarrow ^{4}_{2}He + 2\,^{0}_{1}e$

C. $^{2}_{1}H + ^{3}_{2}He \rightarrow ^{4}_{2}He + ^{1}_{1}H$

D. $^{1}_{0}n + ^{239}_{94}Pu \rightarrow ^{134}_{54}Xe + ^{103}_{40}Zr + 3\,^{1}_{0}n$

Answer:

D. Correct.

$^{1}_{0}n + ^{239}_{94}Pu \rightarrow ^{134}_{54}Xe + ^{103}_{40}Zr + 3\,^{1}_{0}n$

Some of the products have a lower mass number and lower atomic number, meaning larger atoms were split into smaller ones.

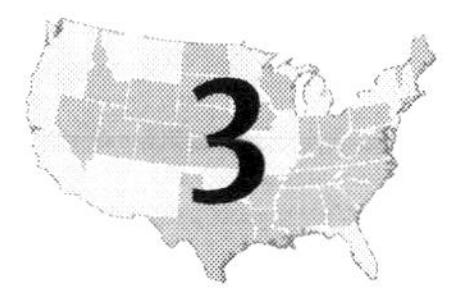

Bonding

Ionic Bonds

Ionic bonds tend to form between elements toward the left side of the periodic table, which have low ionization energies, and elements on the right side, with large negative electron affinities. Both the atoms losing electrons and those gaining electrons are stabilized by attaining a full outer shell, or octet configuration, of s^2p^6, except for Li and Be, which yield a $1s^2$ filled outer shell.

The attraction between the positive and negative ions results in the formation of a regular crystal, or lattice, in which each positive ion interacts with several negative ions around it, and vice versa. The energy released by the stabilizing effect of lattice formation is called the **lattice energy**. The formation of ionic compounds is exothermic due to the stabilizing effects of a full outer electron shell and a lattice that balances the attractive and repulsive forces of the ions. Sodium chloride, NaCl, is a typical ionic compound. Na loses an electron to Cl, and the resulting Na^+ and Cl^- ions form a lattice in which each ion is surrounded by six ions of the opposite charge.

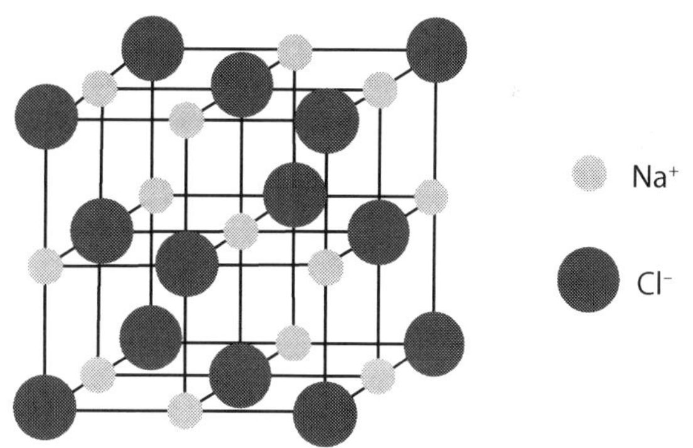

Figure 3.1. A Lattice of Na^+ and Cl^- ions

To form a filled outer shell, elements in family 1 lose one electron and form ions with a charge of 1^+. Elements in family 2 lose two electrons and form 2^+ cations. Cations are smaller than the corresponding neutral atom. The halogens accept an electron to form anions

HELPFUL HINT

The noble gases are highly stable because they have filled outer shells and do not ionize.

with a charge of 1^-. Atoms in family 16 tend to accept two electrons to form anions with a charge of 2^-. Anions are larger than the corresponding atoms.

QUICK REVIEW

Explain the changes in atomic size when electrons are gained or lost in terms of the change in electron-electron repulsion in the outer orbitals.

The transition metals also form cations. Most of them can have multiple charges. They lose their outer *s* electrons first and then their outer *d* electron(s).

In addition to ions formed by single atoms, there are also polyatomic ions, such as NH_4^+, CO_3^{2-} and CrO_4^{2-}. Most are negatively charged and contain oxygen. The atoms within these ions are covalently bonded, and the whole molecule has a charge and can bond with oppositely charged ions.

SAMPLE QUESTION

1) **Which of the following pairs of atoms is most likely to form an ionic bond?**

A. O and H

B. Li and F

C. Be and Ne

D. Ni and Cu

Answers:

A. Incorrect. Both oxygen and hydrogen are in the upper right corner of the periodic table and do not form ionic bonds.

B. **Correct.** Lithium is an alkali metal and forms the ion Li^+, and fluorine is a halogen that forms the ion F^-. The two ions form an ionic bond to make LiF.

C. Incorrect. Neon is a noble gas and does not form ionic bonds.

D. Incorrect. Both nickel and copper are metals and do not form ionic bonds.

Covalent Bonds

In **covalent** molecules, electrons are shared between atoms. Nonmetals occupying the top of family 13 and extending down and across the periodic table to encompass all the halogens are capable of forming covalent bonds. Covalent bonding stabilizes the molecule by giving each participant in the bond a completely filled outer octet. Hydrogen also forms covalent bonds, resulting in two electrons filling its *s* shell.

POLARITY

Covalent bonds may be nonpolar or polar. In a **nonpolar bond**, electrons are shared equally between the atoms. Diatomic gases, such as Cl_2 and N_2, exhibit nonpolar bonding.

When one of the atoms has a stronger attraction for electrons than the other, it attracts more of the electron density toward itself, resulting in a **polar bond**. Atoms with high ionization energies and high electron affinities have a high attractive force for electrons, or electronegativity, in bonds.

HELPFUL HINT

The chemical interactions of polar molecules are dependent on the orientation of the molecules, so a little arrow is often drawn over the molecule to show the direction of charge. Nonpolar molecules have no dipole (and no arrow), so the interaction is less dependent on the orientation of the molecule.

C ——— Cl

δ+ δ−

Figure 3.2. Dipole Moment

Polar bonds can be visualized as **dipoles**, where there is a partial negative charge on the more electronegative atom and a partial positive charge on the less electronegative atom. **Dipole moment** is a measure of the strength of a dipole and is expressed in a unit called a debye. The formula for dipole moment is $\mu = \delta d$, where δ is the effective charge and d is the distance between the charges. The charge δ is a function of the difference in electronegativity between the atoms participating in the dipole. Longer distances between charges translate into larger dipole moments.

A molecule is considered polar if it contains polar bonds that do not balance each other out. In other words, it has a net dipole moment. CH_3Cl is polar, but, in contrast, CCl_4 is not. Although the C—Cl bond is polar, in CCl_4, the bonds are symmetrically distributed around the central carbon and are all equally polar so there is no net dipole moment. Likewise, the linear molecule O=C=O has no dipole moment because the two opposing C=O dipoles cancel each other out.

SAMPLE QUESTION

2) **Put the bonds C—H, H—F, and H—Br in order of increasing polarity.**

A. C—H, H—F, H—Br

B. C—H, H—Br, H—F

C. H—Br, C—H, H—F

D. H—Br, H—F, C—H

Answer:

B. **Correct.** The difference in electronegativities of the halogens and hydrogen is much greater than the difference between carbon and hydrogen. Fluorine is higher in family 17 than bromine and more electronegative.

HYBRIDIZATION

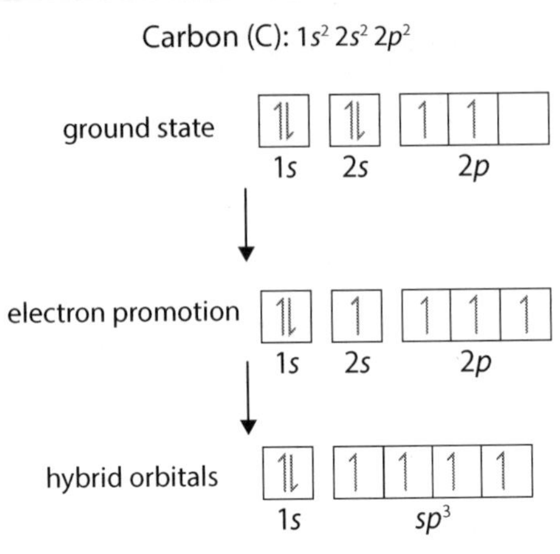

Figure 3.3. Electron Promotion and Hybrid Orbitals

When electrons are shared between atoms, the outer atomic orbitals can hybridize to form orbitals that are of the same average energy as the atomic orbitals from which they formed. For this to happen, atoms "promote" paired electrons to higher-energy orbitals, freeing unpaired electrons for covalent bonds. Carbon, for example, promotes one electron from its 2*s* orbital to its 2*p* orbital, creating four orbitals with one electron each. These orbitals hybridize to form four sp^3 orbitals of equal energy.

Mixing a certain number of orbitals results in the same number of hybrid orbitals. An *s* orbital can hybridize with one, two, or three *p* orbitals, and *d* orbitals may also hybridize with *s* and *p* orbitals for elements in period 3 and below. These hybridizations result in the following hybrid orbitals:

- $s + p$ = two *sp* orbitals
- $s + p + p$ = three sp^2 orbitals
- $s + p + p + p$ = four sp^3 orbitals
- $s + p + p + p + d$ = five sp^3d orbitals
- $s + p + p + p + d + d$ = six sp^3d^2 orbitals

SAMPLE QUESTION

3) **In BeF_2, the orbitals of the Be atom hybridize to form**

A. two *sp* orbitals.

B. three sp^2 orbitals.

C. four sp^3 orbitals.

D. five sp^3d orbitals.

Answer:

A. Correct. Be promotes one electron from its filled 2*s* shell to its empty 2*p* shell, creating two *sp* orbitals.

SIGMA (σ) AND PI (π) BONDS

Sigma (σ) bonds are formed by two orbitals lined up end to end. They are usually single bonds, and are the strongest type of covalent bond.

Sigma bonds can be formed from regular or hybrid orbitals. The diatomic molecule H_2, for example, includes a σ bond between the *s* orbitals on each atom. In the molecule CH_4, the four sp^3 orbitals bond with the *s* orbital of the hydrogen atoms, giving the molecule a tetrahedral structure that minimizes electron-electron repulsion.

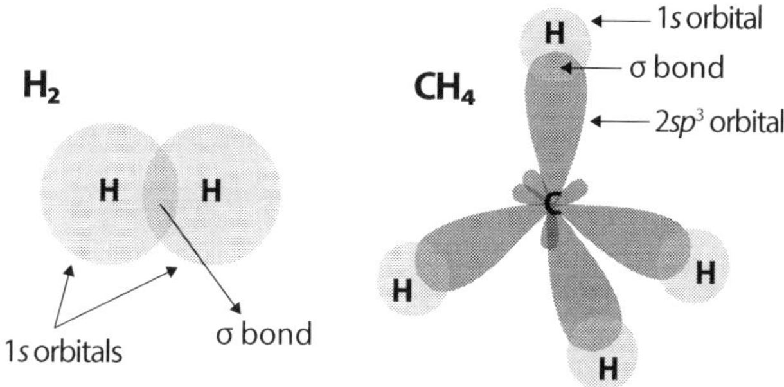

Figure 3.4. Sigma Bonds in Hydrogen Gas and Methane

Pi (π) bonds are formed by the lateral overlap of two *p* or *d* orbitals, and are usually formed between atoms after a σ bond has already formed. A double bond consists of one σ and one π bond; a triple bond consists of one σ bond and two π bonds. For example, in ethene (C_2H_4), the carbons undergo sp^2 hybridization. The sp^2 orbitals overlap to form three σ bonds: one with each hydrogen atom, and one with the other carbon. The remaining *p* orbitals overlap to form a π bond—the second bond of the double bond. In ethyne, two sets of *p* orbitals overlap to form two π bonds (see Figure 3.6).

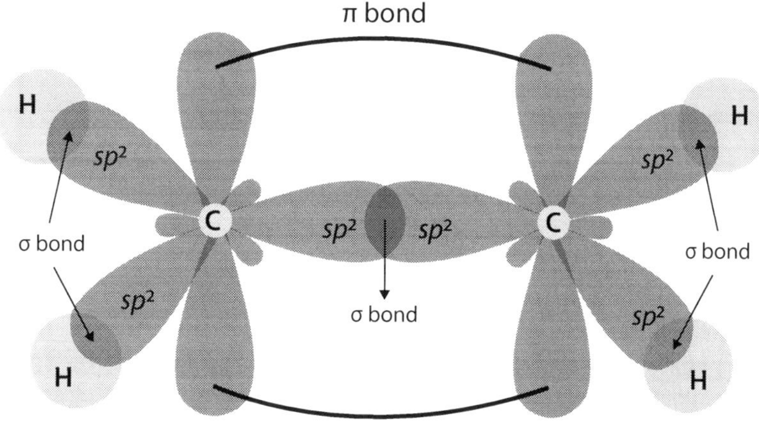

Figure 3.5. sp^2 Hybridization with a π Bond in Ethene (Trigonal Planar)

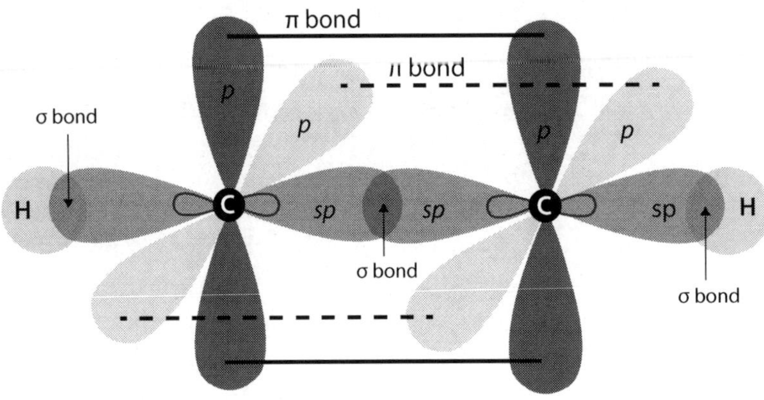

Figure 3.6. *sp* Hybridization with Two π Bonds in Ethyne (Linear)

SAMPLE QUESTION

4) **Which of the following compounds does NOT contain a π bond?**

A. F_2
B. N_2
C. O_2
D. C_2H_4

Answer:

A. Correct. F_2 includes a single covalent bond. The other three compounds all include a double or triple bond, which is a π bond.

Lewis Structures

It can often be difficult to figure out the bonding structure of complex covalent compounds simply from their chemical formulas. **Lewis structures** and formal charge are means of determining the most stable and therefore likely configuration. Lewis structures are based on the octet rule—that atoms will share electrons so that each atom has a complete set of eight of electrons in its outer shell. This configuration mimics the very stable electron configuration of the nearest noble gas. The steps in determining a Lewis structure are as follows:

1. Calculate the total number of valence electrons for all the atoms.
2. Place the least electronegative atom in the center position.
3. Place H and F in terminal positions.
4. Connect the terminal atoms to central atoms with single bonds.
5. Calculate the remaining number of electrons.
6. Place lone pairs of electrons around the terminal atoms to give an octet—except for H, which gets two electrons.

7. Place any remaining electrons around the central atom as lone pairs.
8. Check the number of electrons around each atom.
9. Move electrons from terminal atoms to the central atom, creating multiple bonds if necessary to achieve an octet on the central atom.

In some cases, it is possible to draw multiple nonequivalent Lewis structures for a molecule. Formal charge is used to determine which structure is correct. **Formal charge** (FC) is the difference between the number of valence electrons of a free atom and the number of electrons assigned in the Lewis structure. It is calculated for each atom in the molecule, and the structure that yields the lowest formal charge value is the most stable. Formal charge is calculated for each atom as:

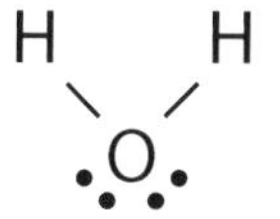

Figure 3.7. Lewis Structure of H_2O

$$FC = \text{valence electrons} - \text{lone pair electrons} - \frac{1}{2}\text{bonding electrons}$$

Sometimes there is more than one equivalent Lewis structure, called **resonance structures**, for a molecule. For example, SO_2 can be drawn two ways. In these cases, the electron density is on average evenly divided between the two bonds, so the true structure is an average of the two forms.

HELPFUL HINT

Boron has only six electrons in its outer shell. Therefore, BF_3 tends to react with molecules, such as NH_3, that can donate two electrons to form a bond.

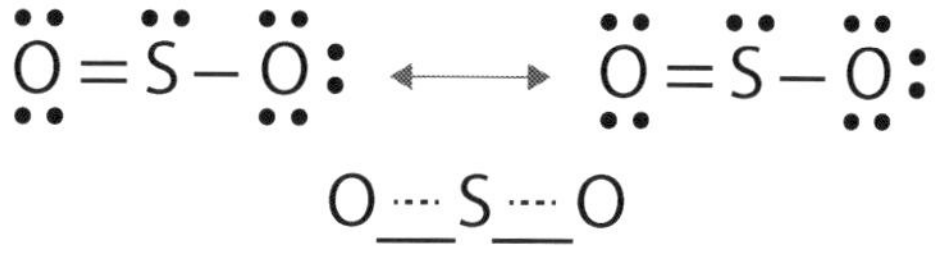

Figure 3.8. Resonance Forms of SO_2

There are three exceptions to the octet rule. These exceptions have Lewis structures that do not always follow the rules given above.

- Incomplete octets—these usually form with F or H. Fluorine is too electronegative to donate electrons to a double bond. Hydrogen can only accommodate two electrons in its outer and only shell. An example of a compound with an incomplete octet is BF_3.

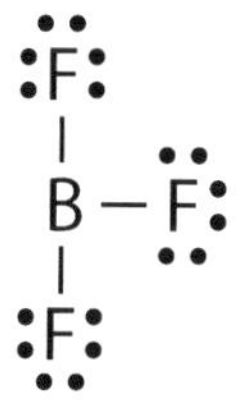

Figure 3.9. Incomplete Octet in BF_3

- Molecules with odd numbers of electrons. An example is NO_2.

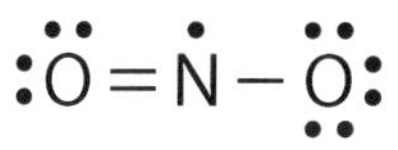

Figure 3.10. Odd Numbers of Electrons in NO_2

- Elements with an expanded valence shell—elements in the third period and below—have empty *d* orbitals and can accommodate more than an octet around the central atom. An example is PCl_5, which has ten electrons around phosphorus.

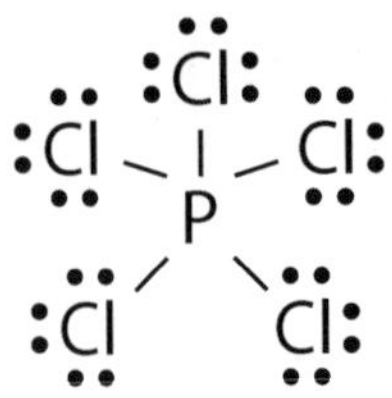

Figure 3.11. Lewis Structure of PCl_5

SAMPLE QUESTIONS

5) **Draw the Lewis structure for CO_2.**

A.  O::C::O

B. :O–C–O:

C. :O–C–O:

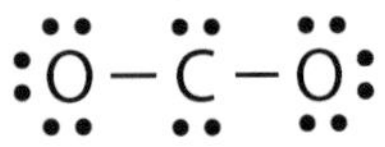

D. 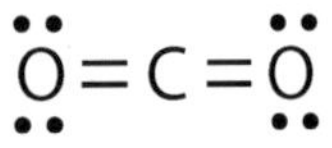 O=C=O

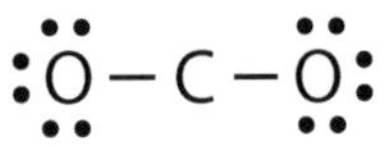

Answers:

A. Incorrect. Lines are used to denote bonds rather than electron pairs.

B. Incorrect. Carbon only has four electrons. It should have an octet.

C. Incorrect. The least electronegative atom goes in the center. Also, there are too many electrons—twenty. C, O, and O only have a total of sixteen valence electrons.

D. Correct. The less electronegative carbon is in the center. Placing single bonds between the atoms and placing the remaining lone pairs on the oxygen atoms leaves carbon with only four electrons. A lone pair is donated from each oxygen to form two double bonds, giving carbon an octet.

6) **Which Lewis structure is correct for $COCl_2$?**

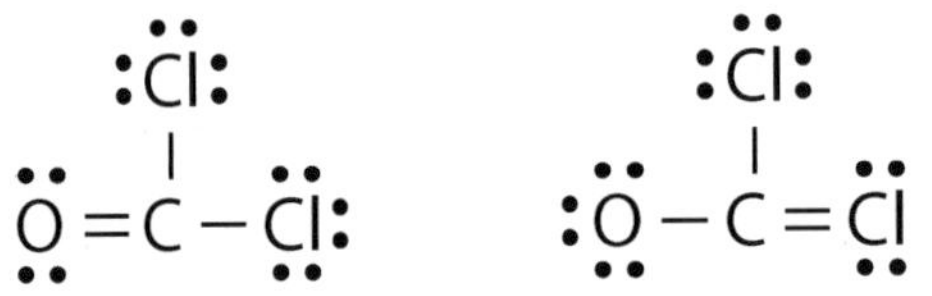

Structure A: O=C(–Cl)–Cl: or Structure B: :O–C(–Cl)=Cl

Structure A or Structure B

Answers:

A. **Structure A is correct.** Structure A minimizes the formal charges—all are zero.

O has 6 valence electrons – 4 lone pair electrons – ½ of 4 bonding electrons = 0.

C has 4 valence electrons – no lone pairs – ½ of 8 bonding electrons = 0.

Cl has 7 valence electrons – 6 lone pair electrons – ½ of 2 bonding electrons = 0.

B. Structure B is incorrect.

For O: 6 valence electrons – 6 lone pair electrons – ½ of 2 bonding electrons = –1.

For C: Same as in structure A: 0.

For singly bonded Cl: same as in structure A: 0.

For doubly bonded Cl: 7 valence electrons – 4 lone pair electrons – ½ of 4 bonding electrons = 1.

THE VSEPR MODEL

The valence shell electron pair repulsion (VSEPR) model predicts **molecular geometry** based on Lewis structures. Valence electrons are both attracted to the central nucleus and repelled by each other. VSEPR places both the bonding electrons and the lone pairs around the central atom in the geometric arrangement that minimizes the repulsion between them. The model predicts the measured bond angles of many molecules perfectly and is a good approximation for most others.

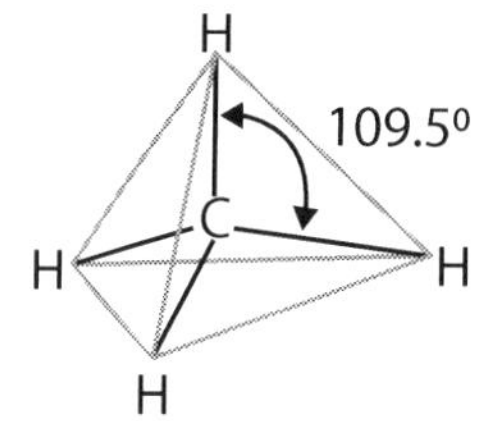

Figure 3.12. VSEPR Structure of Methane

For the simple molecule CH_4, VSEPR predicts a tetrahedral arrangement that places each bonding pair as far as possible from its nearest neighbor. The angles in a tetrahedron are 109.5 degrees, and that is the measured bond angle for CH_4.

The VSEPR model holds that lone pairs of electrons occupy more space than bonding pairs because the bonding pairs are attracted to two nuclei, whereas the lone pairs only experience the attractive force of the central nucleus. Therefore, lone pairs repel bonding pairs a bit more than bonding pairs repel each other. This effect can be seen in the geometry of NH_3 shown next.

QUICK REVIEW

Carbon has four valence electrons and is the element that makes up diamond and graphite. Graphite is a two-dimensional sheet, where three valence electrons are equally spaced (at angles of 120°) in a plane while the fourth is perpendicular to the plane. In diamond, the valence electrons are equally spaced in a three-dimensional crystal. What are the ideal bond angles for diamond?

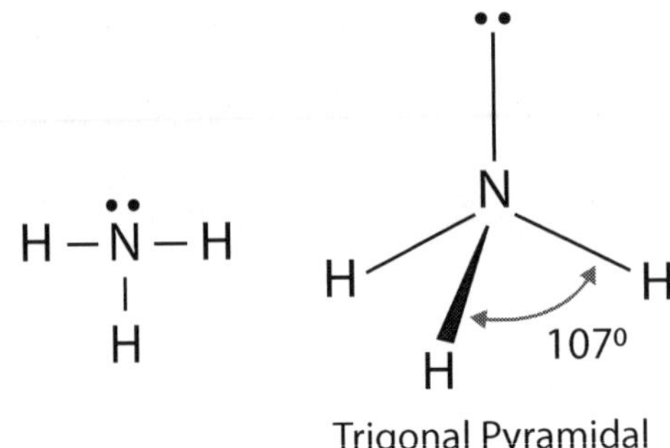

Figure 3.13. Lewis Structure and Molecular Geometry of NH^3

The bond angles are 107 degrees rather than 109.5 degrees because the lone pair repels the bonding electrons more strongly than they repel each other. The description of the molecule as "trigonal pyramidal" refers to the position of the bonded atoms and does not include the position of the lone pair. Spectroscopy and diffraction are used to determine the actual positions of the atoms and bond angles.

When there are double bonds or triple bonds, they are treated like single bonds except that they are expected to take up somewhat more space and will push out adjacent bonds a bit more.

Table 3.1 shows the VSEPR geometries predicted for various Lewis structures. The steric number is the number of atoms bonded to the central atom plus the number of lone pairs on the central atom.

Table 3.1. VSEPR Molecular Geometries

Bonding Electron Pairs	Lone Pairs	Electron Domains (Steric Number)	Shape Name	Ideal Bond Angle	Example	Shape
4	0	4	tetrahedral	109.5°	CH_4	
6	0	6	octahedral	90°, 180°	SF_6	
9	0	9	tricapped trigonal prismatic		$ReHg^{2-}$	

Bonding Electron Pairs	Lone Pairs	Electron Domains (Steric Number)	Shape Name	Ideal Bond Angle	Example	Shape
2	1	3	bent	120° (119°)	SO_2	
2	2	4	bent	109.5° (104.48°)	H_2O	
2	0	2	linear	180°	CO_2	
2	3	5	linear	180°	XeF_2	
7	0	7	pentagonal bipyramidal	90°, 72°, 180°	IF_7	
5	2	7	planar pentagonal	72°, 144°	XeF_5^-	
6	1	7	pentagonal pyramidal	72°, 90°, 144°	$XeOF_5^-$	
3	1	4	trigonal pyramidal	109.5° (107.8°)	NH_3	

Table 3.1. VSEPR Molecular Geometries (continued)

Bonding Electron Pairs	Lone Pairs	Electron Domains (Steric Number)	Shape Name	Ideal Bond Angle	Example	Shape
4	1	5	seesaw	ax-ax 180° (173.1°) eq-eq 120° (101.6°) ax-eq 90°	SF_4	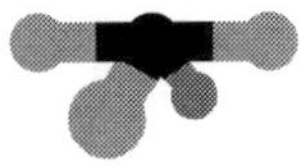
8	0	8	square antiprismatic		XeF_8^{2-}	
4	2	6	square planar	90°, 180°	XeF_4	
5	1	6	square pyramidal	90° (84.8°)	BrF_5	
3	2	5	T-shaped	90° (87.5°), 180° (175°)	ClF_3	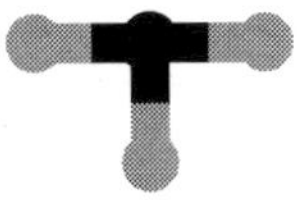
3	0	3	trigonal planar	120°	BF_3	
5	0	5	trigonal bipyramidal	90°, 120°, 180°	PCl_5	

SAMPLE QUESTION

7) **Why is BF_3 trigonal planar as opposed to trigonal pyramidal like NH_3?**

A. The B—F bond is stronger than the N—H bond.

B. NF_3 has a lone electron pair while BF_3 does not.

C. F is more electronegative than H.

D. The B—F bond is more polar than the N—H bond.

Answers:

A. Incorrect. The overall shape is not related to bond strength.

B. **Correct.** For BF_3, a planar structure with 120-degree bond angles minimizes the repulsion between the three B—F bonding pairs. There is no lone pair. For NH_3, the lone pair occupies the fourth axis of a tetrahedron with the three N—H bonds forming the other three axes. The shape formed by the three N—H bonds is trigonal pyramidal.

C. Incorrect. Electronegativity does not determine overall shape.

D. Incorrect. The polarity of a molecule does not determine its shape (although its shape can influence the strength and direction of its dipole moment).

METALLIC BONDS

Elements in families 1 and 2, as well as the transition metals and some of the heavier members of families 3–6, can form tightly packed arrays in which each atom is in close contact with many neighbors. So many atomic orbitals overlap with each atom that they form very large molecular orbitals that in turn overlap with each other, creating a continuous band in which electrons can move. This type of delocalized bonding is called **metallic bonding**.

Any excitation, such as an electrical current, can cause the electrons to move throughout the array. The high electrical and thermal conductivity of metals is due to this ability of electrons to move throughout the lattice. Metals are ductile—or can be bent without breaking—because the atoms can slide past each other without breaking the delocalized bonds.

SAMPLE QUESTION

8) **The valence electrons in a metallic bond are NOT**

A. evenly distributed.

B. held in place by their attraction to the cations.

C. shared between two atoms.

D. free to move.

Answers:

A. Incorrect. This statement is true—valence electrons in a metallic bond are evenly distributed throughout the metal.

B. Incorrect. This statement is true—while they are free to move within the metal, valence electrons in a metallic bond are held within the metal by their attraction to the cations.

C. **Correct.** The valence electrons in a metallic bond are shared equally by all the atoms in the metal.

D. Incorrect. This statement is true—valence electrons in a metallic bond can move freely, as happens when a voltage is applied to the metal.

Bond Strength and Bond Length

The strength of a chemical bond is reflected in the **bond length**, with stronger bonds tending to be shorter because the attractive force between atoms is greater. Bond length can be measured by X-ray diffraction in crystals and by spectroscopy. Bond lengths are related to the atomic radii of the bonded atoms and tend to decrease going across the periodic table and increase going down families.

Bond strength can be measured as the energy required to break apart a bond and is known as the **bond energy**. Stronger bonds are harder to break and make a more stable molecule.

Covalent molecules have characteristic bond strengths based on the atoms participating in the bonds, and, to a smaller extent, on the rest of the molecule. When atoms form double and triple bonds with each other, bond strength increases as more electrons are shared between the atoms. In general, as bond strength goes up, bond length gets shorter, as the atoms are more tightly held together. So bonds between smaller atoms tend to be shorter and stronger than those between larger atoms.

SAMPLE QUESTION

9) **How would the bond lengths and bond strengths of C—C, C=C, and C≡C compare?**

A. Bond length: C—C > C=C > C≡C
Bond strength: C—C > C=C > C≡C

B. Bond length: C—C > C=C > C≡C
Bond strength: C—C < C=C < C≡C

C. Bond length: C—C < C=C < C≡C
Bond strength: C—C > C=C > C≡C

D. Bond length: C—C < C=C < C≡C
Bond strength: C—C < C=C < C≡C

Answer:

B. **Correct.** Triple bonds are shorter and stronger than double bonds, which in turn are shorter and stronger than single bonds.

INTERMOLECULAR FORCES

TYPES OF INTERMOLECULAR FORCES

Covalent molecules experience a variety of intermolecular forces due to electrostatic interactions between molecules. These forces are responsible for the physical properties of liquids and solids.

Table 3.2. Intermolecular Forces

Force	Strength	Occurs Between
Hydrogen	High	Permanent dipoles in molecules with an H and an F, O, or N
Dipole-Dipole	Medium	Permanent dipoles in polar molecules
Dipole-Induced Dipole	Medium	Temporary dipoles induced in nonpolar molecules by polar molecules
London	Low	Temporary dipoles in nonpolar molecules

The strongest of the forces between polar molecules is **hydrogen bonding**. It occurs in molecules that have N—H, O—H, and F—H bonds. These bonds are quite polar, with N, O, and F being much more electronegative than H. An attraction is produced between the relatively positive H and the unpaired electrons on N, O, and F so that hydrogen bonds of the form X—H—X form, where X can be N, O, F or an anion. The molecule containing the relatively positive H is called the donor, and the molecule containing the electronegative atom bonding to H is called the acceptor.

Hydrogen bonding is the reason that H_2O has a high boiling point and is a liquid at room temperature, while H_2S, H_2Se, and H_2Te, the larger hydrides of family 16, are all gases. Hydrogen bonding is also the reason ice floats, a property necessary for aquatic life. When water freezes, the molecules adopt a regular structure that maximizes the number of hydrogen bonds. There are regular spaces in the structure, causing water, unlike most substances, to be less dense in the solid phase than the liquid phase. Hydrogen bonding plays an important role

HELPFUL HINT

Water is often called the *universal solvent* because of its strong intrinsic dipole and hydrogen bond. Materials that don't dissolve in water (oil is a common example) have forces holding them together that are stronger than the van der Waals forces from water that could separate them.

in biological systems, holding the DNA double helix together and causing proteins to fold into globular shapes.

There are three weaker intermolecular forces collectively called **van der Waals forces**. They are dipole-dipole interactions, dipole-induced dipole forces, and London forces.

Dipole-dipole interactions occur between polar molecules resulting from the attraction between the negative and positive ends of dipoles. When a dipole comes close to a nonpolar molecule or atom, it can induce a dipole by distorting the electron cloud, creating a **dipole-induced dipole force**. Electrons will be repelled from the negative end of a dipole and attracted to the positive end. Such interactions are important in allowing some nonpolar molecules to dissolve in water. For instance, the negative dipole on H_2O can induce a dipole on O_2 gas, allowing it to dissolve.

London forces refer to the ability of any atom or molecule to induce a temporary dipole in another atom or molecule that is very close. It arises because electrons are constantly in motion. Although on average the electrons are evenly distributed, at any given moment a temporary dipole may occur where there is more electron density on one side of an atom or molecule. This may in turn induce dipoles and result in attraction between adjacent atoms or molecules.

The London force increases with atomic and molecular weight because the electrons are farther from the nucleus and more easily distorted. In general, boiling points increase as atomic and molecular size increase due to increased London forces. The shape of the molecule also has an effect. The boiling point of n-pentane is 27 degrees higher than that of neopentane. The straight chain of n-pentane allows for more London interactions between molecules than the relatively spherical shape of neopentane.

SAMPLE QUESTION

10) Which intermolecular force causes n-pentane to be a liquid at room temperature, while neopentane, also known as 2,2-dimethylpropane, is a gas?

A. dipole-induced dipole

B. dipole-dipole

C. hydrogen bonding

D. London force

Answers:

A. Incorrect. Both molecules are nonpolar and do not have significant dipole interactions.

B. Incorrect. Both molecules are nonpolar.

C. Incorrect. Neither molecule contains —OH, —NH, or —FH bonds, so there is no hydrogen bonding.

D. **Correct.** London forces operate between all molecules and generally increase with increasing molecular weight. Molecular shape also affects them. Although n-pentane and neopentane have identical molecular weights, n-pentane is a long chain where multiple interactions with nearby molecules are possible along the length of the molecule. Neopentane is roughly spherical with fewer opportunities for intermolecular interaction.

INTERMOLECULAR FORCES AND PHYSICAL PROPERTIES

The combinations of bonding and intermolecular interactions determine the physical properties of compounds, including their boiling and melting points. To boil a liquid, heat has to provide molecules with the kinetic energy needed to overcome the intermolecular forces holding them together so the molecules can enter the gas phase. Thus, the stronger the intermolecular forces are in a substance, the higher that substance's boiling point will be. Similarly, the application of heat gives ions and molecules the kinetic energy to overcome the strong stabilizing and attractive forces in a solid and begin to melt. The stronger those attractive forces, the higher the substance's melting point.

Ionic compounds, because of the strong attraction between ions and the stabilizing effect of the lattice energy, have very high melting points, typically several hundred to a 1,000°C. In molten salts, there are still strong attractions between oppositely charged ions. These attractions must be overcome for vaporization, so salts have low equilibrium vapor pressures and boiling points in the thousands of degrees Celsius. Ionic attractions are stronger when the ionic radii are smaller, with more concentrated charge and closer interactions leading to higher melting and boiling points. Higher nominal values of charge also produce stronger attractions and higher melting and boiling points.

The intermolecular interactions between covalent molecules are much weaker than the attractions between ions, so covalent compounds have much lower melting and boiling points. For compounds with similar structures, as molecular weight increases, melting and boiling points increase and equilibrium vapor pressure decreases due to attractive London forces. Introducing polar groups increases boiling and melting points due to dipole-dipole and dipole-induced dipole forces. Introducing hydrogen bonding significantly increases the boiling and melting points of otherwise similar compounds.

Table 3.3. Effects of Dipole–Dipole Interactions on Boiling Point

Formula	Molecular Mass (amu)	Dipole Moment (D)	Boiling Point (K)
$CH_3CH_2CH_3$	44	0	231
CH_3OCH_3	46	1.3	249
CH_3CHO	44	2.7	293

In terms of polarity, like tends to dissolve like. Nonpolar liquids tend to be miscible with each other, being stabilized by London forces. Polar liquids tend to dissolve in water because of dipole-dipole interactions between the polar molecules and water. Compounds that form hydrogen bonds with water tend to be soluble, especially when a large proportion of the molecule participates in the hydrogen bonding.

Electrostatic interactions also play a role in solubility. Simple gases tend to become more soluble in water as molecular weight increases due to greater London forces.

SAMPLE QUESTIONS

11) $CH_3CH_2CH_3$, CH_3OCH_3, and CH_3CHO have similar molecular weights with dipole moments of 0, 1.3, and 2.7 D, respectively. Put them in order of increasing boiling points.

A. $CH_3CH_2CH_3$, CH_3CHO, CH_3OCH_3

B. CH_3CHO, CH_3OCH_3, $CH_3CH_2CH_3$

C. $CH_3CH_2CH_3$, CH_3OCH_3, CH_3CHO

D. CH_3OCH_3, CH_3CHO, $CH_3CH_2CH_3$

Answers:

A. Incorrect. CH_3CHO is more polar than CH_3OCH_3.

B. Incorrect. $CH_3CH_2CH_3$ is nonpolar.

C. **Correct.** The compounds are in order of increasing polarity and so increasing dipole-dipole attraction, leading to increasing boiling points.

D. Incorrect. $CH_3CH_2CH_3$ is nonpolar.

12) Which is more soluble in water—ethanol or n-butanol?

A. ethanol

B. n-butanol

Answers:

A. **Correct.** The —OH group constitutes a larger part of the molecule for ethanol.

B. Incorrect. n-butanol has a larger nonpolar chain so would be less soluble. Compounds that react with water tend to be more soluble than expected due to intermolecular interactions.

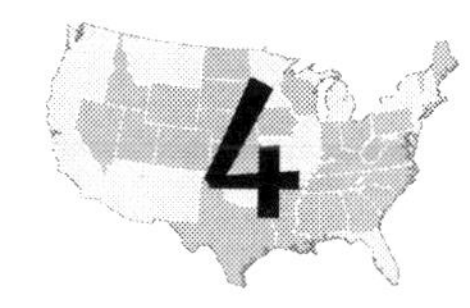

Naming Compounds

The practice and advancement of science requires that scientists have a common language to describe their work. As early as the nineteenth century, chemists from around the world recognized the need for a standardized naming system for chemical compounds. A committee formed in 1860 to develop a standard nomenclature for organic compounds; this committee evolved into the International Union of Pure and Applied Chemistry or **IUPAC**, the organization responsible for naming elements, molecules, and compounds.

Nomenclature and Chemical Composition

Inorganic Compound Nomenclature

A chemical compound by definition is composed of more than one element. **Ionic binary compounds** consist of two elements: a cation, which is positively charged, and an anion, which is negatively charged. They are generally formed between metals and nonmetals. When naming a binary ionic compound, the name of the cation comes first followed by the root of the name of the anion with an *-ide* suffix. For example, NaCl is called sodium chloride, and $MgBr_2$ is named magnesium bromide.

> **CONSIDER THIS**
>
> The most abundant mineral on the Earth's surface is quartz, which is a primary component of sand and is used to make glass. Its chemical formula is SiO_2—what is its IUPAC name?

Most of the transition metals, except for Ag^+, Zn^{2+}, and Sc^{3+} can have more than one charge. A Roman numeral is used to denote the charge in this case. For example, CuCl is written as *copper(I) chloride*, whereas $CuCl_2$ is *copper(II) chloride*. $ZnCl_2$ would simply be zinc chloride.

For covalent binary compounds, which are generally formed between nonmetals, the name of the element that is further left in the periodic table comes first. If the elements are in the same column, the one that is lower comes first. The second element gets an *–ide* suffix as with ionic compounds. The Greek prefixes *mono–*, *di–*, *tri–*, *tetra–*, *penta–*, *hexa–*, etc., are used to denote the number of atoms of each element. For example, P_2O_5 is named *diphosphorus pentoxide.*

Acids are compounds that yield a proton, H^+, when dissolved in water. For binary acids, the prefix *hydro–* and suffix *–ic* are added to the root of the anion followed by the word *acid*. For example, HF is *hydrofluoric acid.*

Ternary acids are composed of hydrogen and polyatomic anions. Most of these acids form from oxyanions. In the most common case, an oxyanion that ends in *–ate*, like carbonate, yields an oxyacid that ends in *–ic acid*, like carbonic acid. Some elements form multiple oxyanions. The nomenclature for an oxyacid is related to the names of the oxyanions. For each element that forms multiple oxyanions, there is a most common oxyanion that ends in *–ate*. For instance, sulfate, SO_4^{2-}, is the most common oxyanion of sulfur, but it also forms SO_3^{2-}, SO_2^{2-}, and SO_5^{2-}. (Table 4.1 explains how compounds formed from oxyanions are named.) Some common oxyanions include:

- SO_4^{2-} Sulfate
- NO_3^- Nitrate
- PO_4^{3-} Phosphate
- ClO_3^- Chlorate
- BrO_3^- Bromate
- IO_3^- Iodate
- CO_3^{2-} Carbonate
- $CH_3CO_2^-$ Acetate

Table 4.1. Naming Oxyanions

Number of Oxygen Atoms	Name of Oxyanion	Name of Oxyacid
2 < most common	hypo– (root) –ite	hypo– (root) –ous acid
1 < most common	(root) –ite	(root) –ous acid
most common	(root) –ate	(root) –ic acid
1 > most common	per– (root) –ate	per– (root) –ic acid

Example: Naming Sulfur Compounds

Oxyanion Formula	Name of Oxyanion	Acid Formula	Name of Acid
SO_2^{2-}	hyposulfite	H_2SO_2	hyposulfous acid
SO_3^{2-}	sulfite	H_2SO_3	sulfous acid
SO_4^{2-}	sulfate	H_2SO_4	sulfuric acid
SO_5^{2-}	persulfate	H_2SO_5	persulfuric acid

Bases yield hydroxide ions (OH^-) when dissolved in water. The naming of bases is similar to the naming of binary ionic compounds. The name of the cation formed when the base dissociates comes first followed by the word *hydroxide*. NaOH is *sodium hydroxide*. $Ca(OH)_2$ is *calcium hydroxide*. NH_3 has the common name *ammonia* and is a weak base. NH_4OH is *ammonium hydroxide*.

Salts are ionic compounds formed when an acid neutralizes a base yielding water and the salt. The name of the salt is the name of the cation followed by the name of the anion. Some examples are NaCl, which is called sodium chloride, and NH_4NO_3, which is called ammonium nitrate. For transition metals, which can have multiple charges, Roman numerals denote the charge, as with $FeCO_3$, which is *iron(II) carbonate*.

> **EXCEPTIONS TO THE RULE**
>
> Note the bottom 2 acids in Table 4.1 have a *–ur* added to the root. Similarly, phosphoric acid (not *phosphic* acid) is formed from the phosphate ion.

Hydrates are salts bound in a specific ratio to water molecules within a crystal. The name of the salt is followed by a Greek prefix indicating the number of water molecules bound. For instance, $CoCl_2 \cdot 6H_2O$ is expressed as *cobalt(II) chloride hexahydrate*.

SAMPLE QUESTIONS

1) **What is the name of the acid HNO_2?**

A. nitrous acid

B. nitric acid

C. pernitric acid

D. nitrite

Answers:

A. Correct. NO_2^- has one less oxygen atom than the most common oxyanion of nitrogen, NO_3^-. So NO_2^- is nitrite and the corresponding acid, HNO_2, is nitrous acid.

B. Incorrect. Nitric acid is HNO_3 formed from the most common oxyanion of nitrogen NO_3^-.

C. Incorrect. Pernitric acid is HNO_4 with one more oxygen than nitric acid.

D. Incorrect. Nitrite is an oxyanion, not an acid.

2) **What is the name of $ZnSO_4 \cdot 7H_2O$?**

A. zinc(II) sulfate heptahydrate

B. zinc sulfate pentahydrate

C. zinc sulfate heptahydrate

D. zinc(II) sulfite heptahydrate

Answers:

A. Incorrect. Zn, Ag, and Sc are the three transition metals that can have only one charge, so it is not necessary to denote the charge.

B. Incorrect. Pentahydrate indicates five H_2O, not seven.

C. Correct. Heptahydrate indicates seven H_2O bound, and it is unnecessary to denote the charge on zinc, as it can only have one charge of +2.

D. Incorrect. The anion is sulfate, not sulfite.

Organic Compound Nomenclature

Organic compounds contain carbon and are the basis of life. The simplest organic molecules contain just carbon and hydrogen and are called *hydrocarbons*. Carbon participates in four bonds and hydrogen participates in one bond. Hydrocarbons that are composed of all single bonds are called **alkanes**. The nomenclature for alkanes is based on the number of carbons in the molecule.

Table 4.2. Naming Alkanes

Chemical Formula	Name	Chemical Formula	Name
CH_4	methane	$C_{11}H_{24}$	undecane
C_2H_6	ethane	$C_{12}H_{26}$	dodecane
C_3H_8	propane	$C_{13}H_{28}$	tridecane
C_4H_{10}	butane	$C_{14}H_{30}$	tetradecane
C_5H_{12}	pentane	$C_{15}H_{32}$	pentadecane
C_6H_{14}	hexane	$C_{16}H_{34}$	hexadecane
C_7H_{16}	heptane	$C_{17}H_{36}$	heptadecane
C_8H_{18}	octane	$C_{18}H_{38}$	octadecane
C_9H_{20}	nonane	$C_{19}H_{40}$	nonadecane
$C_{10}H_{22}$	decane	$C_{20}H_{42}$	eicosane

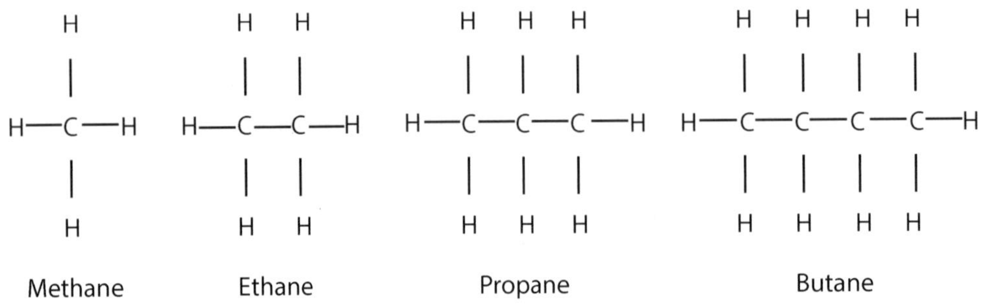

Methane Ethane Propane Butane

Figure 4.1. Alkanes

Starting with butane, there are multiple configurations possible for the same chemical composition, as shown in Figure 4.2. As the number of carbons in the molecule increases, there are too many possible configurations to use common names. It becomes necessary to have a naming system, which the IUPAC has defined.

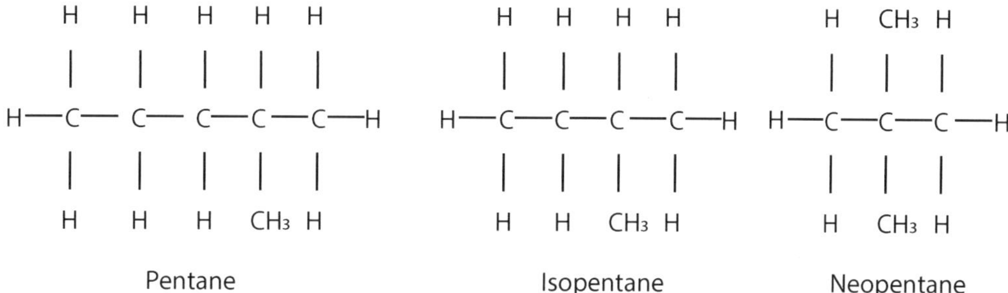

Figure 4.2 Isomers of Pentane

For branched alkanes, the groups attached to the longest chain are called alkyl groups and are named with the same roots as above but end in *-yl* as opposed to *-ane*. Common names of branched groups are also converted from *-ane* to *-yl*, such as isopropyl, isobutyl, etc. For alkyl groups of six or fewer carbons, common names are often intermingled with IUPAC conventions for the overall molecule. There is a common convention of prefixes for the alkyl groups that depends on the configuration of the group and how many carbons are bonded to the carbon at the point of attachment to the main chain:

- *n*– refers to a straight chain.
- *iso*– refers to the configuration $(CH_3)_2CH$—.
- *sec*– refers to a carbon at a point of attachment to the main chain, which is attached to two other carbons.
- *tert*– refers to a carbon that at a point of attachment to the main chain is attached to three other carbons.

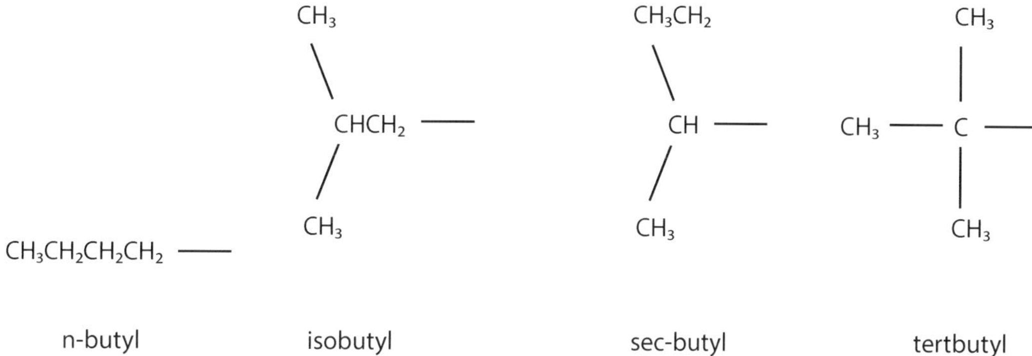

Figure 4.3. Branched Alkanes

The first step in naming a compound is to identify the longest carbon chain. Numbers are used to denote the position on the long chain where the groups are attached. Numbering starts at the end that produces lower numbers. If several of the same group are attached, the Greek prefixes *di–*, *tri–*, *tetra–*, etc, are used. If there are several different groups attached, they are named in order of increasing size or alphabetically.

In addition to forming single bonds, carbon atoms can form double and triple bonds. Compounds with double bonds between carbon atoms are called **alkenes** and those with triple bonds are called **alkynes**.

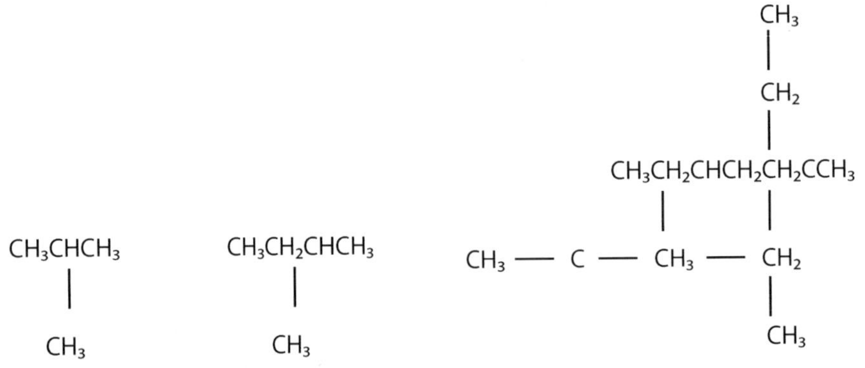

CH_3CHCH_3 | CH_3

methylpropane

$CH_3CH_2CHCH_3$ | CH_3

2-methylbutane

CH_3 | CH_2 | $CH_3CH_2CHCH_2CH_2CCH_3$ | $CH_3 — C — CH_3$ … $— CH_2$ | CH_3

2,2-diethyl-5-isopropylheptane

Figure 4.4. Naming Alkanes with Attached Groups

For **alkenes**, roots are the same as alkanes but with a suffix of *–ene* instead of *–ane*. The location of the double bond is denoted by a number corresponding to the position in the chain of the first carbon in the double bond. Counting starts from the end closest to the double bond. The same names and numbers denote alkyl groups and their positions as for alkanes.

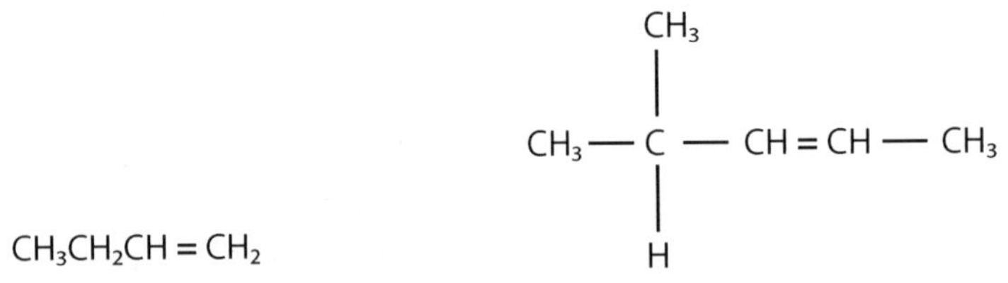

$CH_3CH_2CH = CH_2$

1-butene

CH_3 | $CH_3 — C — CH = CH — CH_3$ | H

4-methyl-2-pentene

Figure 4.5. Alkenes

Alkynes have a triple bond between carbons. The nomenclature is the same as for alkenes, except the names end in *-yne* instead of *–ene*. The smallest alkyne, $HC \equiv CH$, has the common name *acetylene* and the IUPAC name *ethyne*.

Organic compounds can also have functional groups that give them specific chemical properties. Some of the most common groups contain oxygen or nitrogen. These include alcohols, ethers, aldehydes, ketones, and amines.

Alcohols contain an —OH group. The smaller alcohols have frequently used common names that consist of the name of the alkyl groups followed by *alcohol.* The *iso–*, *sec–*, and *tert–* prefixes are used to indicate the alkyl groups bonded to —OH. For example, isopropyl alcohol is $(CH_3)_2CHOH$.

DID YOU KNOW?

Ethanol, CH_3CH_2OH, an alcohol that is commonly called "alcohol," is a polar molecule and can therefore dissolve easily in water, a requirement for its use in drinks.

Alcohols have similar IUPAC names as alkanes, except they end in *-ol.* A number is used to designate the position of the —OH group, starting from the closest end of the chain.

```
       CH3
        |
  CH3CHCHCH3              CH3 — CH — CH2 — OH
     |                          |
     OH                         CH3

 3-methyl-2-butanol        2-methyl-1-propanol
```

Figure 4.6. Alcohols

Another class of organic molecule with single C—O bonds are ethers. **Ethers** have the general structure R—O—R, where R is an alkyl or aromatic group. There are two common ways of naming ethers. The first is to name the alkyl/aromatic groups followed by the word ether. If the two R groups are the same, the alkyl group is named just once.

The second way of naming ethers is used most often when one group is large and doesn't have a common alkyl name. The larger group is named following alkane naming rules. A number denotes where on the main chain the oxygen is attached, and the smaller group containing the oxygen is named by its common root followed by *-oxy.*

```
                      CH3
                      |
  CH3OCH3        CH3— C — O — CH2CH3      CH3CH2CH2CH2CHCH3
                      |                                |
                      CH3                              OCH3

  methyl ether   ethyl tert-butyl ether      2-methoxyhexane
```

Figure 4.7. Ethers

The two types of organic compounds that contain carbon-oxygen double bonds are the aldehydes and ketones.

Not surprisingly, the smaller **aldehydes** have common names. Those names are derived from the names of the corresponding carboxylic acids—of the form RCOOH—which in turn get their names from where they naturally occur. The general structures and names are given in the table below.

Table 4.3. Naming Aldehydes

Chemical Formula	Common Name	IUPAC name
H_2CO	formaldehyde	methanal
CH_3CHO	acetaldehyde	ethanal
CH_3CH_2CHO	propionaldehyde	propanal
$CH_3(CH_2)_2CHO$	n-butyraldehyde	butanal
$CH_3(CH_2)_3CHO$	n-valeraldehyde	pentanal
$CH_3(CH_2)_4CHO$	n-caproaldehyde	hexanal

In conjunction with the common names, the Greek letters α, β, δ, and γ designate distance from the carbonyl carbon—CHO—with α being next to the carbonyl and β, δ, and γ getting progressively farther away.

The IUPAC system takes the alkane name of the longest chain containing the CHO group and replaces *-ane* with *-al*. Numbers denote the position of the substituents, with the carbonyl carbon being number one. H_2CO is *methanal*. CH_3CHO is *ethanal* and so on.

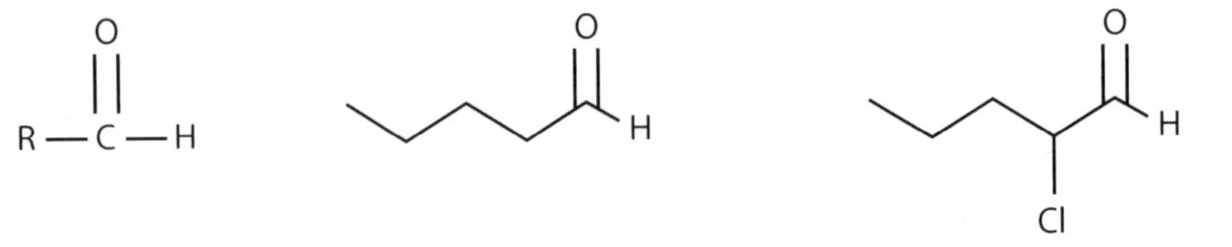

O
R—C—H
aldehyde

O
H
pentanal
(valeraldehyde)

O
H
Cl
2-chloropentanal
(α-chlorovaleraldehyde)

Figure 4.8. Aldehydes

As with aldehydes, there are two naming systems for **ketones**. In the common system, the smallest ketone CH_3COCH_3 is called acetone. Larger ketones are named with the names of the alkyl groups attached to the carbonyl and the word *ketone*. For instance, $CH_3CH_2COCH_3$ is methyl ethyl ketone. When the carbonyl is attached to a benzene ring, it is called a *phenone*.

The IUPAC system takes the alkane name of the longest straight chain containing the carbonyl and replaces the end *-e* with *-one*. Substituent positions and the position of the carbonyl are denoted by numbers, starting from the end of the chain closest to the carbonyl. $(CH_3)_2CHCOCH_3$ is called *3-methyl-2-butanone.*

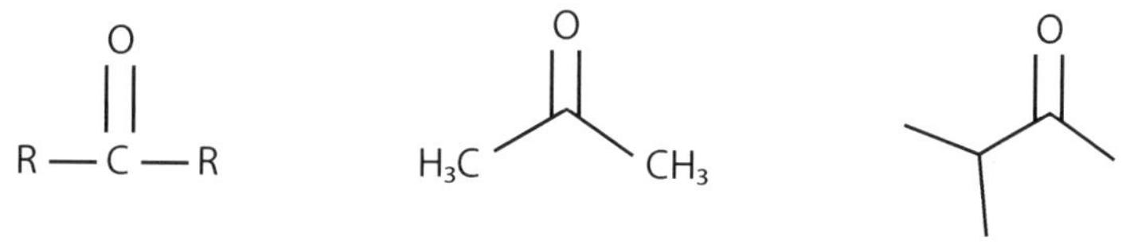

ketone

propanone (acetone)

3-methyl-2-butanone (methyl isopropyl ketone)

Figure 4.9. Ketones

Amines are a class of organic compounds containing nitrogen. They are described as primary (RNH_2), secondary (R_2NH), or tertiary (R_3N). Smaller amines often have common names corresponding to the alkyl group(s) attached followed by amine. For instance, $CH_3NHCH_2CH_3$ is called *methylethylamine.*

IUPAC names are based on the alkane name of the longest straight chain attached to nitrogen, where the suffix *-amine* replaces *-e*. A number denotes the position of the amine group. For secondary and tertiary amines, the shorter chains attached are treated as alkyl groups and given the label *N-* to denote they are attached to nitrogen. For example, $CH_3CH_2CH_2N(CH_3)_2$ is called *N,N-dimethyl-1-propanamine.*

QUICK REVIEW

What are the similarities and differences between the names for functional groups? What patterns can you see that would help students learn the rules for naming organic compounds?

When amines are found in most oxygen-containing organic molecules, the amine is treated as a substituent attached to the main chain containing the oxygen group. The amine group is given the name *amino* preceded by *N-alkyl* describing any other alkyl group(s) attached to N.

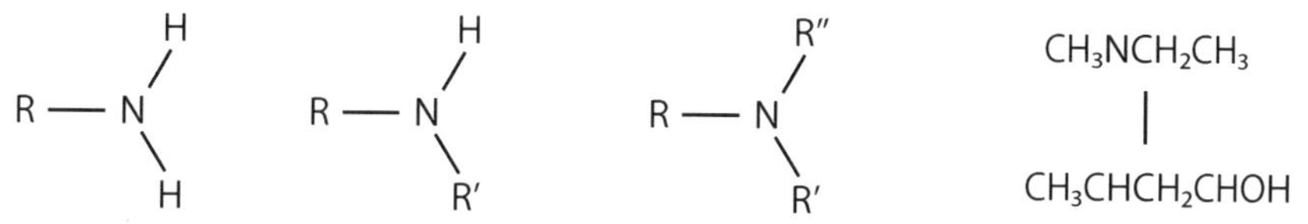

primary amine

secondary amine

tertiary amine

$CH_3NCH_2CH_3$ | CH_3CHCH_2CHOH

3-(N-methyl-N-ethylamino)-1-butanol

Figure 4.10. Amines

Go on

SAMPLE QUESTIONS

3) **What is the name of the following molecule?**

$$
\begin{array}{llllll}
CH_3 & & & & & \\
| & & & & & \\
\multicolumn{6}{l}{CHCH_2CH_2CHCH_2CHCH_3} \\
| & & & | & | & \\
CH_2 & & & CH_3 & CH_2 & \\
| & & & & | & \\
CH_3 & & & & CH_3 &
\end{array}
$$

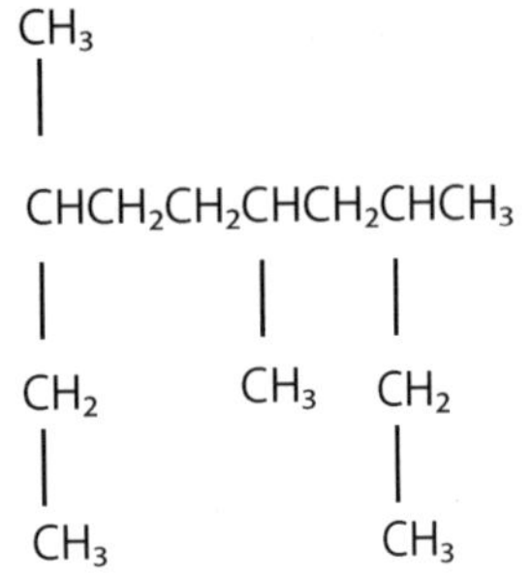

A. 1-methyl-1-ethyl-4-methyl-6-ethylheptane

B. dimethyl-diethyl-heptane

C. 1,4-dimethyl-1,6-diethylheptane

D. 3,5,8-trimethyldecane

Answers:

A. Incorrect. Identical groups should be combined with a Greek prefix for the number of like groups, as in *dimethyl* and *diethyl*. Also, the longest chain is longer than seven carbons.

B. Incorrect. Numbers are used to denote the position on the longest straight chain of the alkyl groups. Also, the longest chain is longer than seven carbons.

C. Incorrect. This would be correct if the longest chain was as drawn with seven carbons. Numbers denote the position of the groups on the main chain. Identical alkyl groups are denoted together with the Greek prefix *di–* for the number of them: two each of methyl and ethyl. However, the two ethyl groups can be considered part of a ten-carbon straight chain.

D. Correct. The longest straight chain possible is ten carbons long with methyl groups attached at positions three, five, and eight.

4) **What are the common and IUPAC names for the following molecule?**

$$
\begin{array}{ccc}
 & CH_3 & \\
 & | & \\
CH_3CH_2 - & C & - CH_3 \\
 & | & \\
 & OH &
\end{array}
$$

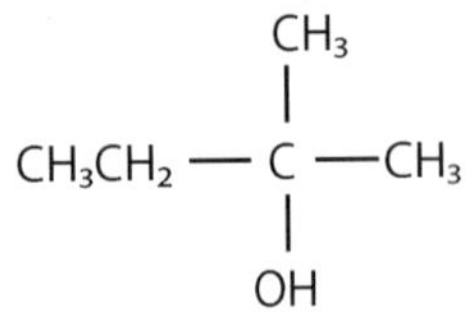

A. methylbutanol, 2-methyl-2-butanol

B. tert-pentyl alcohol, 3-methyl-3-butanol

C. isopentyl alcohol, 2-methyl-2-butanol

D. tert-pentyl alcohol, 2-methyl-2-butanol

Answers:

A. Incorrect. *Methylbutanol* is ambiguous. It doesn't designate where the methyl group is.

B. Incorrect. IUPAC numbering starts from the end closest to the hydroxyl group.

C. Incorrect. Isopentyl alcohol would have the methyl group attached to the next to last carbon on the chain, that is, the three position.

D. **Correct.** *tert–* indicates that the carbon bonded to —OH is bonded to three carbons; there are five carbons total, so by common naming conventions, this is a *pentyl alcohol*. IUPAC names the alcohol by the number of carbons in the main straight chain containing the —OH group: butanol. Counting starts from the end of the chain nearest the —OH, yielding 2-methyl-2-butanol.

5) **Give the common and IUPAC names of the following molecule.**

$CH_3CH_2CCH_2CH_2CH_3$

A. ethyl n-propyl ketone, 4-hexanone

B. ethyl propyl ketone, 3-hexanone

C. n-propyl ethyl ketone, 3-pentanone

D. ethyl n-propyl ketone, 3-hexanone

Answers:

A. Incorrect. IUPAC numbering starts at the end closest to the carbonyl.

B. Incorrect. Propyl is ambiguous. n-propyl should be used to denote a straight chain.

C. Incorrect. For common names, the name of the smaller alkyl group is generally listed first. For the IUPAC name, the main chain containing the carbonyl has a total of six carbons, so it is *hexanone*.

D. **Correct.** The smaller ethyl group is listed first, and n-propyl indicates a straight propyl chain. For the IUPAC name, the position of the carbonyl is counted from the closest end, and the six-carbon chain is called *hexanone*.

Chemical Reactions

Atomic Mass and the Mole

Each element has a specific atomic mass, measured in atomic mass units (amu), that is the result of the number of protons, neutrons, and electrons in the atom. (The periodic table lists the atomic masses for all the elements.) For elements with isotopes, the atomic mass of each isotope is weighted based on its prevalence, and the resulting values are averaged. Carbon, for example, which exists mostly as ^{12}C (98.9 percent) but also as ^{13}C (1.1 percent) and ^{14}C (0.001 percent), has a mass of 12.01 amu.

Likewise, molecules and compounds have molecular mass or formula mass values that are equal to the sum of the masses of the atoms that compose them. CO_2, for example, has a molecular mass of $12.01 + (2 \times 16) = 44.01$ amu.

Avogadro's number, 6.02×10^{23}, is the number of atoms or molecules in a mole of any given element or compound. The number relates atomic or molecular mass to weight in grams, the unit typically used when working with chemical reactions. A mole of an element weighs the same in grams as the atomic weight. So, a mole of carbon, or 6.02×10^{23} atoms of carbon, weighs 12.01 g. The weight of a mole of an element or compound is called its **molar mass**.

> **DID YOU KNOW?**
>
> Tin (Sn), has ten stable isotopes, the most of any element on the periodic table. The most abundant in nature is ^{120}Sn, but large percentages of ^{118}Sn and ^{116}Sn, among others, result in an atomic mass for Tin of 118.71 amu.

The molar mass of an element or compound can be used as a conversion factor to convert between moles and grams:

3 g C	1 mol	= 0.25 mol C
	12.01 g	

$$\frac{5 \text{ mol } O_2 \;\Big|\; 32 \text{ g}}{\;\Big|\; 1 \text{ mol}} = 160 \text{ g } O_2$$

Avogadro's number can be used as a conversion factor to convert between moles and number of atoms or molecules:

$$\frac{3 \text{ mol } CH_4 \;\Big|\; 6.02 \times 10^{23} \text{ molecules}}{\;\Big|\; 1 \text{ mol}} = 1.8 \times 10^{24} \text{ molecules } CH_4$$

Molar mass can be used to calculate the percent composition by mass of each element in a compound. The percent composition by mass is simply the percentage of a compound's mass contributed by each element.

$$\% \text{ mass of element} = \frac{\text{no. of atoms of element} \times \text{molar mass of element}}{\text{molar mass of compound}} \times 100$$

Percent composition can, in turn, be used to find the empirical formula for a given compound. The **molecular formula** of a compound is the number of each type of atom in the molecule, while the **empirical formula** gives the smallest whole number ratio of different atoms in a molecule. For example, the molecular formula of ethane is C_2H_6, and the empirical formula is CH_3.

An empirical formula can be determined from mass percent data using the following steps:

1. Starting with mass percentages for each element, find the mass of each element in a 100 g sample.
2. Convert the mass of elements to moles of elements.
3. Divide each number of moles by the smallest number of moles to determine the smallest whole number ratio of elements.
4. Write the empirical formula with elements and subscripts.

If the molar mass of the compound is known, the molecular formula can be determined from the empirical formula. The molar mass of the compound divided by the empirical molar mass yields the number that the empirical subscripts are multiplied by to get the molecular formula. If the molar mass of the compound equals the molar mass of the empirical formula, then the empirical formula is the molecular formula.

SAMPLE QUESTIONS

1) **How many moles of NaCl are in 5 g of NaCl?**

A. 0.09 mol

B. 11.69 mol

C. 3.01×10^{24} mol

D. 8.31×10^{-24} mol

Answer: A.

Find the molar mass of NaCl and use dimensional analysis.

Na: 22.99 g

Cl: 35.45 g

NaCl: 22.99 + 35.45 = 58.44 g

5 g	1 mol	**= 0.09 mol**
1	58.44 g	

2) **What is the mass percent of O in $CaCO_3$?**

A. 12.00 percent

B. 15.99 percent

C. 40.04 percent

D. 47.96 percent

Answer: D.

$$\%\text{ mass of element} = \frac{\text{no.of atoms of element} \times \text{molar mass of element}}{\text{molar mass of compound}} \times 100$$

$$= \frac{\text{no.of atoms of O} \times \text{molar mass of O}}{\text{molar mass of } CaCO_3}$$

$$= \frac{3(16)}{40.08 + 12.01 + 3(16)} \times 100 = \mathbf{47.96\%}$$

3) **Find the empirical formula of a compound that is 68.54% carbon, 8.63% hydrogen, and 22.83% oxygen.**

A. C_2HO

B. C_4H_6O

C. CH_6O_4

D. CHO

Answer: B.

Convert percentages to masses assuming 100 grams of the substance is present.

68.54 g C

8.63 g H

22.83 g O

Convert mass to moles.

68.54 g C	1 mol C	= 5.70 mol C
1	12.01 g C	

8.63 g H	1 mol H	= 8.54 mol H
1	1.01 g H	

22.83 g O	1 mol O	= 1.42 mol O
1	16 g O	

Divide by the smallest value.

$C = \frac{5.70}{1.42} = 4$

$H = \frac{8.54}{1.42} = 6$

$O = \frac{1.42}{1.42} = 1$

The empirical formula for the compound is: $\mathbf{C_4H_6O}$

Chemical Reactions and Equations

Chemical reactions involve the conversion of reactants into products and are described by chemical equations. The left side of a chemical equation shows the **reactants**, those elements or compounds present at the beginning of a reaction. The right side of the equation shows the **products**, the elements and compounds that result from the reaction. In the chemical equation, chemical formulas are used to represent the reactants and products, and the arrow symbol indicates the direction of the reaction. A plus sign is used to show the relationship of multiple reactants and products (i.e., reactant A plus B yields product C plus D). All chemical reactions must obey the law of conservation of matter, which states that matter can neither be created nor destroyed (i.e., the mass of the reactants must be equal to the mass of the products).

A common chemical reaction is the reaction between baking soda and vinegar. Baking soda is a chemical compound called sodium bicarbonate ($NaHCO_3$), and vinegar is dilute acetic acid (CH_3COOH). Their reaction results in the formation of gas, water, and sodium acetate.

$$NaHCO_3\ (s) + CH_3COOH\ (l) \rightarrow CO_2\ (g) + H_2O\ (l) + NaC_2H_3O_2\ (aq)$$

In this equation, $NaHCO_3$ and CH_3COOH are the reactants and CO_2, H_2O, and $NaC_2H_3O_2$ are the products. The arrow in the equation indicates that the reaction will form or yield the products and moves in the forward direction. The physical state of the compounds is indicated in the parentheses next to them: *s* = solid, *l* = liquid, *g* = gas, and *aq* = aqueous.

Types of Chemical Reactions

There are several types of chemical reactions. One of the most common is a **combustion** reaction, which is when an element or compound burns in air or oxygen. This happens every time natural gas is used to produce heat and gasoline is used to power a vehicle. Combustion reactions are exothermic, meaning they give off heat. When elements are burned, the products are typically the most common oxide of the element; for example, sulfur produces sulfur dioxide and iron produces iron oxide. When an organic compound (a compound made of C, H, and O) combusts in oxygen, the reaction products are always carbon dioxide and water. The general chemical equation for this is:

$$C_xH_y + Z\,O_2 \rightarrow X\,CO_2 + \frac{Y}{2}\,H_2O$$

Neutralization reactions, also called acid-base reactions, occur when acids and bases react with each other. The reaction between strong acids and bases always produces salt and water, neutralizing their acidic and basic effects. This occurs because there are no longer excesses of hydrogen or hydroxide ions in the solution, resulting in a pH of 7 for strong acid-base neutralizations. For weak acids and bases, the pH of the solution will depend on the acid strength of the reactants.

It is easy to determine the products of a neutralization reaction since Acid + Base → Salt + Water. The salt will form from the anion of the acid and the cation of the base. The following is an example of a neutralization reaction involving a strong acid and base:

$$HCl\,(aq) + NaOH\,(aq) \rightarrow NaCl\,(aq) + H_2O\,(l)$$

In a **decomposition** reaction, one compound decomposes or breaks down into two or more products. The products can be elements or simpler compounds, and the number of products will be greater than the number of reactants. This is the opposite of a combination reaction or chemical synthesis. The general formula for a decomposition reaction is:

$$AB \rightarrow A + B$$

A decomposition reaction can occur spontaneously and may be an unwanted reaction. For example, hydrogen peroxide will decompose into water and oxygen over time. The decomposition of hydrogen peroxide is spontaneous, which is why bottles of hydrogen peroxide slowly lose their effectiveness over time. The equation for the decomposition of hydrogen peroxide is:

$$2\,H_2O_2\,(aq) \rightarrow 2\,H_2O\,(l) + O_2\,(g)$$

Some decomposition reactions occur so spontaneously, they are explosive. Nitroglycerine will violently decompose with very little provocation. Decomposition reactions that occur with the addition of heat are called *thermal decomposition reactions*. With the addition of heat, some metal oxides decompose into the component metal and oxygen.

In a **dehydration** reaction, the reacting molecules combine in such a way that a water molecule is lost from a reactant. Dehydration reactions are often used in organic synthesis. Two monosaccharides (sugars) can be joined together to form a disaccharide via the loss of water. The opposite of a dehydration reaction is a hydration or hydrolysis reaction in which water is a reactant. The conversion of alcohols to ethers is an example of a dehydration reaction:

$$2\,CH_3CH_2-OH \rightarrow CH_3CH_2-O-CH_2CH_3 + H_2O$$

In a **single-replacement** (or **displacement**) reaction, the reactant element replaces one of the elements in the reactant compound, releasing another element as a product. The general equation for this type of reaction is:

$$A + BC \rightarrow AC + B$$

For this reaction to occur, A and B must be different metals or halogens. The single replacement can be the replacement of one cation for another or one anion for another. An example of a cation single replacement reaction is:

$$3\ Na + AlCl_3 \rightarrow 3\ NaCl + Al$$

An example of an anion single replacement reaction is:

$$Br_2 + 2\ KI \rightarrow 2\ KBr + I_2$$

A **double-replacement** (or **displacement**) reaction is similar to a single replacement reaction but occurs between two compounds instead of a compound and an element. The two compounds react to form two new compounds. The general equation for a double-replacement reaction is:

$$AB + CD \rightarrow AD + CB$$

This can also be called an exchange reaction because the two compounds exchange partners. The neutralization reaction is a type of double-replacement reaction.

In some double composition reactions, one of the products will be a solid precipitate. In the reaction shown below, the aqueous reactants silver nitrate and sodium chloride react to form aqueous sodium nitrate and silver chloride, which is a solid:

$$AgNO_3\ (aq) + NaCl\ (aq) \rightarrow AgCl\ (s) + NaNO_3\ (aq)$$

SAMPLE QUESTION

4) **Identify the type of reaction shown below:**

$Pb(NO_3)_2\ (aq) + K_2CrO_4\ (aq) \rightarrow PbCrO_4\ (s) + 2\ KNO_3\ (aq)$

A. neutralization reaction

B. decomposition reaction

C. double-displacement reaction

D. single-replacement reaction

Answers:

A. Incorrect. A neutralization reaction includes an acid and a base as the reactants.

B. Incorrect. In a decomposition reaction, a reactant breaks down into multiple products.

C. **Correct.** In the reaction, the Pb and K exchange their anions in a double-displacement reaction.

D. Incorrect. In a single-replacement reaction, a single element reacts with a compound.

BALANCING CHEMICAL EQUATIONS

The law of conservation of mass states that matter can neither be created nor destroyed during a reaction. Accordingly, a chemical equation must be balanced to ensure that an equal number of each type of atom appears on both sides. This is not always the case when a chemical equation is initially written. Sometimes the coefficients, the numbers in front of the reactants and products, must be changed to balance the equation.

To balance a chemical reaction, use the following simple steps:

1. Write the chemical equation for the reaction. Determine if the equation needs to be balanced.
2. If the equation needs to be balanced, choose an element and balance it by adding the appropriate coefficient to the reactant or product as needed.
3. Balance the atoms of the remaining elements by adding coefficients. Only the coefficients can be changed, not the subscripts. Changing the subscripts would change the compound, not just the number of the compound.
4. Verify that the number of atoms of each element is balanced.

A simple combustion reaction of methane with oxygen results in carbon dioxide and water. With just the reactants and products, the chemical equation is:

$$CH_4\,(g) + O_2\,(g) \rightarrow CO_2\,(g) + H_2O\,(l)$$

However, this equation is not balanced. There are four reactant hydrogen atoms but only two hydrogen atoms in the product. Additionally, there are two reactant oxygen atoms but three product oxygen atoms. This equation can be balanced by adding more product or reactant molecules as needed.

The product side of the equation needs two additional hydrogen atoms, which must come from one of the two products. Since CO_2 does not have any hydrogen, H_2O is the only option for balancing hydrogen. Adding a two in front of the H_2O indicates that two molecules of water are produced in the reaction, resulting in a total of four hydrogen atoms.

This step balances the hydrogen atoms in the equation, but now there are four oxygen atoms on the product side and two on the reactant side. Since O_2 is the only reactant that contains oxygen, it is the only option for balancing the equation. By putting a 2 in front of the O_2, there will be a total of four oxygen atoms on both sides of the equation. The following is the balanced equation:

$$CH_4\,(g) + 2\,O_2\,(g) \rightarrow CO_2\,(g) + 2\,H_2O\,(l)$$

This combustion reaction requires two molecules of diatomic oxygen to move forward and results in two molecules of water being formed.

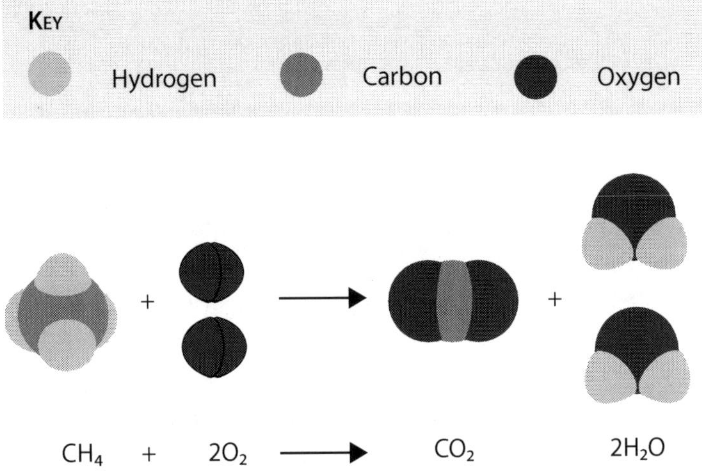

Figure 5.1. Combustion Reaction

SAMPLE QUESTIONS

5) **Balance the following combustion equation: $C_8H_{18} + O_2 \rightarrow CO_2 + H_2O$**

A. $C_8H_{18} + O_2 \rightarrow CO_2 + H_2O$

B. $C_8H_{18} + 6\ O_2 \rightarrow 8\ CO_2 + H_2O$

C. $4\ C_8H_{18} + 48\ O_2 \rightarrow 32\ CO_2 + 16\ H_2O$

D. $2\ C_8H_{18} + 25\ O_2 \rightarrow 16\ CO_2 + 18\ H_2O$

Answer: D.

$C_8H_{18} + O_2 \rightarrow 8\ CO_2 + H_2O$	Start by balancing the carbon atoms on each side of the equation.
$C_8H_{18} + O_2 \rightarrow 8\ CO_2 + 9\ H_2O$	Next, balance the hydrogen atoms on each side of the equation.
$C_8H_{18} + 12.5\ O_2 \rightarrow 8\ CO_2 + 9\ H_2O$	Then, balance the oxygen on each side of the equation.
$2\ C_8H_{18} + 25\ O_2 \rightarrow 16\ CO_2 + 18\ H_2O$	Finally, remove the decimal by multiplying each coefficient by 2.

6) **Predict the missing product for the following reaction:**

$CuCO_3 \rightarrow CuO +$ ___

A. CuO_2

B. CO_2

C. CO

D. C_2

Answers:

A. Incorrect. This product would leave the right side with no C atoms.

B. Correct. The reaction is the decomposition of $CuCO_3$ into CuO and CO_2.

C. Incorrect. This reaction could not be balanced.

D. Incorrect. This reaction could not be balanced.

Oxidation and Reduction Reactions

Both single- and double-replacement reactions are types of **oxidation-reduction** reactions, also known as redox reactions. These reactions involve the exchange of electrons; one species is reduced while the other is oxidized. The reactant that is **oxidized** (that undergoes oxidation) loses electrons. The reactant that is **reduced** (that undergoes reduction) has gained electrons. In the reaction, the oxidizing agent accepts electrons, causing the oxidation of another species. The reducing agent donates electrons, causing the reduction of another species.

Both oxidation and reduction must occur together and in equal proportion, and the number of electrons lost and gained must be the same. Because of this, individual oxidation and reduction reactions are referred to as half reactions since they are only half of the electron exchange process.

Oxidation Numbers

The transfer of electrons in redox reactions also results in a change in the oxidation number of species involved in the reaction. The **oxidation number** is the charge of an atom in a compound compared with its charge as an uncombined atom. The oxidation number of an atom can be determined using the following set of rules and the periodic table.

> **HELPFUL HINT**
>
> Two mnemonic devices can help in remembering which species gain or lose electrons:
>
> LEO the lion says, "GER!" (Loss of Electrons is Oxidation. Gain of Electrons is Reduction.)
>
> OIL RIG (Oxidation Involves Loss of electrons. Reduction Involves Gain of electrons.)

Oxidation Number Rules:

1. The oxidation number of a pure element is always 0.
2. The sum of the oxidation numbers in a neutral species is 0, and in an ion it is equal to the charge of the ion.
3. The oxidation number of an ion is equal to its charge.
4. Some elements will always have the same oxidation number. These elements can be used to determine the oxidation number of other elements in a compound.

- Group 1 metals have an oxidation number of +1.
- Group 2 metals have an oxidation number of +2.
- Hydrogen has an oxidation number of +1 unless it is combined with a metal, in which case its number is –1.
- Fluorine has an oxidation number of –1.
- Oxygen usually has an oxidation number of –2. The exception is peroxides, in which oxygen has an oxidation number of –1.
- In binary metal compounds, Group 17 elements have an oxidation number of –1, Group 16 an oxidation number of –2, and Group 15 an oxidation number of –3.

SAMPLE QUESTION

7) **Determine the oxidation numbers for the species in the following reaction.**

Fe (*s*) + H_2SO_4 (*aq*) → $FeSO_4$ (*aq*) + H_2 (*g*)

A. Fe (0), H (−1), S (+4), O (−2) → Fe (0), S (+4), O (−1), H (−1)

B. Fe (+1), H (+1), S (+6), O (−2) → Fe (0), S (+4), O (−1) , H (0)

C. Fe (0), H (+1), S: (+6), O (−2) → Fe (+2), S (+6), O (−2), H (0)

D. Fe (0), H (−1), S (+4), O (−2) → Fe (+2), S (+4), O (−1) , H (0)

Answer: C.

- The elemental reactant (Fe) and product (H) are assigned 0.
- H is assigned +1 and O is assigned −2.
- Use the oxidation numbers of H and O to find the oxidation number for S.

  H_2SO_4: 2(1) + S + 4(−2) = 0

  S – 6 = 0

  S = +6

Reduction Potentials

To balance redox reactions, the reaction must be separated into two half reactions, the oxidation reaction and the reduction reaction. Most half reactions are well known and have a standard potential associated with them. These potentials are all written for the reduction reaction and, as such, are called **standard reduction potentials**. The value of the reduction potential, $E°_{red}$, indicates how strongly the reduced species on the right wants the electrons, and it is measured in volts, the SI unit for electrical potential. The values for E° are for a certain specific set of conditions (e.g., a 1 M solution of an aqueous ion at 1 atm and 25 °C) and are called the voltages for the half cell. The symbol ° indicates the conditions are standard.

$$Li+ (aq) + e^- \rightarrow Li (s) \qquad E°_{red} = -3.04 \text{ V}$$

All standard potentials are measured against the standard hydrogen electrode (SHE) reaction, which is assigned a potential of zero volts. When the E° value for the lithium reduction reaction is –3.04, this really means that it is –3.04 volts compared to the reduction of hydrogen by the SHE reaction.

The reduction potentials indicate the spontaneity of the half reactions. A positive potential indicates a spontaneous forward reaction. Fluorine has a high affinity for electrons and a standard reduction potential of +2.87 volts, which indicates that the reaction is spontaneous. The more positive the E°, the more easily the substance on the left side of the reaction can be reduced. The more negative the E°, the less likely the substance on the left side of the reaction will be reduced and more likely an oxidation will occur.

If the half reaction is written in the reverse direction, the sign of E° must be reversed (i.e., a positive value becomes negative, and a negative value becomes positive). It is important to remember that the half reactions can occur in either direction.

Standard reduction potentials are used to form the **electrochemical reactivity series**. This series can be used to determine which elements oxidize more easily than others by ranking the reducing and oxidizing agents. Hydrogen is used as the reference point. The strongest reducing agents are the most reactive metals and are at the top of the table (for instance, Li, Na, and Mg). The metals at the bottom of the table are relatively unreactive.

Table 5.1. The Electrochemical Activity Series

Metal	Oxidation Reaction	E°_{red}
Lithium	$Li\ (s) \rightarrow Li^{+}\ (aq) + e^{-}$	−3.05
Potassium	$K\ (s) \rightarrow K^{+}\ (aq) + e^{-}$	−2.92
Barium	$Ba\ (s) \rightarrow Ba^{2+}\ (aq) + 2e^{-}$	−2.90
Calcium	$Ca\ (s) \rightarrow Ca^{2+}\ (aq) + 2e^{-}$	−2.76
Sodium	$Na\ (s) \rightarrow Na^{+}\ (aq) + e^{-}$	−2.71
Magnesium	$Mg\ (s) \rightarrow Mg^{2+}\ (aq) + 2e^{-}$	−2.37
Aluminum	$Al\ (s) \rightarrow Al^{3+}\ (aq) + 3e^{-}$	−1.66
Manganese	$Mn\ (s) \rightarrow Mn^{2+}\ (aq) + 2e^{-}$	−1.18
Zinc	$Zn\ (s) \rightarrow Zn^{2+}\ (aq) + 2e^{-}$	−0.76
Chromium	$Cr\ (s) \rightarrow Cr^{3+}\ (aq) + 3e^{-}$	−0.73
Iron	$Fe\ (s) \rightarrow Fe^{2+}\ (aq) + 2e^{-}$	−0.44
Cobalt	$Co\ (s) \rightarrow Co^{2+}\ (aq) + 2e^{-}$	−0.28
Nickel	$Ni\ (s) \rightarrow Ni^{2+}\ (aq) + 2e^{-}$	−0.23
Tin	$Sn\ (s) \rightarrow Sn^{2+}\ (aq) + 2e^{-}$	−0.14
Lead	$Pb\ (s) \rightarrow Pb^{2+}\ (aq) + 2e^{-}$	−0.13

EASE OF OXIDATION INCREASES ↑

Table 5.1. The Electrochemical Activity Series (continued)

Metal	Oxidation Reaction	E°_{red}
Hydrogen	H_2 (*g*) → $2H^+$ (*aq*) + $2e^-$	0.00
Copper	Cu (*s*) → Cu^{2+} (*aq*) + $2e^-$	0.16
Silver	Ag (*s*) → Ag^+ (*aq*) + e^-	0.80
Mercury	Hg (*l*) → Hg^{2+} (*aq*) + $2e^-$	0.80
Platinum	Pt (*s*) → Pt^{2+} (*aq*) + $2e^-$	1.23
Gold	Au (*s*) → Au^{3+} (*aq*) + $3e^-$	1.50

EASE OF OXIDATION INCREASES

SAMPLE QUESTION

8) **Which of the following ions is the strongest reducing agent?**

A. Mg^{2+}

B. Ba^{2+}

C. Fe^{3+}

D. K^+

Answer: D.

D. Ions with negative reduction potentials will be oxidized, and so will act as reducing agents. According to Table 5.1, potassium has the most negative reduction potential (E°_{red} = −2.92 V) among the four answer choices.

Balancing Redox Reactions

Balancing redox reactions is a bit more complicated than balancing other types of chemical equations because it involves changes in the oxidation states of elements.

To balance redox reactions, first, determine the oxidation state for each element in the reaction. If the oxidation states change, this is a redox reaction.

Once it has been established the reaction is a redox reaction, separate the reaction into its two half reactions, the oxidation and reduction reactions. Include only the reaction compounds that change oxidation states in these half reactions. The other ions that do not change oxidation states are referred to as spectator ions because they do not participate in the redox reaction.

When the half reactions have been identified, balance the atoms that are not oxygen or hydrogen. After all other atoms are balanced, balance the oxygen atoms by adding H_2O to one side of each half reaction, and balance the hydrogen atoms by adding H^+.

Once all the atoms are balanced, balance the charges in each half reaction by adding electrons. If the half reactions do not have the same number of electrons, multiply the half reactions by a coefficient so they do have the same number of electrons.

Finally, combine the half reactions and simplify by removing the compounds that appear on both the reactant side and product side.

Below is a step-by-step example showing how to balance a redox reaction.

$$HNO_3\ (aq) + Cu\ (s) \rightarrow Cu^{2+}\ (aq) + NO\ (g)$$

1. This is a redox reaction because the oxidation state of copper changes from 0 to +2 and the oxidation state of nitrogen changes from +5 to +2.
2. The two half reactions are:
   $Cu(s) \rightarrow Cu^{2+}\ (aq)$ and $HNO_3\ (aq) \rightarrow NO\ (g)$
3. None of the ions are spectator ions in this example, so none of the ions are left out.
4. Because the atoms of copper and nitrogen are equal, no balancing is needed for those elements. However, the oxygen and hydrogen atoms in the nitric acid half reaction must be balanced.
5. Adding two molecules of water to the right side of the equation balances the number of oxygen atoms:
   $HNO_3\ (aq) \rightarrow NO\ (g) + 2\ H_2O\ (l)$
6. Now, hydrogen atoms need to be added.
   $3\ H^+ + HNO_3\ (aq) \rightarrow NO\ (g) + 2\ H_2O\ (l)$
7. This step balances the atoms in the equations, but the charges still need to be balanced by adding electrons. The 2+ charge is balanced by adding 2 electrons, which have a negative charge.
   $Cu\ (s) \rightarrow Cu^{2+}\ (aq) + 2\ e^-$
8. The 3+ charge from the added hydrogen atoms must be balanced by adding 3 electrons.
   $3\ e^- + 3\ H^+ + HNO_3\ (aq) \rightarrow NO\ (g) + 2\ H_2O\ (l)$
9. Next, the number of electrons in both half reactions must be equal. This can be done by multiplying the equations by 3 and 2, respectively.
   $3\ [Cu\ (s) \rightarrow Cu^{2+}\ (aq) + 2\ e^-]$ and
   $2\ [3\ e^- + 3\ H^+ + HNO_3\ (aq) \rightarrow NO\ (g) + 2\ H_2O\ (l)]$
10. Now the reactions can be added back together to give the balanced redox reaction:
    $3\ Cu\ (s) + 6\ H^+(aq) + 2\ HNO_3\ (aq) \rightarrow 3\ Cu^{2+}\ (aq) + 2\ NO\ (g) + 4\ H_2O\ (l)$

SAMPLE QUESTIONS

9) **Find the coefficients for the following redox reaction:**

$C_2H_6\ (g) + O_2\ (g) \rightarrow CO_2\ (g) + H_2O\ (g)$

A. 1:4:2:2

B. 2:7:4:6

C. 2:6:4:2

D. 2:7:4:2

Answer: B.

$C_2H_6\ (g) + O_2\ (g) \rightarrow 2\ CO_2\ (g) + H_2O\ (g)$	Start by balancing the carbon atoms on each side of the equation.
$C_2H_6\ (g) + O_2\ (g) \rightarrow 2\ CO_2\ (g) + 3\ H_2O\ (g)$	Next, balance the hydrogen atoms on each side of the equation.
$C_2H_6\ (g) + 3.5\ O_2\ (g) \rightarrow 2\ CO_2\ (g) + 3\ H_2O\ (g)$	Then, balance the oxygen on each side of the equation.
$\mathbf{2\ C_2H_6\ (g) + 7\ O_2\ (g) \rightarrow 4\ CO_2\ (g) + 6\ H_2O\ (g)}$	Finally, remove the decimal by multiplying each coefficient by 2.

10) **Find the coefficients for the following redox reaction:**

$HNO_3\ (aq) + H_3AsO_3\ (aq) \rightarrow NO\ (g) + H_3AsO_4\ (aq) + H_2O\ (l)$

A. 1:3:1:3:2

B. 2:3:2:3:2

C. 2:3:2:3:1

D. 4:2:2:4:1

Answer: C.

$HNO_3\ (aq) + 3\ H_3AsO_3\ (aq) \rightarrow NO\ (g) + H_3AsO_4\ (aq) + H_2O\ (l)$	First, work to balance the hydrogen atoms on each side.
$HNO_3\ (aq) + 3\ H_3AsO_3\ (aq) \rightarrow NO\ (g) + 3\ H_3AsO_4\ (aq) + H_2O\ (l)$	Then, balance the arsenic atoms in the products.
$2\ HNO_3\ (aq) + 3\ H_3AsO_3\ (aq) \rightarrow NO\ (g) + 3\ H_3AsO_4\ (aq) + H_2O\ (l)$	Next, continue to work to balance the hydrogen.
$\mathbf{2\ HNO_3\ (aq) + 3\ H_3AsO_3\ (aq) \rightarrow 2\ NO\ (g) + 3\ H_3AsO_4\ (aq) + H_2O\ (l)}$	Finally, balance the nitrogen and oxygen atoms in the products.

ELECTROCHEMICAL CELLS

An **electrochemical cell** is set up so that a redox reaction takes place, but electrons move through an outside conductor. Electrochemical cells are batteries and can generate electrical energy from chemical reactions or introduce electrical energy to facilitate a chemical reaction.

Electrochemical cells are composed of electrodes and a salt bridge. A common electrochemical cell that will be used to illustrate the components of the cell consists of Zn and Cu. There are two half reactions that occur in the cell, but they are separated into half cells. Each half cell comprises an electrode and an electrolyte. An electrode moves electrons (conducts electrical current). In the following example, the electrodes are metal plates of Zn and Cu, but electrodes can also be other metals, graphite, or another conductor. There are two types of electrodes: the **cathode**, where reduction takes place, and the **anode**, where oxidation occurs. Zn is the anode and Cu is the cathode in this example:

$$Zn \rightarrow Zn^{2+} + 2e^{-}, \text{ oxidation (anode)}$$

$$Cu^{2+} + 2e^{-} \rightarrow Cu, \text{ reduction (cathode)}$$

$$\text{Net reaction: } Cu^{2+} + Zn\ (s) \rightarrow Cu\ (s) + Zn^{2+}$$

The electrons flow from the anode to the cathode via a filament. If the electrons flowed continually with no other reactions, the half cells would very quickly build up a positive charge in the anode and a less positive charge in the cathode (charge difference), stopping the flow of electrons. This buildup is avoided by using a salt bridge to connect the two half cells. The salt bridge is a solution of a salt that allows negative and positive ions to pass freely while keeping the contents otherwise separated, allowing a steady-state charge distribution. In this example, Na_2SO_4 is used as the salt bridge. As the electrons flow in the cell, the negative ions (SO_4^{2-}) move to the anode, and the positive ions (Na^+) move toward the cathode. In general, anions always flow to the anode and cations to the cathode. This flow allows the current to flow by preventing charge buildup.

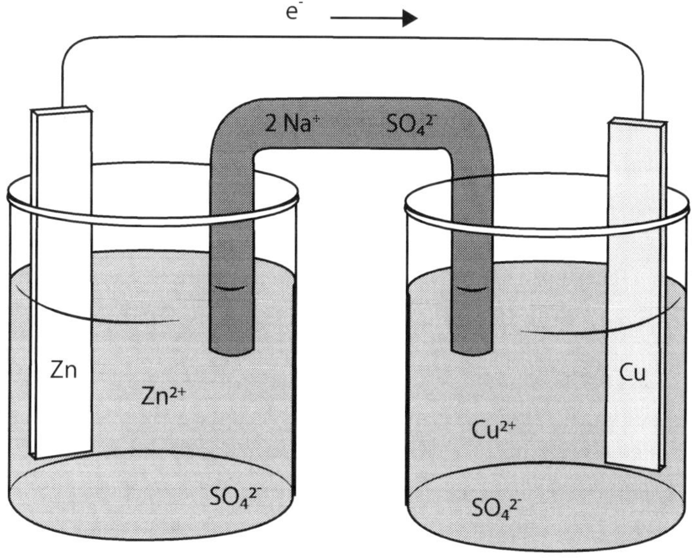

Figure 5.2. Electrochemical Cell

The following are rules for the operation of batteries (electrochemical cells):

- The redox reaction in the cell must favor the formation of products.
- There must be an external circuit for the electrons to flow through.
- All cells must have a salt bridge or some means of allowing ions to flow between the half cells.

SAMPLE QUESTION

11) In an electrochemical cell, oxidation occurs at the __________.

A. salt bridge

B. cathode

C. anode

D. ion channels

Answers:

A. Incorrect. The salt bridge is used as a barrier between the two parts of the cell to prevent a charge difference.

B. Incorrect. Reduction occurs at the cathode.

C. Correct. Oxidation reactions occur at the anode. In the example above, the anode contains Zn ions.

D. Incorrect. Ion channels are not associated with electrochemical cells.

Chemical Equilibrium

A **chemical equilibrium** occurs when the concentrations of reactants and products remain constant in a reaction system. This does not mean that the chemical reaction has stopped, just that the forward and backward reactions are occurring at equal rates. Because of this, chemical equilibria are often called *dynamic equilibria* and are represented in equations with a double arrow. An example of a system in chemical equilibrium is a weak acid, which only partially ionizes in water.

$$CH_3COOH\ (aq) + H_2O\ (l) \leftrightarrow CH_3COO^-\ (aq) + H_3O^+\ (aq)$$

While more than 90 percent of the acid remains in its molecular form (CH_3COOH) at equilibrium, both the forward and backward reactions are occurring at the same rates.

There are two important facts to know about chemical equilibrium. First, the equilibrium state is independent of how the equilibrium was reached if the temperature is constant. This means that the same number of moles of the reactants and products will be there at equilibrium whether the reaction starts with *x* moles of reactant or *x* moles of product. The Haber process for synthesizing ammonia is often used to illustrate this concept because the reaction does not go to completion, but instead reaches an equilibrium with all three components present.

$$N_2\ (g) + 3\ H_2\ (g) \leftrightarrow 2\ NH_3\ (g)$$

It does not matter whether N_2 and H_2 or NH_3 are added to the container; either situation will result in an equilibrium with the same concentrations of N_2, H_2, and NH_3.

Second, the equilibrium is not affected by catalysts. Catalysts can speed up the rate at which equilibrium is achieved, but they cannot change the equilibrium concentrations.

EQUILIBRIUM CONSTANTS

Each equilibrium has an equilibrium constant, K. This is a quotient of the equilibrium concentrations of reactants and products for a given reaction at a given temperature. K is independent of the initial concentrations of the reactants and products in a reaction, but is dependent on the temperature of the reaction system.

A mathematical expression, called the *equilibrium constant expression*, can be derived from the chemical equation for any equilibrium process. The equilibrium constant can reveal whether the reaction favors products or reactants, the direction the reaction will proceed in, and the concentration of products and reactants at equilibrium.

The equilibrium constant, K, is written with the concentrations of products in the numerator and the concentration of reactants in the denominator. The concentrations of both products and reactants are also raised to the power of their stoichiometric coefficients. However, only the concentrations of gases and dilute solutions should be included. The concentrations of pure solids and liquids do not appear in equilibrium constant expressions because their concentrations do not change as the reaction occurs.

The following general equilibrium reaction illustrates how the equilibrium constant is written:

$$aA + bB \leftrightarrow cC + dD$$

$$K = \frac{[C]^c[D]^d}{[A]^a[B]^b}$$

If $K > 1$: The reaction strongly favors products. The concentrations of products at equilibrium are much greater than those of the reactants.

If $K < 1$: The reaction strongly favors the reactants. The concentrations of the reactants at equilibrium are much greater than those of the products.

If $K \approx 1$: The reaction favors neither the reactants nor the products. The equilibrium mixture contains significant concentrations of reactants and products.

SAMPLE QUESTION

13) Write the equilibrium constant for the following reaction:

$Cl_2O_7\ (g) + 8\ H_2\ (g) \leftrightarrow 2\ HCl\ (g) + 7\ H_2O\ (g)$

A. $K = \frac{[H_2O]^1[HCl]^2}{[Cl_2O_7][H_2]^1}$

B. $K = \frac{[H_2O]^7[HCl]^2}{[Cl_2O_7][H_2]^8}$

C. $K = \frac{[H_2O]^2[HCl]^7}{[Cl_2O_7][H_2]^8}$

D. $K = \frac{[Cl_2O_7][H_2]^8}{[H_2O]^7[HCl]^2}$

Answer: B.

The products are always in the denominator and the reactants in the numerator. Additionally, the concentrations of both the products and reactants must be raised to the power of their coefficients from the equation.

Le Châtelier's Principle

Le Châtelier's principle states that if a chemical reaction system is at equilibrium, and the conditions are changed so it is no longer at equilibrium, the system will react to counteract the change and reach a new equilibrium. This applies to changes in the concentration of reactants or products, temperature, and to changes in pressure or volume in a gas-phase equilibrium.

Applying changes to a system in equilibrium is known as *shifting the equilibrium.* The equilibrium can shift to either the right (forward direction, products) or left (reverse direction, reactants). If reactants are added to a system in equilibrium, the equilibrium will shift to the right (forward direction), but if reactants are removed from the system, the equilibrium will shift to the left (reverse direction). If products are added to the system, the equilibrium will also shift to the left (reverse direction), but if products are removed from the system, the equilibrium will shift to the right (forward direction).

Changing the temperature, pressure, or volume of a chemical reaction will also result in a change in the equilibrium of the system. If the temperature of a system is increased, the heat of the reaction system increases, and if the temperature is lowered, the heat of the reaction system decreases.

QUICK REVIEW

Transferring gas into and out of the blood is an equilibrium process. For oxygen, it is represented by $Hb_4 + 4O_2 \leftrightarrow Hb_4O_8$, where Hb is hemoglobin. How would this reaction maintain equilibrium when it occurs (1) in the lungs with high oxygen concentration and (2) near tissues with low oxygen concentration?

The effect of changes in temperature depend on whether the reaction is endothermic or exothermic. If a reaction is endothermic, heat can be considered a reactant, and the addition of heat to the system will push the equilibrium in the forward direction. If a reaction is exothermic, heat is a product, and the addition of heat will push the equilibrium in the reverse direction.

Table 5.2. Le Châtelier's Principle

Change	Shift	Effect on K
Increase in reaction concentration	To products	No change
Increase in product concentration	To reactants	No change
Increase pressure Decrease volume	Toward fewer moles of gas	No change
Decrease pressure Increase volume	Toward more moles of gas	No change
Increase temperature	Toward endothermic direction	Increases if products are favored
Decrease temperature	Toward exothermic direction	Decreases if reactants are favored
Addition of catalyst	No shift	No change

If a system has an equal number of moles of gas on each side of the chemical reaction, a change in the volume and partial pressures will not have an effect. However, if the product and reactant sides have different numbers of moles, a change in the volume will affect the reaction. If the volume decreases, increasing the partial pressure, the reaction shifts to the side of the equilibrium with fewer moles in an attempt to decrease the pressure. If the volume increases, decreasing the partial pressure, the reverse is true, and the equilibrium side with more moles is favored.

SAMPLE QUESTION

13) **Consider that the following reaction is in equilibrium: $BaSO_4$ (*s*) $\leftrightarrow$ Ba^{2+} (*aq*) + SO_4^{2-} (*aq*)**

What will happen to the concentration of Ba^{2+} if more $BaSO_4$ is added to the reaction?

A. It will increase.

B. It will decrease.

C. There is insufficient information to determine the effect.

D. There will be no change.

Answer:

A. **Correct.** Adding more reactants will push the reaction forward toward the products to reach a new equilibrium.

STOICHIOMETRY

Stoichiometry uses the relative quantities of the molecules in a chemical equation to calculate the amount of reactants used or products made in a reaction. Stoichiometry problems are worked using dimensional analysis (or railroad tracks), which requires three basic steps:

1. Identify the given or initial value.
2. Add conversion factors that will leave the desired units when cancelled.
3. Multiply across the top and across the bottom, and then divide.

Common conversion factors used in stoichiometry are shown in the table below.

Table 5.3. Common Conversion Factors in Stoichiometry

Use...	To go between...	Example
mole ratio	moles of different substances in a chemical reaction	$\frac{1 \text{ mol } O_2}{2 \text{ mol } CO_2}$
molar mass	moles and grams	$\frac{1 \text{ mol } O_2}{32 \text{ g } O_2}$
Avogadro's number	moles and molecules	$\frac{1 \text{ mol } O_2}{6.02 \times 10^{23} \text{ molecules } O_2}$
molar volume	moles and volume of gas (at STP)	$\frac{1 \text{ mol } O_2}{22.4 \text{ L}}$

THE AMOUNT OF PRODUCTS AND REACTANTS

The main tool of stoichiometry is the **mole ratio**, which is simply a ratio of the number of moles of two substances in the equation. For example, in the combustion of methane (shown below), 2 moles of O_2 produce 1 mole of CO_2.

$$CH_4 + 2\,O_2 \rightarrow CO_2 + 2\,H_2O,$$

The mole ratio of O_2 and CO_2 is written as $\frac{2 \text{ mol } O_2}{1 \text{ mol } CO_2}$ or $\frac{1 \text{ mol } CO_2}{2 \text{ mol } O_2}$. This ratio can be used to determine how many moles of a specific reactant or product are required for the given amount of a reactant or product.

- If 0.4 mol of CH_4 reacts completely with oxygen, how many moles of water are produced?

0.4 mol CH_4	2 mol H_2O	= 0.8 mol H_2O
1	1 mol CH_4	

- How many moles of O_2 are needed to produce 5 moles of CO_2?

5 mol CO_2	2 mol O_2	= 10 mol O_2
1	1 mol CO_2	

Combining the mole ratio with molar mass allows for the calculation of the mass of the required reactant or product.

- How many moles of water are formed from the complete reaction of 4.32 g of methane with oxygen?

4.32 g mol CH_4	1 mol CH_4	2 mol H_2O	= 0.54 mol H_2O
1	16 g mol CH_4	1 mol CH_4	

SAMPLE QUESTION

14) Which statement is NOT true of the chemical reaction $2\ BiCl_3 + 3\ H_2S \rightarrow Bi_2S_3 + 6\ HCl$?

A. When 4 grams of $BiCl_3$ react, 12 grams of HCl are formed.

B. When 20 molecules of $BiCl_3$ react, 10 molecules of Bi_2S_3 are produced.

C. When 3 moles of H_2S react, 2 moles of $BiCl_3$ also react.

D. When 34.08 grams of H_2S react, 109.38 grams of HCl are produced.

Answers:

A. Correct. When 4 g of $BiCl_3$ react, 1.39 g of HCl is produced.

4g $BiCl_3$	1 mol BiCl	6 mol HCl	36.46 g HCl	= 1.39 g HCl
1	315.33 g BiCl	2 mol $BiCl_3$	1 mol HCl	

B. Incorrect. According the equation, for every 2 moles of $BiCl_3$, 1 mole of Bi_2S_3 is formed.

C. Incorrect. According the equation, 3 moles of H_2S react with 2 moles of $BiCl_2$.

D. Incorrect. When 34.08 g of H_2S react, 109.38g of HCl is produced.

34.08 g H_2S	1 mol H_2S	6 HCl	36.46 g HCl	= 109.38 g HCl
1	34.08 g H_2S	2 H_2S	1 mol HCl	

LIMITING REACTANTS

In a chemical reaction where both reactants are present, it is possible for one reactant to be used up before the other. Once this reactant is gone, the reaction ceases and no further product can be made. The reactant that is used up, stopping the reaction, is the **limiting**

CONSIDER THIS

Think of stoichiometry as cooking, and the chemical equation as the recipe. If there is not enough of one ingredient (the limiting reactant), the amount of the other ingredients and the amount of food the recipe produces will change.

reactant. When calculating the amount of product made, it's important to use the amount of the limiting reactant (not any other reactants) as the initial value.

There are several ways to find the limiting reactant, but simplest is to find the amount of product made by each reactant. The reactant that produces the smallest amount of product will be the limiting reactant.

In the reaction below, what is the limiting reactant if 5 g of SiO_2 and 5 g of C are used?

SiO_2 (*s*) + 3 C (*s*) → SiC (*s*) + 2 CO (*g*)

5 g C	0.416 mol C	1 mol SiC	40.1 g SiC	= 2.32 g SiC
1	12 g C	3 mol C	1 mol SiC	
5 g SiO_2	0.0832 mol SiO_2	1 mol SiC	40.1 g SiC	= 0.28 g SiC
1	60.19 g SiO_2	1 mol SiO_2	1 mol SiC	

Since the amount of SiO_2 present can produce only 0.28 g of SiC, the reaction is limited by SiO_2.

SAMPLE QUESTION

15) Determine the limiting reactant and the mass of $C_9H_8O_4$ produced when 1 g of $C_7H_6O_3$ and 3 g of $C_4H_6O_3$ react.
2 $C_7H_6O_3$ (*s*) + $C_4H_6O_3$ (*l*) → 2 $C_9H_8O_4$ (*s*) + H_2O (*l*)

A. $C_4H_6O_3$, 2 g of $C_9H_8O_4$
B. $C_7H_6O_3$, 2 g of $C_9H_8O_4$
C. $C_7H_6O_3$, 1.3 g of $C_9H_8O_4$
D. $C_4H_6O_3$, 1.3 g of $C_9H_8O_4$

Answer: C.

Find the number of moles of each reactant.

3 g $C_4H_6O_3$	1 mol	= 0.029 mol $C_4H_6O_3$
1	102.1 g	

1 g $C_7H_6O_3$	1 mol H	= 0.007 mol $C_7H_6O_3$
1	138.12 g	

Determine which is the limiting reactant.

0.029 mol $C_4H_6O_3$	2 mol $C_7H_6O_3$	= 0.058 mol $C_7H_6O_3$
1	1 mol $C_4H_6O_3$	

In this reaction, 0.058 moles of $C_7H_6O_3$ are required for every 0.029 mol $C_4H_6O_3$. Because only 0.007 moles of $C_7H_6O_3$ are available, it is the limiting reactant.

Use the limiting reactant to determine yield for $C_9H_8O_4$.

0.007 mol $C_7H_6O_3$	2 mol $C_9H_8O_4$	180.17 g	= **1.3 g $C_9H_8O_4$**
	2 mol $C_7H_6O_3$	1 mol	

PERCENT YIELD

When the maximum quantity of the product is formed in a reaction, the yield is 100%. This is the theoretical yield of a reaction, and it is often different from the **actual yield** of a reaction, which is the quantity of the product actually created from the chemical reaction. Dividing the actual yield by the theoretical yield gives the **percent yield**.

$$\text{percent yield} = \frac{\text{actual yield}}{\text{theoretical yield}} \times 100\%$$

The percent yield can differ from the theoretical yield for a number of reasons. For example, the product can be lost during purification or the reactants can be used in unwanted side reactions.

SAMPLE QUESTION

16) **Consider the equation: CO (*g*) + 2 H_2 (*g*) → CH_3OH (*l*). If 100 g of CO reacts with excess H_2 and produces 100 g of CH_3OH, what is the percent yield?**

A. 100%

B. 92%

C. 80%

D. 87.5%

Answer: D.

Find the theoretical yield.

100 g CO	1 mol CO	1 mol CH_3OH	32 g CH_3OH	114.24 g CH_3OH
	28.01 g CO	1 mol CO	1 mol CH_3OH	

Use the formula for percent yield.

$$\text{percent yield} = \frac{\text{actual yield}}{\text{theoretical yield}} \times 100\%$$

$$= \frac{100\text{ g}}{114.24\text{ g}} \times 100\% = \mathbf{87.5\%}$$

Chemical Kinetics

Rate Laws

Chemical kinetics, the study of rates and mechanisms of chemical reactions, can be used to determine how quickly chemical reactions will occur. The **rate** of a chemical reaction describes how fast the reaction is; it is written as a change in the concentration of reactants or products per unit of time. The reaction rate's relationship with the reactant concentration can be described by a mathematical equation known as a **rate law**. The rate law uses a proportionality constant, k, called the **rate constant**. The rate constant is specific to each reaction, applies at a specific temperature, and is independent of concentration.

> HELPFUL HINT
>
> An uppercase K represents the equilibrium constant of a reaction. A lowercase k represents the rate constant for a reaction.

The rate law must be determined experimentally. For most homogeneous reactions, the rate law has the following general form:

$$\text{Rate} = k\,[A]^m[B]^n$$

where A and B are the reactants, products, or catalysts, and the exponents define the order of reaction.

The **reaction order**, or order of reaction, is the exponent to which each concentration term in the rate equation is raised. For the generic equation given above, the reaction order for A is m and for B it is n. The overall reaction order is $m + n$.

- In zero-order reactions, the rate is independent of the reactant concentration. Rate $= k\,[A]^0 = k$

Most reactions occur in two or more steps during which intermediate substances are formed and then consumed. Each step in a reaction will have its own reaction rate, with the slowest step determining the overall rate of the reaction.

- First-order reactions are reactions in which the reaction rate depends only on a single reactant that has an exponent of one. All unimolecular elementary reactions are first order. Rate $= k\,[A]$
- Second-order reactions are reactions with an overall order of two. This can be because the reaction is proportional to one concentration squared or to the product of two concentrations. Rate $= k\,[A]^2$ or $k\,[A][B]$

> SAMPLE QUESTION
>
> 17) **For the following reaction, determine the order based on the given rate law.**
>
> **$2\ NO_2\ (g) \rightarrow 2\ NO\ (g) + O_2\ (g)$, Rate $= k\ [NO_2]^2$**
>
> A. second order

B. first order

C. zero order

D. There is not enough information to determine the answer.

Answer:

A. The only exponent is a 2, so this rate law has an overall order of 2.

REACTION RATES

Various factors can affect the speed of a reaction or reaction rate. In homogeneous reactions, in which all the reactants and products are in one phase, there are four main factors:

- the properties of the reactants and products (i.e., molecular structure and bonding)
- the concentrations of the reactants and sometimes the products
- the reaction temperature
- the presence and concentration of a catalyst

Heterogeneous reaction rates depend on those factors, but because those reactions take place at the surface/interface (e.g., where a solid and gas meet), their rates also depend on the surface area and nature of the surface. A heterogeneous reaction with a larger surface area will proceed more quickly.

It is possible to predict how certain factors will change the reaction rate. For example, as the reactant concentration increases, the reaction rate will also increase. This is explained by collision theory: Reactants must collide (meet) to react. If there are more reactants (i.e., a higher concentration), there is a higher probability of collision. Pressure also influences the reaction rate of gaseous reactions. An increase in the pressure results in an increase in the reaction rate, because increasing the pressure of a gas is equivalent to increasing the concentration. Finally, temperature changes the reaction rate. An increase in temperature typically delivers more energy to a system, increasing the collision rate and thus the reaction rate.

SAMPLE QUESTION

18) How will an increase in the concentration of the reactants affect the reaction rate?

A. It will slow down the reaction rate.

B. It will increase the reaction rate.

C. It will not change the reaction rate.

D. The effect can't be determined without knowing the reaction's rate law.

Answer:

B. A higher concentration of reactants increases the rate of reaction by increasing the number of collisions between reactant molecules.

Activation Energy

All chemical reactions require some energy to change reactants into products. The amount of energy required to overcome the energy barrier for a reaction is the **activation energy, E_a,** which can vary greatly from reaction to reaction. A reaction profile diagram shows the activation energy required to turn reactants into products.

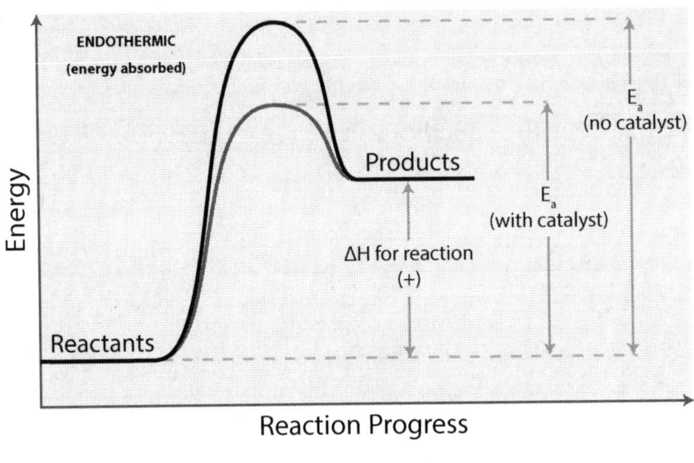

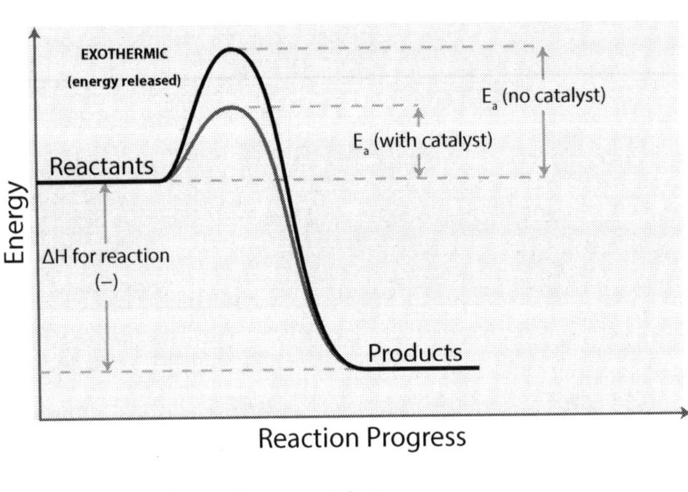

Figure 5.3. Reaction Profile Diagrams

> **DID YOU KNOW?**
>
> Catalytic converters in gasoline engines use a heterogeneous catalyst. A solid, metal is used to catalyze the reaction of harmful exhaust products, like carbon monoxide, nitrogen oxides, and unused fuel, into less harmful emissions, such as carbon dioxide, water, oxygen, and nitrogen.

If the activation energy is too high, a reaction may not proceed or may proceed only at a very slow rate. The activation energy can be modified by the addition of a **catalyst**. Overall, a catalyst is a compound that lowers the activation energy of a reaction by changing the mechanism to a new mechanism with a lower activation energy. By lowering the activation energy, a catalyst speeds up the rate of the reaction. Catalysts are not consumed by the chemical reaction and do not appear in the overall chemical equation. The presence of a catalyst is often indicated by placing the catalyst above or below the reaction arrow:

$$O_3 + O \xrightarrow[Cl]{} 2O_2$$

There are two types of catalysts: homogeneous and heterogeneous. **Homogeneous catalysts** are in the same phase as the reactants (dissolved in the solvent with the reactants). **Heterogeneous catalysts** are in a different phase from the reactants. These are usually solid catalysts used in a liquid- or gas-phase reaction. Heterogeneous catalysts rely on their surface area to help speed up a reaction; a larger surface area results in a faster rate of reaction.

SAMPLE QUESTION

19) What is the role of a catalyst in a reaction?

A. to decrease the rate of the reaction

B. to increase the rate of the reaction

C. to change the chemical equilibrium

D. to increase the amount of product produced

Answers:

A. Incorrect. A catalyst is used to increase the rate of reaction, not to decrease it.

B. Correct. A catalyst increases the rate of reaction by changing the reaction mechanism.

C. Incorrect. Chemical equilibrium refers to a reaction where the forward and reverse reactions are occurring at the same rate. A catalyst is used to speed up a reaction, not to shift the equilibrium.

D. Incorrect. A catalyst does not influence the amount of product that results from a reaction.

Thermodynamics

Energy, work, and heat all play a crucial role in chemical reactions and changes of state. The study of the relationship between these three factors is called **thermodynamics**. By looking at the balance of energy gained and lost during chemical and physical changes, it is possible to determine whether these changes will occur spontaneously.

In thermodynamics, variables can be divided into two categories. **State functions** have a value that does not depend on the path taken by the process to reach its final state. Mass, volume, and pressure (along with many of the variables defined in this chapter) are state functions. A property that does depend on the path taken by the process is called **path function** or **process function**. Work and heat are both path functions.

To understand the laws of thermodynamics, it is necessary to understand systems and surroundings. A **system** is the part of the universe where an actual process takes place or where observations are made; the rest of the universe is the **surroundings**.

There are three types of systems:

- Open systems: Exchange of energy or matter between the system and its surroundings is possible.
- Closed systems: Only exchange of energy between the system and its surroundings is possible; exchange of matter is not possible.
- Isolated systems: No exchange of energy or matter between the system and its surroundings is possible.

HELPFUL HINT

The laws of thermodynamics govern the initial and the final states of the system—not the rate at which a reaction or a process occurs.

The Basics of Chemical Thermodynamics

Types of Energy

Energy (measured in Joules, J) is a property needed to perform work on or to heat an object. There are two kinds of energy: kinetic and potential. **Kinetic energy** is the energy possessed by objects in motion, and **potential energy** is possessed by objects that have the potential to be in motion due to their position. Potential energy is defined in relation to a specific point. For example, a book held 10 feet off the ground has more potential energy than a book held 5 feet off the ground, because it has the potential to fall farther (i.e., to do more work). Both kinetic and potential energy can be further broken down into other types of energy (shown in Table 6.1).

Table 6.1. Types of Energy

Kinetic	Thermal	Energy possessed by an object due to the movement and vibration of atoms or molecules, which generate heat.
	Sound	Energy associated with the vibration of an object because of a force and the subsequent transference of energy through the object in a wave.
	Motion	Energy associated with the motion of an object.
	Radiant	Energy from the sun, or the energy possessed by vibrating particles is electromagnetic energy.
Potential	Chemical	Energy that exists in the bonds between molecules and atoms.
	Elastic	Energy that is stored due to the deformation of an elastic object.
	Nuclear	Energy that is responsible for holding the nucleus of an atom together.
	Gravitational	Energy possessed by an object by the virtue of its height.
	Electrical	Energy that is stored in a battery.

The total amount of energy remains constant and can neither be created nor destroyed, a property known as the **law of conservation of energy**. Energy can, however, be transformed from one form into another. In the example above, dropping one of the books turns potential energy into kinetic energy. Conversely, picking up a book and placing it on a table turns kinetic energy into potential energy. Solar panels are another example of the law of conservation of energy: the panels transform solar energy into chemical energy, which is eventually transformed into mechanical energy.

SAMPLE QUESTION

1) **Compressing a spring increases the spring's**

   A. thermal kinetic energy.
   B. radiant kinetic energy.
   C. gravitational potential energy.
   D. elastic potential energy.

Answer:

D. **Correct.** A compressed spring has elastic potential energy, which can be turned into kinetic energy when the spring is released and begins to move.

THE LAWS OF THERMODYNAMICS

The **first law of thermodynamics** states that change in energy for a closed system is the difference between the heat supplied to the system and the work done by the system on its surroundings. It is essentially the law of conservation of energy extended to the principles of thermodynamics and heat. The law can be mathematically represented as

$$\Delta U = Q - W$$

where ΔU is the change in internal energy, Q is the heat added to the system, and W is the work done by the system.

In this equation, the signs of the variables depend on whether work is done on or by the system, and on whether heat is added to or lost from the system:

- When work is done on the system, W is positive.
- When work is done by the system, W is negative.
- When heat is added to the system, Q is positive.
- When heat is lost by the system, Q is negative.

The **second law of thermodynamics** states that, in an isolated system, the total entropy of the system always increases with time. This law is also called the *law of increased entropy.*

Entropy (S) is often described as a measure of randomness or chaos in a system. It can also be thought of as the number of possible configurations, or **microstates**, within a system. Increasing the number of possible microstates in a system will increase the chaos or randomness of a system: with increasing possible configurations, it is less likely that molecules will be in a particular microstate. This principle explains why gases spontaneously expand: molecules have more possible arrangements when they have more space to move around.

Systems will favor processes that create more possible configurations for the molecules in the system. Entropy will increase when:

- temperature increases
- volume increases
- the number of molecules in a system increases
- a solid or liquid changes to a gas
- a solid changes to a liquid
- a solution forms from a solid

In thermodynamics, change in entropy equals heat added to the system divided by the temperature at which heat is added. It is important to note that entropy is a state function (it does not depend on the path of the process), and its value is always positive.

The **third law of thermodynamics** states that the entropy of a pure crystalline substance at absolute zero is 0. This is because all the molecules in a pure substance at 0 degrees K would have no energy and would be locked in place, meaning there is only one possible microstate.

According to the **zeroth law of thermodynamics**, two objects are said to be in thermal equilibrium when they have the same temperature. Similarly, if three or more substances are at the same temperature, all three of them will be in thermal equilibrium.

SAMPLE QUESTION

2) **Which of the following will increase the entropy of a system?**

A. 2 moles of liquid water are broken apart to form 2 moles of hydrogen gas and 2 moles of oxygen gas.

B. 2 moles of water vapor condense to form a liquid.

C. 2 moles of water are cooled from 25°C to 15°C.

D. 2 moles of water vapor are moved from a 1 L container to a 0.5 L container.

Answers:

A. Correct. Increases in the number of molecules in a system increases entropy.

B. Incorrect. The phase transition from gas (a high-energy state) to liquid (a low-energy state) decreases entropy.

C. Incorrect. Decreasing the temperature of a system decreases its entropy.

D. Incorrect. Decreasing the volume of a system decreases its entropy.

ENDOTHERMIC AND EXOTHERMIC REACTIONS

A chemical reaction always involves breaking the bonds of the reactants and forming the bonds of the products. Depending on whether the energy required to break the bonds is greater or smaller than the energy released when the products are formed, the reaction will either absorb or release energy. Based on whether energy is released or absorbed, a reaction can be called endothermic or exothermic.

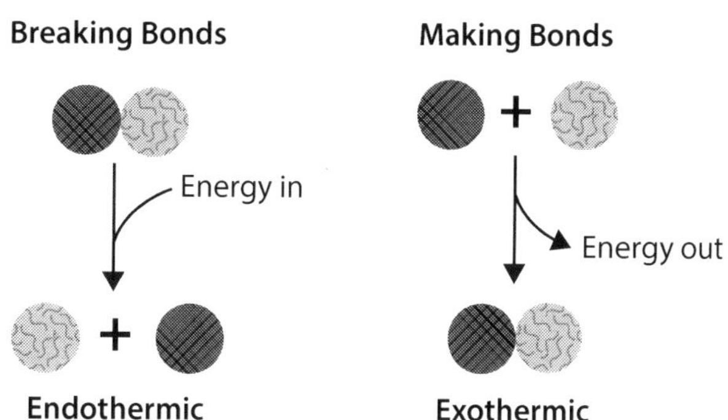

Figure 6.1. Endothermic and Exothermic Reactions

An **endothermic** process absorbs energy in the form of heat. In an endothermic reaction, the energy required to break the existing bonds is greater than the energy released when the new bonds form. These reactions have a positive change in enthalpy (ΔH) because the system is gaining heat. Examples of endothermic processes include:

- liquid water evaporation (an endothermic process)
- photosynthesis (an endothermic reaction)

> **HELPFUL HINT**
>
> Endothermic processes feel cold because they absorb heat from the environment.

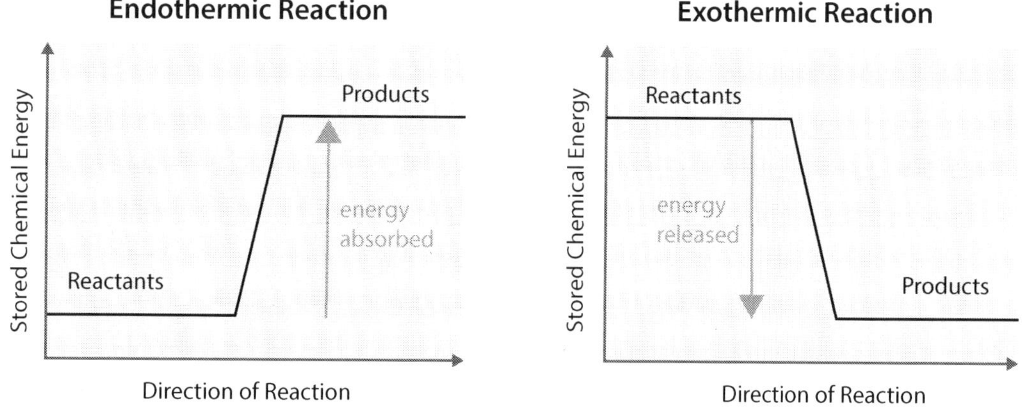

Figure 6.2. Stored Energy in Endothermic and Exothermic Reactions

An **exothermic** process releases energy from the system into the environment. This energy release is usually in the form of heat but can also be in the form of sound or light. An exothermic reaction occurs when the energy required to break bonds is less than the energy released when new bonds form. These reactions have a negative change in enthalpy ($-\Delta H$) because the system is losing heat. Examples of exothermic processes include:

- water vapor condensation (an exothermic process)
- hydrogen combustion (an exothermic reaction)

SAMPLE QUESTION

3) **Which of the following is an endothermic process?**

A. sublimation

B. freezing

C. deposition

D. condensation

Answer:

A. Correct. Energy is required to turn a solid into a gas, making the process endothermic. Energy is released during the processes of freezing, deposition, and condensation because they are transitions from high-energy states to low-energy states.

Temperature and Phase Transitions

Temperature and Heat

While it might look like a substance is not in motion, in fact, its atoms have kinetic energy and are constantly spinning and vibrating. **Temperature** is the name given to the kinetic energy of all the atoms or molecules in a substance. The more energy the atoms have (meaning the more they spin and vibrate) the higher the substance's temperature.

HELPFUL HINT

Use this equation to convert between temperature scales:

$$\frac{(F-32)}{180} = \frac{C}{100} = \frac{(K-273)}{100}$$

Temperature can be measured using the Celsius, Fahrenheit, or Kelvin scale. Most equations in chemistry require the use of the Kelvin scale. Below are the equations for converting between each scale:

- Celsius to Kelvin: $T_K = T_C + 273.15$
- Celsius to Fahrenheit: $T_F = \frac{9}{5}T_C + 32$
- Fahrenheit to Celsius: $T_C = \frac{5}{9}(T_F - 32)$

Table 6.2. The Three Temperature Scales

	Celsius Scale (°C)	Fahrenheit Scale (°F)	Kelvin Scale (K)
Boiling Point of Water	100	212	373.16
Melting Point of Ice	0	32	273.16
Absolute Zero	–273	–460	0

Heat is the movement of energy from one substance to another. Energy will spontaneously move from high-energy (high-temperature) substances to low-energy (low-temperature) substances. This can be seen in phase changes. When an ice cube is put in water, energy moves from the water (which is warmer) to the ice (which is colder). The heat added to the ice will increase the kinetic energy of the molecules in the ice, causing them to move farther apart. With enough heat, the ice will melt and become water.

SAMPLE QUESTION

4) **Convert 89°F to °C.**

Answer:

Use the conversion formula where T_c = temperature in Celsius and T_F = temperature in Fahrenheit.

$T_c = \frac{5}{9}(T_F - 32°)$

$= \frac{5 \times (89 - 32)}{9} = \mathbf{31.66}$

HEAT CAPACITY

Heat capacity (*C*) is the amount of energy required to raise the temperature of a substance by 1 K or 1°C. The unit for measuring specific heat is J°C^{-1} or J K^{-1}. Heat capacity can be mathematically denoted as

$$C = \frac{Q}{\Delta T}$$

where *C* is heat capacity, *Q* is heat supplied to the substance, and ΔT is the difference between the final and initial temperatures.

Specific heat (*c*) is the amount of energy needed to increase the temperature of a unit mass of a sample by 1 K or 1°C. The unit for specific heat is J kg^{-1} °C^{-1} or J kg^{-1} K^{-1}. It can be mathematically represented as

$$c = \frac{Q}{m\Delta T} \text{ or } Q = mc\Delta T$$

HELPFUL HINT

Heat capacity is an *extensive* property that depends on the mass of the substance. More mass requires more energy to raise its temperature. Specific heat is an *intensive* property because it does not depend on the mass of any specific sample.

where c is specific heat, Q is heat supplied to the substance, m is the mass of the substance, and ΔT is the difference between the final and initial temperatures.

> HELPFUL HINT
>
> Even though the numerical values for temperature in °C or K are different, ΔC and ΔK for two given temperatures will be same. This is NOT true when comparing the changes on the Fahrenheit scale.

Change in temperature of a substance is directly proportional to the heat supplied and inversely proportional to its mass (specific heat is a property of the substance and thus a constant). In other words, applying a certain amount of heat to a substance with a high specific heat will produce a smaller change in temperature than applying that same amount of heat to a substance with a low specific heat. Water, for example, has a relatively high specific heat and, therefore, is often used as a coolant in industrial applications because it can absorb more thermal energy.

SAMPLE QUESTIONS

5) **What is the specific heat for a 5 g metal block that experiences a rise in temperature of 27°C after 1,019 J of heat is added?**

Answer:

Use the formula for specific heat.

$c = \frac{Q}{m\Delta T}$

$c = \frac{1019}{5(27)}$

$=$ **7.54 J/g°C**

6) **How much heat is required to raise the temperature of 250 g of water from 15°C to 65°C? (The specific heat of water is 4.18 J/g°C.)**

Answer:

Use the formula for specific heat.

$Q = mc\Delta T$

$= (250\text{ g})(4.18\text{ J/g°C})(65\text{°C} - 15\text{°C})$

$=$ **52,250 J**

Phase Transitions

A **phase transition** in a substance happens when it changes from a solid, liquid, or gas phase to a different phase. Temperature and pressure play an important role in the phase transitions because for any substance, change in phase takes place at a set temperature-pressure combination.

Table 6.3. Phase Transitions

Name	Process	Sign of Enthalpy Change
Condensing	gas to liquid	heat of vaporization (–)
Evaporating	liquid to gas	heat of vaporization (+)
Freezing	liquid to solid	heat of fusion (–)
Melting	solid to liquid	heat of fusion (+)
Deposition	gas to solid	heat of sublimation (–)
Sublimation	solid to gas	heat of sublimation (+)

The effect of temperature and pressure on the state of a substance is shown in a **phase diagram**. Every element and compound has a unique phase diagram that depends on that substance's chemical properties. The diagram shows temperature on the *x*-axis and pressure on the *y*-axis. Lines on the diagram show where the substance is a solid, liquid, and gas, and also where transitions between states occur. The diagram also shows when a substance becomes a **supercritical fluid**, a state that has the properties of both gas and liquid. Notable points on the diagram include:

DID YOU KNOW?

It is possible for two phases of a substance to coexist at the same time; this is called a *two-phase state*. A common example of a two-phase state is melting ice, where both solid and liquid water exist at the same time.

- melting point (T_m): temperature and pressure at which the solid melts to liquid
- boiling point (T_b): temperature and pressure at which liquid evaporates to gas

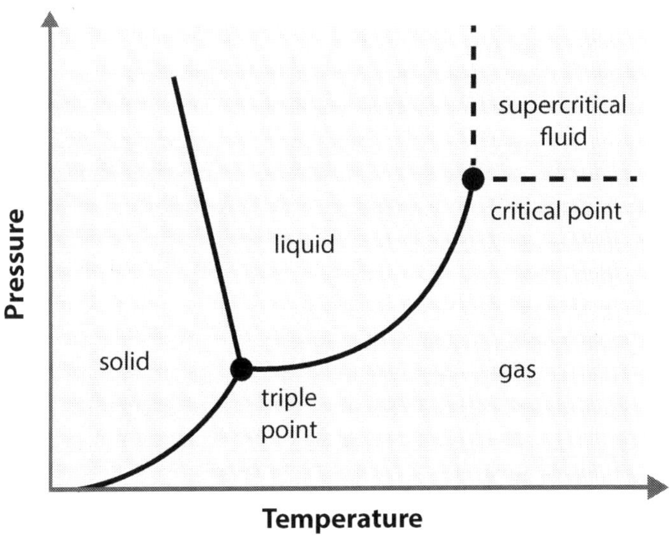

Figure 6.3. Phase Diagram

- triple point (T): temperature and pressure at which the solid, liquid, and gas states are in equilibrium
- critical point (C): temperature and pressure at which the substance becomes supercritical fluid

DID YOU KNOW?

Supercritical fluids have many household and industrial applications. For example, supercritical carbon dioxide is used in dry cleaning and is being introduced as a refrigerant in some parts of the world.

Every phase transition is accompanied by a change in enthalpy. The **heat of vaporization** (ΔH_{vap}) is the energy needed to transform a liquid to a gas at constant pressure. **Heat of fusion** (ΔH_{fus}) is the energy needed to change a substance from solid to liquid at constant pressure. Lastly, **heat of sublimation** (ΔH_{subl}) is the amount of energy needed to change a solid to gas without going through the liquid phase (again at constant pressure). The **molar heat** of vaporization, fusion, and sublimation is the amount of energy needed to change the substance between the relevant states.

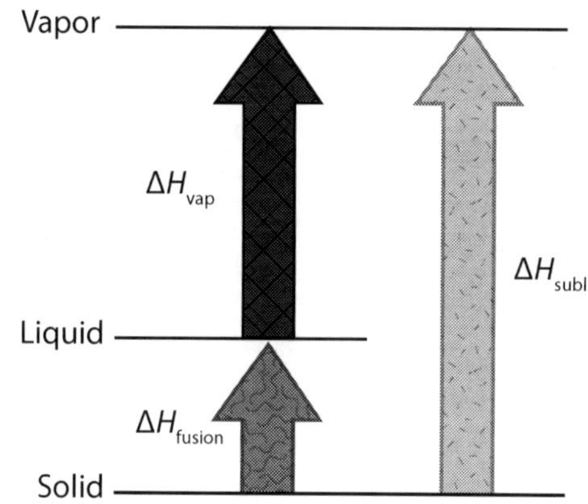

Figure 6.4. Changes in Enthalpies in Phase Transition

The heat of vaporization, fusion, and sublimation for a substance depend on the chemical properties of that substance. More energy is required to separate molecules within a substance that has strong intermolecular forces, so the heat of vaporization, fusion, and sublimation will be high. Conversely, substances with weak intermolecular forces will have lower heat values. For example, the molar heat of vaporization for water is 40.56 kJ/mol, while the molar heat of vaporization for helium is only 0.0845 kJ/mol.

The process of turning ice to vapor illustrates how the enthalpy of phase transitions is calculated. When heat is added to solid water (ice), the ice's temperature increases as molecules in the ice lattice begin vibrating. At 0°C, the heat added to the system no longer increases the temperature of the ice, but instead begins to break the ice's lattice structure, turning it into water. As more heat is added, the ice at 0°C becomes water at 0°C. The energy needed for this step is the heat of fusion.

HELPFUL HINT

The heat required to change between two phases will always be much larger than the heat required to raise the temperature of a substance in either phase.

Similarly, heat can be added to increase the temperature of the water to 100°C. At this point, adding more heat will break the intermolecular forces holding molecules in a liquid state, forming a gas at 100°C. The energy needed for this step is the heat of vaporization. Adding more heat to the gas past this point will increase the temperature of the gas. This process is shown in a **heating curve**.

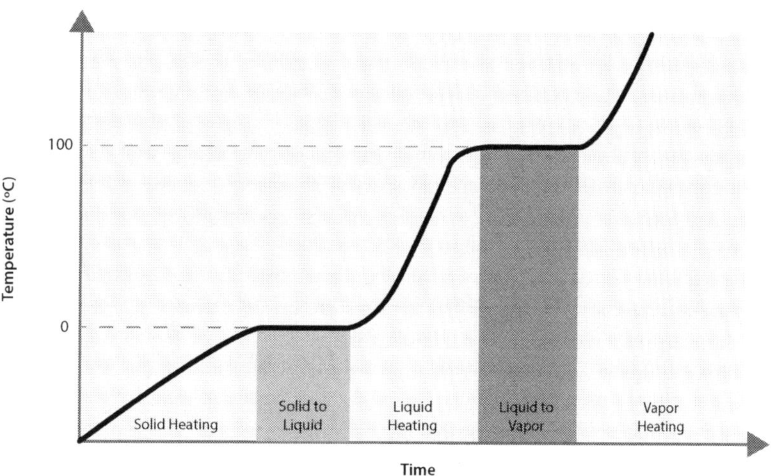

Figure 6.5. Heating Curve of Water

SAMPLE QUESTION

7) **How much energy is needed to turn 100 g of ice at −15°C to water at 45°C? (The specific heat of water is 4.18 J/g°C and the heat of fusion for water is 333.55 J/g.)**

Answer:

$Q = mc\Delta T$ $= (100 \text{ g})(4.18 \text{ J/g°C})(0°\text{C} - (-15 °\text{C}))$ $= 6{,}270 \text{ J}$	Find the energy required to raise the temperature of the ice to 0°C.
$\Delta H_{fus} = (333.55 \text{ J/g})(100 \text{ g}) = 33{,}355 \text{ J}$	Use the heat of fusion to find the energy required to turn the ice to water.
$Q = mc\Delta T$ $= (100 \text{ g})(4.18 \text{ J/g°C})(45°\text{C} - 0°\text{C})$ $= 18{,}810 \text{ J}$	Find the energy required to increase the temperature of the water to 45°C.
6,270 J + 33,355 J + 18,810 J = **58,435 J**	Add the three values to find the total energy for the process.

ENTHALPY

Enthalpy (H) is the heat content of a system at constant pressure. The sign of ΔH describes whether the system has gained or lost heat. When ΔH is positive, the system has gained heat. When ΔH is negative, the system has lost heat. Like entropy, enthalpy is a state function. Enthalpy is given by the formula

$$\Delta H = \Delta U + P\Delta V$$

where ΔH is the change in enthalpy, ΔU is the change in the total internal energy of the system, P is pressure, and ΔV is the change in volume. ($P\Delta V$ is the work done when gases are expanded or compressed.)

A substance's **standard enthalpy of formation** ($\Delta H_f°$) is the change in enthalpy when a substance is formed under standard conditions (0°C and 10^5 Pa, denoted °). In a chemical reaction, the **enthalpy of reaction** (ΔH_{rxn}) is the sum of the enthalpy of formation of the reactants subtracted from the sum of the enthalpy of formation of the products:

$$\Delta H_{rxn} = \Sigma n \Delta H_{\text{f products}} - \Sigma m \Delta H_{\text{f reactants}}$$

where n and m are the stoichiometric coefficients in the chemical equation.

Table 6.4. Enthalpies of Formation

Substance	(kJ/mol)
Benzene	49.0
Carbon dioxide	–393.5
Carbon monoxide CO (*g*)	–110.5
Glucose	–1273
Hydrogen chloride HCl (*g*)	–92.30
Water	–285.8
Water vapor	–241.8

Because enthalpy is a state function, the ΔH of a chemical reaction depends only on the amount of matter in the reaction, and not on the path taken to reach the final state. Accordingly, **Hess's law** states that the ΔH for a reaction that occurs in a series of steps can be found by adding the enthalpy changes for each individual step. To use Hess's law, line up the equations for each step and reverse and/or multiply equations (and ΔH values) as necessary so that the intermediate products cancel. Then, add the ΔH values.

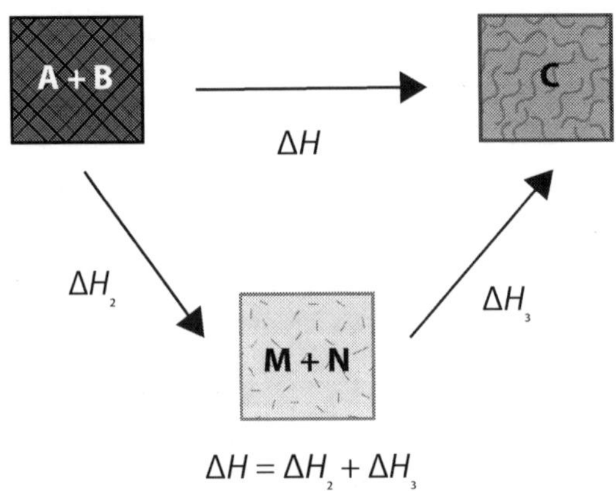

Figure 6.6. Hess's Law

$$A + B \overset{\Delta H_1}{\rightarrow} C$$

$$A + B \overset{\Delta H_2}{\rightarrow} M + N \overset{\Delta H_3}{\rightarrow} C$$

$$\Delta H_1 = \Delta H_2 + \Delta H_3$$

Enthalpies of reactions can also be found by looking at the enthalpy changes that result from the individual bonds that are broken and formed during the reaction. **Bond enthalpy** (*D*) is the ΔH for breaking a bond in one mole of a gaseous substance. The enthalpy of reaction can be estimated by subtracting the enthalpy of the bonds formed from the enthalpy of the bonds broken:

> **HELPFUL HINT**
>
> When reversing a reaction, change the sign of the corresponding ΔH value.

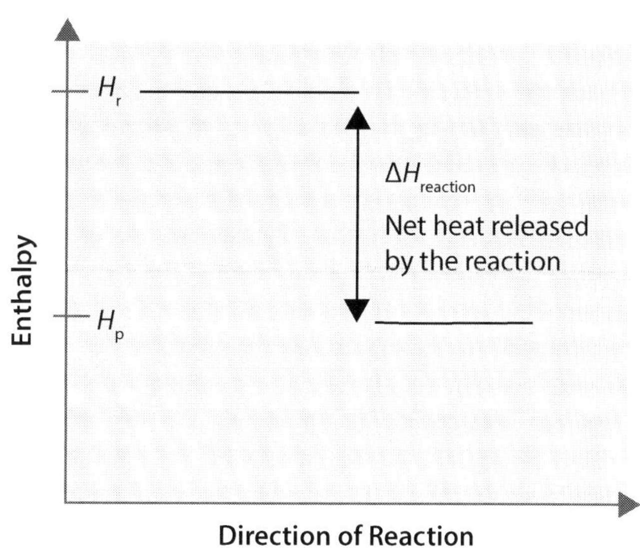

Figure 6.7. Enthalpy for Endothermic Reactions

$$\Delta H_{rxn} = \sum(\text{bond enthalpies of bonds broken}) - \sum(\text{bond enthalpies of bonds formed})$$

If ΔH is positive, meaning more energy was needed to break bonds than was released when new bonds formed, the reaction is endothermic. Conversely, when more energy is released by the formation of new bonds than was used to break bonds, ΔH is negative and the reaction is exothermic.

> **HELPFUL HINT**
>
> Bond enthalpy is always positive because breaking bonds always requires energy.

Go on →

SAMPLE QUESTIONS

8) **Find the enthalpy of reaction for the reaction 4 NH_3 (*g*) + 5 O_2 (*g*) → 4 NO (*g*) + 6 H_2O (*g*) given the following enthalpies of reaction:**

N_2 (*g*) + O_2 (*g*) → 2 NO (*g*) ΔH = –180.5 kJ

N_2 (*g*) + 3 H_2 (*g*) → 2 NH_3 (*g*) ΔH = –91.8 kJ

2 H_2 (*g*) + O_2 (*g*) → 2 H_2O (*g*) ΔH = –483.6 kJ

Answer:

	2[N_2 (*g*) + O_2 (*g*) → 2 NO (*g*)]	ΔH = 2(–180.5 kJ) Multiply by 2.
	2[2 NH_3 (*g*) → N_2 (*g*) + 3 H_2 (*g*)]	ΔH = 2(91.8 kJ) Multiply by 2 & reverse.
+	3[2 H_2 (*g*) + O_2 (*g*) → 2 H_2O (*g*)]	ΔH= 3(–483.6 kJ) Multiply by 3.
	4 NH_3 (*g*) +5 O_2 (*g*) → 4 NO (*g*) + 6 H_2O (*g*)	ΔH = **–1,628 kJ**

9) **Use the given enthalpies of formation to determine whether the following reaction is endothermic or exothermic.**

2 HCl → H_2 + Cl_2

ΔH_f° [HCl] = 428 kJ

ΔH_f° [H_2] = 436 kJ

ΔH_f° [Cl_2] = 239 kJ

Answer:

2 ΔH_f° [HCl] = 2(428 kJ) = 856 kJ	Calculate the total enthalpy of the reactants.
ΔH_f° [H_2] + ΔH_f° [Cl_2] = 436 + 239 = 675 kJ/mol	Calculate the total enthalpy of the products.
$\Delta H_{rxn} = \Sigma n \Delta H_{f\,reactants} - \Sigma m \Delta H_{f\,products}$ = 856 kJ – 675 kJ = 181 kJ/mol *ΔH* is positive, so the reaction is **endothermic**.	Find the difference between the products and reactants.

Gibbs Free Energy

Spontaneous processes are processes that are thermodynamically favorable, meaning that under a given set of conditions, these processes take place on their own. To determine whether a process will occur spontaneously, it is necessary to look at the resulting changes in both enthalpy and entropy. The difference between the process's enthalpy and entropy is called the **Gibbs free energy** (G), which is represented as

> **HELPFUL HINT**
>
> Spontaneity of a process describes the direction of a reaction, not the reaction's speed.

$$\Delta G = \Delta H - T\Delta S$$

where ΔG is the change in Gibbs free energy, ΔH is the change in enthalpy, T is the absolute temperature, and ΔS is the change in entropy.

The sign of ΔG for a process determines whether that process occurs spontaneously:

- $\Delta G < 0$: Process is spontaneous in the forward direction.
- $\Delta G > 0$: Process is nonspontaneous (but is spontaneous in the reverse direction).
- $\Delta G = 0$: Process is at equilibrium.

As with enthalpy, the **standard free energy of formation** ($\Delta G_f°$) describes the free energy change that results when a substance is formed. The **standard free energy change** for a process is the difference between the sum of the standard free energies of formation of the products and the reactants:

$$\Delta G_{\text{reaction}} = \Sigma n \Delta G_{\text{f products}} - \Delta m \Sigma G_{\text{f reactants}}$$

Table 6.5. Effects of Enthalpy and Entropy on Spontaneity

$\Delta G = \Delta H - T\Delta S$

ΔH	ΔS	ΔG	Spontaneous?
+	–	+	No
–	+	–	Yes
+	+	+ or –	At high temperatures
–	–	+ or –	At low temperatures

SAMPLE QUESTION

10) **Calculate the Gibbs free energy change at 25°C for a reaction where ΔH is – 750 kJ and ΔS is 0.5 kJ/K, and determine whether the reaction is spontaneous.**

Answer:

$\Delta G = \Delta H - T\Delta S$ $\Delta H = -750$ kJ $\Delta S = 0.5$ kJ/K	Identify the appropriate equation and variables.
$T = 25 + 273 = 298$ K	Find temperature in Kelvins.
$\Delta G = -750 - (298 \times 0.5)$ **$\Delta G = -899$ kJ** **ΔG is negative, so the reaction is spontaneous.**	Plug in the values and solve.

7

Solutions and Acid–Base Chemistry

SOLUTIONS AND SOLUBILITY

A solution consists of a solute and a solvent. The **solute** is the substance that is dissolved, and the **solvent** is the substance that dissolves the solute. For example, when making a salt water solution, the salt (NaCl) is the solute and water (H_2O) is the solvent. The concentration of a solution is the amount of solute dissolved in the solvent.

The **solubility** of a solution is the maximum amount of solute that will dissolve in a specific quantity of solvent at a specified temperature. A concentrated solution contains an amount of solute near the solubility limit (i.e., a large amount of dissolved solute). A dilute solution contains less solute and more solvent than a concentrated solution.

Solutions can be saturated, unsaturated, or supersaturated based on the amount of solute dissolved in the solution. A **saturated solution** has the maximum amount of solute (i.e., the solute concentration equals the solute solubility in the solvent). There is a dynamic equilibrium in a saturated solution between the undissolved and dissolved solute, and the solution is in equilibrium with its solute and solvent. If the solute is a solid, the solid is observed in the solution.

An **unsaturated solution** contains the solute at a concentration less than the solubility of the solute. Therefore, an unsaturated solution can dissolve more solute without additional solvent. As solute is added to an unsaturated solution, it can become a saturated solution.

A **supersaturated solution** is a solution that contains more than the solubility (equilibrium concentration) of the solute at a specified temperature. A supersaturated solution can be made by heating the solution to dissolve additional solute and then slowly cooling it down to a specified temperature. For example, a saturated solution of ammonia chloride can be made at 80°C and cooled to 25°C, at which point it becomes a supersaturated solution. If the solution is cooled slowly, none of the ammonia chloride will precipitate out immediately. Eventually, the excess solute will slowly precipitate, or crystallize, out of the solution, but this may take days or months.

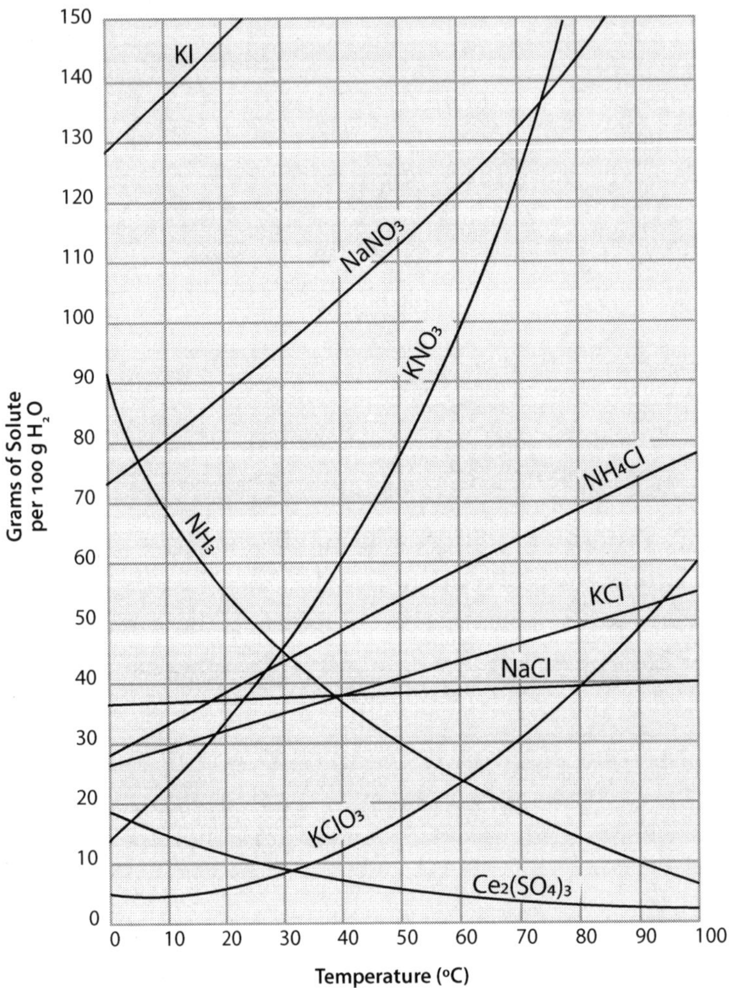

Figure 7.1. Solubility Curves Based on Temperature

A solubility curve (see Figure 7.1) can be used to determine the solubility of a solute at a particular temperature. These diagrams are specific for each compound/molecule and indicate the number of grams of the solute that can be dissolved in *X* grams or milliliters of a solvent at specific temperatures. The curve in the diagram represents the solubility and indicates the concentration required for a saturated solution at each temperature. The area above the curve represents supersaturated solutions, and the area below the curve represents unsaturated solutions.

Temperature-based solubility diagrams and curves can be used to describe the solubility of solids, liquids, and gases. Typically, the solubility of a solute in a solvent increases with an increase in temperature, but this is not always true. When a solute is dissolved in a solution, the process is analogous to melting, and heat or energy is required to break the bonds holding the solute together. Heat is also given off by the formation of new solvation/solvent bonds. In the uncommon event that the heat given off by the formation of the solvent bonds is greater than that needed to break the solute bonds, an increase in temperature will decrease the solubility. However, in most cases, an increase in temperature will increase the solubility by providing additional energy to break apart (dissolve) the solute. The solubility of gases in solution typically decreases with an increase in temperature because of an increase in the energy in the solution, allowing the gas molecules to "escape" the solution.

A pressure-dependent solubility curve is often used to describe the solubility of gases. As the pressure increases, the solubility of a gas increases. The increased pressure "forces" the gas molecules into solution. The pressure does not have an impact on the solubility of liquids and solids.

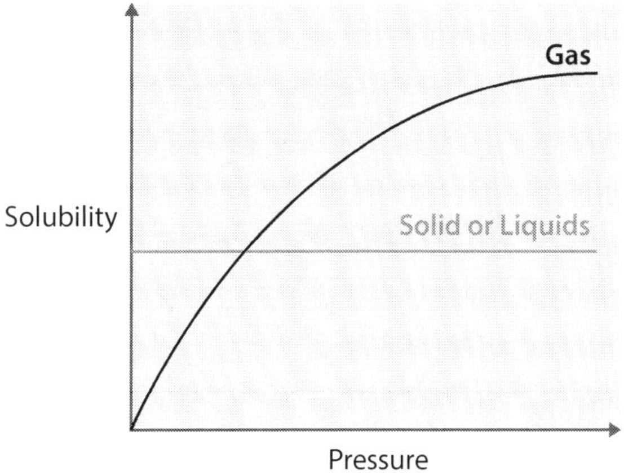

Figure 7.2. Solubility Curves Based on Pressure

There are many different ways to describe the concentration of a solution. **Molarity** (molar concentration) is commonly used in chemistry to describe the concentration of a solution. The molarity of a solution is the number of moles of solute per liter (volume) of the solution and is abbreviated as M (mol/L).

$$\text{Molarity} = \frac{\text{moles of solute}}{\text{liters of solution}}$$

Because molarity is based on volume and volume is temperature dependent, molarity is temperature dependent. A temperature-independent unit to define concentration is molality. **Molality** (*b*) is the concentration of a solute (in moles) in a given mass of the solvent and is abbreviated m (mol/kg).

$$\text{Molality} = \frac{\text{moles of solute}}{\text{kilograms of solvent}}$$

> **DID YOU KNOW?**
>
> Decompression sickness, also called the bends, is an ailment that afflicts divers who come to the surface too quickly. The high pressure deep in the ocean allows more gas to be dissolved in the fluid inside the diver's body. A quick drop in pressure (rising to the surface quickly) will lower the solubility of the gas, causing the gas to come out of solution and form bubbles inside the diver's body.

The **mass fraction** of a solute is the fraction of the solution's total mass that the solute contributes. This is commonly expressed as the **weight percent**, which is calculated by multiplying the mass fraction by 100%. To calculate the weight percent of sucrose in a solution, the masses of the sucrose and total solution are needed:

$$\text{mass fraction of sucrose} = \frac{\text{mass of sucrose}}{\text{mass of the solution}} = \frac{25\text{ g}}{100\text{ g}} = 0.25$$

$$\text{weight percent} = 0.25 \times 100\% = 25\%\text{ wt. solution of sucrose}$$

The weight percent can be converted to molarity if the density of the solution is known.

In addition to weight percent, **volume percent** can be used. In volume percent, the amount of solute and solution are both measured in volume.

$$\text{volume percent} = \frac{\text{volume of solute}}{\text{volume of solution}} \times 100$$

The **mole fraction** of a solution is similar to the mass fraction, but uses the number of moles instead of the mass. The mole fraction is the moles of the solute (or solution component) divided by the total number of moles in the solution.

$$\text{mole fraction} = \frac{\text{moles of solute}}{\text{moles of the solution}}$$

When a solution is very dilute, the concentration units previously described can be too large to usefully describe the solution. In this case the mass fraction of the solution can be described using parts per million or per billion. *Parts per million* (ppm) is equivalent to one gram of solute per one million grams of solution or 1 milligram of solute per 1 kilogram of solution. *Parts per billion* (ppb) is equivalent to one gram of solute in one billion grams of solution or 1 microgram of solute per 1 kilogram of solution.

Frequently, a series of solutions that vary in concentration is needed for experiments. To come up with a series of solutions, a concentrated solution of known concentration is used and diluted to the needed concentrations. During dilution, the number of moles of the solute remains constant, but the volume changes, which changes the molarity of the solution. A simple relationship can be used to determine how much solution and solvent are needed for the dilutions:

$$M_sV_s = M_dV_d$$

The **dissolution rate** of a solution is the rate at which the solute is dissolved in the solvent to form a solution. The dissolution rate can be affected by a number of factors such as the temperature, pressure, surface area, and solution agitation (stirring). Changes in the solubility change the dissolution rate, and an increase in the solubility will increase the dissolution rate. Because of this, an increase in temperature for solids and liquids will likely increase the dissolution rate, and an increase in the pressure for gases will increase the dissolution rate. An increase in the surface area of a solid will increase the dissolution rate by providing more surface for the solvent to solvate, and stirring or agitating a solution will increase the dissolution rate by providing more energy to break the solute bonds.

SAMPLE QUESTIONS

1) **What is the molarity of a solution if 12 grams of NaCl are added to 100 mL of water?**

A. 1.2 M

B. 2.05 M

C. 4 M

D. 12 M

Answer: B.

Convert the grams of NaCl into moles to calculate the molarity.

$12 \text{ g NaCl} \times \frac{1 \text{ mole of NaCl}}{58.44 \text{ grams}} =$

0.205 moles of NaCl

Divide the moles of the solute by the liters of solution to find the molarity.

$\text{Molarity} = \frac{0.205 \text{ moles of NaCl}}{0.1 \text{ L}}$

= 2.05 M NaCl

2) **What is the molality of a 100 mL solution of water with 20 g of $NaNO_3$?**

A. 1 m

B. 2.35 m

C. 20.1 m

D. 3.33 m

Answer: B.

Convert grams of $NaNO_3$ into moles.

$20 \text{ g } NaNO_3 \times \frac{1 \text{ mole } NaNO_3}{84.995 \text{ g } NaNO_3} = 0.235 \text{ moles } NaNO_3$

Use the formula for molality. Assume a density of 1 g/mL for water.

$\text{Molality} = \frac{0.235 \text{ moles NaNO3}}{0.1 \text{ kg solvent}}$

= 2.35 m $NaNO_3$

3) **To make 100 mL of 1 M HCl from a 6 M HCl solution, how many mL of a 6 M solution are needed?**

A. 6 mL

B. 7.6 mL

C. 12.2 mL

D. 16.7 mL

Answer: D.

Use the formula for finding the volume of a diluted solution.

$M_sV_s = M_dV_d$

$(6 \text{ M})(V_s) = (0.1 \text{ L})(1 \text{ M})$

$V_s = \frac{0.1 \text{ L} \times 1 \text{ mol}}{6 \text{ mol/L}} = 0.0167 \text{ L}$

Colligative Properties of Solutions

A colligative property of a solution depends only on the concentration of the solute particles in the solution and not on the type of particles present. There are four colligative properties: vapor pressure, boiling point, freezing point, and osmotic pressure. All colligative properties can be understood by looking at the differences in entropy between the pure solvent and the solution.

Vapor Pressure

The liquid in a closed system is in equilibrium with its vapor. In this equilibrium, the rate at which molecules escape the liquid is equal to the rate at which the vapor molecules return to the liquid. The pressure created by the vapor at equilibrium is that substance's **vapor pressure.** Liquids that have a vapor pressure are described as **volatile**; those that have no vapor pressure (meaning the liquid does not vaporize), are **non-volatile**.

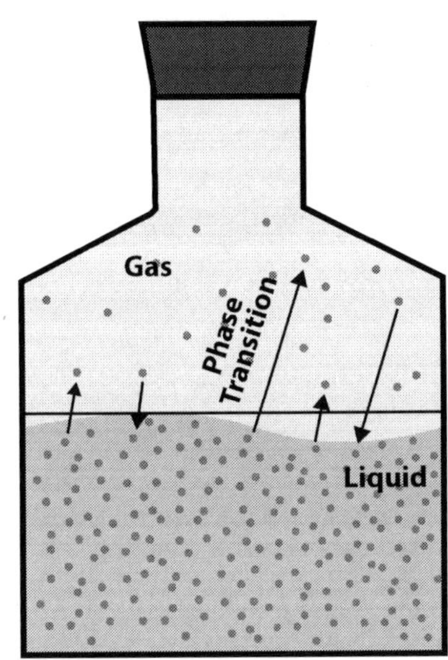

Figure 7.3. Vapor Pressure

A substance's vapor pressure increases with temperature, as molecules have more energy to escape the liquid. The addition of a nonvolatile solute to a volatile substance will lower that substance's vapor pressure. The amount that the vapor pressure decreases depends on the solute concentration, and can be described by Raoult's law:

$$P_1 = X_1 P_1^\circ$$

where P_1 is the vapor pressure of the solvent over the solution, P_1° is the vapor pressure of the pure solvent, and X_1 is the mole fraction of the solvent in the solution.

SAMPLE QUESTION

4) **Calculate the vapor pressure of water for a solution containing 0.5 moles of sucrose and 10 moles of water at 25°C. The vapor pressure of pure water at 25°C is 23.76 mm Hg.**

A. 22.63 mm Hg
B. 24 mm Hg
C. 23.76 mm Hg
D. 21 mm Hg

Answer: A.

$\frac{10 \text{ mol water}}{10.5 \text{ mol}} = 0.952$	Calculate the mole fraction of water.
$P_1 = 0.952 \times 23.76$ mm Hg **= 22.63 mm Hg**	Use Raoult's law.

BOILING POINT AND FREEZING POINT

The boiling point of a solvent or solution is the temperature at which the vapor pressure of the solution is equal to 1 atm. Because a solution has a lower vapor pressure than the solvent, the solution must now reach a higher temperature to have a vapor pressure equal to the atmospheric pressure. The difference between the normal boiling point of a solvent and the higher boiling point of a solution is referred to as boiling point elevation. The increase in the boiling point is related to the concentration of the solute. In this case, the concentration of the solute needs to be expressed in molality because molality is independent of temperature. The increase in the boiling point can be calculated by:

$$\Delta Tb = T_{B\,(solution)} - T_{B\,(solvent)} = K_b m$$

where K_b is the molal boiling point elevation constant of the solvent and m is the molality of the solute.

The freezing point of a liquid is the temperature at which the first molecules begin to cluster together into a crystal lattice to form a solid. At the freezing point, there is a dynamic equilibrium between crystallization and melting. When a solution freezes, the pure solvent clusters together to form solid solvent, and an equilibrium between the solution and solid solvent is established. In a solution, all of the molecules in contact with the frozen solvent are not solvent molecules, causing a slower dynamic equilibrium between crystallization and melting. The slower rate also correlates to a lower freezing point, meaning the freezing temperature for a solution is lower than that of the pure solvent. The lowering of the freezing point, called freezing point depression, can be calculated in the same way as the boiling point elevation:

QUICK REVIEW

Why is salt used to keep water from freezing on the roads in the winter?

$$\Delta T_f = K_f m$$

where K_f is a constant that depends only on the solvent and m is the molality of the solute.

SAMPLE QUESTION

5) **Calculate the boiling and freezing points of an aqueous solution containing 39.5 g of ethylene glycol (MW 62.07 g) dissolved in 750 mL of water. The K_b for water is 0.52 °C kg mol^{-1} and the K_f is 1.86 °C kg mol^{-1}.**

A. Boiling: 101 °C
Freezing: 0 °C

B. Boiling: 100.75 °C
Freezing: −1.8 °C

C. Boiling: 110 °C
Freezing: −5 °C

D. Boiling: 100.44 °C
Freezing: −1.58 °C

Answer: D.

Determine the molality of the solution (moles of solute per kilogram of solvent).

$$39.5 \text{ g ethylene glycol} \times \frac{1 \text{ mol ethylene glycol}}{62.07 \text{ g}}$$

$= 0.636$ mol ethylene glycol

Find the molality of the solution. The density of water is 1 g/mL, so 750 mL is equal to 750 g or 0.75 kg

$$b = \frac{0.636 \text{ mol}}{0.75 \text{ kg}} = 0.848 \text{ m}$$

Determine boiling point elevation.

$\Delta T_b = (0.52°\text{C kg mol}^{-1})(0.848 \text{ mol/kg}) = 0.44\ °\text{C}$, which gives a boiling point of **100.44 °C**.

Determine freezing point depression.

$\Delta T_f = (1.86°\text{C kg mol}^{-1})(0.848 \text{ mol/kg}) = 1.58°\text{C}$, which gives a freezing point of **−1.58 °C**.

Osmotic Pressure

Osmosis is the movement of a solvent through a semipermeable membrane from a region with a lower solute concentration to a region with a higher solute concentration (i.e., the solvent moves from a higher solvent concentration to a lower solvent concentration region). When a solution is separated from pure water by a semipermeable membrane, water (the solvent) will move from across the membrane into the solution. The pressure required to prevent this osmosis is a solution's **osmotic pressure** (Π).

As with other colligative properties, osmotic pressure depends on the concentration of the solution: a higher concentration in the solute increases the pressure required to prevent mixing. The osmotic pressure can be calculated using the following equation:

$$\pi = \left(\frac{n}{V}\right)RT = MRT$$

where n is the number of particles per formula unit of solute, V is the volume of solution, R is the gas constant, T is the absolute temperature (in Kelvin), and M is the molarity of the solution.

SAMPLE QUESTION

6) **What is the osmotic pressure of a 1.50 M solution of sucrose at 25°C?**

A. 3.08 atm

B. 36.7 atm

C. 37.5 atm

D. 447.225 atm

Answer: B.

Use the equation for osmotic pressure.

$\pi = (1.50\text{ M})\left(0.08206\ \frac{\text{L} \times \text{atm}}{\text{mol} \times \text{K}}\right)(298.15\text{ K}) = \mathbf{36.7\ atm}$

SOLUBILITY EQUILIBRIA

Most ionic compounds are completely soluble in water, meaning they dissociate into their component ions. However, some ionic compounds are only slightly soluble and partially dissociate, while others are insoluble in water. The solubility of ionic compounds in water is determined by two competing forces: the force of attraction between the ions and water, and the force of attraction between the ions. It is not easy to predict which of these forces will prevail in ionic compounds, but there are rules to help determine solubility.

Solubility Rules:

- All ammonium and alkali metal salts are soluble.
- All nitrates are soluble.
- All chlorides, bromides, and iodides are soluble except for: AgCl, Hg_2Cl_2, $PbCl_2$, AgBr, Hg_2Br_2, $PbBr_2$, AgI, Hg_2I_2, PbI_2.
- Most sulfates are soluble except for: $CaSO_4$, $SrSO_4$, $BaSO_4$, $PbSO_4$.
- All chlorates are soluble.
- All perchlorates are soluble.
- All acetates are soluble.
- All phosphates are insoluble except for: NH_4^+ and alkali metal phosphates.

- All carbonates are insoluble except for: NH_4^+ and alkali metal carbonates.
- All hydroxides are insoluble except for: NH_4^+ and alkali metal hydroxides; $Sr(OH)_2$, $Ba(OH)_2$, and $Ca(OH)_2$ are slightly soluble.
- All oxides are insoluble except for alkali metal oxides.
- All oxalates are insoluble except for: NH_4^+ and alkali metal oxalates.
- All sulfides are insoluble except for: NH_4^+ and alkali metal sulfides; MgS, CaS, and BaS are sparingly soluble.

HELPFUL HINT

If a compound contains at least one of the ions listed for soluble compounds in the solubility rules, the compound is at least partially soluble.

In the case of saturated solutions of ionic compounds, a solubility equilibrium is established between the dissolved and undissolved ions. The equilibrium constant that describes this relationship is called the **solubility product constant**, K_{sp}. The value of K_{sp} indicates the extent to which a solid will dissolve into its component ions in solution. A general equilibrium expression for the dissolution of a slightly soluble salt is:

$$A_xB_y(s) \leftrightarrow x\,A^{n+}\,(aq) + y\,B^{m-}\,(aq); \qquad K_{sp} = [A^{n+}]^x\,[B^{m-}]^y$$

Note that the K_{sp} is related only to the concentration of the ions in solution.

When a reaction between two aqueous solutions results in an insoluble product, a solid will form. This solid is called a precipitate, and the process is called **precipitation**. For example, when two soluble compounds, $BaCl_2$ and Na_2SO_4, react, they form $BaSO_4$ and NaCl. NaCl is soluble, but a check of the solubility rules shows that $BaSO_4$ is not soluble and will precipitate from the solution.

Additional factors that can influence the solubility of ionic compounds include temperature, pressure, formation of ion pairs, competing equilibria, pH, the formation of complex ions, and the presence of common ions. The **common ion effect** occurs when the presence of a second solute with a common ion decreases the solubility of an ionic compound. The common ion shifts the equilibrium in the solution to the left, based on Le Châtelier's principle, making the compound less soluble. For example, the solubility of $BaSO_4$ can be reduced by adding $NaSO_4$ to the solution. The increased concentration of the SO_4^{2-} ions decreases the solubility of $BaSO_4$ by shifting the equilibrium to offset the additional sulfate ions by forming solid $BaSO_4$.

DID YOU KNOW?

Precipitation can be used to make water drinkable by turning dissolved contaminants into solids that can be removed.

Table 7.1. Effects of Temperature and Pressure on Solubility

Factor	Solute State	Effect
Temperature	Solid	In an endothermic reaction, an increase in temperature increases solubility.
		In an exothermic reaction, an increase in temperature reduces solubility.
	Gas	An increase in temperature reduces solubility.
Pressure	Gas	An increase in the pressure above a solution increases solubility.

SAMPLE QUESTIONS

7) **Predict the solubility of the following compounds:**

1. NH_4Cl

2. $Mg_3(PO_4)_2$

3. $Ba(OH)_2$

4. $Ca(NO_3)_2$

A. Soluble: 1, 3, and 4
Insoluble: 2

B. Soluble: 1, 2, and 4
Insoluble: 3

C. Soluble: 2 and 4
Insoluble: 1, 3

D. Soluble: 1, 2, 3, and 4

Answer: A.

All common chlorides are soluble. All phosphates are insoluble. $Ba(OH)_2$ is an exception to the rule that all hydroxides are insoluble; and all nitrates are soluble.

8) **In a saturated CaF_2 solution, the calcium concentration is 9.1 mg/L. Calculate the K_{sp} for CaF_2 assuming the compound dissociates completely into Ca^{2+} and F^-.**

A. 4.9×10^{-11}

B. 6×10^{-8}

C. 9.1×10^{-4}

D. 7.6×10^{-13}

Answer: A.

$CaF_2\ (s) \leftrightarrow Ca^{2+}\ (aq) + 2\ F^-\ (aq)$	Write the chemical equilibrium equation.
$K_{sp} = [Ca^{2+}]\ [F^-]^2$	Write the equilibrium constant expression, K_{sp}.
$\frac{9.1\ mg\ Ca^{2+}}{1\ L} \times \frac{1\ g\ Ca^{2+}}{1000\ mg\ Ca^{2+}} \times \frac{1\ mol\ Ca^{2+}}{40\ g\ Ca^{2+}}$ $= 2.3 \times 10^{-4}\ M\ Ca^{2+}$ Based on the balanced equation, 2 moles of F ions are produced for every mole of Ca ions, so the F ion concentration must be 4.6×10^{-4} M.	Determine the molar concentrations of the Ca and F ions.
$K_{sp} = (2.3 \times 10^{-4})(4.6 \times 10^{-4})^2$ $\mathbf{= 4.9 \times 10^{-11}}$	Determine the K_{sp} using these concentrations.

Introduction to Acid–Base Chemistry

Definitions of Acids and Bases

There are three main definitions for acids and bases. The first is the Arrhenius definition. An **Arrhenius acid** is a substance that dissociates in water to form hydrogen ions, and an **Arrhenius base** is a substance that dissociates in water to form hydroxide ions. The Arrhenius definition is restricted to aqueous solutions and refers to the concentration of the solvent ions. An Arrhenius acid must increase the hydrogen ion concentration or decrease the hydroxide concentration in an aqueous solution; an Arrhenius base must increase the hydroxide ion concentration or decrease the hydrogen ion concentration in an aqueous solution.

The second definition is the Brønsted-Lowry definition. A **Brønsted-Lowry acid** is a hydrogen ion donor, and a **Brønsted-Lowry base** is a hydrogen ion acceptor. Under this definition, all acids donate hydrogen ions and all bases accept the hydrogen ions. Thus, the acid-base reaction is the removal of a hydrogen ion from the acid and its addition to the base.

A conjugate acid-base pair is a pair of molecules or ions that are related to each other via the loss or gain of a hydrogen ion. The removal of the hydrogen ion from the acid produces the conjugate base, and the addition of the hydrogen ion to the base results in the formation of the conjugate acid.

$$HA + B \rightarrow BH^+ \text{ (conjugate acid)} + A^- \text{ (conjugate base)}$$

To act as a Brønsted-Lowry base, a molecule or ion must have an unshared pair of electrons so it can accept a hydrogen ion. According to the Brønsted-Lowry definition, water can act as either an acid or a base, depending on whether an acid or a base is present, since water can both donate and accept hydrogen ions to become either OH^- or H_3O^+. All hydrogen-containing substances are acids according to this definition.

The third and final definition is the Lewis definition. A **Lewis acid** is a compound that can receive an electron pair to form a new bond, and a **Lewis base** is a compound that can donate an electron pair to form a new bond. Based on this definition, an acid-base reaction occurs when there is a molecule with a lone pair of electrons and a molecule that can accept the lone pair. Lewis acids tend to be cations or neutral molecules with an empty orbital, and Lewis bases tend to be anions or neutral molecules with a lone pair of electrons. All metal cations are potential Lewis acids. Water acts as a Lewis base when it forms a coordinate covalent, both with metal ions.

An example of a typical Lewis acid-base reaction is the reaction of boron trifluoride with a flouride ion to produce the ion tetrafluoroborate: $BF_3 + F^- \rightarrow BF_4^-$

Table 7.2. The Three Definitions of Acids and Bases

	Arrhenius	Brønsted-Lowry	Lewis
Acid	provider of H^+ in HOH	proton donor	electron pair acceptor
Base	provider of OH^- in HOH	proton acceptor	electron pair donor
Neutralization	formation of water	proton transfer	coordinate covalent bond formation
Equation	$H^+ + OH^- \rightarrow HOH$	$HA + B \rightarrow BH^+ + A^-$	$A + B \rightarrow A{:}B$
Limitation	water solution only	proton transfer reactions only	generalized theory

SAMPLE QUESTION

9) $HBr\ (aq) + H_2O\ (l) \rightarrow H_3O^+\ (aq) + Br^-\ (aq)$

Which of the following is the conjugate base in the reaction shown above?

A. HBr
B. H_2O
C. H_3O^+
D. Br^-

Answer: D.

The acid HBr loses a proton, creating the conjugate base Br^-.

THE PH SCALE

The pH scale (see Figure 7.5) is used to indicate how acidic or basic an aqueous solution is. **pH** is the negative of the base 10 logarithm (log) of the hydronium ion concentration (H_3O^+).

$$pH = -\log[H_3O^+] \text{ or } -\log[H^+]$$

> HELPFUL HINT
>
> The hydronium ion and hydrogen ion are often used interchangeably when talking about acid-base reactions. It was initially thought that hydrogen ions existed in solution, but it was later shown that they exist as the hydronium ions in water.

The concentrations of H_3O^+ and OH^- vary widely in aqueous solutions, from 10 M to 10^{-15} M, depending on the acid and base present. The pH scale ranges from 0 to 14 with 7 representing a neutral solution (pure water). pH values less than 7 are acidic and pH values greater than 7 are basic.

The pOH of a solution can also be calculated based on the hydroxide ion concentration.

$$pOH = -\log[OH^-]$$

pH and pOH are related by the following expression:

$$pH + pOH = 14$$

When one value is known, the other value can be determined. For example, a 0.1 M solution of a strong base, such as NaOH, has an $[OH^-]$ of 0.1 M and a pOH of 1, which gives a pH of 13.

Water undergoes self-ionization to form a hydroxide ion and a hydronium ion. This equilibrium applies to pure water and any aqueous solution. The ionization constant for water at 25°C is:

$$K_w = [H_3O^+]\,[OH^-] = 1.0 \times 10^{-14}$$

The K_w is related to pH and pOH via the equation:

$$-\log K_w = pK_w = pH + pOH = 14$$

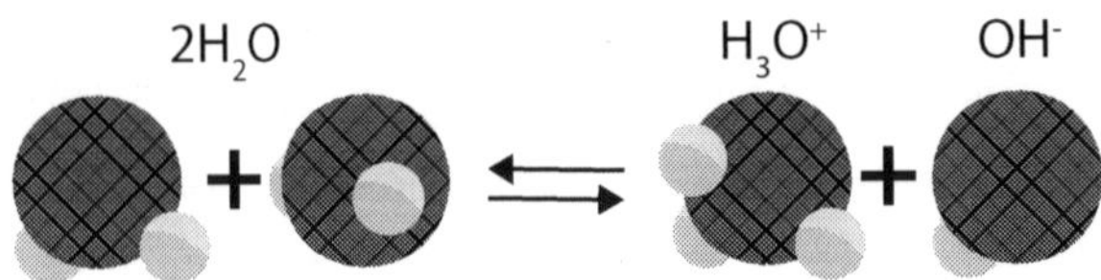

Figure 7.4. Self-Ionization of Water

The ionization constant decreases as the temperature and pressure increase, and it changes with the electrolyte concentration.

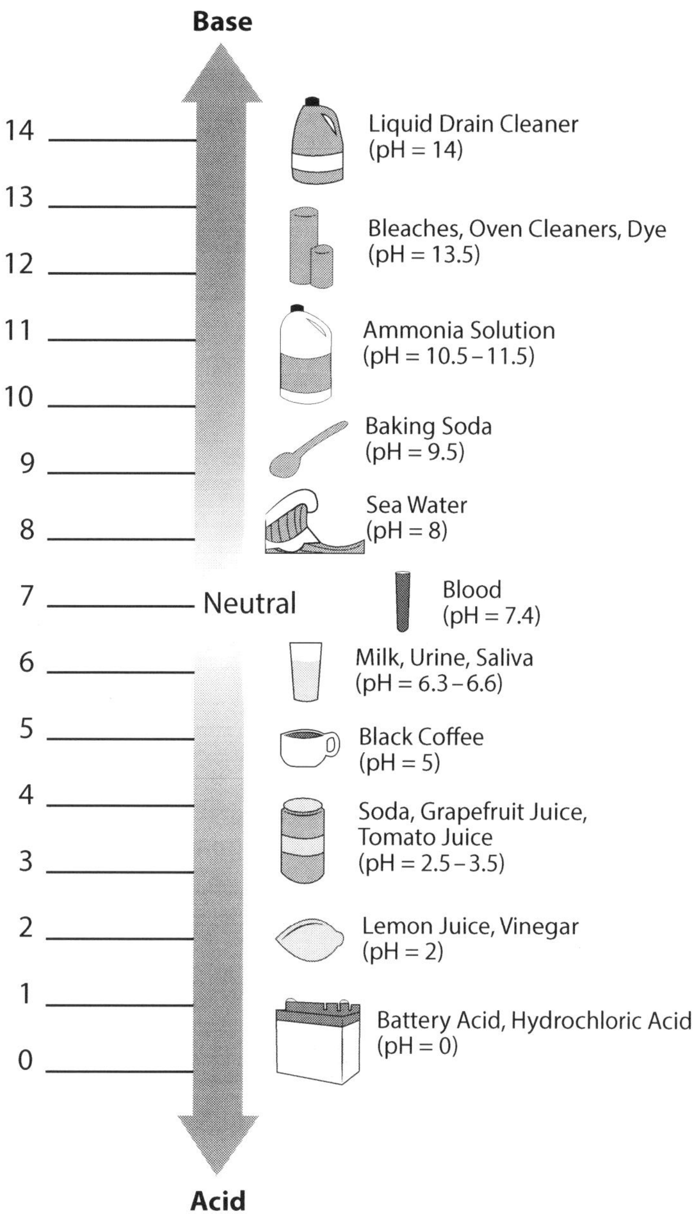

Figure 7.5. The pH Scale

SAMPLE QUESTIONS

10) **What is the pH of a 500 mL solution containing 1.25 g of HCl?**

A. 1

B. 0.5

C. 1.16

D. 2.25

Answer: C.

$1.25 \text{ g HCl} \times \frac{1 \text{ mol HCl}}{36.46 \text{ g HCl}} = 0.034 \text{ mol HCl}$	Determine the number of moles of HCl.

$[H_3O^+] = \frac{0.034 \text{ mol HCl}}{0.5 \text{ L}} = 0.069 \text{ M} = 0.069 \text{ M}$ $pH = -\log(0.069)$ **= 1.16**	Because HCl is a strong acid, the moles of H_3O^+ are equal to the moles of the acid.

11) **What is the $[H_3O^+]$ for a solution with a pH of 8.3?**

A. 5×10^{-7} M

B. 5×10^{-9} M

C. 8.3×10^{-5} M

D. 8.3×10^{-9} M

Answer: B.

To determine the $[H_3O^+]$, use the equation for pH.

$pH = -\log[H_3O^+]$

$8.30 = -\log[H_3O^+]$

$10^{-8.3} = [H_3O^+]$

$\mathbf{[H_3O^+] = 5 \times 10^{-9}}$ **M**

Neutralization and Titration

When acids and bases react quantitatively with each other, the hydrogen and hydroxide ions react with each other to form water, neutralizing the solution. Water is neutral and the remaining ions form a salt in the solution. For example, when HCl (a strong acid) and NaOH (a strong base) react, they create water and NaCl.

The general neutralization reaction is:

$$HX\ (aq) + MOH\ (aq) \rightarrow H_2O\ (l) + MX\ (aq)$$

To neutralize an acid an equivalent quantity of base must be added, and vice versa, to ensure that the concentrations of hydrogen and hydroxide ions are zero. The point of neutralization, the **equivalence point**, is the point in an acid-base reaction at which chemically equivalent quantities of the acid and base have been mixed. For strong acids and bases the neutralization endpoint results in a neutral pH of 7.

> QUICK REVIEW
>
> What acidic and basic solutions do you use on a daily basis?

An acid-base **titration** is a method to determine the concentration of an acid or base in an aqueous solution by adding known amounts of an acid or base. A standard solution of an acid or base (a titrant) is prepared and placed in a burette, which accurately measures the volume of the solution as it is added to the unknown solution. An indicator is also added to the unknown solution that will show when the unknown solution has been neutralized.

During the titration, small amounts of the titrate are added to the unknown solution. When the moles of acid and base are equal (at the equivalence point), the indicator will change color. The volume of titrant added can then be used to determine the initial concentration of the unknown acid or base. For strong acids and bases the equivalence point is at pH 7. For a strong acid titration with a weak base, the pH will be less than 7, and for a strong base titration with a weak acid, the pH will be greater than 7.

Titrations are typically plotted as titration curves (see Figure 7.6), with the volume of the added acid or base on the *x*-axis and the pH on the *y*-axis. Near the equivalence point the pH tends to change very quickly, so it is important to add small increments of the titrant as the equivalence point is approached to accurately determine the equivalent volume.

In a typical titration of HNO_3 with NaOH, a standardized solution of NaOH is placed in the burette, and a known amount of the HNO_3 solution is placed in an Erlenmeyer flask with phenolphthalein, a commonly used acid-base indicator. In its acidic form, phenolphthalein is colorless; in its basic form, it is red. NaOH is stirred into the HNO_3 solution until the solution turns pink, indicating the reaction is complete and the endpoint has been reached. The volume of NaOH added is measured and used to calculate the concentration of the HNO_3.

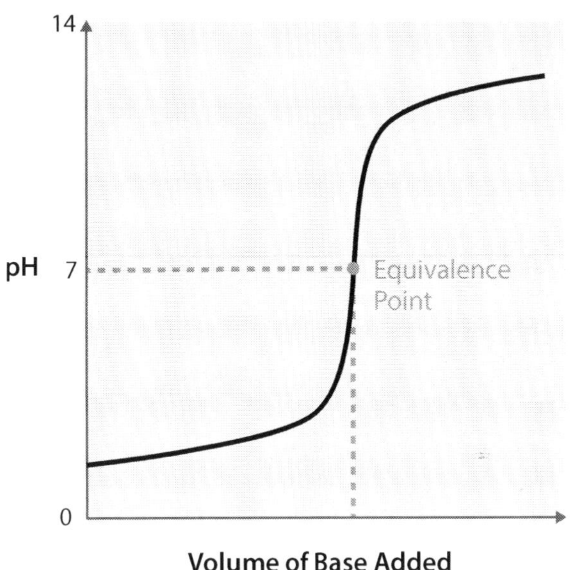

Figure 7.6. Titration Curve

SAMPLE QUESTION

12) **If 20 mL of a 0.5 M NaOH solution is used to titrate a 50 mL solution of HNO_3, what is the concentration of the HNO_3?**

A. 0.5 M

B. 0.25 M

C. 0.2 M

D. 0.35 M

Answer: C.

Use dimensional analysis to find the molarity of the HNO_3 solution.

20 mL NaOH	1000 mL	0.5 mol NaOH	1 mol HNO_3	**0.2 M HNO_3**
50 mL HNO_3	1 L	1000 mL	1 mol NaOH	

Acid–Base Equilibria

Strong Acids and Bases

Strong acids ionize completely in water while **weak acids** only partially ionize. The strength of an acid can depend on the electronegativity of the conjugate base, the atomic radius of the resultant anion, the charge of the species, and the equilibrium of the dissociation reaction. Because strong acids completely dissociate in aqueous solutions, the concentration of the hydronium ions in water is equal to the concentration of the acid added to the solution. The dissociation of weak acids must be represented by an equilibrium of the acid molecules and constituent ions.

Strong and weak bases are categorized in the same way. Strong bases completely dissociate in water, and weak bases only partially dissociate. Weak bases exist as an equilibrium of the base and its component ions. Strong bases completely dissociate into ions in aqueous solution. Weak bases do not completely dissociate and exist as an equilibrium of the base and its component ions. See Table 7.3 for a list of common acids and bases.

Table 7.3. Common Acids and Bases

Strong acids	HCl	Hydrochloric acid
	HNO_3	Nitric acid
	H_2SO_4	Sulfuric acid
	$HClO_4$	Perchloric acid
	HBr	Hydrobromic acid
	HI	Hydroiodic acid
Strong bases	LiOH	Lithium hydroxide
	NaOH	Sodium hydroxide
	KOH	Potassium hydroxide
	$Ca(OH)_2$	Calcium hydroxide
	$Ba(OH)_2$	Barium hydroxide
	$Sr(OH)_2$	Strontium hydroxide
Weak acids	H_3PO_4	Phosphoric acid
	CH_3COOH	Acetic acid
	H_2CO_3	Carbonic acid
	HCN	Hydrocyanic acid
	HCOOH	Formic acid
	C_6H_5COOH	Benzoic acid

Table 7.3. Common Acids and Bases (continued)

Weak bases	NH_3	Ammonia
	CH_3NH_2	Methylamine

SAMPLE QUESTION

13) **Which of the following is a strong acid?**

A. HClO

B. HBr

C. HF

D. HN_3

Answer: B.

HBr is one of the strong acids.

EQUILIBRIUM EQUATIONS FOR ACIDS AND BASES

The previous section introduced the pH calculations for strong acids and bases. Because strong acids and bases completely dissociate, the concentration of H^+ and/or OH^- is easily determined based on the concentration of the acid or base. This is not the case for weak acids and bases. Because weak acids only partially ionize in water, a different approach must be used to calculate the pH of a solution containing a weak acid.

The equilibrium equation for a weak acid is:

$$HA\ (aq) + H_2O\ (l) \rightarrow H_3O^+\ (aq) + A^-\ (aq)$$

or

$$HA\ (aq) \rightarrow H^+\ (aq) + A^-\ (aq)$$

The equilibrium constant expression, K_a, is the acid dissociation constant:

$$K_a = \frac{[H_3O^+][A^-]}{[HA]} \text{ or } \frac{[H^+][A^-]}{[HA]}$$

The larger the K_a value is, the stronger the acid is. The K_a value can also be used to calculate the pH of a solution if the initial concentration of the weak acid is known.

Weak bases react with water to form the conjugate acid of the base and hydroxide ions. The general equilibrium expression is:

$$B\ (aq) + H_2O\ (l) \leftrightarrow HB^+\ (aq) + OH^-\ (aq)$$

The equilibrium constant expression K_b is the base dissociation constant:

$$K_b = \frac{[HB^+][OH^-]}{[B]}$$

SAMPLE QUESTIONS

14) Calculate the pH of a 0.3 M solution of acetic acid (CH_3COOH), which has a K_a of 1.8 × 10–5.

A. 2.64

B. 1.3

C. 1.8

D. 3

Answer: A.

$CH_3COOH\ (aq) \leftrightarrow CH_3COO^-\ (aq) + H^+\ (aq)$	Write the ionization equilibrium for the acid.
$K_a = \frac{[H^+][CH_3COO^-]}{[CH_3COOH]} = 1.8 \times 10–5$	Write the equilibrium constant expression, K_a.
$K_a = \frac{(x)(x)}{0.3 - x} = 1.8 \times 10^{-5}$	Now determine the concentrations of the components. The concentration of H^+ can be assigned as x and will be equal to the concentration of CH_3COO^-. The concentration of CH_3COOH will be equal to 0.3 – x.
$\frac{x^2}{0.3} = 1.8 \times 10^{-5}$ $x = 2.3 \times 10^{-3}$ M pH = $-\log(2.3 \times 10^{-3})$ **= 2.64**	x is assumed to be negligible compared to 0.3 M so the equation can be simplified and solved.

15) Calculate the [OH^-] in a 0.15 M solution of NH_3, which has a K_b of 1.8 × 10^{-5}.

A. 0.1 M

B. 0.001 M

C. 0.0016 M

D. 0.016 M

Answer: C.

$NH_3\ (aq) + H_2O\ (l) \leftrightarrow NH_4^+\ (aq) + OH^-\ (aq)$	Write the ionization equilibrium equation.
$K_b = \frac{[NH_4^+][OH–]}{[NH_3]} = 1.8 \times 10^{-5}$	Write the expression for K_b.
$[NH_4^+] = [OH^-] = x$ and $[NH_3] = 0.15$ M $- x$ $K_b = \frac{(x)(x)}{0.15 - x} = 1.8 \times 10^{-5}$	The concentration of NH_4^+ will equal the concentration of OH^-, so both can be assigned the variable x. The concentration of NH_3 will be equal to 0.15 – x.

$\frac{x^2}{0.15} = 1.8 \times 10^{-5}$

$\mathbf{x = 0.0016\ M = [OH^-]}$

The concentration of x compared to 0.15 M can again be assumed to be negligible, so the equation can be simplified and solved.

MONOPROTIC AND POLYPROTIC ACIDS

Acids that have one ionizable proton are called **monoprotic acids**. These acids are described by the dissociation equation given earlier:

$$HA\ (aq) + H_2O\ (l) \leftrightarrow H_3O^+\ (aq) + A^-\ (aq)$$

Acids that have more than one ionizable proton are called **polyprotic acids**. These acids will lose protons in successive steps, each of which will have its own dissociation constant:

$$H_2A\ (aq) + H_2O\ (l) \leftrightarrow H_3O^+\ (aq) + HA^-\ (aq) \quad K_{a_1}$$

$$HA^-\ (aq) + H_2O\ (l) \leftrightarrow H_3O^+\ (aq) + A^{2-}\ (aq) \quad K_{a_2}$$

Sulfurous acid is a polyprotic acid that can ionize in successive steps:

$$H_2SO_3\ (aq) \leftrightarrow H^+\ (aq) + HSO_3^-\ (aq) \quad K_{a_1} = 1.7 \times 10^{-2}$$

$$HSO_3^-\ (aq) \leftrightarrow H^+\ (aq) + SO_3^{2-}\ (aq) \quad K_{a_2} = 6.4 \times 10^{-8}$$

For polyprotic acids, removing the first proton is always easier than removing the second. This is also true for acids with three protons. The K_a values become increasingly smaller as more protons are removed. Because the K_a values for the second and third proton removals are so small, it is typically possible to estimate the pH of a polyprotic acid by using only K_{a_1}.

SAMPLE QUESTION

16) **In polyprotic acids, the K_a value is always _________ for the first dissociation compared to the K_a value for the second dissociation.**

A. higher

B. lower

C. the same

D. halved

Answer: A.

The K_a value is always the highest for the first dissociation and decreases for each subsequent dissociation.

Ions in Solution

An **electrolyte** is a substance that dissolves into anions and cations in water to produce an electrically conducting solution. This occurs when a salt, acids, and bases are dissolved in water. The overall solution is still electrically neutral, but if an electrical potential is applied, the cations are drawn to the electrode with an abundance of electrons and the anions are drawn to the electrode with a deficit of electrons. The movement of the ions results in a current.

Electrolytes can be either strong or weak. A weak electrolyte does not completely dissociate in the solvent, while a strong electrolyte completely or nearly completely dissociates in the solvent.

Nonelectrolytes do not dissociate in solution nor do they produce ions. Because they do not form ions, nonelectrolytes are poor conductors of electricity. Polar covalent substances such as sugar and alcohols are examples of nonelectrolytes.

Almost all salts are strong electrolytes and completely dissociate in water. Many salts have acid-base properties that come from their component ions reacting with water. When ions react with water to generate H^+ or OH^-, a hydrolysis reaction occurs. The pH of an aqueous salt solution can be predicted by considering the ions of the salt.

Anions can be considered conjugate bases of acids. For example, Cl^- is the conjugate base of HCl and CH_3COO^- is the conjugate base of acetic acid. If an anion is a conjugate base of a strong acid, such as Cl^-, the anion will not have a tendency to take protons from water and will not affect the pH. However, if the anion is a conjugate base of a weak acid, it will react with water to produce the weak acid and hydroxide ions, affecting the pH.

$$X^- (aq) + H_2O (l) \leftrightarrow HX (aq) + OH^- (aq)$$

Polyatomic cations with one or more protons can be considered conjugate acids of weak bases. The cation NH_4^+ can donate protons to water to produce hydronium ions and decrease the pH.

$$NH_4^+ (aq) + H_2O (l) \leftrightarrow NH_3 (aq) + H_3O^+ (aq)$$

Overall, if an aqueous salt solution contains anions and cations that do not react with water, the pH will be neutral.

To summarize the effects of cations and anions on an aqueous solution:

1. An anion that is a conjugate base of a strong acid will not change the pH.
2. An anion that is the conjugate base of a weak acid will increase the pH.
3. A cation that is the conjugate acid of a weak base will decrease the pH.
4. With the exception of Group 1 ions and Ca, Sr, and Ba, metal ions decrease the pH.
5. When a solution contains the conjugate base of a weak acid and the conjugate acid of a weak base, the ion with the larger ionization constant will influence the pH.

SAMPLE QUESTION

17) Which of the following is the product of a reaction between a polyprotic acid and water?

A. H_2O

B. OH^-

C. H_3O^+

D. H^+

Answer:

A. Incorrect. Water is one of the reactants in this example.

B. Incorrect. The hydroxide ion (OH^-) is increased when a base is added to water.

C. Correct. Adding an acid to water increases the concentration of the hydronium ion (H_3O^+) as the acid "donates" a proton to water to become H_3O^+.

D. Incorrect. Hydrogen ions (H^+) typically represent protons in acid/base reactions.

BUFFERS

A **buffer**, or buffer solution, is a chemical system that resists changes in pH when small quantities of acids or bases are added. A buffer can do this because it contains a weak acid to react with any added base and a weak base to react with any added acid. The acid and base components of the buffer must not react with each other. Typically, a weak acid and its conjugate base or a weak base with its conjugate acid are used to create buffers in a 1:1 ratio.

Human blood is an example of a buffer solution. Blood contains CO_2, which reacts in water to form H_2CO_3. This results in the following equilibria:

$$CO_2\,(aq) + H_2O\,(l) \leftrightarrow H_2CO_3\,(aq)$$

$$H_2CO_3\,(aq)\text{ (weak acid)} + H_2O\,(l) \leftrightarrow H_3O^+\,(aq) + HCO_3^-\,(aq)\text{ (conjugate base)}$$

If a strong acid is added to this solution, the conjugate base will react with the hydronium ions to form more of the weak acid. If a strong base is added to the solution, the weak acid will react with the hydroxide ions to form more of the conjugate base.

The pH of a buffer solution can be calculated based on the $[H_3O^+]$ in the K_a expression, if the K_a and concentration of the conjugate acid and base are known; it can also be calculated using the Henderson-Hasselbach equation:

$$pH = pK_a + \log\frac{[\text{conjugate base}]}{[\text{conjugate acid}]} = pK_a + \log\frac{[A^-]}{[HA]}$$

SAMPLE QUESTION

18) **Which of the following statements about buffers are true?**

   I. A buffer solution could consist of equal concentrations of ammonia and ammonium bromide.

   II. A buffer solution could consist of 1 mole of HF and 0.5 mole of NaOH in one liter of water.

   III. A buffer solution will change only slightly in pH upon addition of acid or base.

   A. I only

   B. III only

   C. II and III only

   D. I, II, and III

   Answer: D.

   All three statements are true.

Scientific Inquiry and Procedures

The Nature of Scientific Inquiry

If science is defined as the study of the natural world, then **scientific inquiry** is defined as the myriad ways in which scientists examine and form explanations about the natural world. There is no one set path that all scientists must follow in order to conduct scientific inquiry, but observations, hypotheses, variables, controls, drawing conclusions, using sources, and communicating findings all play major roles in the process.

The Scientific Method

Observations, or the receipt of knowledge of the natural world using senses or technology, are considered the core element of scientific inquiry. Observations can be quantitative or qualitative in nature. **Quantitative observations** are ones which can be measured, such as number, length, mass, or volume. Conversely, **qualitative observations** cannot be measured and are general qualities, such as color, shape, or texture.

Scientists observe the natural world in order to collect data of **natural phenomena**, or any state or process that occurs in nature. These observations are used to propose scientific **explanations** that describe how and why these phenomena occur. A proposed explanation of natural phenomena is also known as a **hypothesis**. Once a testable hypothesis is formed, then a scientific investigation can begin.

> HELPFUL HINT
>
> A hypothesis consists of more than an educated guess. Instead, a hypothesis is a **testable proposition** that scientists can use as the basis for an investigation. If it is not capable of being tested scientifically, it is not a hypothesis.

The data produced by scientific investigation must be analyzed and interpreted. By contextualizing the data, scientists seek to incorporate new information into the existing body of knowledge within the field. Once many hypotheses have been substantiated by data, a **theory** is developed. A theory provides an explanatory framework for observations. Although a theory may be shown to be incorrect, a theory may never be fully proven to be true. A scientific **law** is more firmly established than a theory, as it is a well-substantiated statement about a fundamental aspect of the universe.

A law differs from a theory in that it does not include mechanistic propositions. In other words, laws are statements about *what* is observed and theories are statements about *why* that observation is made. For instance, Boyle's law states that, at constant pressure, the volume of a gas is inversely proportional to the pressure to which it is subjected. No proposition is included in this law regarding how this relationship is maintained; simply, the relationship is observed. The theories of acid–base reactivity, however, such as the Arrhenius theory and the Brønsted-Lowry theory, propose specific mechanisms for acid–base reactions. The Arrhenius theory states that an acid donates an H^+ and a base donates an OH^-. The Brønsted–Lowry theory presents a slightly different model, stating that an acid donates an H^+ and a base accepts an H^+.

SAMPLE QUESTION

1) **Which of the following best defines a hypothesis?**

A. A hypothesis is a proposed explanation for an observed phenomenon.

B. A hypothesis is a question that a scientist seeks to answer.

C. A hypothesis is a widely accepted and substantiated theory that demonstrates applicability.

D. A hypothesis is a simplified version of a concept or observed phenomenon.

Answers:

A. **Correct.** A hypothesis is stated with regard to an observed phenomenon that is not understood, and it provides a suggested explanation for that phenomenon.

B. Incorrect. The process of scientific inquiry seeks to answer questions about observed phenomenon, and a hypothesis is a suggested answer to such questions.

C. Incorrect. A widely accepted and substantiated theory that demonstrates applicability is considered a law.

D. Incorrect. A simplified version of a theory is considered to be a model.

Experimental Design

A key characteristic of a hypothesis is that it must be testable. An **experimental design** is then established, which is a set of experiments carefully and deliberately chosen for the purpose of testing the stated hypothesis. The successful adherence to the scientific method may result in either the support or rejection of the hypothesis. Rejection of the hypothesis does not imply poor scientific practice, but in fact it implies successful scientific inquiry. Scientists must approach inquiry with openness and honesty, allowing their findings to shape their formulation of hypotheses and theories.

One possible outcome of an experimental investigation is the formation of a **null hypothesis.** A null hypothesis is a statement that there is no relationship between two measured phenomena, or no association between groups under observation. The investigator must remain open to the possibility that no true relationship exists.

In the design of an experiment, factors that can be manipulated, changed, or measured in experiments are defined as **variables. Independent variables** are deliberately changed in the course of experimentation, and **dependent variables** are those variables that are measured or observed. Dependent variables rely on independent variables. For example, imagine that a chemist is conducting an experiment in which she is heating a liquid to the point of evaporation. As the reaction progresses, she measures the mass of the liquid remaining in the container, and also records the temperature of the solution at each of these points in time. Temperature is the independent variable because it is the parameter she is deliberately changing over the course of the reaction, whereas liquid mass is the dependent variable because it is the measured parameter whose value depends on the value of the independent variable.

TYPES OF VARIABLES

independent: the variable changed by the experimenter

dependent: the variable being measured or observed

control: variables that do not change

confounding: outside variables that influence the results of the experiment

To properly design an experiment, it is necessary to include a control in the experimental design. A scientific **control** is used to measure the effects of variables other than the independent variables. In the control, the samples are treated identically to those being tested but are not subject to the independent variable. For example, if an experiment is designed to determine the effects of a pharmaceutical agent on cellular growth, a control sample of cells of the same type would be grown in conditions identical to those of the experimental groups. At the time of treatment, the control experimental group would be left untreated with the pharmaceutical agent. Inclusion of an experimental control increases the reliability of experimental outcomes, and provides confirmation that the experimental design is successfully testing the targeted phenomenon.

When analyzing data collected in a scientific investigation, it is important to recognize the role of confounding variables. **Confounding variables** are factors that are not directly manipulated or measured in a scientific study, but may have an effect on the variables included in the study. To avoid being misled by confounding variables, experimental controls should be included in the experimental design. In this way, the scientist can distinguish between correlative and causal relationships among variables.

Reproducibility is an essential feature of a scientific finding. Under the same conditions and using the same experimental methods, multiple researchers should be able to produce identical results. If a result is irreproducible, it will not be trusted and accepted in the science community.

In the course of scientific inquiry, the scientist seeks to minimize sources of human error. Human error occurs when unintentional events obscure the accuracy of the findings in an experiment. Errors originate from a variety of sources. It is possible that the observed phenomenon may be disrupted in the process of making the measurements that are part of the experimental design. Familiarity with a specific subject matter allows scientists to carefully plan experiments in a way that allows for minimal disruption of the natural phenomena they are investigating. Human error is distinct from poor experimental design; human error is an unintended error, whereas poor experimental design is the outcome of oversight or misinformation in the experimental design process.

CONSIDER THIS...

Confounding variables are a significant challenge in the development of scientific understanding. Can you think of a historical scientific development in which confounding variables initially halted progress?

SAMPLE QUESTION

2) **A chemist is studying a chemical reaction and has hypothesized that increasing the amount of a copper catalyst will increase the reaction yield. She observes that the percent yield is unchanged by increasing the amount of copper. She does an additional series of experiments in which she decreases the amount of copper, and observes that the percent yield is unchanged in these conditions as well. What can she conclude about her hypothesis?**

A. The hypothesis is supported by the observations in the experimental design.

B. The null hypothesis is true in this situation.

C. Further experiments are needed to determine whether the hypothesis may be confirmed.

D. The opposite of the hypothesized relationship is supported by her observations.

Answers:

A. Incorrect. For the hypothesis to be supported, there would be an observed direct correlation between the increase in amount of copper and the percent yield.

B. Correct. The null hypothesis, which is a statement that there is no relationship between the independent variable (amount of copper) and the dependent variable (percent yield), is true in this case.

C. Incorrect. The experimental design has provided sufficient information to show that the independent and dependent variables are unrelated to one another.

D. Incorrect. If the opposite of the hypothesized relationship were correct, lowering the amount of copper would have decreased the percent yield.

SCIENTIFIC MODELS

A useful tool for the scientist is the **model**, which is a simplified version of an observed phenomenon or concept. The purpose of using a model is to make complex concepts easier to visualize, quantify, observe, or simulate. Models make abstract or complicated concepts more accessible, facilitating their further investigation. To produce useful theories, models, and laws, it is necessary to make some assumptions, given the limited nature of observational skills. It is the goal of the scientist, however, to minimize the assumptions as much as possible.

Different models are selected for different purposes of investigation. **Physical models** are physical copies of a phenomenon that are built to scale and are used to physically visualize processes and phenomena, such as solar system movement. **Conceptual models** are also used to provide a visual representation of abstract concepts while also describing behavior, such as the fluid mosaic model. Models can also be **mathematical** or **graphical**. Mathematical models are used to describe and predict behavior or phenomena, such as population growth, while graphical models are used in probability and statistics. Graphical models are also used prominently in disciplines such as genetics in order to analyze genetic links.

Scientific models are representations of natural phenomena and processes, but cannot be exact replicas. In order to provide simple, useful explanations, scientists must make trade-offs regarding details, approximations, and accuracy of information. All models must be evaluated for their potential **limitations**. For example, the Bohr atomic model is limited by the fact that it is only useful for describing hydrogen atoms. To

> **DID YOU KNOW?**
>
> Many models are used in the process of **simulation**, or imitating a natural phenomenon or process. Simulations play a major role in both scientific investigations as well as engineering, which applies information learned from simulations to design real-world technology.

compensate for model limitations, scientists will often use multiple models in their investigations as well as modify existing models to explain new observations.

SAMPLE QUESTION

3) **The Bohr model, which is an atomic model that describes the concept of how components of an atom behave, is an example of which of the following types of models?**

A. physical model

B. graphical model

C. mathematical model

D. conceptual model

Answers:

A. Incorrect. Physical models are physical representations; the Bohr model is a conceptual diagram.

B. Incorrect. The Bohr model is a conceptual diagram and does not factor in probability or statistics like a graphical model does.

C. Incorrect. Mathematical models represent phenomena by using equations, while the Bohr model is a conceptual diagram.

D. **Correct.** The Bohr model is an example of a conceptual model that describes and explains the behavior of atoms.

Data Collection and Interpretation

Working in the laboratory involves dealing with a lot of measurements, that is, dealing with a lot of numbers. Managing measurements can become overwhelming at times, so specific scientific techniques are used to organize data. Furthermore, that data needs to be presented properly. Without being able to present results with clarity, a scientist's research and time spent in the laboratory will have no impact.

Precision and Accuracy

In science, it is important to have precise and accurate results because the results of one finding may be used as a baseline for another finding, and if the results of the first finding are not accurate, it increases the inaccuracy of the second finding, which can lead to the propagation of inaccuracy if the same results are used in subsequent experiments.

- **Precision** refers to how close together a series of measurements of the same quantity are to each other. If several measurements of the same quantity exist, and all the measurements are very similar to one another, then that set of measurements is precise.

- **Accuracy** refers to how close a measured value is to an accepted value (true value).

So, most measurements can fall in one of the following categories:

1. neither precise nor accurate
2. precise but not accurate
3. precise and accurate

To better understand the preceding three scenarios, consider a bucket filled with dirty water; turbidity measurements are taken to estimate the quality of water. Three sets of measurements are taken, and each set includes five measured values with the help of a turbidimeter (a digital instrument that displays the turbidity value on the screen). The measurements are compared to each other and to the true value of turbidity, which is 100 NTUs (Nephelometric Turbidity Units). The results are displayed in Table 8.1.

HELPFUL HINT

Turbidity is the cloudiness of the water due to the presence of a large number of individual particles, suspended solids, or dirt.

Table 8.1. Precision versus Accuracy

Set 1 (NTU)	Set 2 (NTU)	Set 3 (NTU)
130	151	100
180	151	101
200	152	100
150	150	99
120	150	100
Set 1: The values are neither close to one another nor close to the correct value of turbidity (100 NTUs). Hence, the set of measured values is neither precise nor accurate.	Set 2: The values are close together, but they are way off the correct value of turbidity. Hence, the set of measured values is precise but not accurate.	Set 3: The values are close together as well as very close to/the same as the correct value of turbidity. Hence, the set of measured values is precise and accurate.

Go on

SAMPLE QUESTION

4) **Which of the following targets shows accuracy, but not precision?**

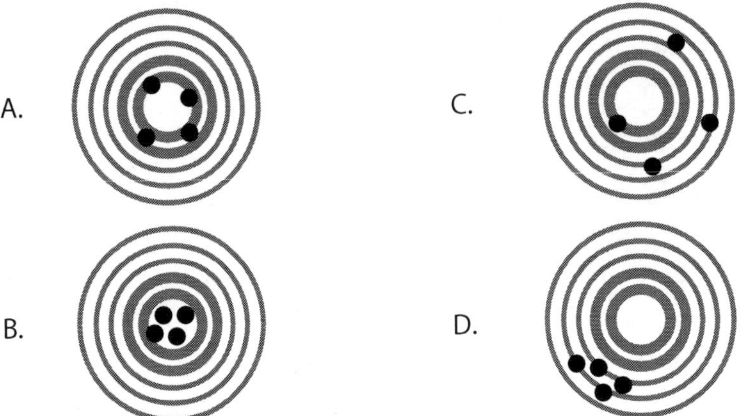

Answers:

A. **Correct.** This shows measurements that are accurate, but not precise.

B. Incorrect. This shows measurements that are both accurate and precise.

C. Incorrect. This shows measurements that are neither accurate nor precise.

D. Incorrect. This shows measurements that are precise, but not accurate.

Significant Figures

The concept of significant figures helps estimate uncertainty in the measured results; in other words, the uncertainty in an experimental result or a calculated value is indicated by the number of significant figures. **Significant figures** can be found by adding one uncertain digit to the number of certain digits in an experiment measurement. The rules for determining significant figures are as follows:

- All nonzero digits are significant; 15.36 has four significant figures.
- Zeros that are to the left of the first nonzero digit in the number are not considered significant; 023 has two significant figures, and 0.0673 has three significant figures.
- Zeros that are present between two nonzero digits are significant; 205 has three significant figures, and 0.7089 has four significant figures.
- Zeros that are present to the right of the decimal point are significant; 2.00 has three significant figures, and 0.3000 has four significant figures.

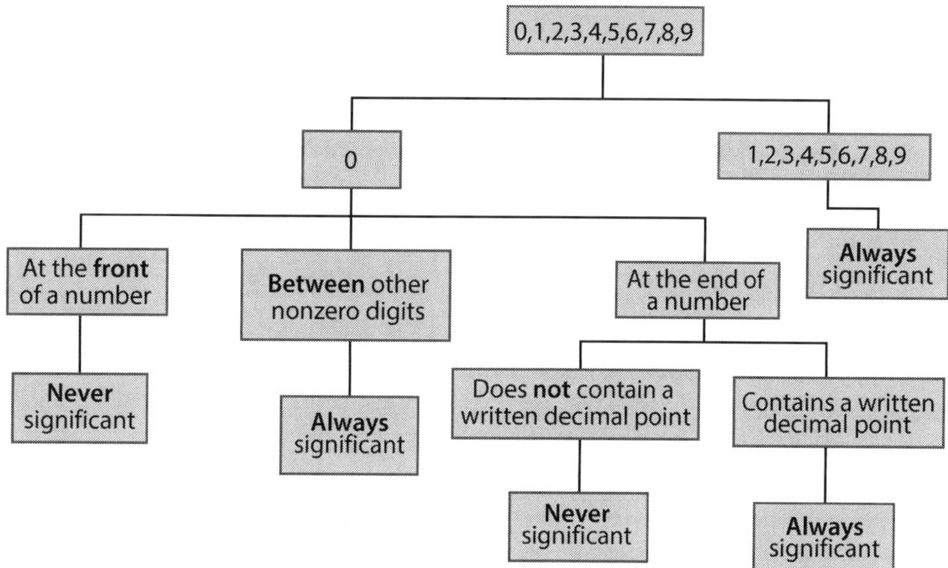

Figure 8.1. Significant Figures

The numbers involved in the addition and subtraction of significant figures can have different decimal places; however, the result should always be reported to the same number of decimal places as that of the number with the smallest number of decimal places.

For example, in the addition of 93.35, 2.1, and 28.013, the result will be reported with one decimal point because one of the numbers involved has just one decimal point (2.1). Hence, the result will be 123.4.

In multiplication and division of significant figures, the result should have as many significant figures as there are in the original number with the least significant figures. For example, the calculation $12.8 \times 5.678 = 72.6784$ would be reported as 72.7.

SAMPLE QUESTIONS

5) **How many significant figures are in the number 51800?**

Answer:

Determine if any nonzero digits exist and if there are any zeros between them. They are all significant: 5, 1, 8.

Trailing zeros are not significant because there is no decimal point.

Thus, total number of significant figures is three: 5, 1, 8.

6) **How many significant figures are in the number 78,340.00?**

Answer:

Determine if any nonzero digits exist and if there are any zeros between them. They are all significant: 7, 8, 3, 4.

Trailing zeros are significant because there is a decimal point. Thus, the total number of significant figures is seven: 7, 8, 3, 4, and the three trailing zeros.

Interpreting Results and Drawing Conclusions

Once collected, data must be analyzed in order to draw conclusions from it, and to interpret it so that the data can be used to make an impact on society or to support further studies. To make sure the data collected is relevant and helps develop the research, the following points should be kept in mind:

- making sure the data being collected is relevant to the research
- making sure that the pattern formed with the data is correct
- noting if the pattern formed by the collected data matches the expected pattern
- noting and analyzing the deviations from the expected pattern
- making sure to collect data that could explain the expected deviations
- making sure the data collected and the patterns formed answer the unanswered question
- making sure the results are worthy of further use

To further make sense of the data, descriptive analysis and inferential analysis are used. **Descriptive analysis** involves transforming raw data into a version that can be easily understood—for example, organizing data in tables and charts—whereas **inferential analysis** involves drawing conclusions from the results.

Data can be visually displayed with the help of graphs and charts. The types of graphs widely used to display data are the line graph, scatter graph, bar graph, histogram, and pie chart. It is important to know and identify the differences between these graphs because different graphs are used for displaying different kinds of data.

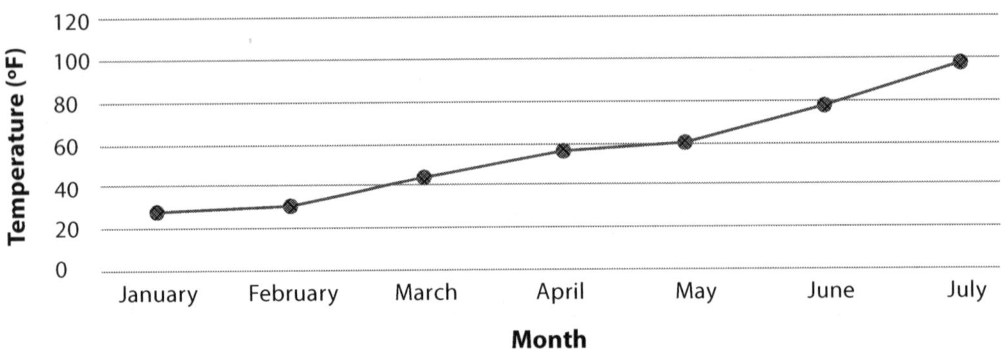

Figure 8.2. Line Graph

Line graphs show change over time. In chemistry experiments, line graphs are used extensively to show a trend in the collected data.

Scatter plots are used when correlating two sets of data. In cases where one variable is dependent on the other variable, the scatter plot shows the effect of the changes in one variable on the other variable. The scatter plot provides a way to analyze the nature of the data as quantitative changes are made to some parameters. A **line of best fit** is often included on scatter plots to show trends in the data.

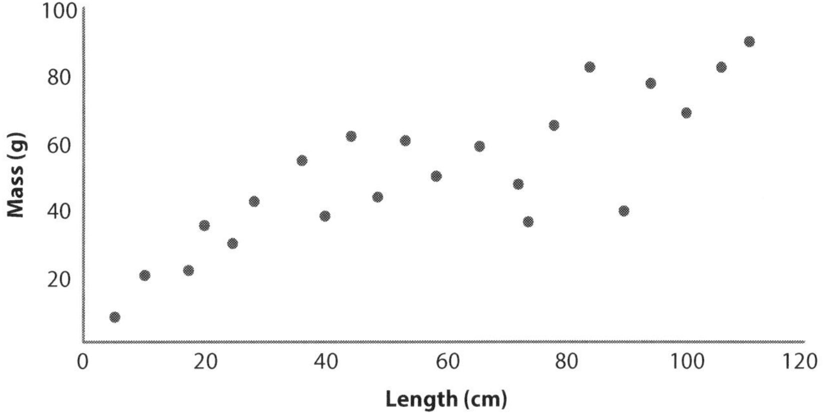

Figure 8.3. Scatter Plot

Bar graphs compare two or more groups. Most times the bar represents an average or mean of the data. In a bar graph, the length of the bar represents the magnitude of the quantity. Bar graphs are helpful in comparing qualitative data that exists in small numbers. In a bar graph, bars do not touch—in Figure 8.5 there is a small gap between the bars, which can make it difficult to differentiate between a bar graph and a histogram (explained next). However, if a gap exists between the bars, it implies it is a bar graph.

> HELPFUL HINT
>
> The base of the bars is the independent variable. The height or length of the bars shows the dependent variable.

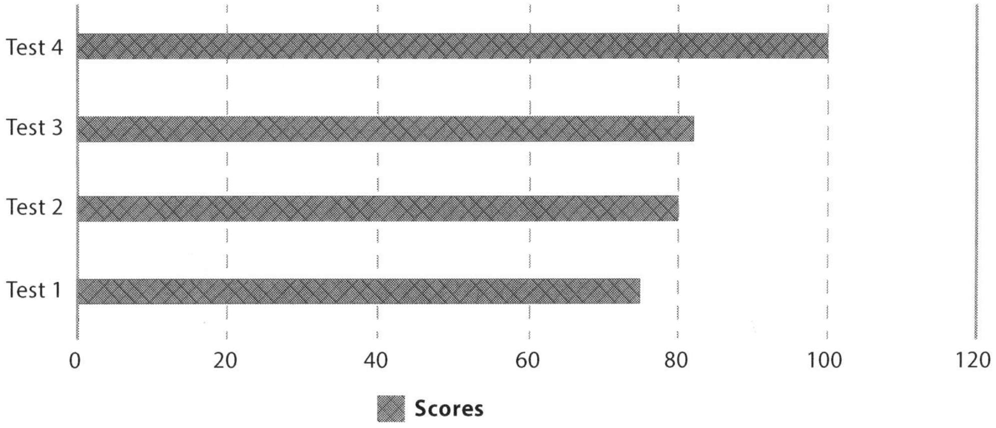

Figure 8.4. Bar Graph

Histograms are used to look at distribution of data. In a histogram, bars touch one another. A histogram might look like a bar graph, but it differs in a few ways. In a histogram, the length of the bars represents measurements that fall into a set of values, that is, along with the magnitude of an effect, a histogram gives a good idea about the spread of the measured values. Unlike bar graphs, which usually involve categories, histograms involve quantities.

Pie charts illustrate a part of the whole. A pie chart is a statistical graphic, circular in shape, and is divided to show different numerical proportions. There is a direct relation between the quantity represented and the arc length of each section in the pie chart.

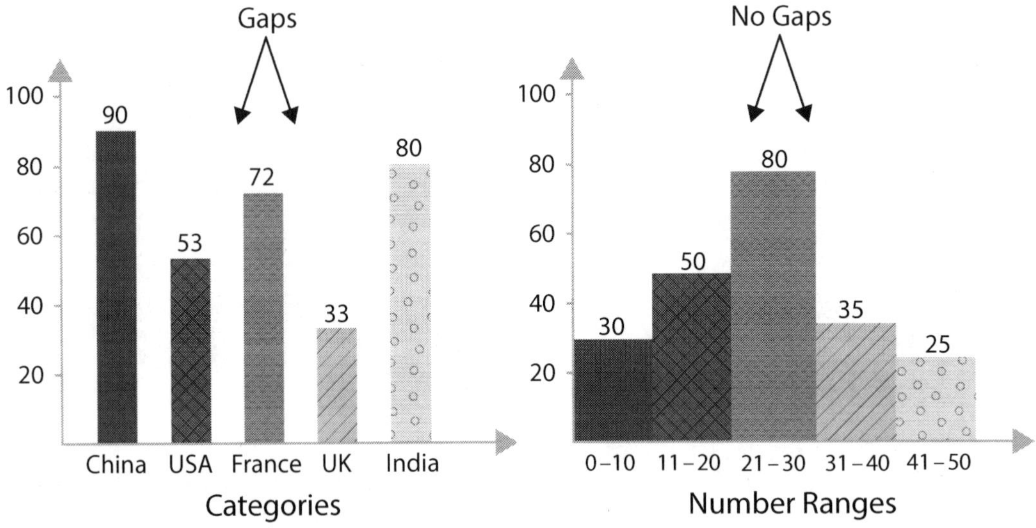

Figure 8.5. Bar Chart vs Histogram

No matter what kind of image is used, effective data presentation is impossible without considering the audience. The graphs or charts should be self-explanatory. The following steps will help ensure best representation of data:

- It is important to make sure the data is represented in the simplest way so that the audience is able to comprehend it. The best results are obtained when the most complicated data is broken down and represented in the simplest terms. Along with the use of basic Excel charts and graphs, many other options are available for the visual representation of the data.

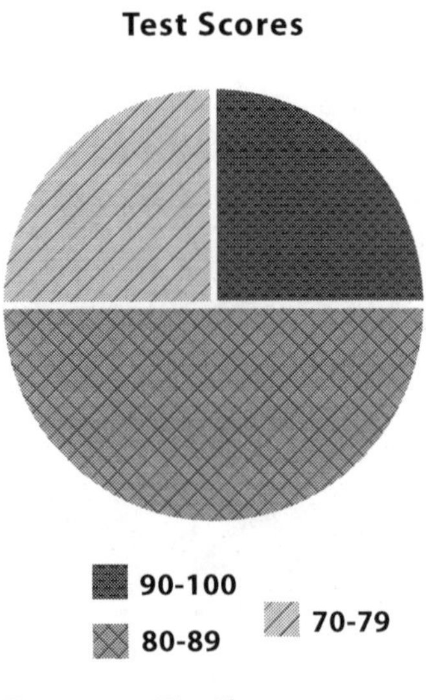

Figure 8.6. Pie Chart

- The data should be clear. Simple things should be kept in mind, like using bar graphs instead of histograms wherever it makes most sense. In addition to using different colors in the graph, different shapes can be used to make graphs clearer.
- Visual data must be labeled properly, and *everything* in the chart or graph should be labeled. Nothing should be left ambiguous; all the axes should be labeled. No matter how much effort went into the research, if the visual presentation is bad and fails to convey the message, the research is no good. Hence, to make the effort worthwhile, time and energy should be invested in the proper analysis and representation of the data.

SAMPLE QUESTION

7) **Which of the following types of graphs best shows the quantitative relationship between an independent and dependent variable over time?**

A. scatter plot

B. histogram

C. bar graph

D. pie chart

Answers:

A. **Correct.** Scatter plots show trends among quantitative independent and dependent variables.

B. Incorrect. Histograms show data in ranges of numbers.

C. Incorrect. Bar graphs show the relationship between categories of individual data, some of which may be qualitative.

D. Incorrect. Pie charts are best suited for showing data as a percentage compared to the entire data set.

UNITS AND NOTATION SYSTEMS

SCIENTIFIC NOTATION

In science, certain commonly used values are extremely big or extremely small, and writing such values again and again can become inconvenient. For example, the size of an electron is 0.00000000000000285 m. Writing this number multiple times in a calculation would be tedious. Writing it over and over also increases the possibility of error because there is a greater chance of leaving out one of the zeros. Scientific notation is important because it reduces the possibility of error and makes it easier to use these values multiple times.

When using scientific notation, there are two possible scenarios:

The number is *less* than 1: an extremely small number such as 0.00000000000000285 m

1. Place a decimal point after the first significant digit of the given number. In this example, this would result in 2.85.
2. Then, count the number of places that will be required to move the decimal point from where it currently exists to the right of the first significant figure. The number of places moved becomes the power of 10 and is multiplied by the number expressed as a decimal in step 1 (2.85). Because the shift of the decimal point was from left to right, the exponent is negative: 0.00000000000000285 m = 2.85×10^{-15} m

The number is *greater* than 1: an extremely large number such as 3,800,000,000,000 m

1. Place a decimal point after the first significant digit of the given number. In this example, this would result in 3.8.
2. Rewrite the number with a decimal place, which is usually placed at the end of the number. Here, this would result in 3,800,000,000,000.
3. Count the number of places that will be required to move decimal point from where it currently exists to the right of the first significant figure. The number of places moved becomes the power of 10 and is multiplied with the number expressed as a decimal in step 1 (3.8). Because the shift of the decimal point was from right to left, the exponent is positive: 3,800,000,000,000 m = 3.8×10^{12} m

SAMPLE QUESTION

8) **Which of the following is the correct scientific notation for 844,000?**

A. 84.4×10^4

B. 84.4×10^5

C. 8.44×10^6

D. 8.44×10^5

Answers:

A. Incorrect. The decimal is moved to the second significant figure, instead of the first. The power of 10 is also off by one digit.

B. Incorrect. The decimal is moved to the second significant figure, instead of the first.

C. Incorrect. The decimal is moved over 5 spots to the first significant figure, not 6 like this answer suggests.

D. **Correct.** The decimal is moved over 5 spots to the first significant figure.

STANDARD UNITS OF MEASUREMENT

The **metric system** is a decimal measurement system based on a consistent set of **metric units**, indicated by a prefix paired with a base unit. The metric system, which originated in the 1700s, was expanded upon and standardized in 1960 as the International System of Units, or **SI units**. SI units are used consistently across all disciplines in order to coordinate research efforts and reduce communication errors. There are seven base SI units (shown in Table 8.2).

Table 8.2. Standard Base Units

Physical Quantity	Name of Unit	Abbreviation
mass	kilogram	kg
length	meter	m
time	second	s
temperature	kelvin	K
electric current	ampere	A
amount of substance	mole	mol
luminous intensity	candela	cd

Derived units are made by combining one or more base units. Density, area, acceleration, and speed are all examples of derived units.

- area: $A = m \times m = m^2$
- speed: $\frac{distance}{time}$ (m/s)
- density; ρ: $\frac{mass}{volume}$ (kg/m^3)

Metric prefixes are placed in front of the base unit or the derived unit to indicate quantity. Since quantities can have a wide range of values, prefixes—like scientific notation—simplify expressing them. Each metric prefix is represented by a symbol and denotes what multiple of 10 it is. The detailed description of the metric prefixes can be found in Table 8.3.

Table 8.3. Metric Prefixes

Prefix	Symbol	Meaning	Exponential
exa	E	1,000,000,000,000,000,000	10^{18}
peta	P	1,000,000,000,000,000	10^{15}
tera	T	1,000,000,000,000	10^{12}
giga	G	1,000,000,000	10^{9}
mega	M	1,000,000	10^{6}
kilo	k	1,000	10^{3}
hecto	h	100	10^{2}
deka	da	10	10^{1}

Table 8.3. Metric Prefixes (continued)			
Prefix	**Symbol**	**Meaning**	**Exponential**
–	–	1	10^{0}
deci	d	0.1	10^{-1}
centi	c	0.01	10^{-2}
milli	m	0.001	10^{-3}
micro	μ	0.000001	10^{-6}
nano	n	0.000000001	10^{-9}
pico	p	0.000000000001	10^{-12}
femto	f	0.000000000000001	10^{-15}
atto	a	0.000000000000000001	10^{-18}

Although the US Customary System is not commonly used in chemistry, it's helpful to be familiar with the common US units and the conversion factors needed to move between the US and SI systems.

Table 8.4. Commonly Used Measurements in the US Customary System		
Category	**Name of Unit**	**Conversion Factor**
Length	inch	1 in. = 1/12th ft.
	foot	1 ft.
	yard	1 yd. = 3 ft.
	mile	1 mi. = 5,280 ft.
	nautical mile	1 nautical mile = 6,076.12 ft.
Area	acre	1 ac. = 43,560 sq. ft.
Volume	fluid ounce	1 fl. oz. = 1/16th pt.
	pint	1 pt.
	quart	1 qt. = 2 pt.
	gallon	1 gal. = 8 pt.
Weight	ounce	1 oz. = 1/16th pt.
	pound	1 lb.
	stone	1 st. = 14 lb.
	ton	1 ton = 2,000 lb.

Table 8.5. US Customary to Metric Conversion Factors

1 in. = 2.54 cm	1 lb. = 0.454 kg
1 yd. = 0.914 m	1 cal = 4.19 J
1 mi. = 1.61 km	$°F = \frac{9}{5}°C + 32$
1 gal. = 3.785 L	1 cm^3 = 1 mL
1 oz. = 28.35 g	1 hr = 3600 s

SAMPLE QUESTION

9) **Which of the following is NOT a base SI unit?**

A. meter
B. gram
C. second
D. ampere

Answers:

A. Incorrect. The meter is the base SI unit for length.
B. **Correct.** The base SI unit for mass is the kilogram.
C. Incorrect. The second is the base SI unit for time.
D. Incorrect. The ampere is the base SI unit for electric current.

UNIT CONVERSION

The **factor-label method**, also known as dimensional analysis, is a **unit conversion** process to convert one set of units to another. It includes conversion factors, which are fractions where the numerator and denominator are given quantities expressed in different units. The numerator and denominator can also be reversed, that is, the reciprocal can be used as well.

HELPFUL HINT

The factor-label method is often referred to as **railroad tracks** because of the appearance of the lines on the page.

$$1000 \text{ m} = 1 \text{ km}$$

$$\frac{1 \text{ km}}{1000 \text{ m}} = \frac{1000 \text{ m}}{1 \text{ km}}$$

Conversion factors connect the new unit of measurement to the unit being converted. In this method, units are multiplied together, and the conversion factors are arranged in a manner where all units, except the required unit, cancel.

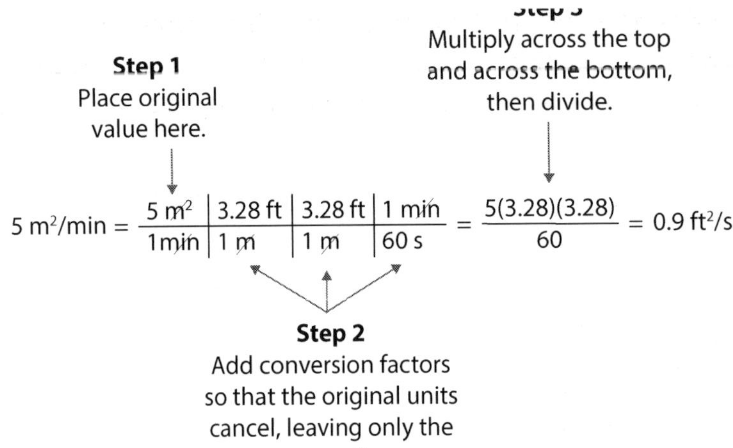

Figure 8.7. Dimensional Analysis

SAMPLE QUESTION

10) Convert 8 miles/hour into metric units (meters/second).

Answer:

Use dimensional analysis.

8 ~~miles~~	1.609 ~~km~~	1000 m	1 ~~hr.~~	1 ~~min.~~	**= 3.57 m/s**
~~hr.~~	1 ~~mile~~	1 ~~km~~	60 ~~min.~~	60 s	

Error Analysis

Performing a study or an experiment always involves noting measurements, and uncertainty in the measured results is always possible. There could be numerous reasons for the uncertainty—it could be a human error, machine error, lack of ideal conditions, or improper calibration. However, there are ways to minimize uncertainty in measurements to ensure precise and accurate results.

Because it is impossible to avoid uncertainty in measurements during experiments, focus should be on accurately reporting the uncertainties. It is important to highlight what the measurement errors are and how they propagate through the equation.

Errors in scientific experiments can be categorized as

1. systematic error or determinate error
2. random error or indeterminate error

Systematic error is a result of faulty experiment design or faulty equipment. This type of error can be reproduced if the experiment is carried out in the same way multiple times. The error values in such cases are either too high or too low. It is possible to eliminate systematic errors by making corrections to the equipment or the experiment design. In the case of uncertainties due to systematic errors, the resultant uncertainty is calculated by adding or subtracting uncertainty in each term.

Random error, on the other hand, is a result of uncontrollable factors. Random errors can be reduced but cannot be eliminated completely. It is usually difficult to identify the root cause for a random error because they may be due to environmental factors or human error.

The uncertainty calculation for random error can be figured using the following formulas:

- **Absolute uncertainty** is the margin of uncertainty associated with a measurement; for example, the absolute uncertainty of a measuring cylinder can be reported as 0.01 mL.
- **Relative uncertainty** is the ratio of the absolute uncertainty to the actual value of the measurement. For example, the relative uncertainty of a measuring cylinder reading of 8.47 mL with an absolute uncertainty of 0.01 is 0.001 (0.01 mL/8.47 mL).
- **Percent relative uncertainty** is the relative uncertainty expressed as a percentage. In the preceding example, the percent relative error would be 0.1 (0.01 mL/8.47 mL × 100).

Summing up uncertainties within an experiment can be complex. There may be numerous uncertainties involved in an experiment; some could be positive and the rest negative. They may even cancel each other out.

HELPFUL HINT

Overall uncertainty is the sum of absolute uncertainties.

SAMPLE QUESTION

11) Which of the following types of errors can alter the precision of a scientific investigation?

A. procedural flaws

B. systematic errors

C. analyzed error

D. random errors

Answers:

A. Incorrect. A procedural flaw is a root cause of a systematic error, which can alter the accuracy of an investigation.

B. Incorrect. Systematic errors impact the accuracy of an investigation, not the precision.

C. Incorrect. All error is analyzed error; only the random error impacts the precision of an investigation.

D. Correct. Random errors—or unpredictable changes—alter the precision of a measurement or how close measurements are to one another.

Laboratory Equipment

Although the subject matter and focus of investigations vary widely, there are many common pieces of equipment used across all disciplines. All equipment must be appropriately and safely used and maintained in order to preserve a safe laboratory space and ensure the accuracy, precision, validity, and reliability of the investigations taking place. Before using any equipment, all components must be checked for potential damage and all manufacturer instructions must be read and followed. Equipment and its components should also be used and stored in cool, dry laboratory spaces. If working with potentially hazardous equipment, such as powerful industrial magnets, warning signs need to be posted in the work area. Equipment components should be regularly cleaned, maintained, and replaced according to the manufacturer's instructions.

Optical Equipment

Optical lab equipment includes any equipment that disperses, concentrates, or redirects light using **lenses**, mirrors, or **prisms**. **Microscopes** and **telescopes** both commonly use an objective lens and eyepiece lens to magnify objects. Microscopes are used to magnify small objects at a short distance, while telescopes are used to magnify large objects from a great distance. Light Amplification by Stimulated Emission of Radiation, or **LASERs**, produce high-energy, narrow beams of concentrated, monochromatic light that can travel great distances and are used in a wide variety of applications, ranging from CD/DVD technology to anti-missile defense. **Spectrometers** are used to measure and record light properties and wave spectrums. Glass or plastic mirrors, prisms, and lenses used in any of these instruments must be cared for appropriately. Dust covers or lens caps should be placed over glass when the equipment is not in use, stored in a cool, dry area, and cleaned at appropriate intervals according to manufacturer instructions.

SAMPLE QUESTION

12) **Which of the following is an example of safe, appropriate use of a piece of optical equipment?**

A. leaving a spectrometer open and accessible for the next use

B. storing spectrometers in a humid storage space

C. cleaning glass lenses but not plastic lenses

D. placing a dust cover over a telescope after use is complete

Answers:

A. Incorrect. Optical equipment should be stored appropriately when not in use.

B. Incorrect. Optical equipment should be stored in a cool, dry place.

C. Incorrect. All lenses—both glass and plastic—must be cleaned at appropriate intervals.

D. **Correct.** Dust covers are an important piece of protective equipment that maintains the safety, cleanliness, and accuracy of the instrument.

SEPARATION EQUIPMENT

Separation lab equipment is used to **separate** a mixture into its distinct, separate components. There are several methods commonly used to complete this task. **Mechanical separation** is the separation of components using physical machines. This includes **filtration** via **funnels**, sieves, and other equipment to remove large particles from liquid and a **centrifuge** to separate a mixture by spinning it at high speeds. Centrifuges can be used to separate organelles or to isolate nucleic acid. The individual tubes must be balanced when placing in the equipment to avoid a large force unbalance as it spins at high speeds.

Chemical separation relies on chemically removing compounds through procedures such as **distillation**, which purifies and separates liquids through a heating and cooling process using burners, tubing, and flasks; and **chromatography**, which separates mixtures by allowing a gas or liquid to flow over a material, which causes the various components to separate as they flow at different rates. Chromatography systems typically involve the use of columns, detectors, and pumps.

Magnetic separation occurs when magnetic devices are used to attract and remove magnetic components out of the non-magnetic substance in the mixture. Scientific applications of this technology include magnetic-activated cell sorting (MACS), in which magnetic nanoparticles are used to separate cells based on their surface antigens. This equipment is highly specialized and includes separators and columns.

Separation on the cellular level can also be conducted using **electric separation**. A primary example of this is gel electrophoresis, which uses electrical pulses to separate DNA, RNA, and/or proteins. This process requires the use of a power supply, a series of chambers, and tables, trays, and combs for the gel.

SAMPLE QUESTION

13) Columns, pumps, and detectors are examples of primary equipment commonly used for which of the following methods of separation?

Go on →

A. electric separation
B. chromatography
C. mechanical separation
D. filtration

Answers:

A. Incorrect. Electric separation also requires a power supply and separation chambers.

B. Correct. This is a basic list of equipment that is required to complete separation using chromatography.

C. Incorrect. Mechanical separation could use these components, but the primary definition of this type of equipment is that it relies on machines.

D. Incorrect. This is not the defining list of equipment for filtration methods, as it does not contain a sieve, mesh, or any filter.

Measurement, Mixing, and Heating Equipment

Measurement lab equipment includes **meter sticks** to measure lengths in meters, **graduated cylinders** to measure volume, **balances** to measure mass, and **thermometers** to measure temperature in Celsius or Kelvin. All measurement instruments must use **the metric system** and be able to read SI units in accordance with worldwide scientific standards. The **pH** of a substance is measured according to the 14-point pH scale using pH meters, which use probes. These devices should be carefully cleaned and calibrated before use. Precise, traceable **timers**—including decimal stopwatches and clocks—are used to measure and record time elapsed.

Mixing lab equipment includes any of the individual pieces of equipment used to move materials and mix together. **Pipettes** are used to transport precise amounts of liquids from one container to another. Containers include beakers, flasks, and test tubes. **Stirrers** are used to physically mix substances. These can be as simple as glass or plastic rods in small investigational settings, or as advanced as mechanical overhead stirrers, magnetic stirrers, or shakers in order to mix components at high speeds and/or at controlled temperatures.

There are multiple varieties of **heating lab equipment** that are used depending on the type and size of the laboratory investigation. When using any heating device, great care should be taken to remove all flammable materials from the work area. Plastic, closed or narrow-necked containers, such as flasks or reagent bottles, should be avoided. When heating things at very high temperatures, crucibles, which are resistant to high temperatures, should be used. Protective clothing should be worn and protective equipment, such as tongs or hot pads, should be used when transporting.

Some heating equipment uses open flames. **Alcohol burners** produce low, open flames at relatively low temperatures. **Bunsen burners** are similar in nature but produce higher, hotter flames. Both are used for heating and sterilizing non-flammable materials. When using any open flame heating equipment, all loose clothing or hair should be secured. Flames should never be leaned over or left unattended. Other heating equipment does not use open flames. This includes **hot plates**, which are used when controlled temperatures are required for heating substances, and **ovens**, which are used to uniformly heat and dry materials.

SAMPLE QUESTION

14) Which of the following extra care steps should be taken when using pH meters?

A. Calibrate the probe before use.
B. Remove flammable material from work area.
C. Attend to pH meters constantly, never leaving them unattended.
D. Inspect all parts before use.

Answers:

A. Correct. Due to the sensitive nature of the probe, pH meter probes should be cleaned and calibrated before each use.
B. Incorrect. This is a step necessary when using heating equipment.
C. Incorrect. This is a step necessary when using heating equipment that uses an open flame.
D. Incorrect. This is a step that is taken when using any piece of laboratory equipment.

STERILIZATION EQUIPMENT

Highly specialized **sterilization lab equipment** is used in laboratory settings to sterilize, effectively removing bacteria or any other microorganism that could present a hazard or manipulate the investigation. Quick, small scale sterilization can be completed by wiping materials with appropriate solvents or by heating in ovens or over burners. For larger scale sterilization, and in the case of potential biohazards, industrial **sterilizers** or **autoclaves** can be used. Autoclaves are strong vessels that use high pressure and temperatures, and autoclaving is considered the most reliable form of sterilization. Equipment and materials can be sterilized by placing in a high-pressure autoclave at a sustained temperature of 250 degrees for 15 minutes.

HELPFUL HINT

Autoclave machines have uses other than sterilization. The combination of pressure and heat applied appropriately can also inactivate potential biohazards, vulcanize rubber, and cure composites.

SAMPLE QUESTION

15) **Which of the following correctly describes the definition of sterilization?**

A. eliminating hazards from equipment

B. removing microorganisms from a surface

C. storing equipment at high pressures and temperatures

D. removing all sources of investigation manipulation

Answers:

A. Incorrect. Sterilization removes potential biohazards from equipment by removing microorganisms but does not eliminate all potential hazards.

B. Correct. Sterilization uses solvents and heat to denature and remove microorganisms.

C. Incorrect. This process can be used to sterilize but is not the definition of sterilization itself.

D. Incorrect. Sterilization removes potentially unintentional biological manipulations from equipment used in an investigation by removing microorganisms, but it does not eliminate sources of potential data manipulation.

Laboratory Safety

Working in a chemistry laboratory comes with a lot of personal responsibility. While most of the accidents that occur in the lab are minor and result from ignorance of safety procedures, serious or fatal accidents can occur. Hence, safety procedures are of utmost importance. Moreover, the instruments used for operations and experiments in laboratories are generally very expensive and require ongoing maintenance. Everyone working in the lab is responsible for the proper care of these instruments to prevent damage to them and ensure the most accurate results possible.

Safety Equipment and Guidelines

Accidents are always a risk in the lab. However, with proper implementation of safety guidelines and procedures, they can be avoided. Most accidents are minor, but major accidents can and do occur. Hence, it is the combined responsibility of the instructor and the students to make sure all the important precautions are taken while performing experiments.

In industrial settings, mandatory Occupational Safety and Health Administration (OSHA) training emphasizes how employees can protect themselves and their surroundings, making enforcement of safety procedures rigorous. However, such training in educational institutions has been slow to catch on. Students do not generally have hands-on training in laboratory experiments or handling chemicals.

It is important to ensure that students' enthusiasm about learning new concepts and conducting experiments does not override the need to understand the safety procedures. Students must understand the risks involved with the experiments, how to cope with an emergency, and how to protect themselves and their surroundings.

The first step to ensuring safety is to wear proper clothing. **Personal protective equipment (PPE)** and **proper clothing** can prevent serious injuries and ensures a safe working environment. The general laboratory PPE requirements are a lab coat, gloves, and safety glasses. While working with volatile or reactive chemicals, chemical aprons are required to protect the body from splash hazards. Special chemical-resistant safety glasses protect the eyes from splash hazards instead of the usual safety glasses; normal safety glasses only protect against flying debris. Respirators protect workers from harmful vapors (proper respirator training is required).

Safety gloves protect the hands; they must always be worn. Although safety gloves are nonabsorbent, chemicals can leach, so lab workers must change gloves frequently and wash their hands often. Thermal and puncture-resistant gloves are used for handling extremely hot or cold materials like dry ice, using an autoclave, or dealing with sharps. Gloves must be properly removed and discarded before leaving the laboratory and touching personal or public items.

In general, lab workers should cover the body properly by wearing long sleeves and pants and avoiding baggy clothes. In addition, instead of sandals, closed-toe shoes should be worn at all times. Anyone working in the lab should tie back long hair and remove jewelry before entering the lab. Lastly, all personal items should be kept outside the laboratory to prevent contamination.

A good knowledge of **safety equipment** found in the lab can help minimize the effects of an accident. When working in the laboratory for the first time, it is important to look around and identify the safety equipment.

A **safety shower** and an **eye wash station** are must-haves for every laboratory, and weekly testing is necessary to ensure they are always working and have clean water. In case of flame exposure, the safety shower should be immediately used on the affected area and 911 should be called. Similarly, if a worker's eyes are injured, he or she should use the eye wash, keeping the eyes open while rinsing them.

The fire extinguisher is another extremely important piece of safety equipment. There are four types of fires:

1. Class A fires involve ordinary combustible products like wood, cloth, paper.
2. Class B fires include organic solvents and flammable liquids.
3. Class C fires involve electrical equipment.
4. Class D fires involve combustible metals.

Class A fires can be extinguished using water and general purpose fire extinguishers. For Class B and Class C fires, chemical smoke extinguishers must be used because putting water on them can worsen the situation by increasing the chances of spreading the fire or electrocution. Dry chemical fire extinguishers are installed in most labs close to the exit in case Class A, Class B, or Class C fires occur. In large fires, the building should be evacuated immediately, 911 should be called, and no attempt should be made to extinguish the fire unless someone has been trained by a certified trainer.

All workers should know where fire blankets are located because these are used to douse small fires. If someone's clothing is on fire, the person should lie on the ground and others should roll him or her on a fire blanket until the flame is out. A fire blanket must not be used to douse the fire while the person is standing because the flame can travel upward toward the person's face.

Other pieces of safety equipment include a first aid kit and the chemical fume hood. The first aid kit can be used to treat minor injuries. The chemical fume hood is a closed ventilated area that helps a person escape toxic vapors. The exhaust must be switched on and chemicals should not be left in the hood after work is done. Also, evacuation routes must be posted near the exits and should be clear and easy to follow.

Everyone working in the lab should be aware of the locations of all safety equipment to take prompt action in case of emergency. In addition, safety equipment must be tested regularly to ensure proper working in case of an emergency.

SAMPLE QUESTIONS

16) Which of the following can NOT be considered PPE?

A. safety gloves

B. safety glasses

C. closed-toe boots

D. slippers

Answers:

A. Incorrect. Safety gloves protect lab workers from chemicals, sharps, and extreme temperatures.

B. Incorrect. Safety glasses protect the eyes from flying debris and splash hazards.

C. Incorrect. Closed-toe boots protect the feet from debris and splash hazards; their sturdiness also helps prevent trips and falls.

D. Correct. Slippers are not sturdy enough to protect the feet from debris or chemicals, and they may cause the wearer to slip and fall.

17) **During a college camping trip, the flame from the campfire grew unexpectedly and spread to the surrounding twigs and shrubs. This is an example of which of the following?**

A. Class A fire
B. Class B fire
C. Class C fire
D. Class D fire

Answers:

A. Correct. This is a Class A fire because it involves an ordinary combustible product (in this case, wood).
B. Incorrect. A Class B fire involves organic solvents and flammable liquids.
C. Incorrect. A Class C fire is an electrical fire.
D. Incorrect. A Class D fire involves combustible metals.

Preparation, Use, and Storage of Laboratory Materials

It is important to note the safe handling of the chemicals. One must take care to never leave the caps of the chemical bottles open and never remove chemicals from the lab. A secondary container should be used to transport chemicals between labs, and an acid/base should be added to the solvent, never vice versa. Care must be taken to wear appropriate PPE depending on the requirements of the chemical. In case of breaking a large chemical bottle, it is important to evacuate the lab, as the vapors could be potentially dangerous, and not reenter until advised. Special attention must be given to flammable and explosive chemicals by making sure they are always kept away from ignition sources. Flammable chemicals must be stored in dedicated cabinets, and when disposing of chemicals, chemical-resistant plastic containers must be used. Paper towels used to wipe chemicals are also considered hazardous and must be disposed of appropriately.

Thus, it is important to prepare for each laboratory activity and determine the possible risks, wear the appropriate PPE, and know what protective measures to take in case of emergency. Knowing the emergency procedures and exit procedures can help mitigate the effects of an accident.

Many chemicals used in the lab can be dangerous, so lab workers need all the information they can get. Each chemical has a technical document called the Material Safety Data Sheet (MSDS), which lists important information about the chemical's properties, hazards, and safety precautions. This information helps people prepare to use the chemicals in the lab. Anyone using the lab should know where these safety data sheets are stored. Furthermore, chemicals should be labeled according to the Globally Harmonized System of classification and labeling of chemicals (also called the GHS).

The MSDS is organized into sixteen sections:

1. **Identification**: chemical name, chemical description, and manufacturer's contact address.
2. **Hazard Identification**: safety symbols and warnings.
3. **Composition**: a list of ingredients.
4. **First Aid**: the treatment when a person is exposed to the chemical.
5. **Fire Fighting Measures**: instructions for taking correct measures depending on the type of fire caused by the chemical.
6. **Accidental Release**: instructions for cleanup and evacuation, if needed.
7. **Handling and Storage**: instructions listing the specific storage method for each type of chemical.
8. **Personal Protection and Exposure Control**: the type of PPE needed for each chemical and OSHA's exposure limit for each chemical.
9. **Physical and Chemical Properties**: physical and chemical characteristics of a chemical, such as color, odor, appearance, solubility, pH, evaporation rate, and other chemical properties.
10. **Stability and Reactivity**: ways to avoid hazardous reactions by detailing how reactive a chemical can be under various conditions.
11. **Toxicological Information**: long-term and short-term toxic effects of the chemical.
12. **Ecological**: information about how a chemical can affect the environment.
13. **Disposal**: instructions to safely dispose of a chemical based on its reactivity, flammability, and similar properties.
14. **Transport**: transportation methods for each chemical. Wrong decisions here can be disastrous.
15. **Regulatory Information**: legal requirements applicable to the chemical.
16. **Other Information**: when the Safety Data Sheet was last prepared or revised, other pertinent information.

The other way to obtain information about a chemical apart from the MSDS is the labels on the chemical bottles. The information lists the name of the product, signal word (indicates danger level), hazards, precautions, first aid instructions, supplier's contact information, and pictograms (represents specific hazards posed by the chemicals). It is important to understand if a chemical is flammable, is toxic, contains compressed gases or oxidizers, is explosive, poses skin and eye harm danger, is environmentally unsafe, or is acutely toxic.

Table 8.6. shows a list of pictograms along with the type of hazard they represent.

Table 8.6. Pictograms Depicting Hazards

PICTOGRAM	TYPE OF HAZARD
	Flammability
	Toxicity
	Health
	Compressed gases
	Oxidizers
	Unstable explosives
	Skin and eye exposure
	Environmental hazards
	Acute toxicity

Thus, it is clear how safety data sheets and the chemical labels provide important information regarding the safe use of chemicals in the laboratory.

The National Fire Protection Association (NFPA) has also developed widely used guidelines to identify safety hazards. The NFPA diamond uses colors to represent hazards.

The **blue diamond** represents a health hazard. Numbers indicate the extent of the hazardous effect:

- 4—deadly
- 3—extreme danger
- 2—hazardous
- 1—slightly hazardous
- 0—normal material

The **red diamond** represents a fire hazard. Numbers indicate flash point levels.

- 4—below 73°F
- 3—below 100°F
- 2—above 100°F, not exceeding 200°F
- 1—above 200°F
- 0—will not burn

The **yellow diamond** represents reactivity. Numbers indicate the extent of the hazardous effect.

- 4—may detonate
- 3—shock and heat may detonate
- 2—violent chemical change
- 1—unstable if heated
- 0—stable

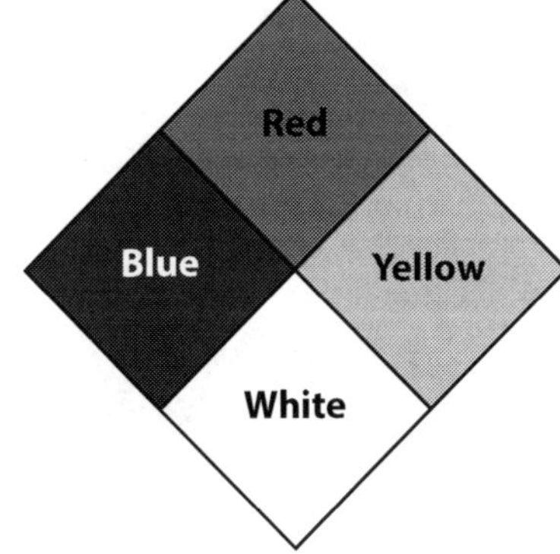

Figure 8.8. NFPA Diamond

The **white diamond** represents a specific hazard.

- ACID—acid
- ALK—shock and heat may detonate
- 2—alkali
- COR—corrosive
- OXY- oxidizer
- ☢—radioactive
- W—use no water

SAMPLE QUESTION

18) **What hazards are represented by the two symbols below?**

Answer:

The symbol on the left marks a flammable substance, and the symbol on the right marks oxidizers.

9

Practice Test

Read the question and choose the most correct answer.

1

Which ion has the greatest number of electrons?

A. Ca^{2+}

B. Cl^{-}

C. Ca^{+}

D. P^{3-}

2

Using the following equation, how many moles of P_4O_6 would be produced from 6 moles of O_2, assuming excess P_4 is present?

$P_4 + 3O_2 \rightarrow P_4O_6$

A. 1

B. 2

C. 3

D. 6

3

A student performed an experiment, forming a gas. When testing the gas with red litmus paper, the paper turned blue. What is the gas?

A. hydrogen chloride

B. methane

C. ammonia

D. helium

4

Which of the following should have the highest boiling point?

A. NH_3

B. H_2O

C. HF

D. H_2S

5

For which of the following elements is the aufbau principle NOT followed?

I. chromium
II. iron
III. copper

A. I only
B. II only
C. I and III only
D. I, II, and III

6

If the following reaction is at equilibrium, what would happen if the pressure of the reaction was decreased?

$N_2(g) + 3H_2(g) \leftrightarrows 2NH_3(g)$

A. There would be no effect on the equilibrium.
B. The reaction will shift toward the products.
C. The reactions will shift toward the reactants.
D. It cannot be determined which way the reaction will shift.

7

Which of the following solvents will have the greatest effect on the freezing point when 1.0 g of naphthalene is dissolved in 100 g of each solvent?

A. Benzene: $K_f = 5.12$°C/molal
B. Carbon disulfide: $K_f = 3.83$°C/molal
C. Chloroform: $K_f = 4.70$°C/molal
D. All will be equally affected.

8

Which of the following is NOT a typical property of metals?

A. Metals have low densities.
B. Metals are malleable.
C. Metals are good conductors of electricity and heat.
D. Metals in solid state consist of ordered structures with tightly packed atoms.

9

What is the oxidation number of P in $MgNaPO_4$?

A. −3
B. 0
C. +3
D. +5

10

What is the formula for tin(IV) chloride pentahydrate?

A. $Sn_4Cl \cdot 5H_2O$
B. $SnCl_4 \cdot H_20$
C. $SnCl_4H_5$
D. $SnCl_4 \cdot 5H_20$

11

Which statement is true for ionization energy?

A. It increases moving left to right in a periodic table.
B. It remains constant moving left to right in a periodic table.
C. It decreases moving left to right in a periodic table.
D. It increases initially and then decreases moving left to right in a periodic table.

12

Which of the following is true of a solution?

A. It is a heterogeneous mixture.

B. It consists of only one kind of atom.

C. It is easy to separate using filtration.

D. It may be separated using distillation.

13

Sublimation is the change from

A. gas to solid

B. liquid to solid

C. gas to liquid

D. solid to gas

14

How many electrons can the *s* orbital hold?

A. two

B. three

C. eight

D. nine

15

A chemistry student is conducting an experiment in which she tests the relationship between reactant concentration and heat produced by a reaction. In her experiment, she alters the reactant concentration and measures heat produced. The independent variable in the experiment is the

A. reactant concentration.

B. reaction rate.

C. amount of heat produced by the reaction.

D. product concentration.

16

Which acids require the same number of moles of hydroxide to be titrated to the equivalence point?

I. hydrofluoric acid

II. nitric acid

III. phosphoric acid

A. I and II only

B. I and III only

C. II and III only

D. I, II, and III

17

Which of the following elements has chemical properties most similar to sulfur?

A. fluorine

B. argon

C. phosphorus

D. oxygen

18

Which of the following is a biological function of lipids?

A. genetic expression

B. energy storage

C. catalysis

D. molecule transportation

19

Which of the following actinides has the greatest number of *f* electrons?

A. actinium

B. thorium

C. uranium

D. plutonium

20

Isotones are

A. atoms that belong to different elements that have the same mass number but a different atomic number.

B. atoms that have the same number of neutrons.

C. atoms containing the same number of electrons or having the same electron configurations.

D. atoms belonging to the same element that have the same number of protons but a different number of neutrons.

21

Which of the following functional groups is found in the molecule below?

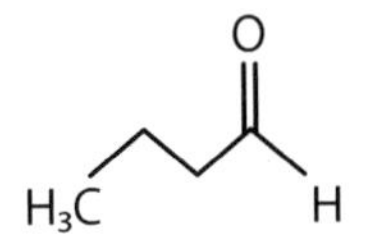

O

H_3C H

A. aldehyde

B. carboxylic acid

C. alcohol

D. ketone

22

How many neutrons are in an atom of the element $^{88}_{38}Sr$?

A. 38

B. 88

C. 50

D. 126

23

For a spontaneous process,

A. $\Delta G > 0$.

B. $\Delta S < 0$.

C. $\Delta G < 0$.

D. $\Delta S = \Delta G$.

24

What is the approximate mass percent of carbon in ethanol, CH_3CH_2OH?

A. 15

B. 25

C. 35

D. 50

25

Acetic acid has a K_a of 1.8×10^{-5}. If equal concentrations of acetic acid (HOAc) and conjugate base acetate ion are present, the pH of the acid is between

A. 2 and 3.

B. 3 and 4.

C. 4 and 5.

D. 5 and 6.

26

What is the specific chemical basis of magnetic resonance imaging (MRI) technology?

A. nuclear magnetic resonance

B. atomic theory

C. acid–base chemistry

D. thermodynamics

The graph below shows temperature versus heat added to water. Use the figure to answer questions 27 – 29.

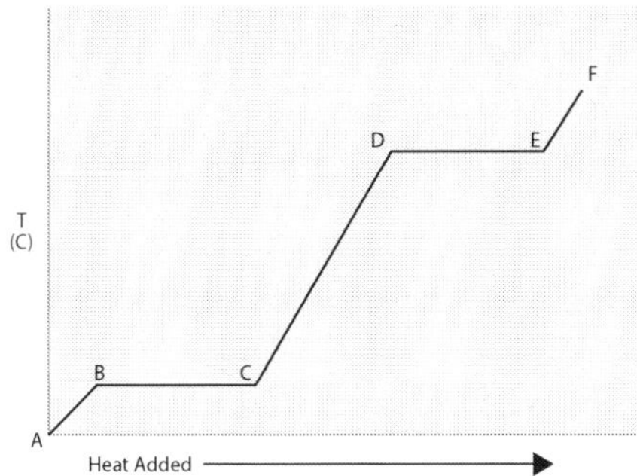

27

What does Point C represent?

A. boiling point
B. melting point
C. latent heat of vaporization
D. freezing point

28

Which of the following is NOT true about point E?

A. Molecules at point E have greater average kinetic energy than molecules at point C.
B. Evaporation occurs at point E.
C. Point E has higher entropy than point D.
D. Melting occurs at point E.

29

Between points B and C the water is

A. boiling.
B. melting.
C. depositing.
D. sublimating.

30

Which of the following is NOT an organic compound?

A. C_3H_8
B. CH_3COOH
C. H_2CO_3
D. HCOOH

31

Which of the following elements has the lowest first ionization energy?

A. Ca
B. K
C. Na
D. Mg

32

Balance the following chemical equation:

$P_4 + O_2 + H_2O \rightarrow H_3PO_4$

A. 1:8:6:4
B. 1:2:2:4
C. 1:2:6:4
D. 1:5:6:4

33

The E° for the reduction of Cu^{2+} is +0.34 V. The E° of Zn^{2+} is −0.76 V. What is the emf of a galvanic cell where the concentration of Cu^{2+} and Zn^{2+} are the same?

A. −1.10 V
B. −0.42 V
C. 0.42 V
D. 1.10 V

34

Which statements are true of a buffer?

I. A buffer solution could consist of equal concentrations of ammonia and ammonium bromide.

II. A buffer solution could consist of one mole of HF and 0.5 mole of NaOH in one liter of water.

III. A buffer solution will change only slightly in pH upon addition of acid or base.

IV. In a buffer solution containing benzoic acid, C_6H_5COOH, and sodium benzoate, NaC_6H_5COO, the species that reacts with added $[OH^-]$ is the benzoate ion.

A. I and IV only

B. II and III only

C. I, II, and III only

D. II, III, and IV only

35

A confounding variable is a variable that is

A. directly measured in an experiment.

B. deliberately changed over the course of an experiment.

C. not directly measured or manipulated, but has an effect on the experimental results.

D. has no direct relationship with the independent and dependent variables.

36

Electrons were discovered by

A. Ernest Rutherford.

B. J.J. Thomson.

C. John Dalton.

D. Niels Bohr.

37

Which of the following describes the temperatures reached by methane, ethane, propane, and n-butane at an equilibrium vapor pressure of 1 atm?

A. methane > ethane > propane > butane

B. methane = ethane = propane = butane

C. methane < ethane < propane < butane

D. methane < ethane = propane < butane

38

Which transition metal is the easiest to oxidize to the +2 cation?

A. copper

B. iron

C. zinc

D. cobalt

39

Which of the following is a decomposition reaction?

A. $2Na + Cl_2 \rightarrow 2NaCl$

B. $Zn + 2HCl \rightarrow ZnCl_2 + H_2$

C. $CH_4 + 2O_2 \rightarrow CO_2 + 2H_2O$

D. $H_2CO_3 \rightarrow H_2O + CO_2$

40

Use the bond energies given below to find the enthalpy for the reaction of carbon with oxygen to form carbon dioxide.

$C(s) + O_2(g) \rightarrow CO_2(g)$

Bond	Bond Energy
C=O	745 kg/mol
O=O	495 kg/mol

A. -9.95×10^2 kJ/mol

B. -2.56×10^2 kJ/mol

C. 2.56×10^2 kJ/mol

D. 9.95×10^2 kJ/mol

41

Which element is a metalloid?

A. rubidium

B. vanadium

C. antimony

D. iodine

42

Which element is INCORRECTLY matched with its group name?

A. lithium – alkaline earth metal

B. iodine – halogen

C. argon – noble gas

D. iron – transition metal

43

How many significant figures are in the number 0.0200?

A. two

B. one

C. three

D. five

44

A student uses a scale to find the mass of a metal block and records the readings below.

8.114 kg

8.119 kg

8.111 kg

If the reported true value for the block is 6.115 kg, what can be said about the measured values?

A. The results are both accurate and precise.

B. The results are accurate but not precise.

C. The results are precise but not accurate.

D. They are neither accurate nor precise.

45

A 0.10 M solution of a weak acid has $[H_3O^+] = 7.08 \times 10^{-3}$ M. What is the percent dissociation of the acid?

A. 3.2%

B. 7.1%

C. 9.4%

D. 14%

46

Which of the following is true of an atom of Ar with a mass number of 40 and the ion S^{2-} with a mass number of 32?

A. They have the same number of protons.

B. They have the same number of electrons.

C. They have the same number of neutrons.

D. They have the same atomic radius.

47

Which statement about melting points is FALSE?

A. Diamond has a very high melting point since it is a network covalent solid.

B. Table salt has a high melting point because it is an ionic solid.

C. Tungsten carbide has a high melting point because it is an ionic solid.

D. Silicon carbide has a very high melting point because it is a network covalent solid.

48

A compound has an empirical formula of BH_3. If its molar mass is 27.67 g/mol, what is its molecular formula?

A. BH_3

B. B_2H_6

C. H_3BO_3

D. B_3H_9

49

Which of the following is a possible set of quantum numbers for an atom's electron configuration?

A. $n = 0, l = 0, ml = 0, ms = +1/2$

B. $n = 1, l = 0, ml = 0, ms = -1/2$

C. $n = 1, l = 1, ml = 0, ms = +1/2$

D. $n = 3, l = 3, ml = -3, ms = +1/2$

50

Which of the following is a chemical bond?

I. polar covalent bond

II. ionic bond

III. hydrogen bond

A. I only

B. I and II only

C. II and III only

D. I, II, and III

51

Which of the following is true when sodium acetate is added to acetic acid in solution?

A. The pH will go down.

B. The pH will stay the same.

C. The acetate ion will react with water to form hydronium ions.

D. The acetate ion will react with water to form hydroxide ions.

52

Which of the following is NOT a colligative property of a solution?

A. vapor pressure lowering

B. osmotic pressure

C. heat of solution

D. boiling point elevation

53

Which type of sensor can be used to detect colon cancer?

A. gas

B. liquid

C. solid

D. liquid crystal

54

The process that takes place when water reaches its boiling point is called

A. condensation.
B. evaporation.
C. melting.
D. sublimation.

55

Cathode rays are made of

A. positively charged particles.
B. neutral particles.
C. negatively charged particles.
D. X-rays.

56

Which statement about radioactive particles is true?

A. Alpha particles consist of two protons and two electrons.
B. Alpha particles are NOT deflected by electric and magnetic fields.
C. Beta particles are positively charged and are deflected by electric and magnetic fields.
D. Gamma rays are not deflected by the electric and magnetic fields because they do not possess any charge.

57

Which organic compound is INCORRECTLY matched with the functional group?

A. CH_3COOH—carboxyl
B. CH_3OH—hydroxyl
C. CH_3CN—carbonyl
D. CH_3COOCH_3—ester

58

Which of the following is amphoteric?

I. water
II. sodium hydrogen sulfate
III. sodium phosphate

A. I only
B. II only
C. I and II only
D. I, II, and III

59

Which of the following is NOT an example of a combustion reaction?

A. methane gas burning on a stove
B. hydrogen reacting with oxygen to give water
C. carbon reacting with oxygen to give carbon dioxide
D. an egg being boiled in water

60

Which of the following may NOT be determined by kinetics?

A. the mechanism of the reaction
B. the overall order of the reaction
C. how reaction concentrations will affect the rate
D. how product concentrations will affect the rate

Go on →

61

Which of the following elements is the most electronegative?

A. Mg
B. Si
C. S
D. Cl

62

Atomic number is defined as the number of

A. electrons in the nucleus.
B. protons in the nucleus.
C. protons and neutrons in the nucleus.
D. orbitals in an atom.

63

Which of the following bases has the highest pH if they all have the same molarity?

A. barium hydroxide
B. sodium hydroxide
C. potassium hydroxide
D. ammonium hydroxide

64

Which of the following is a double-replacement reaction?

I. Silver nitrate reacting with sodium chloride.
II. Hydrochloric acid reacting with sodium hydroxide.
III. Aluminum metal reacting with zinc chloride solution.

A. I only
B. II only
C. III only
D. I and II only

65

Which of the following is defined as the average kinetic energy of molecules?

A. pressure
B. mass
C. thermal energy
D. enthalpy

66

Which of the following is NOT a homogeneous mixture?

A. air
B. sandy water
C. brass
D. salt dissolved in water

67

What happens to the atomic radius when moving left to right on the periodic table?

A. It decreases.
B. It increases.
C. It stays constant.
D. It does not follow a set pattern.

68

Which of the following is a decomposition reaction?

A. $2HBr + Ba(OH)_2 \rightarrow BaBr_2 + 2H_2O$
B. $CH_4 + 2O_2 \rightarrow CO_2 + 2H_2O$
C. $MgSO_3 \rightarrow MgO + SO_2$
D. $Cu + 2AgNO_3 \rightarrow 2Ag + Cu(NO_3)_2$

69

When ordering different types of radiation in order of their frequency, which statement is true?

A. Microwave radiation has a higher frequency than radio waves.

B. Infrared radiation has a higher frequency than ultraviolet rays.

C. Gamma rays have a higher frequency than X-rays, but a lower frequency than ultraviolet rays.

D. Ultraviolet and X-ray radiations have a lower frequency than microwaves.

70

For a closed system, which of the following is true?

A. No exchange of matter is possible between a system and its surroundings, although exchange of energy is possible.

B. No exchange of energy is possible between a system and its surroundings, although exchange of matter is possible.

C. No exchange of energy or matter is possible between a system and its surroundings.

D. Exchange of energy and matter is possible between the system and its surroundings.

71

Which element will form a +2 ion?

A. Mg

B. C

C. Cl

D. Na

72

What is the name of the compound $CaCl_2$?

A. calcium chloride

B. calcium dichloride

C. chlorine calcide

D. calcium(II) chloride

73

What is the Lewis structure for Br_2O?

A. :Br=O=Br:

B. :Br — O — Br:

C. :Br — Br — O:

D. :Br — O — Br:

74

What is the equilibrium constant for $PCl_5(g) \leftrightarrows PCl_3(g) + Cl_2(g)$?

A. $K = \frac{[Cl_2][PCl_3]^2}{[PCl_5]}$

B. $K = \frac{[Cl_2][PCl_3]}{[PCl_5]}$

C. $K = \frac{[PCl_5]}{[Cl_2][PCl_3]}$

D. $K = \frac{[PCl_3]}{[PCl_5]}$

75

The vapor pressure lowering of a solution containing a nonvolatile solute is directly proportional to the

A. mole fraction of solute.

B. mole fraction of solvent.

C. molality of the solution.

D. osmotic pressure of the solute.

76

Which of the following is NOT true for systematic errors?

A. They are the result of faulty experimental design.

B. They are not reproducible.

C. It is not possible to eliminate these errors.

D. It is possible to eliminate these errors.

77

The heat energy required to change 1 g of a substance from a solid to a liquid state at the same temperature is

A. entropy.

B. specific latent heat of vaporization.

C. sensible heat.

D. specific latent heat of fusion.

78

What is the name of the compound $Cr(NO_3)_3$?

A. chromium trinitrate

B. chromium nitrate

C. chromium(III) nitrate

D. chromium(II) nitrate

79

Which of the following was NOT demonstrated by Niels Bohr with respect to the absorption and emission spectra?

A. When a heavy nucleus splits, the energy released is the calculated difference in the mass of products and reactants multiplied by velocity of light squared.

B. When an electron goes from a lower energy level to higher energy level, it absorbs some color of light.

C. When going from the fourth energy level to the second energy level, ultraviolet light is emitted.

D. When a beam of light passes through an atom, if the energy of this beam of light is sufficient, the electron moves from the ground state to a higher energy state.

80

Which of the following is NOT a Brønsted conjugate acid-base pair?

A. H_3O^+ and H_2O

B. Na_2S and NaS^-

C. HCl and Cl^-

D. H_2CO_3 and HCO_3^-

81

The entropy of the universe is

A. increasing.

B. decreasing.

C. constant.

D. zero.

Use the information below to answer questions 82 and 83.

An unknown liquid is experimentally determined to be 39.99 percent carbon, 6.73 percent hydrogen, and 53.28 percent oxygen. It also determined to have a formula mass of 60.06 amu.

82

What is the liquid's empirical formula?

A. CH_2O

B. $C_4H_7O_5$

C. CH_4O

D. $C_3H_6O_3$

83

What is the liquid's molecular formula?

A. $C_2H_4O_2$

B. CH_2O

C. $C_3H_6O_3$

D. $C_2H_3O_2$

84

Place these compounds in order of increasing bond strength: NaCl, $MgCl_2$, $MgBr_2$.

A. NaCl, $MgCl_2$, $MgBr_2$

B. $MgBr_2$, $MgCl_2$, NaCl

C. $MgCl_2$, NaCl, $MgBr_2$

D. NaCl, $MgBr_2$, $MgCl_2$

85

What is the mass number of $^{12}_{24}Mg$?

A. 2

B. 12

C. 24

D. 36

86

Determine the reaction type and the missing compound for the following reaction:

$BaCO_3$ (*s*) → BaO (*s*) + ____ (*g*)

A. neutralization reaction; H_2O

B. decomposition reaction; CO_2

C. single replacement reaction; CO

D. oxidation-reduction reaction; OH^-

87

A catalyst increases a reaction rate by

A. increasing the activation energy.

B. increasing the concentration of the reactants.

C. changing the relative partial pressures of the reactants.

D. changing the reaction mechanism.

88

What is the concentration of Ni^{2+} ions in a saturated solution of NiS? (The K_{sp} for NiS is 4×10^{-20}.)

A. 16×10^{-40} M

B. 4×10^{-20} M

C. 2×10^{-20} M

D. 2×10^{-10} M

89

What is the molar mass of $ZnCl_2$?

A. 136.29 amu

B. 100.83 g

C. 136.29 g

D. 100.83 amu

90

According to the ideal gas law, which of the following could NOT happen when the number of moles of a gas increase?

A. Pressure increases as temperature and volume stay constant.

B. Volume increases as temperature and pressure stay constant.

C. Pressure and volume decrease while temperature stays constant.

D. Temperature decreases as pressure and volume stay constant.

91

Which statement about the periodic table is FALSE?

A. While moving from left to right on the periodic table, atomic radii decrease.

B. When moving from top to bottom on the periodic table, atomic radii increase.

C. While moving left to right on the periodic table, the ionization energy increases.

D. While moving from top to bottom on the periodic table, ionization energy increases.

92

What is the name of the acid H_2SO_3?

A. sulfuric acid

B. sulfurous acid

C. hyposulfurous acid

D. persulfuric acid

93

Order these bonds in terms of increasing polarity: C—H, C—C, C—N, C—O, C—F

A. C—H, C—C, C—N, C—O, C—F

B. C—C, C—H, C—N, C—O, C—F

C. C—F, C—O, C—N, C—H, C—C

D. C—C, C—N, C—H, C—O, C—F

94

If the following exothermic reaction is at equilibrium, which of the following statements is true?

$$N_2(g) + 3H_2(g) \leftrightarrows 2NH_3(g)$$

A. The addition of heat to the system will push the equilibrium in the forward direction.

B. The addition of heat to the system will have no effect on the equilibrium.

C. The addition of heat to the system will push the equilibrium in the reverse direction.

D. The addition of heat to the system will result in a higher equilibrium constant.

95

What will happen to the pH of a nitric acid solution that is diluted by a factor of ten?

A. The pH will go up ten units.

B. The pH will go down ten units.

C. The pH will go up one unit.

D. The pH will go down one unit.

96

In general, the solubility of a

A. solid in a solid decreases with increasing temperature.

B. gas in a liquid increases with decreasing temperature.

C. solid in a liquid decreases with increasing temperature.

D. liquid in a liquid is independent of temperature.

97

Which of the following is a balanced equation?

A. $Cl_2(g) + KBr(aq) \rightarrow KCl(aq) + Br_s(g)$

B. $6CO_2(g) + 6H_2O(l) \rightarrow C_6H_{12}O_6(s) + 6O_2(g)$

C. $C_2H_4O_2 \rightarrow C_4H_6O_3 + H_2O$

D. $Cu(s) + AgNO_3(aq) \rightarrow Cu(NO_3)_2(aq) + Ag(s)$

98

Class D fires involve

A. combustible metals.

B. organic solvents and flammable liquids.

C. electrical equipment.

D. ordinary combustible products.

99

Which atomic model states that electrons move around the orbit in waves and not in defined paths?

A. Bohr model

B. Schrödinger model

C. Rutherford model

D. Dalton model

100

When benzene burns completely in excess oxygen, which combustion products should form?

A. CO_2 and H_2O

B. CH_4 and H_2O

C. CO_2 and H_2O_2

D. CH_4 and H_2O_2

101

In which compound is the oxidation number of As NOT +3?

A. As_2O_3

B. AsO_3^{-2}

C. AsF_3

D. As_2H_6

102

The equilibrium constant for the reaction to create sulfur trioxide is $K = 4.0 \times 10^{24}$. Based on the equilibrium constant, which of the following is true about the reaction?

A. The reaction strongly favors the reactants.

B. The reaction favors neither the reactants nor the products.

C. The reaction strongly favors the products.

D. There is not enough information to be able to predict how the reaction will proceed.

Go on →

103

Which titration curve could describe the titration of a solution of HCl with the addition of a solution of KOH?

A.

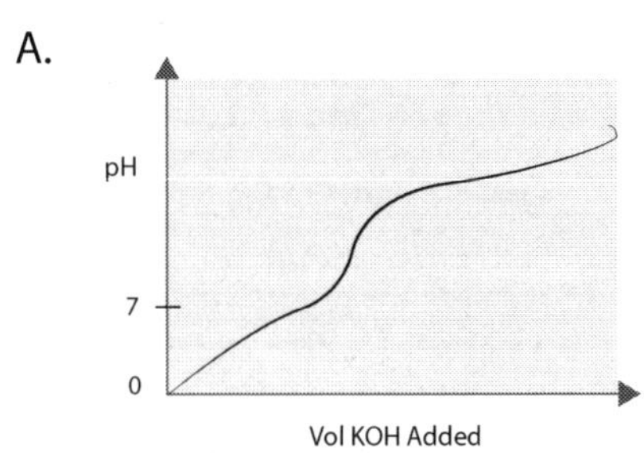

B.

pH
7
0
Vol KOH Added

C.

pH
7
0
Vol KOH Added

D.

pH
7
0
Vol KOH Added

104

When a nonvolatile solute is dissolved in a solvent, which of the following statements is true?

A. The freezing point of the solution is raised.

B. The boiling point of the solution is raised.

C. The osmotic pressure is unchanged.

D. The vapor pressure of the solution is raised.

105

The lines representing a phase transition on a heating curve

A. are vertical.

B. are horizontal.

C. have a positive slope.

D. have a negative slope.

106

What is the IUPAC name of the molecule below?

CH_3 — CH_2 — CH_2—CH—CH—C—C—CH_3
CH_3—CH_2—CH_2—CH_3

A. 4-methyl-5-n-propyl-6-octyne

B. 5-methyl-4-n-propyl-3-octyne

C. 5-methyl-4-n-propyl-2-octyne

D. 5-methyl-4-n-propyl-2-octene

107

What does Avogadro's number represent?

A. the number of atoms in 1 g of an element

B. the number of atoms in a mole of an element

C. the molar mass of an atom

D. the molar mass of carbon

108

What is the predicted geometry for the molecule SiF_4?

A. tetrahedral

B. trigonal planar

C. seesaw

D. linear

109

What intermolecular forces would need to be considered in predicting the relative physical properties of CH_3F, CH_3Cl, CH_3Br, and CH_3I?

A. London force

B. dipole-dipole and London force

C. dipole-dipole and hydrogen bonding

D. dipole-dipole, hydrogen bonding, and London force

110

How many O_2 molecules are required to balance the following reaction?

$CS_2 + O_2 \rightarrow CO_2 + SO_2$

A. 1

B. 2

C. 3

D. 4

111

Order the following equations and their equilibrium constants from most-favored product to least-favored product.

1. $2H_2(g) + O_2(g) \leftrightarrows 2H_2O(g)$ $K = 3.3 \times 10^{81}$
2. $H_2(g) + I_2(g) \leftrightarrows 2HI(g)$ $K = 2.5 \times 10^{1}$
3. $AgCl(s) \leftrightarrows Ag^{+}(aq) + Cl^{-}(aq)$ $K = 1.8 \times 10^{-10}$
4. $HCOOH(aq) + H_2O(l) \leftrightarrows H_3O^{+}(aq) + HCOO^{-}(aq)$ $K = 1.8 \times 10^{-4}$

A. 1 > 4 > 2 > 3

B. 1 > 2 > 4 > 3

C. 3 > 4 > 2 > 1

D. 3 > 2 > 4 > 1

112

Which of the following ALWAYS exists in a state of equilibrium?

I. a weak acid

II. a weak base

III. a hydrolyzed product

A. I only

B. IIII only

C. I and II only

D. I, II, and III

113

What type of reaction is shown below?

$2Na(s) + 2H_2O(l) \rightarrow 2NaOH(aq) + H_2(g)$

A. neutralization reaction

B. decomposition reaction

C. double-displacement reaction

D. single-replacement reaction

114

What are the products of the complete reaction of NaOH and H_2SO_4?

A. H_2O and $NaSO_4$

B. OH^- and $NaSO_4$

C. H_3O^+ and Na_2SO_4

D. H_2O and Na_2SO_4

115

Which of the following phase transitions passes from a low to high energy phase without passing through an intermediate phase?

A. evaporation

B. condensation

C. sublimation

D. fusion

116

What is the name of the compound below?

$$CH_3CHCH_3 \text{ with } OCH_2CH_3 \text{ on the central carbon}$$

CH₃CHCH₃
  |
  OCH₂CH₃

I.	ethyl isopropyl ether
II.	2-ethoxypropane
III.	ethyl isopropyl alcohol

A. I only

B. II only

C. I and II only

D. I, II, and III

117

What is the net ionic equation for the reaction of HNO_3 and KOH?

A. $H^+ + OH- \rightarrow H_2O$

B. $H^+ + NO_3^- + KOH \rightarrow H_2O + KNO_3$

C. $HNO_3 + OH- \rightarrow H_2O + K^+$

D. $H^+ + KOH \rightarrow H_2O + K^+$

118

Which is NOT a definition of an acid?

A. A substance that contains hydrogen and produces H^+ in water.

B. A substance that donates protons to a base.

C. A substance that reacts with a base to form a salt and water.

D. A substance that accepts protons.

119

Which of the following compounds contains a π bond?

I.	ethylene
II.	acetylene
III.	carbon monoxide

A. II only

B. I and II only

C. II and III only

D. I, II, and III

120

Place the compounds below in order of increasing melting points.

CCl_4, KCl, and $CaCl_2$

A. KCl, $CaCl_2$, CCl_4

B. KCl, CCl_4, $CaCl_2$

C. CCl_4, KCl, $CaCl_2$

D. CCl_4, $CaCl_2$, KCl

121

Which of the following is NOT a conclusion of the Rutherford model of the atom?

A. Atoms have a positively charged center (nucleus) that contains most of their mass.

B. Atoms are not just empty spaces with electrons distributed around them.

C. The presence of electrons is confirmed for the first time.

D. The positively charged nucleus of an atom is tiny compared with the size of the entire atom.

122

What is the name of the following compound?

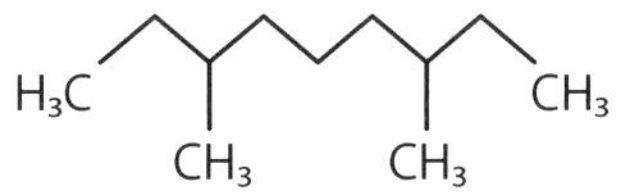

H_3C CH_3 CH_3 CH_3

A. decane

B. 3,7-dimethyloctane

C. 3-methylnonane

D. 3,7-dimethylnonane

123

In which of the following mixtures will a precipitate form? Assume equal volumes of 0.1 M solutions.

A. KCl and NH_4NO_3

B. $Ba(OH)_2$ and H_2SO_4

C. Na_2SO_4 and $Al(NO_3)_3$

D. CsI and $MgCl_2$

124

In the reaction $SnCl_2(s) + 2\ Cl^-(aq) \leftrightarrows SnCl_4^{-2}(aq)$,

A. $SnCl_2$ is a Lewis acid, and Cl^- is a Lewis base.

B. $SnCl_2$ is a Lewis base, and Cl^- is a Lewis acid.

C. $SnCl_4^{-2}$ is a Lewis acid, and Cl^- is a Lewis base.

D. $SnCl_4^{-2}$ is a Lewis base, and Cl^- is a Lewis acid.

125

While working in the laboratory, someone breaks a large bottle of chemicals. Which of the following actions must be taken?

A. The spill must be cleaned up appropriately.

B. Everyone must evacuate the laboratory immediately.

C. A qualified person must be called to clean the spill, but work may continue.

D. Experiments should be completed before evacuating.

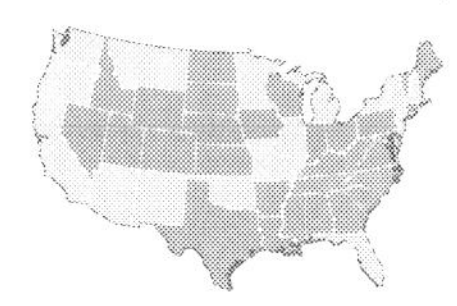

Answer Key

1)

C. **Correct.** Ca^{+} has nineteen electrons. All the other ions have eighteen electrons.

2)

B. **Correct.** Use dimensional analysis.

$$\frac{6 \text{ mol } O_2 \times 1 \text{ mol } P_4O_5}{3 \text{ mol } O_2} = \mathbf{2 \text{ mol } P_4O_5}$$

3)

A. Incorrect. Hydrogen chloride is an acid, which turns blue litmus paper red.

B. Incorrect. Methane is a neutral compound, which does not turn red litmus paper blue.

C. **Correct.** Ammonia is a base, which turns red litmus paper blue.

D. Incorrect. Helium is a neutral noble gas, which does not turn red litmus paper blue.

4)

A. Incorrect. NH_3 has hydrogen bonding, which increases the boiling point. However, the hydrogen bonding is not as strong as that with water since the three lone pairs on the fluorine atom are more stabilized than the one on oxygen in water, due to fluorine's higher electronegativity.

B. **Correct.** H_2O has hydrogen bonding, which increases boiling point and has two lone pairs on each oxygen atom, one more than that on nitrogen in ammonia.

C. Incorrect. HF has hydrogen bonding, which increases boiling point, but the hydrogen bonding is not as strong as that within water since there is only one lone pair on each nitrogen atom.

D. Incorrect. H_2S does not have hydrogen bonding, thus lowering the boiling point despite having the second-highest molar mass among the chemicals listed.

5)

C. **I and III only**

I. Chromium does not follow the aufbau principle since the ground state electron configuration is $4s^1 3d^5$.

II. Iron does follow the aufbau principle since the ground state electron configuration is $4s^2 3d^6$.

III. Copper does not follow the aufbau principle since the ground state electron configuration is $4s^1 3d^{10}$.

6)

C. **Correct.** An equilibrium always responds to a change by trying to reverse it. The equilibrium will shift to the reactants to increase the number of moles of gases and thus increase the pressure.

7)

A. **Correct.** Because $\Delta T_f = K_f m_{solute}$, the solvent with the largest K_f will have the greatest effect on the freezing point.

8)

A. **Correct.** Because metals tend to consist of ordered, tightly packed atoms, their densities are typically high. The properties in choices B, C, and D apply to metals.

9)

D. **Correct.** Mg has an oxidation number of +2, Na an oxidation number of +1, and O an oxidization number of −2; thus, P has to be +5 to result in a neutral compound.

10)

A. Incorrect. The Roman numeral IV denotes the charge on Sn, not the number of Sn ions.

B. Incorrect. Pentahydrate indicates five H_2O molecules bound per $SnCl_4$.

C. Incorrect. Hydrate indicates water molecules bound not hydrogen atoms.

D. **Correct.** Tin, with a charge of +4, has four Cl^- ions bound to balance the charge, and *pentahydrate* indicates five water molecules bound.

11)

A. **Correct.** Ionization energy increases while moving left to right in the periodic table. As the atomic size decreases left to right, more energy is needed to remove electrons.

12)

A. Incorrect. A solution is a homogeneous mixture.

B. Incorrect. A solution is a mixture, so it cannot have just one kind of atom.

C. Incorrect. A solution is a homogeneous mixture, and it cannot be separated using a filter.

D. **Correct.** A solution is a homogeneous mixture that may be separated using distillation.

13)

A. Incorrect. Deposition is when matter changes from a gas to a solid.

B. Incorrect. Freezing is when matter changes from a liquid to a solid.

C. Incorrect. Condensation is when matter changes from a gas to a liquid.

D. **Correct.** Sublimation is when matter changes from a solid to a gas.

14)

A. **Correct.** The *s* orbital holds a maximum of two electrons with opposite spins.

15)

A. **Correct.** The independent variable is deliberately changed in the course of the experiment.

B. Incorrect. The reaction rate is not directly manipulated or measured in the experiment.

C. Incorrect. The amount of heat produced by the reaction is being measured in the reaction, and is defined as the dependent variable.

D. Incorrect. The product concentration is not directly manipulated or measured in the experiment.

16)

A. I and II only

I. True. Hydrofluoric acid (HF) has one proton per formula unit.

II. True. Nitric acid (HNO_3) has one proton per formula unit.

III. False. Phosphoric acid (H_3PO_4) has three protons per formula unit.

17)

D. Correct. Oxygen is in the same group as sulfur and is also a non-metal.

18)

B. Correct. Lipids are used for energy storage.

19)

D. Correct. Plutonium has the highest atomic number out of the actinide elements listed and thus the greatest number of *f* electrons.

20)

A. Incorrect. This is the definition of isobars.

B. Correct. This is the correct definition of isotones.

C. Incorrect. This is the definition of isoelectric species.

D. Incorrect. This is the definition of isotopes.

21)

A. Correct. This is butanal, which contains aldehyde (—CHO).

22)

C. Correct. Subtracting the atomic number from the mass number gives the number of protons: $A - Z = 88 - 38 = 50$.

23)

A. Incorrect. Total Gibbs free energy change is not positive for a spontaneous process.

B. Incorrect. For a spontaneous process, entropy increases.

C. Correct. Gibbs free energy change is negative for a spontaneous process.

D. Incorrect. ΔG must be negative for a spontaneous reaction, and may or may not be equal to ΔS.

24)

D. Correct. Find the formula mass of ethanol.

CH_3CH_2OH

C = 12.01 amu

H = 1.01 amu

O = 16 amu

$2(12.01) + 6(1.01) + 1(16) = 46.08$ amu

Divide the mass of carbon in ethanol by the total formula mass to find the mass percent of carbon.

$\frac{2(12.01}{46.08} = 0.5213 = \mathbf{52.13\%}$

25)

C. Correct. Use the acid dissociation expression.

$HOAc(aq) \rightarrow H^+(aq) + OAc^-(aq)$

$K_a = \frac{[H+][OAc-]}{[HOAc]}$

$[HOAc] = [OAc^-]$ and $K_a = [H^+]$

$pH = pK_a = -\log(1.8 \times 10^{-5}) = \mathbf{4.74}$

26)

A. Correct. MRI technology is based on the chemical principle of nuclear magnetic resonance.

27)

A. Incorrect. Boiling point is represented by point E.

B. Correct. Melting point is represented by point C.

C. Incorrect. Point C deals with the solid-to-liquid transition, whereas latent heat of vaporization refers to the liquid-to-gas phase.

D. Incorrect. Freezing represents the conversion of liquid to solid, whereas point C represents melting, which is conversion of solid to liquid.

28)

A. Incorrect. This statement is true about point E because point E has more heat added to it compared to point C.

B. Incorrect. This statement is true because at point E, the phase change from liquid to gas takes place.

C. Incorrect. This statement is true because there is more heat at point E and more heat implies more entropy.

D. Correct. This statement is NOT true for point E because evaporation, not melting, occurs at point E.

29)

A. Incorrect. Boiling occurs between points D and E.

B. Correct. The water is melting between points B and C.

C. Incorrect. Deposition—the change from gas to solid—is not shown on the graph.

D. Incorrect. Sublimation—the change from solid to gas—is not shown on the graph.

30)

C. Correct. H_2CO_3 (carbonic acid) is not an organic compound since each H is bonded to an O, not to C. All the others have C–H bonds.

31)

B. Correct. Elements in Group 1 have the lowest first ionization energy because they will form a noble gas when one electron is removed. Elements toward the bottom of a group will have a lower first ionization energy because the valence electrons are farther from the nucleus. Thus, potassium (K) will have the lowest first ionization energy of all the choices.

32)

D. Correct.

$\_P_4 + \_O_2 + \_H_2O \rightarrow \_H_3PO_4$

Add a 4 on the right side to balance the four P atoms on the left.

$\_P_4 + \_O_2 + \_H_2O \rightarrow 4H_3PO_4$

There are now twelve H atoms on the right, so add a 6 to H_2O on the left.

$\_P_4 + \_O_2 + 6H_2O \rightarrow 4H_3PO_4$

There are sixteen O on the right, so add a 5 to O_2 on the left.

$P_4 + 5O_2 + 6H_2O \rightarrow 4H_3PO_4$

33)

D. Correct. Use the equation $E^\circ_{cell} = E^\circ_{cathode} - E^\circ_{anode}$

Cu is the cathode because it has a higher E°.

$0.34 \text{ V} - (-0.76 \text{ V}) = 1.10 \text{ V}$

34)

C. Correct. The benzoate ion does not react with added hydroxide ions, so IV cannot be correct. All the other statements are true.

35)

A. Incorrect. A variable that is directly measured in an experiment is a dependent variable.

B. Incorrect. A variable that is deliberately changed over the course of an experiment is an independent variable.

C. Correct. Confounding variables are not accounted for in the experimental design, but have an effect on the outcome of the experiment.

D. Incorrect. Confounding variables have an effect on the experimental results.

36)

A. Incorrect. Ernest Rutherford's gold foil experiment proved that atoms contain a positively charged nucleus. However, he did not discover electrons.

B. Correct. J.J. Thomson's cathode ray experiment detected the presence of electrons.

C. Incorrect. John Dalton's contribution to atomic theory was the proposition that atoms are indivisible, atoms belonging to the same element are identical, and atoms combine in whole number ratios to form compounds.

D. Incorrect. Niels Bohr developed the quantum model and determined that electrons exist in specific energy levels.

37)

C. Correct. For chemically similar molecules, as molecular weight increases, so do London forces. So, the kinetic energy required to overcome those forces and reach the vapor phase increases with molecular weight.

38)

A. Incorrect. Oxidation to Cu^{2+} results in $3d^9$ as the valence electrons, which is a less stable configuration than $3d^{10}$ with Zn^{2+}.

B. Incorrect. Oxidation to Fe^{2+} results in $3d^6$ as the valence electrons, which is a less stable configuration than $3d^{10}$ with Zn^{2+}.

C. Correct. Oxidation to Zn^{2+} results in $3d^{10}$ as the valence electrons, which is a stable configuration since filled orbitals are preferred.

D. Incorrect. Oxidation to Co^{2+} results in $3d^7$ as the valence electrons, which is a less stable configuration than $3d^{10}$ with Zn^{2+}.

39)

A. Incorrect. This is a synthesis or metathesis reaction.

B. Incorrect. This is a single replacement or displacement reaction.

C. Incorrect. This is a combustion reaction.

D. Correct. This is a decomposition reaction since one reactant gives two products.

40)

A. Correct. Subtract the bond energy for two C=O bonds from the bond energy for O=O.

$495\frac{kJ}{mol} - 2\left(745\frac{kJ}{mol}\right) =$

$\mathbf{-9.95 \times 10^2 \frac{kJ}{mol}}$

41)

A. Incorrect. Rubidium is a metal.

B. Incorrect. Vanadium is a transition metal.

C. Correct. Antimony is a metalloid.

D. Incorrect. Iodine is a halogen.

42)

A. Correct. Li is an alkali metal, not an alkaline earth metal.

43)

C. Correct. There are three significant figures in this number. Trailing zeros (zeros after the last nonzero digit) are significant when there is a decimal point. So in this case, the nonzero digit *2* and the two trailing zeros count as significant figures—the three underlined digits 0.0200.

44)

C. **Correct.** The values are close to each other (precise) not are not close to the actual value (accurate).

45)

B. **Correct.** The percent dissociation is the percent of the acid that dissociated.

$[H_3O^+] = 7.08 \times 10^{-3} = 0.00708$ M

$\frac{0.00708 \text{ M}}{0.1 \text{ M}} = 0.0708 \times 100 = \mathbf{7.1\%}$

46)

A. Incorrect. Ar has eighteen protons and S^{2-} has sixteen protons.

B. **Correct.** They both have eighteen electrons.

C. Incorrect. Ar has twenty-two neutrons and S^{2-} has sixteen neutrons.

D. Incorrect. They are not the same size since S^{2-} has a larger radius because it has two fewer protons than Ar but the same number of electrons.

47)

C. **Correct.** Tungsten carbide is a network covalent solid. All the other statements are true.

48)

B. **Correct.** Divide the molar mass by the mass of the empirical formula and multiply the empirical formula by that ratio.

$\frac{27.67 \text{ g/mol}}{13.84 \text{ g/mol}} \approx 2$

$2(BH_3) = \mathbf{B_2H_6}$

49)

A. Incorrect. *n* can never equal 0.

B. **Correct.** This set is possible (1s).

C. Incorrect. If $n = 1$, l can only be 0 (and not 1).

D. Incorrect. If $n = 3$, l can only be 0, 1, or 2.

50)

B. **I and II only**

I. A polar covalent bond is a type of intramolecular bond that creates a compound.

II. An ionic bond is a type of intramolecular bond that creates a compound.

III. A hydrogen bond is not a chemical bond, but an intermolecular force that acts between molecules.

51)

D. **Correct.** The acetate ions react with water to form hydroxide ions, which causes the pH to go up.

52)

C. **Correct.** The heat of solution is not a colligative property of a solution because it is determined by the properties of the specific substance being dissolved.

53)

A. **Correct.** VOCs (volatile organic compounds) in breath or intestinal gases contain biomarkers for colorectal cancer.

54)

A. Incorrect. Condensation is the process of conversion from liquid to solid.

B. **Correct.** Evaporation is the process of conversion from liquid to gas that occurs at the boiling point.

C. Incorrect. Melting is the process of conversion of solid to liquid.

D. Incorrect. Sublimation is the process of conversion of solid to gas.

55)

C. Correct. Cathode rays are made up of negatively charged particles called electrons.

56)

A. Incorrect. Alpha particles consist of two protons and two neutrons.

B. Incorrect. Alpha particles are positively charged and are deflected by electric and magnetic fields.

C. Incorrect. While beta particles are deflected by electric and magnetic fields, they have a negative charge.

D. Correct. Gamma rays are neutral in charge and are not deflected by electric and magnetic fields.

57)

C. Correct. The carbonyl group is –C=O. All the other groups are matched correctly.

58)

C. I and II only

I. True. Water can form hydroxide or a proton.

II. True. Sodium hydrogen sulfate can form sulfuric acid or a sulfate ion.

III. False. Sodium phosphate can only form an acid such as sodium hydrogen phosphate.

59)

A. Incorrect. Methane burns or combusts by reacting with oxygen to form carbon dioxide and water.

B. Incorrect. The reaction is a combustion reaction since hydrogen is being oxidized with oxygen.

C. Incorrect. The reaction is a combustion reaction since carbon is being oxidized with oxygen.

D. Correct. When an egg is boiled in water, the proteins in the egg white and yolk become entangled and clump together. No oxygen is involved in this process.

60)

A. Incorrect. Kinetics can be used to determine the rate determining step, which helps to explain the mechanism of a reaction.

B. Incorrect. The overall order is determined by adding the order of each reactant, which is part of kinetics.

C. Incorrect. Reaction rate can be determined from the rate equation, which includes reactant concentrations.

D. Correct. Product concentration is used in equilibrium calculations but not in kinetics.

61)

D. Correct. The electronegativity of an element increases up and to the right on the periodic table. Cl is one of the most electronegative elements since it is in group 17.

62)

A. Incorrect. There are no electrons in the nucleus.

B. Correct. Atomic number is defined as the total number of protons in the nucleus of an atom.

C. Incorrect. The total number of protons and neutrons in a nucleus is given by the mass number.

D. Incorrect. The total number of orbitals is not given by the atomic number.

63)

A. Correct. Barium hydroxide is a strong base and has two hydroxide ions per formula unit.

B. Incorrect. Sodium hydroxide is a strong base but has only one hydroxide ion per formula unit.

C. Incorrect. Potassium hydroxide is a strong base but has only one hydroxide ion per formula unit.

D. Incorrect. Ammonium hydroxide is a weak base.

64)

D. I and II only

I. This is a double-replacement reaction: the silver and sodium ions "replace" each other.

II. This is a double-replacement reaction: the hydrogens from the acid and the sodium ions "replace" each other.

III. This is a single-replacement reaction: the aluminum "replaces" the zinc ions, creating a metal and aluminum chloride.

65)

A. Incorrect. Pressure is the force exerted by molecules against a surface.

B. Incorrect. Mass is the amount of matter in a substance.

C. Correct. Thermal energy is defined as the average kinetic energy of molecules.

D. Incorrect. Enthalpy is the net heat from the surroundings needed for the reaction.

66)

A. Incorrect. Air is a homogeneous mixture of N_2, O_2, H_2O, and CO_2.

B. Correct. Sandy water is not a homogeneous mixture. Sand and water can be easily separated, making it a heterogeneous mixture.

C. Incorrect. Brass is an alloy—a homogeneous mixture.

D. Incorrect. Salt dissolved in water is a homogeneous mixture with salt ions dispersed evenly throughout the mixture.

67)

A. Correct. Atomic radius decreases from left to right on the periodic table because, as the number of protons in the nucleus increases, the attraction between the nucleus and the electrons increases.

68)

A. Incorrect. This reaction is a neutralization reaction.

B. Incorrect. This reaction is a combustion reaction.

C. Correct. This reaction is a decomposition reaction in which one substance breaks up or decomposes to two substances.

D. Incorrect. This reaction is a simple replacement reaction.

69)

A. Correct. The types of radiation in order of increasing frequency are: radio waves < microwaves < infrared rays < visible rays < ultraviolet rays < X-rays < gamma rays.

70)

A. Correct. In a closed system, exchange of energy is possible between the system and its surroundings, but exchange of matter is not.

B. Incorrect. This type of system does not exist.

C. Incorrect. In an isolated system, there is no exchange of energy or matter between the system and its surroundings.

D. Incorrect. In an open system, there is exchange of both energy and matter between the system and its surroundings.

71)

A. **Correct.** Mg tends to lose its two valence electrons to form a +2 ion.

B. Incorrect. C does not tend to form ions.

C. Incorrect. Cl tends to gain one electron, forming a −1 ion and completing an octet in the third energy level.

D. Incorrect. Na tends to lose its one valence electron to form a +1 ion. This leaves Na^{+1}, which has a filled second energy level.

72)

A. **Correct.** For binary ionic compounds, the element farther left in the periodic table comes first followed by the root of the second element with an *–ide* suffix.

B. Incorrect. For binary ionic compounds, it is not necessary to specify the number of ions.

C. Incorrect. The element farther to the left in the periodic table is named first.

D. Incorrect. It is only necessary to indicate charge with a Roman numeral for those transition metals that can have multiple charges.

73)

A. Incorrect. There are a total of twenty valence electrons: seven for each Br and six for O. This diagram only shows sixteen. Also, Br does not tend to form double bonds.

B. Incorrect. This diagram only shows eighteen valence electrons. There are twenty.

C. Incorrect. The number of valence electrons is correct, but the least electronegative atom—oxygen—should be in the middle.

D. **Correct.** There are twenty valence electrons. Oxygen being less electronegative than Br is in the middle connected by single bonds to Br. The valence electrons are distributed to give each Br atom an octet and the remaining are placed on oxygen giving it an octet.

74)

B. **Correct.** $K = \frac{[Cl_2][PCl_3]}{[PCl_5]}$ is the equilibrium constant expression for the equation. The expression for the equilibrium constant is the product of the product concentrations divided by the product of the concentrations of the reactants. The coefficients of the balanced equation become exponents of the concentrations in the expression for the equilibrium constant.

75)

A. **Correct.** Colligative properties are changed based on the solute concentration.

B. Incorrect. The solvent mole fraction does not affect the vapor pressure lowering.

C. Incorrect. The overall molality of the solution does not change the vapor pressure.

D. Incorrect. The osmotic pressure is not directly related to the vapor pressure.

76)

A. Incorrect. Systematic errors are the result of faulty experimental design.

B. Incorrect. Systematic errors are reproducible.

C. **Correct.** It is possible to eliminate these errors by correcting the error in the measuring device.

D. Incorrect. It is possible to eliminate systematic errors.

77)

A. Incorrect. Entropy refers to randomness of the system.

B. Incorrect. The specific latent heat of vaporization is the energy required to change a substance from liquid to gas at the same temperature.

C. Incorrect. Sensible heat refers to heat that changes the phase of a substance (as opposed to latent heat).

D. Correct. The specific latent heat of fusion is the heat energy required to change 1 g of a substance from a solid to a liquid at the same temperature.

78)

A. Incorrect. Prefixes are not used to denote the number of anions in a salt. The correct number is assumed to balance the charge on the cation.

B. Incorrect. Chromium can have multiple charges. Roman numerals denote the charge.

C. Correct. A nitrate ion has a charge of −1, so the Roman numeral III denotes the correct charge on chromium to generate a neutral salt.

D. Incorrect. Chromium has a charge of III not II as in this salt.

79)

A. Correct. This concept was introduced by Albert Einstein. Choices B, C, and D were all demonstrated by Niels Bohr.

80)

B. Correct. A Brønsted acid-base pair must have hydrogen atoms.

81)

A. Correct. The entropy of the universe is increasing.

82)

A. Correct. Assume there are 100 g of liquid. Find the moles of each element.

39.99 g C	1 mol C	= 3.33 mol C
	12.01 g	

6.73 g H	1 mol H	= 6.66 mol H
	1.01 g	

53.28 g O	1 mol O	= 3.33 mol O
	16 g	

Divide each number of moles by the smallest number of moles to find the empirical formula.

$\frac{3.33 \text{ mol C}}{3.33 \text{ mol C}} = 1$

$\frac{6.66 \text{ mol H}}{3.33 \text{ mol H}} = 2$

$\frac{3.33 \text{ mol O}}{3.33 \text{ mol O}} = 1$

→ **CH_2O**

83)

A. Correct. The molecular weight of CH_2O is 30.03 amu. The subscripts must be multiplied by two to give a compound with a molecular weight of 60.06 amu.

B. Incorrect. CH_2O is the empirical formula, but it only has a formula mass of 30.03 amu.

C. Incorrect. This compound has a greater formula mass than 60.06 amu.

D. Incorrect. The subscripts must all be the same multiple of those in the empirical formula.

84)

A. Incorrect. Br^- has a larger ionic radius than Cl^- being farther down family

7A, so bonds will be weaker in $MgBr_2$ than in $MgCl_2$.

B. Incorrect. Since Mg is to the right of Na in the periodic table, it will have a smaller atomic radius, and the Mg^{2+} ion having a higher positive charge will also have a significantly smaller ionic radius leading to tighter bonding with Cl^-.

C. Incorrect. The more positive charge and smaller ionic radius of Mg^{2+} versus Na^+ is the more significant effect on bond strength.

D. **Correct.** Na only has a +1 charge versus the +2 charge (and smaller atomic radius) of Mg, so Mg^{2+} has a stronger attractive force. Br^- is larger than Cl^-, so it forms weaker bonds.

85)

C. **Correct.** The number at the bottom, 24, represents mass number, or the total number of protons and neutrons.

86)

A. Incorrect. No hydrogen is involved in the reaction.

B. **Correct.** $BaCO_3$ decomposes into BaO (barium oxide) and CO_2 gas.

C. Incorrect. Only one reactant is involved.

D. Incorrect. No hydrogen is involved in the reaction.

87)

D. **Correct.** A catalyst reduces the activation energy by creating an alternative reaction mechanism for the reaction.

88)

D. **Correct.** Use the formula for the solubility product constant.

$K_{sp} = [Ni^{2+}][S^{2-}]$

$4 \times 10^{-20} = [Ni^{2+}][S^{2-}]$

$[Ni^{2+}] = \sqrt{4 \times 10^{-20}} = \mathbf{2 \times 10^{-10}\ M}$

89)

C. **Correct.** The molar mass of $ZnCl_2$ equals the molar mass of Zn (65.38 g) plus two times the molar mass of Cl (2 × 35.453 g). Molar mass is expressed in grams, not in atomic mass units.

90)

C. **Correct.** According to the ideal gas law, $PV = nRT$, if n decreases and T stays constant, then either P or V will have to decrease.

91)

D. **Correct.** This statement is false: moving down the periodic table, the ionization energy decreases because electrons in the valence shells are shielded from the attraction of the nucleus by the core electrons. Choices A, B, and C are true.

92)

A. Incorrect. SO_4^{2-} is the most common oxyanion of sulfur and forms sulfuric acid.

B. **Correct.** SO_3^{2-} has one less oxygen than sulfur's most common oxyanion and forms sulfurous acid.

C. Incorrect. Hyposulfurous acid is H_2SO_2.

D. Incorrect. Persulfuric acid is H_2SO_5.

93)

B. **Correct.** C—C is the least polar bond. C—H is somewhat less polar than C—N, and polarity increases with increasing differences in electronegativities going to the right in the periodic table.

94)

C. **Correct.** An equilibrium always responds to a change by trying to reverse it. Because this is an exothermic reaction, heat is considered a product; the addition of heat will push the equilibrium in reverse to use up the additional heat.

95)

C. **Correct.** The pH will go up one unit because the proton concentration will go down by a factor of 10 ($pH = -\log[H^+]$).

96)

A. Incorrect. Typically, the solubility of two solids would increase with temperature.

B. **Correct.** Decreasing the temperature decreases the ability of gas to escape the liquid, thus increasing its solubility.

C. Incorrect. The solubility of a solid in a liquid typically increases with increasing temperature.

D. Incorrect. The solubility of two liquids is not independent of temperature.

97)

B. **Correct.** This is the balanced equation for photosynthesis.

98)

A. **Correct.** Class D fires involve combustible metals.

B. Incorrect. Class B fires involve organic solvents and flammable liquids.

C. Incorrect. Class C fires involve electrical equipment.

D. Incorrect. Class A fires involve ordinary combustible products.

99)

A. Incorrect. Niels Bohr developed the quantum model and determined that electrons exist in specific energy levels.

B. **Correct.** According to Erwin Schrödinger, electrons move around the orbit in waves and not in defined paths.

C. Incorrect. By performing the gold foil experiment, Ernest Rutherford proved that the atom consisted of a nucleus, a positively charged core at the center.

D. Incorrect. The John Dalton model stated that atoms are indivisible, atoms belonging to same element are identical, and atoms combine in whole number ratios to form compounds.

100)

A. **Correct.** Benzene, like all hydrocarbons, gives carbon dioxide and water when completely combusted.

101)

A. Incorrect. The oxidation number of As is +3 and the oxidation number of O is −2.

B. **Correct.** The oxidation number of As is +4 and the oxidation number of O is −2.

C. Incorrect. The oxidation number of As is +3 and the oxidation number of F is −1.

D. Incorrect. The oxidation number of As is +3 and the oxidation number of H is −1.

102)

C. **Correct.** A large *K*-value indicates the reaction heavily favors product formation. A large equilibrium constant means the concentrations of the products are much larger than the concentrations of the reactants.

103)

A. Incorrect. A strong acid/strong base titration curve would have a very steep equivalence point; this curve is too gradual.

B. **Correct.** The titration curve for a strong acid/strong base titration will have a very steep equivalence point. The addition of the base will result in an increase in the pH.

C. Incorrect. Since the addition of the base will result in an increase in the pH, this curve is incorrect because it shows a decrease in pH.

D. Incorrect. Adding a base causes an increase in pH; this curve is thus incorrect because it shows a decrease in pH.

104)

A. Incorrect. The freezing point is typically decreased.

B. **Correct.** The boiling point is increased with the addition of a nonvolatile solute.

C. Incorrect. The osmotic pressure would be changed.

D. Incorrect. The vapor pressure of the solution would decrease.

105)

A. Incorrect. A vertical line would show that the temperature was increasing without heat being added.

B. **Correct.** Horizontal lines show that heat is being added but the temperature of the substance is not increasing.

C. Incorrect. The slope of the graph shows the change in temperature that accompanies heat transfer within a phase.

D. Incorrect. The slope of the graph shows the change in temperature that accompanies heat transfer within a phase.

106)

A. Incorrect. Counting starts from the end of the straight chain closest to the triple bond.

B. Incorrect. The location of the triple bond is denoted as the position of the first carbon participating in the bond, which is the second carbon in this example.

C. **Correct.** Counting begins at the end closest to the triple bond. The suffix *–yne* indicates a triple bond.

D. Incorrect. The suffix *–ene* denotes a double bond.

107)

A. Incorrect. Avogadro's number is the number of atoms or molecules in a mole of a substance.

B. **Correct.** Avogadro's number is 6.02×10^{23} and is the number of atoms or molecules in a mole of a substance.

C. Incorrect. Each element has its own characteristic atomic mass based on the number of protons, neutrons, and electrons in the atom.

D. Incorrect. The molar mass of carbon is the mass of 6.02×10^{23} atoms of carbon.

108)

A. **Correct.** SiF_4 is tetrahedral with four equivalent bonds and no lone electron pairs on Si.

109)

B. **Correct.** These molecules are polar and so are subject to both dipole-dipole and London forces. There are no hydrogen atoms bound to high electronegative atoms, so there will be no hydrogen bonding.

110)

C. **Correct.** The balanced equation has the coefficients 1:3:1:2.

$\_CS_2 + \_O_2 \rightarrow \_CO_2 + \_SO_2$

Carbon is already balanced (one atom on each side). There are two S atoms on the left, so add 2 to SO_2 on the right.

$\_CS_2 + \_O_2 \rightarrow \_CO_2 + 2SO_2$

There are six O atoms on the right, so add 3 to O_2 on the left.

$\mathbf{CS_2 + 3O_2 \rightarrow CO_2 + 2SO_2}$

111)

B. **Correct.** The larger the equilibrium constant, the more the equilibrium favors products. To order these equations from most product favored to least product favored, the equilibrium constant should be listed from greatest to least.

112)

C. **I and II only**

I. True. All weak acids are in an equilibrium.

II. True. All weak bases are in an equilibrium.

III. False. A hydrolysis process may be irreversible, which means it is not in a state of equilibrium.

113)

D. **Correct.** In the reaction, the Na displaces hydrogen from water in a single-replacement reaction.

114)

D. **Correct.** This reaction is a neutralization reaction, which always produces water and a salt. Sodium is a +1 ion and sulfate is a −2 ion, so the resulting salt is Na_2SO_4.

115)

A. Incorrect. Evaporation is a phase transition from liquid to gas.

B. Incorrect. Condensation does not skip a phase.

C. **Correct.** Sublimation skips a phase—it goes from solid to gas without passing through the liquid phase.

D. Incorrect. Fusion is a phase transition from solid to liquid.

116)

C. **I and II**

I. True. Ethyl isopropyl ether is the correct name using the common names of the simple alkyl groups attached and the word *ether*.

II. True. The smaller —OR group is treated as an alkoxy group that is a substituent of a longer alkane chain. This is technically correct, although this naming technique is more often used for larger ethers.

III. False. This is an ether of the general form R—O—R, not an alcohol of the general form R—OH.

117)

A. **Correct.** The ions that appear on both the reactant and product sides (spectator ions) are not included in the net ionic equation. The solution of HNO_3 is made up of separated H^{+1} ions and NO_3^{-1} ions and the solution of KOH is made up of separated K^{+1} ions and OH^{-1} ions. When these solutions are mixed together, the H^{+1} ions and the OH^{-1} ions combine to make water. The K^{+1} ions and the NO_2^{-1} ions undergo no change and can thus be omitted. This leaves the net ionic equation $H^{+1} + OH^{-1} \rightarrow H_2O$.

118)

A. Incorrect. This is an acid.

B. Incorrect. An acid donates protons to a base.

C. Incorrect. Salt and water are formed when acids and bases react.

D. **Correct.** Acids increase the concentration of hydrogen ions in solution and do not accept protons.

119)

D. **I, II, and III**

I. True. Ethylene contains one double bond and thus has one pi bond.

II. True. Acetylene contains one triple bond and thus has two pi bonds.

III. True. Carbon monoxide contains a triple bond and thus has two pi bonds.

120)

C. **Correct.** CCl_4 is covalently bonded, so the molecules in the solid are held together by relatively weak intermolecular forces compared to the ionic attractions and stabilizing lattice energy experienced by the salts, KCl and $CaCl_2$. $CaCl_2$, with a smaller ionic radius and +2 charge, forms stronger ionic bonds than KCl and so has a somewhat higher melting point.

121)

C. **Correct.** The presence of electrons was first demonstrated by J.J. Thomson. Choices A, B, and D are all part of the Rutherford model.

122)

D. **Correct.** The longest chain is nine carbons long and has single bonds between carbons. The two methyl groups are on the number 3 and 7 carbons.

123)

A. Incorrect. All chlorides and nitrates are soluble.

B. **Correct.** $BaSO_4$ is not soluble.

C. Incorrect. Most sulfates and all nitrates are soluble.

D. Incorrect. All chlorides and iodines are soluble.

124)

A. **Correct.** A Lewis acid accepts an electron pair, and a Lewis base donates an electron pair.

B. Incorrect. The opposite is true.

C. Incorrect. $SnCl_4^{-2}$ is not a Lewis acid or base.

D. Incorrect. $SnCl_4^{-2}$ is not a Lewis acid or base.

125)

B. **Correct.** Immediate evacuation should be the first action.

Made in the USA
Middletown, DE
18 May 2018

The Tasks *and* Content *of the Steiner-Waldorf Curriculum*

The Tasks *and* Content *of the Steiner-Waldorf Curriculum*

Edited by
KEVIN AVISON *and* MARTYN RAWSON

Floris Books

German edition edited by Tobias Richter
Translated by Johanna Collis

Based on *Pädagogischer Auftrag und Unterrichtsziele vom Lehrplan der Waldorfschule* published by Verlag Freies Geistesleben, Stuttgart

First published in English in 2000 by Steiner Schools Fellowship Publications

English edition © 2000, 2014 Steiner Waldorf Schools Fellowship Publications
Second edition published in 2014 by Floris Books

All rights reserved. No part of this book may be reproduced in any form without written permission of Floris Books, 15 Harrison Gardens, Edinburgh
www.florisbooks.co.uk

British Library CIP Data available
ISBN 978-178250-042-1
Printed in Poland

Table of Contents

Foreword

Caroline von Heydebrand's achievement in piecing together the wide-ranging indications Rudolf Steiner gave to the teachers of the first Waldorf School, in the form of lectures or during meetings, and summarising them in succinct but comprehensive curriculum for Steiner-Waldorf schools, was inspired and deserves enormous credit. Von Heydebrand's style is both precise and concise, and she had the courage to leave gaps in which individual teachers could continue to build. She painted a picture that provided guidance and support for creative teaching without crowding out the space for individual interpretation and adaptation.

Nevertheless, given the developments in education and cultural life generally that have occurred over eight decades, it seemed timely to review, update and extend her work. Furthermore the increasing demand from the authorities for schools to document their curricula have led to more and more Steiner-Waldorf schools presenting their own versions of the curriculum. Meanwhile, Waldorf education has not only moved on in time, it has moved to other places too, each with its own geographical, cultural and educational influences. Translating the original German Waldorf curriculum for a different time and space raises many vital questions about the nature of child development and the role of any curriculum. In an age in which nothing can be taken for granted, no traditions can remain living without consciousness engagement. Thus it seemed right to reformulate the Waldorf curriculum for the present and in as generic a form as possible.

Throughout the 1990s, the need for a renewed curriculum was widely discussed and the need was taken up by groups of experienced teachers and teacher trainers from the Steiner-Waldorf schools movement in Europe and America under the aegis of the Pedagogical Section in Dornach. The conclusion reached was that such an undertaking would require a balancing act. On the one hand there would be the need to explain and confirm the freedom every school must have if it is to succeed to take full account of the developing child (who is, after all, the foundation on which the curriculum must rest). On the other hand, it was felt that it should be possible to document best practice in modern Waldorf schools, giving examples rather than stating norms, and providing general directions to illustrate the substance of the education as envisaged by Rudolf Steiner in relation to children of different ages. At the same time it was recognised that proper account should be taken of the specific requirements of different subjects.

All that was quite a tall order and a start was made by basing the work on a presentation compiled by Tobias Richter with Austrian colleagues, who had prepared a document along these lines for the Vienna (Mauer) school. A number of colleagues from the international Steiner-Waldorf schools' movement shared in this task with Tobias Richter: Georg Kniebe (Germany), Bengt Ulin (Sweden) and Shirley Noakes (Scotland) belonged to the working group, together with Dr Heinz Zimmermann, leader of the Pedagogical Section at the Goetheanum in Switzerland. Nonetheless, it became obvious that this initial effort did not go far enough

It was felt that the new formulation had not taken sufficient account of the freedom of individual teachers, but at the same time, it was seen to offer fewer descriptions than many wanted of how a teacher might actually set about the task of using their freedom purposefully. Led by Georg Kniebe, the *Pädagogische Forschungsstelle* (German education research group) then undertook to sift all the suggestions and, where necessary, have specialist groups work out further ideas. This having been done, two more colleagues, Dietrich Esterl (Germany) and Christof Wiechert (Netherlands), once again made a critical assessment of the whole manuscript, which, in spite of some disagreements, forms the basis for the numerous versions that have followed.

This book has become an essential guide, providing many, if not most, practicing Waldorf teachers with a useful orientation for their work. There are now versions in many other languages and the book has become indispensible for teaching colleagues, academics, school inspections and anyone with a serious interest in Steiner-Waldorf education.

It seems fitting to conclude with the words Tobias Richter wrote for Foreword of the original German edition:

> *By fixing these things in writing, anyone involved in the living flow of teaching cannot help experiencing the limitations of a project that by its very nature inhibits and restricts what ought to remain active, fluid and alive. So the suggestions laid down here resemble a line that is the track left behind by movement; a trace that retains an indication of what has gone before.*
>
> *Nevertheless, we venture to present this attempt at depicting the aims of the education and the possible content of lessons in the hope that every 'artist in the teaching profession' will succeed in creating life from this residual form by sculpting or painting her or his own living path of teaching and learning.*
>
> *Intensive study of Rudolf Steiner's contribution to education never fails to kindle the enthusiasm so much needed in education when it is seen as a force for renewal. First and foremost, therefore, it is to Rudolf Steiner that our thanks are due.*

KEVIN AVISON AND MARTYN RAWSON

Acknowledgements

Many colleagues contributed to the first edition of this curriculum:

Kevin Avison (checklists for class teachers), Martin Baker (Movement curriculum), John Burnett (Curriculum Research Group – CRG), Judy Byford (Eurythmy), Elena Christie (Eurythmy), Linda Churnside (Spelling Checklists and Maths), C. Clouder (Upper School), H. David (Handwork), Michaela Devaris (Eurythmy), Vivien Easton (Geography and Maths), William Forward (German), Bernard Graves (Crafts), Helene Jacquet (Eurythmy), Sally Jenkinson (Early Years), Graham Kennish (Biology and Chemistry), Ewout van Manen (Literacy and Learning Support), Dr. Brien Masters (Music), Monika McGovern (German), Trevor Mepham (CRG), Jenny Milne (Handwork), Janni Nicol (Early Years) Shirley Noakes (CRG), Deborah Pike (French), Ken Power (History), Dorothy Salter (CRG), Martine Scott (French), H. Seufert (Crafts), Rob Sim (Movement curriculum), Jan Swann (quality development and administration), Anne Tandree (CRG), David Urieli (Maths and Physics), Dorothee von Winterfeldt (Foreign Languages), Richard Zienko (Philosophy); Johanna Collis (translation), Anne McNicol (original layout and typesetting), Sue Sim (typing and proof reading), Brien Masters (proof reading), Wilma Rawson (proof reading), David Urieli (translation).

Note to the 2014 edition

Substantial changes have been made to the introduction of this edition. In particular, the sections dealing with young children and early childhood education have been revised by Janni Nicol in the light of continual change made to the Early Years' Foundation Stage over the years, as well as developing practice.

Although many colleagues were invited to contribute amendments to the curriculum sections for this edition, most felt that the essentials of the original remain valid. Some small amendments and corrections have been made, but the vast majority of the original curriculum descriptors remain intact. Nonetheless, wherever possible, we have responded to comments made by colleagues who found the original awkward to refer to or over-wordy. A majority of the revision has thus been completed by Janni Nicol and this editor, in consultation with the Steiner-Waldorf Advisory Service Team. The chapter on Gardening classes benefitted from additions by Helen Morris-Ridout and colleagues of the Steiner Academy Hereford; the chapter on Technology benefitted from reference to the Steiner Education, Australia ICT curriculum.

We would like to thank our colleagues at Floris Books for opportunity to revisit these pages and for their patient tolerance in waiting for the completion of a complicated and delicate task.

A companion volume, *Towards Creative Teaching* (second edition, published by Floris Books 2012, re-edited with additions by Kevin Avison), provides a more detailed outline for class teachers of the 'how' of Waldorf teaching than could be included here.

KEVIN AVISON, MAY 2014

Part I

1

Introduction to Tasks and Content of the Steiner-Waldorf Curriculum

A curriculum could be compared to the list of ingredients for a recipe. However good the recipe, the quality of the ingredients is crucial but to make a start the components also need to be available. When they are to hand, the next question is whether the cook is skilled enough to combine and adjust flavours so that each item plays its part without overwhelming the others. An experienced cook may be able to substitute one ingredient for another, even to improvise in such a way that something new is created. But we should not forget that emotion, even love, goes into the preparation of food and this will influence how it is received. And, of course, the expectations, health and culinary experience of the diners also makes a difference.

A curriculum guides an entire learning process. It should not, like a dish into which a chef has thrown every possible taste, explode in an overwhelming, sensation-bursting blowout; it should bring to the table ingredients that are well-balanced, digestible and nutritious, that promote health and stimulate, not stupefy, the senses. Over time, as with diet, a curriculum can introduce items that may not be immediately appealing, stronger tastes or more subtle and complex ones: intellectual chillis, subjects initially sour or astringent, as well as flavours, textures and scents that help to educate the palate. A primary school curriculum, in particular, sets out ingredients for the hors d'oeuvres of lifelong learning.

Of course, many school curriculums share common ingredients, but the distinctive qualities of the Steiner-Waldorf curriculum framework are, we believe, unique:

* The curriculum unfolds over time, is wide and richly experiential: not merely designed towards narrowly-defined 'achievement', but intended to promote capability for the art of living
* The curriculum is really only a series of 'indications', as Steiner described them, pointers inviting interpretation and free rendering, i.e. it calls on and encourages the creativity (or artistry) of teachers
* The importance of content is fully recognised (young people need certain skills and useful knowledge), but as a creative framework, the Steiner-Waldorf curriculum is embedded within a developing practice and method. The curriculum outline takes its cue from the development of the child: subject, or content, provides a medium for a meeting and collaboration of teacher and learner. Thus,

since meaning and knowledge are built over time, this is co-constructive learning in which understanding unfolds as a process of *learning to learn* encompassing both students and teacher

* Subject content and necessary competence are always relative to the child: the curriculum is midwife to the emerging individuality, rather than suit of clothes into which the child must be made to fit
* The shaping principles of the curriculum are extraordinarily robust and resilient. Many independent educators recognise this fundamental coherence, which has stood the test of time and many generations of children
* The creative freedom within the Waldorf curriculum framework enables it to be successfully adapted for a variety of settings, languages and cultures. Schools founded on the principles and example of the first Waldorf School (Stuttgart 1919), can be found around the world, including every inhabited continent. What started as a central European curriculum has been modified by applying its essential principles to the education of children in the Americas, many parts of Africa, the Middle East, India and the Far East, as well as most of the rest of Europe

Here we need to put aside the image of a recipe. Where people are concerned, and young people in particular, there can be no 'recipe'. Most important of all, a curriculum needs to be a well-spring for enthusiasm and interest, engaging teachers so that they in turn enthuse and interest the pupils as active learners. Whatever the intentions of those who seek to advance narrow prescriptions for education, a centrally-planned curriculum will rarely enlist that sort of engagement and the movers will be forced endlessly to revise and justify their case, usually at great cost to all concerned.

A variety of ways and means are needed to bring vital skills and useful knowledge to young people so that they feel inspired by and invested in learning: education is a process through which culture becomes personalised, and in becoming personalised, culture is also changed and re-charged. For a Steiner-Waldorf educator, alongside heredity and environment there is also a discernible and unique essence which every human being brings with them into life – sometimes called 'the third factor'[1] individual destiny, latent self or personal intention. It is this above all that must be nurtured on the way to adulthood fulfilment. Each child and each generation of children brings something new and it is this that crucially offers the renewal that cultures need if they are not fall into decadence.

> *The question to be asked is not: what does an individual need to know and be capable of doing so as to fit into the existing social order? but rather: what potential does an individual have and what can be developed in him or her? When this is taken into account each new generation can bring forces of continuous renewal to the social order. In this social order there will then live all that the fully mature human beings in it cause it to be. For the existing social order to mould the coming generation in its own image is something that must not happen.*[2]

Children engaged in learning are never passive and education cannot be (to use a buzz word from the recent past) simply 'delivered'. Perhaps one of Steiner's most important ideas was that young people need to feel themselves understood by their teachers so that they are inspired to love learning; to put it another way and in his own words, 'the children *are* the curriculum'. Curriculum content acts as a bridge, mediating between the vital immediacy of young people and the existing order and accumulated wisdom of the world they are growing into. Too much emphasis on the former tends to waywardness, loss of capacity and destructiveness; too much on the latter, to social stagnation, oppression and decadence.

Throughout this book the reader will find examples of the way subjects can be introduced and taught. In that sense it is a conventional curriculum touching on many topics that might be found in other syllabuses and schemes of work. In due course, young people educated in Steiner-Waldorf schools become active, mature and rounded citizens of their home nations, but also citizens of the world with a sense for the wide horizons and opportunities that presents.

Waldorf education had its origin and continues to find relevance in the educational writings and lectures of Rudolf Steiner (1861–1925) and especially in the foundation of the first Waldorf School in Stuttgart in 1919. Steiner's philosophy, which he called anthroposophy ('wisdom of and within humanity', or, as Steiner once put it, 'awareness of the essential nature of human beings'), provides a starting point for those working in Steiner Waldorf schools. But, just as Steiner himself continually checked his intuitive, or spiritual, insights against the science and scholarship of his time, so too is it the duty of teachers and others working with the education to apply an honest scepticism to their practice and to its principles. Steiner-Waldorf schools throughout the world are engaged in realising, refining, reviewing and reframing the plan set out for the first school of their type. International dialogue adds further facets to this evolving educational method and curriculum. The schools stand (with their national associations) in their own terms, implementing a system of education that asks to be reappraised with each class and each generation, a collaborative creation of pupils, teachers, parents and all who engage with it.

> *Today our teachers cannot know what will be good in the Waldorf School in five years' time, for in those five years they will have learned a great deal and out of that knowledge they have to judge anew what is good and what is not good... Educational matters cannot be thought out intellectually; they can only arise out of teaching experience. And it is this working out of experience that is the concern of the collegiate.*[3]

As the authors of the 2010 Cambridge Primary Review[4] noted, any statement of educational aims and purpose is inherently problematic.[5] Nonetheless, as they also recognised without clear intent or purpose, any work in the social sphere will tend to become backward-looking and reactive. An aimless or merely reactive school system is quickly infected by viral expediency, the manipulations and short-term whims of whichever type of politics chooses to exploit it. The principles and educational tasks of Waldorf schools act as a yeast enlivening and informing other ingredients: facilitating collegiality, supporting coherence in management and practice, underpinning curriculum development, and providing a touchstone for the values inherent in educational work generally.

Values too, however, are by no means straightforward. *Issues Paper 6 (Aims and Values)*[6] from the Nuffield Review of 14–19 Education points out that the most important values are embedded in the language used in speaking about schools. Here the authors had in mind the introduction of managerialism into education and the unexplored assumptions that go with this. They demonstrate how language can direct attitudes that clash with other core expectations for education. Small wonder that distinctive types of education evoke misunderstanding and misinterpretation. Small wonder too that governments, and their education departments, prefer to avoid making values explicit. It is safer either not to acknowledge that education, and programmes of 'reform', are pre-eminently a matter of values. To present educational reform in simplistically pragmatic terms such as economic necessity or international league tables is a deception. Education policy is not value-free or value-neutral, even when those values are buried in deepest recesses of the official unconscious. While reluctance to set out aims, principles and values may be in part a response to the danger of bland platitude, curriculum framework that is silent on the subject is seriously deficient.

Steiner-Waldorf values

Steiner-Waldorf education places humane values at the centre of the curriculum. The introduction to the Steiner Waldorf Schools' Fellowship Code of Practice includes five organising principles which need to be embedded in the way each school is organised and operates:

* *Respect* for the integrity (individual essence, or spirit) of each individual and of the living world in general
* *Interest in and positive approach* towards the potential for development in young people in particular, and humanity in general
* Recognition of the central importance of *lifelong learning*
* *Commitment* to the core task of educating children in the light of the above
* Encourage, enable and value the *contribution* of individuals, groups and communities to the improvement of our common human culture

Consequently, the Steiner-Waldorf curriculum is led by values, simultaneously individual and social, which recognise that individualities develop in and with communities. The earlier edition of this volume included the following words:

> *The children in any class come from varied social and cultural backgrounds. These groups of mixed religion, national and ethnic background coalesce into a social group which stays together through their school time. A class is a microcosm of the society around them and young people learn to respect and understand differences in all its forms.*

Ultimately, any education that attempts to include 'spiritual values' such as these is one that is sensitive to and leads to the development of a sense of context in its widest sense: we grow as human beings through and with the humanity of others.

Perhaps the key distinctive quality of Steiner-Waldorf education is its recognition of the 'human spirit'. 'Spirituality' in the English language (at least within Britain) has tended to be associated with religious belief, and secularists view this suspiciously. 'Spiritual, moral, social and cultural education' may be an essential for the registration and inspection of schools[7] but there is little clarity and still less substance to the first of these. For the

Waldorf educator, 'spiritual education' is a concrete intention within the Steiner-Waldorf approach. But the intention is an indirect one: it is not a matter of giving children and young people certain precepts and ideas that are 'spiritual', as might be the case for a religiously-orientated school; rather it is helping students to make a powerful personal connection with idealism, with everything that can inspire them to feel and value a capacity grow as active co-creators in their world. The 'spiritual intention' here is therefore a concern to clear away, so far as is possible, the obstacles and impediments towards a free, clear-sighted appreciation of rich diversity and the underlying coherence of our potential humanity.

Rudolf Steiner emphasised this to the parents and founding teachers of the first school:

> *The wish for a selective, elitist education has no place in a Steiner-Waldorf school. Parents who want such an education are in the wrong place. The right of all children to the highest quality education is not only a social ideal but a social necessity.*[8]

Social harmony today relies upon an integrated, multi-cultural, mixed ability educational environment with equity of opportunity. We can see clearly enough what happens in divided communities, whether in the UK or further afield, when this is not the case and when the schooling system serves to confirm conflict and prejudice.

In Steiner-Waldorf settings, children are not streamed for ability on a permanent basis and the curriculum aims to provide wide scope for different types of intelligence, gifts or learning styles. Although differentiation must be part of the teachers' toolkit, and grouping becomes necessary in a minority of subjects (usually after age fourteen), continuity and a sense of community can still be fostered. The ethos of a class is usually strong, enabling the group to both carry and deal with the kind of crises that occur as part of normal child development. Social difficulties, changeable friendships and occasional fallings out are part of growing up, as they are part of adult relationships, and must be addressed in age-appropriate ways. Kindness, sharing and the ability to listen to others are actively encouraged. An understanding that deeds have consequences is likewise engendered.

In a non-competitive environment the children are encouraged to take pride in their work and achieve the highest standards they are personally capable of. Pupils are also encouraged to evaluate their own and fellow pupils' achievements in an objective, though positive and constructive way.[9]

The teachers try to impart to the children a sense of wonder and reverence for natural phenomena and for other people, and this forms a basis in the young child for interest, respect and the desire for knowledge in the adolescent. With such a foundation, young people can cultivate their own inner voice of conscience and sense of justice and responsibility.

Team work and problem solving are learned through many artistic and practical projects. Through comprehensive work-experience, ecological and social practicals, the students gain not only insight into the world of work but they also learn to empathise with others and to recognise the necessity for mutual support in all realms of life.

In their contacts with the pupils, the enthusiasm of the teachers is a moral force which arises out of their own personal development and growth. Teachers are effective and influential not only in what they know but equally in who they are and what they stand for.

Children are taught to form judgements on the basis of sound observation and to transfer these skills to the personal, social and moral domain.

The school community as a whole reflects these principles, not as a belief system but rather as a recognition of the inherent idealism in all people. The involvement, commitment and not least the work and sacrifice made by the parents, have an exemplary and motivating influence on the pupils. Vandalism, truancy and bullying are rare in Steiner-Waldorf schools, which probably reflects pupils' identification with the ethos of the school.

Much time is given to the resolution of social difficulties in the classroom or school context. Schools have effective bullying and conflict resolution policies which are regularly reviewed in the weekly teachers' meetings and which are implemented as and when difficulties occur. The adult school community likewise seeks to address issues of grievance and conflict in a constructive manner. Both parents and teachers contribute to this process.

The anthroposophical basis for Steiner-Waldorf education

Steiner-Waldorf education is founded on Rudolf Steiner's conceptualisation of child development. This was based on empirical and academic study, enhanced by Steiner's psychological and spiritual insights. The resulting philosophy of education has been interrogated, supplemented and re-evaluated by a considerable practical research over the course of nearly a century. An extensive secondary literature exists in various languages which describes this developmental work.

As has already been mentioned, Steiner's understanding of the nature of the human being formed the central part of a philosophy and cosmology that he called *anthroposophy.*[10] This provides a rich field for study in the form of published books and articles and, mainly, lectures recorded by members of Steiner's audiences, uncorrected by the author. The wide range of subjects testify to his many interests and eclectic studies although it must be emphasised that, of the full range of his work, only the educational lectures and writings are relevant.

Steiner was asked by the industrialist Emil Molt, Director of the Waldorf Astoria Cigarette Factory, to establish the first Waldorf School in Stuttgart in 1919, initially for the children of the workers. Steiner worked as adviser to the school until his death in 1925. During that time he gave a number of courses to the teachers, visited lessons and regularly attended teachers' meetings. The original curriculum designed by Steiner underwent further collegial development as the teachers tested its application. Since then, what has become known as the Waldorf curriculum has evolved and been adapted to changing cultural and geographical circumstances throughout the world and is now used in over 1200 schools in some 60 countries.

Steiner's educational work in Anthroposophy forms the philosophical basis for Steiner-Waldorf education but its content is not taught in the schools. Its insights and ethos, however, inform the curriculum and provide teachers with a body of ideas with which they as individuals work, and from which they derive inspiration. Steiner himself described anthroposophy as '*a path of knowledge that seeks to lead the spiritual in human beings to the spiritual in the universe.*'[11]

Whilst it is not within the scope of this book to give a detailed account of anthroposophy, some aspects relevant to Steiner-Waldorf education should be briefly explained.

Anthroposophy starts from the premise that human being-hood has a threefold character: body (physical), soul (psychological) and spirit (essential being) are integrated during life and the process of human maturation and individuation is one in which a portion of essential being, referred to as the 'I' or Ego, seeks to fashion its physical and sensate vehicle in order to live and express itself. As Steiner himself put it, the human being is a citizen of three different worlds:

> *In body, we both belong to and perceive the outer world; in soul, we build up our own inner world; and in spirit, a third world that is higher than both of the others reveals itself to us.*[12]

This traditional threefold differentiation of body, soul and spirit are existential vessels for three fundamental functions of consciousness (see diagram right): wide-awake thinking (cognition), the more dream-like quality of feeling (affect), and will, which in the moment of action is unconscious, like deep sleep (volition). The vessel for these soul functions is provided by what were called the 'elements' in Classical & medieval thought – earth, water, air and fire – each of which stands in a certain relationship to the structure of life: physical/geosphere; formative/biosphere; and two 'higher' structures that together make up what is sometimes called the cultural or noosphere,[13] including consciousness and individuation. Steiner described these elements of the self from a new point of view. In relation to human development, his account of the maturation of the child proposed a gradual assimilation and synthesis of these qualitative elements so that they can serve the unique essence, or individuality, of the emerging person.

Each of these four elements of the human being permeates and is integrated through childhood. The formative – sometimes called rhythmic or 'ether' – body enfolds and transcends the mineral, so that the physical can function as an organism in time, regulating life rhythms, growth, regeneration and reproductive processes. Living things with just these two principles would have substance and life only: we call these 'plants'. In human beings, the formative self supports higher functions and is the bearer of patterns of habitual behaviour, constitutional characteristics, memory and the capacity for forming mental pictures.

Beyond this and related to consciousness, the sensate, or 'astral', body enfolds and transcends the merely biological, providing the capacity to react to and manipulate stimuli both from the environment and from within the organism. Though consciousness obviously exists at the level of sensation of pain and pleasure, full consciousness

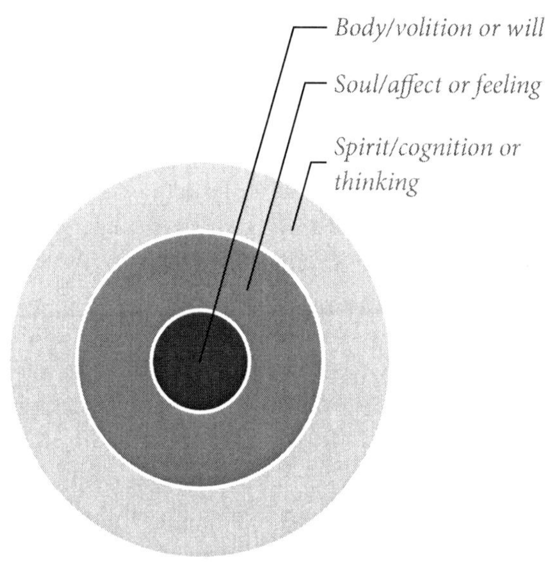

is only present as a entirely human capability when it raises its focus of attention beyond the awareness of bodily states or emotional, subjective content. Through consciousness of self, the individual achieves a sense of identity. In human beings, this enables a highly developed cultural life to emerge, within which motive, individuality and the potential for both freedom and responsibility can be developed. We use the word 'I' to describe the totality of this experience.

Just as the brain is the integrating centre for the physical organism as perceived through the senses, so the 'I' is the focus for the Self. The body and soul react to stimulation from outside. However, through the process of individuation, the 'I' increasingly becomes the centre from which the individual directs intention and becomes able to select motive.

> *We are justified in seeing the 'I' as our true being, and may therefore describe body and soul as the 'garments' in which we live, as the bodily conditions under which we act. In the course of our development we learn to use these instruments more and more as servants of our 'I'.*[14]

Through the 'I', spirit lives and comes to expression in the individual thinker.

Thinking grants us access to higher meaning, to laws and principles that are inherent in the world outside our personality. In seeking knowledge and truth we make a connection to that which, though it arises within ourselves, has an independent existence beyond our experience of it, touching, the objective or universal. As Steiner put it:

> *We must realise that the truth, in itself, endures, even though our thoughts are only transient manifestations of eternal truths.*[15]

This is also true of moral values:

> *What is morally right, like what is true, has an intrinsic eternal value that it receives from the spiritual soul.*[16]

Where a human being is ennobled or enlightened by eternal truth, the spiritual comes to expression, something we may experience in an encounter with people who have fought their way, often through trails of one sort and another, to a certain nobility and presence. At this level the psyche is partially freed from the compulsion of self-orientated desires, such as compulsion, aversion, and instinctive sympathies or antipathies.

What we have set out here is simplified account of what Steiner described in a variety of ways. His multi-perspective account, often conveyed through his use of specialised and unfamiliar terms drawn from contemplative tradition, provides a richer, more nuanced and detailed account than is possible here.

Taking this, however, as a starting point, the individuation process, in which education plays a very significant, supportive role, involves a progressive shift in the activity of the 'I' in integrating into the other elements of the self described above. At birth, the 'I' is primarily active within the physical body. At around the age of seven, some of the forces of the life body gradually become superfluous to their organic functions and emancipate themselves from the physical organism. They thus become available to support the emergence of a distinctive inner life and particularly to enable the process of mental picturing and the formation of memory, two processes essential to learning. Before this emancipation has occurred, the child learns through imitation rather than through understanding, since sense experiences pass relatively unmediated by the mind into the activity of the child. Once the formative forces of the life body begin to free themselves, the child can increasingly form and structure an inner life of experience. Whilst memory is still closely bound to the organism, it will be situational rather than independent. Only once memory can function independently of sensory stimulus is abstract thought possible.

At puberty, the soul activities of thinking, feeling and willing, which have hitherto been at work within the processes of the physical organs and life processes, begin to emancipate themselves. The 'I' becomes active within the soul in aiding the young person to make judgements, form independent concepts and gradually direct their own behaviour according to conscious intentions motivated by ideals.

It will be clear from even this very brief characterisation that it is a central task of education to support the self-activity of the 'I' in each child in integrating the various bodies in such a way that healthy, harmonious development can occur. Supporting the self-activity of the individual is essential in realising his or her potential to the fullest extent. All aspects of education serve that aim.

Rudolf Steiner made the relationship between anthroposophy and Waldorf education very clear when he addressed parents at the newly founded first Waldorf School:

> *You absolutely do not need to be afraid that we are trying to make this school into one that represents a particular philosophy, or that we intend to drum any anthroposophical or other dogmas into the children. That is not what we have in mind. Anyone who says that we are trying to teach the children specifically anthroposophical convictions is not telling the truth. Rather, we are trying to develop an art of education on the basis of what anthroposophy means to us. The 'how' of education is what we are trying to gain from our spiritual understanding. We are not trying to drum our opinions into the children, but we believe that spiritual science differs from any other science in engaging the entire person, in making people skilful in all areas, but especially in their dealings with other human beings. This 'how' is what we are trying to look at, not the 'what'. The 'what' is the result of social necessities; we must apply our full interest to deriving it from a reading of what people should know and be able to do if they are to take their place in our times as good, capable individuals. The 'how', on the other hand, how to teach the children something, can only result from a thorough, profound and loving understanding of the human being. This is what is meant to work and to prevail in our Waldorf School.*[17]

This brief and highly compressed account of the background of Steiner-Waldorf practice will be elucidated further by the following sections, which provide an account of how this finds its way into the practical work of the teacher.

2

The Stages of Development in Relation to the Curriculum

The ideal curriculum must be modelled on the changing nature of the human being passing through different phases while growing up. But like any ideal it is confronted by the reality of life and must accommodate itself accordingly. This reality comprises many things: the individuality of the teacher, the class itself with all the peculiarities of every pupil in it, the moment in history, the education authorities and education laws prevailing at the place where the school wanting to implement the curriculum is located. All these factors modify the ideal curriculum and call for transformation and discussion. The educational task with which the growing human being confronts us can only be achieved if the curriculum remains mobile and pliable.

CAROLINE VON HEYDEBRAND

Steiner-Waldorf education recognises three broad stages of child development: 0 to seven years, seven to fourteen years, and fourteen to young adulthood. In educational terms this covers the Early Years period of three to six years, the Lower School period from six to fourteen years and the Upper School from fourteen to nineteen years. Each of these stages is marked by significant and specific developments in physical, psychological and spiritual maturation. The following descriptions provide a very general summary.

Whilst each stage represents a phase of life, integral and distinct *in its own right*, each metamorphoses into the next. Processes coming to a certain culmination in one phase transform into faculties in the subsequent stage of development. For each stage, however, there is a fundamental, or key-note, which sets the tone and serves to guide the way education can work with the grain of childhood. Thus the Early Years stage, for example, is seen as a valid state of being in its own right, and not merely a preparation for the following stages of life.

From birth to seven: Early Years

The importance of providing the right conditions for early childhood development are, today, fully recognised in theory, if not always in practice. So much depends on the healthy development of the young child's whole being. For this reason, Early Years education has a high profile in Steiner-Waldorf education where practitioners have always been accorded equal status within the profession. Given the increasing pressures on young children and the loss of many traditional forms of nurture and support in the contemporary environment, Early Years education needs greater research, teacher development, parent education and resources than ever before.

In the first three years, the infant is actively growing and adapting to the needs of body and to the environment within which the child is growing. This is a wonderfully complex process that achieves three fundamentals to subsequent development and learning: the achievement of balance and upright walking, the acquisition of language, and the establishing of a basis for cognition. At the same time, the young child begins to relate to other people, becoming a member of human society as represented by the extended circle of those family, friends and others the child encounters. One can only look upon these achievements with the most profound respect. What the very young child needs most of all is a loving environment, and within this healthy nutrition and proper care. Children are interactive beings that thrive on loving attention, communication and the security of being an integral social group.

In this phase, the young child learns primarily through imitation and play. Children absorb and digest their experiences in a largely unconscious way. Learning is *caught rather than taught*; that is to say, through implicit rather than explicit teaching methods. Children need a secure, caring and enabling environment where activities occur in a meaningful context. What they experience is turned into activity, which in turn plays a part in forming their organism as a whole. Imitation actually educates the physical organism as well as establishing the mother tongue, habits, and patterns of behaviour.

Play is a serious and vital activity of early childhood. Through play, the powers of creativity, imagination and initiative are cultivated. It is in play that children learn to relate. In the Early Years phase, the task of education is to provide an environment in which good habits of behaviour – such as memory, reverence, orderliness, listening and enjoyment of the natural world – can be established.

School readiness

During their first six or seven years, children's senses are immensely active even though there is little ability to filter those powerful sense impressions. Small children are uninhibitedly open to their surroundings, accepting everything they find there. What serves them best is an environment and people in it who can set worthy examples. Only once this formative process has reached a certain degree of completion, especially in the brain, can the forces that have shaped the organs and established their life-rhythm be gradually released. This is the moment when children can be considered ready for formal school learning.

Around the age of six these formative forces progressively become accessible to the processes of education, enabling the child to form mental pictures, establish memory, learn and focus attention. If these forces are prematurely called upon, however, for formal learning of literacy or numeracy, for example, there can be a loss of vitality and a narrowing of the experiential basis for subsequent learning to build on. Similarly, if children do not have the opportunity between the ages of five and six years to apply their imaginative will to the social tasks of being with and helping others in an un-reflected and intuitive way, their subsequent social competence may be limited.

Up until the age of around four years, young children tend to play *alongside* other children. From this age on they tend to play increasingly *with* their peers and engage, given the right encouragement, in constructive social interaction through creative play. This marks a significant development, which needs time to mature and become structured. Many children are quite capable of applying their intelligence to tasks such as learning to read and write. The vital question is whether this intelligence should first be given time to develop social awareness through such things as creative play. If this doesn't happen, higher skills may become anti-social, focussed upon controlling rather than communicating and sharing. The listening and oral language skills, the social interaction and initiative that children can develop at this age in a structured kindergarten setting should not be underestimated. If the early years period is essentially characterised by the child's will in activity, this last part of the first seven year phase is important for the development of will in the social and feeling realm.

There is a whole range of symptoms indicating the freeing of the formative forces which show that the child is ready to make the transition to formal learning in school; the change of teeth is one of the more obvious but by no means the only criteria. Others include co-ordination of movement, the ability to form consciously accessible memory, greater emotional independence and strength to leave the relative security of parents and kindergarten. It is becoming increasingly difficult to assess children's readiness for school and it is by no means an automatic question of chronological age, maturity or ability. Long-term factors need to be borne in mind and the advice of a group of professionals – including the kindergarten teacher, the class teacher and school doctor – is often sought. Delaying school entry can sometimes be as unhelpful as pushing precocious children.[1]

Ultimately it is how we understand the nature of the curriculum which proves decisive. Asking if the child ready for Class 1 is one perspective; another is to enquire whether the child *needs* Class 1 in order to begin the process of maturation that comes with formal schooling. Ultimately, school readiness is a complex issue which needs to considered in the light of whether school is ready for the child as much as it is the other way around. Such decisions need to be taken on an individual basis.

From the seventh year to age fourteen

During this stage, children begin formal learning and the intellectual development of the child is fostered through the establishment of basic learning skills and the development of memory in a way that is firmly rooted in practical life. All learning at this stage seeks to engage the feelings of the child so that a strong personal identification with the subject matter can occur. Learning is essentially experiential, and strong and continuous narrative structures with an element of personification enhance direct experience. Imagination is a key quality, and pictorial imagery is a vital factor in making learning a personal inner experience. Art and music play an important role in engaging the child's feelings.

One of the keys, especially during the early part of this phase, is narrative and pictorial thinking.

Through narrative, children develop their conceptual framework so that they can understand themselves and their experiences. Narrative contains beginnings, exposition and conclusion, or outcomes. Thus narrative sequence enables meaning to arise; even when the situation depicted may be beyond the child's immediate grasp, it directs attention to personal experience[2] from the reassuring background of cultural universe. This is why listening to stories being told by a teacher in his or her own words is a powerful experience and deeply engaging. At the same time, linguistic and listening skills are being exercised.

> *Knowledge through narrative rather than mere transmission is constructed afresh by each individual knower on the basis of what is already known and by means of strategies developed both inside and outside the classroom.*[3]
>
> GORDON WELLS

Through storytelling, children become participants in their community and culture; it is collaborative as well as personal, enabling children to 'digest' their experience. Painful and difficult events such as those that bring grief, loss, anger and anxiety can be clothed in story form so that the listener can find ways to come to terms with their feelings. Conflict or tensions between individuals can often be worked through in this indirect way. Paradoxically, story is often more objective than a direct or moralising approach.

Children are told stories from a range of sources: folk and fairy tale, legend, fable, parable, mythology, history, literature. Content is also related in oral form. For younger children this may involve personification and anthropomorphism, e.g. 'number gnomes', dialogue between animals or plants, colours relating to each other in watercolour painting lessons, etc. For older children, biography is an important element in history as a means of helping them to find their own place within past experience of others.

With older pupils there remains a strong element of oral description in all presentations with an emphasis on processes, sequences of events and outcomes. Communicating, exchanging viewpoints, dialogue and debate all have their place in lessons. The groundwork for such abilities is laid down in the younger classes. Narrative furthers this by exemplifying dialogue structure, by helping to shape experience into communicable form, and by cultivating listening, perhaps the key skill in the classroom.

This period has distinct sub-phases: up to the age of nine, between nine and twelve, and from twelve to fourteen. These stages are marked by, among other things, specific cognitive developments and the changing relationship of self to the world.

Ages seven to nine

One of the main characteristics of children between the seventh and ninth year is their desire to learn, without any need to form their own judgements. Memory, imagination, enjoyment of rhythmical repetition, and a desire for universal concepts presented in pictorial form, come to the fore at this stage. Children retain a bias towards accepting the authority of the adult world, but this is not now a matter of imitation but of concentrating attention upon major role models; these affect the child largely through the feeling of their words or moral strength of their actions. A child's inner question to the teacher is: 'Can you really see who I am?'

and 'Can you help me encounter the world?' This determines the teacher's position and relationship in regard to the child. These basic questions are answered in and through the lessons which aim not only to teach about experiencing the world but also to let the children actually experience the world. The teacher who succeeds in meeting these expectations set by the children will be accepted by them as an authority, something very different to attempting to control children as an authoritarian.

The ninth year

An experience of separation from this naive acceptance of the adult world takes place at around nine years of age, i.e. in Class 3. Unconsciously at first, the children begin to question the teacher's authority, which they have hitherto accepted unquestioningly almost like a law of nature. They now want to know whether what the teacher says really is securely based on real experience of the world and of life. On the whole this question remains at the sub-conscious level and is rarely put verbally, except in a growing tendency to criticise. The children now want to know that their admiration is justified. This means that a new teaching method is called for. The aspects of the world presented in school have to take account of this distancing process and the children need to be accompanied and supported in the right way as they step out of what often seems to be the inner 'glow' of childhood into the new reality of a world that is more differentiated and more diverse. But confronting them with the world 'as it really is' does not mean that they must immediately be presented with cold or sobering scientific facts entirely detached from human life. The 'loss of paradise', which is a common theme in nearly every mythology or folk memory, is increasingly felt by each individual child, calling for more individualised centring outwards to the environment.

Between the ages of nine and twelve, rhythmical memory is at its strongest. The teaching method should draw on the child's natural interest in the world and structure the content rhythmically.

Ages nine to twelve

Children begin a new phase of development between their tenth and twelfth years. By the age of twelve, the harmonious physical proportions, typical for the middle period of childhood, are usually lost. The limbs begin to predominate and the muscular system develops.

Psychologically there is an obviously critical attitude, and the children's newly won capacity to think causally must now be taken into account. The intellectuality now preparing to claim its right to be heard must be pointed in appropriate directions. The pupils' questioning, searching attitude needs to be directed increasingly towards inanimate nature and its laws. Finding those laws, which exist independently of humanity and remain valid in spite of this, is a source of delight and satisfaction. Nonetheless, a strong personal and subjective element is retained, with the children knowing that those who are doing the searching and discovering are still human beings and not some incomprehensible instruments. The children sense of space, but also that of time, seeks structure and learning about historical processes gains significance. History is shown to have been shaped by human beings who are in turn changed by historical forces, and not merely peopled by two dimensional historical figures attached to dates in the abstract. History can be both causal and passionate!

Ages twelve to fourteen

The final third of this second seven year phase is characterised by the range of symptoms we label 'puberty'. The visible physiological changes and rapid growth are accompanied by psychological upheaval at least as disorientating and often more so. In both realms the child tends to lose whatever balance and equanimity they may have had during the heart of childhood. Teachers and parents come up against the limits of their abilities to directly influence and boundary issues can cause conflict. Much that has been adopted in terms of behaviour, attitudes or habits is lost or becomes ambivalent. As their inner life and self-experience becomes increasingly introspective and self-centred, the young adolescent increasingly needs a new, more objective orientation from teachers and parents. From twelve onwards, children are increasingly able to form abstract concepts and understand causal relationships. This phase sees the introduction of exact observation and the transition from myth to history.

In this first phase of puberty, children have a strong urge to take hold of, even to 'conquer', the world around them. This essentially aggressive gesture is, however, on the whole a rough kind of playfulness. Challenging them physically can help them extricate themselves from this. The class teacher will endeavour to direct their attention away from themselves and towards the way the natural (and technical) world around them functions. Technology, profession and work become important themes.

> *The most important aspect of educating young people of this age is to educate their will. If this can be achieved, the youngsters can find their home in the 'outside world' step by step. Only by focusing on specific activities in the world can they gain ever new experiences about the partial sovereignty of their own inner being over this world. They also learn that this sovereignty can be extended, although each extension is only achieved as the result of considerable effort.*[4]

When young people seeking to find a new orientation in the world discover that other, older individuals are also engaged in inner battles, it can help them considerably to appreciate others' questions, ideals, frustrations and limitations. But they must be left sufficiently free if these discoveries are to be a help to them. The more isolated young people feel in the world, the more they will long for and seek for an holistic view of the world to provide their orientation. They now have a growing interest in the interrelation of the traditional disciplines of science. These needs and experiences must govern the teacher's decisions as to method and teaching approach.

In Classes 1 to 3 the teacher had to be a master of the 'language of the universe' and make it audible for the children. In the second phase he or she had to articulate the dialogue between world phenomena and the human being. Now, as the youngsters fall silent outwardly in the third phase, the teacher must develop the capacity to hear their inner speech, the young people's hidden words.

Adolescence

With proper encouragement, adolescents set about developing powers of independent judgement, intellect, and striving towards truth. They look to the worlds of culture and nature to reveal their inner principles in clear, objective and, therefore, inspiring ways. Adolescents need to nurture their emerging inner selves with ideals worthy of their attention. Teaching methods become increasingly conceptual and cognitive. While independent inquiry and self-directed tasks are promoted throughout the entire curriculum, the focus now shifts to a more analytical and self-determined approach to learning. Students should learn to view the world from a range of different perspectives. The Upper School curriculum provides a broad basis of learning and prepares the students for access to further and higher education.

School structure

The school structure reflects the major developmental phases. Fully developed Steiner-Waldorf schools are integrated pre-school, primary and secondary (high) schools, usually on one site, under a single management. They comprise:

- Pre-school
  - parent and child groups
  - playgroup or nursery (age three to four)
  - kindergartens (up to age six; groups of up to twenty children with kindergarten teacher and assistant)
  - afternoon care provision
- Lower School
  - Classes 1–8 (age six to fourteen)
- Upper School
  - Classes 9–12 (age fourteen to eighteen/nineteen)

Children enter Class 1 of school at the age of six. In many smaller schools, two age groups are combined in one class, e.g. Class 2/3 are aged seven to nine. All classes are of mixed ability and gender. Class sizes range from twelve to thirty pupils per class.

3

The Steiner-Waldorf Approach

This chapter describes key aspects of the Steiner-Waldorf approach, focusing primarily on the Lower School (age six to fourteen).

The class teacher

Each class has a class teacher who moves up the school with the class. Ideally the class teacher remains with the class for eight years, though sometimes circumstances dictate otherwise.

The class teacher teaches the main morning lesson comprising the first two hours of each day and normally some other lessons with his or her class. Specialist teachers teach foreign languages, music, games and movement, eurythmy, handwork, etc. to each class.

The class teacher provides a focus for the class and continuity over many years of development. He or she aims to be a figure of moral authority based on commitment, care for the children and a close relationship with the parents.

> *A curriculum that, from the outset, lays down the timetable and all sorts of other things completely eliminates the art of teaching... The teacher must be the driving and stimulating force in the whole education system.*[1]

The structure of the school day

Each day begins with a two-hour period known as the main-lesson. This teaching unit is integrated and cross-curricular and includes activities to awaken and focus the children's attention, oral and written practice of basic skills, mental arithmetic, music and drawing, presentation of new material, recall and discussion of the previous day's (or earlier) work, individual working, conversation, narrative and practical work.

This is followed by 40–45 minute subject lessons, often doubled for art and crafts.

Priority is given in the morning to the more academic subjects and the afternoons are usually used for arts and crafts, outdoor activities, sport and practical work. Subjects such as music, eurythmy and foreign languages, which benefit from regular practice, are evenly spaced throughout the middle of the day whenever possible. In making up a school timetable, priority is given to the younger classes for whom a balanced rhythm of lessons and activities is especially important. The older classes are usually more able to cope with less than ideal conditions.

The main-lesson

The main-lesson (also referred to as the 'morning lesson' in some schools) is a central feature of the Steiner-Waldorf approach. This lesson begins each school day and is normally about two hours in length. Subjects are taught in blocks of several weeks. All classes (Classes 1–12, ages six to eighteen), follow a main-lesson programme.

Principles and features

The main-lesson embraces and addresses a varied and progressive range of skills, competencies and faculties in mathematics, English, the arts, science and humanities. Each day's main-lesson is viewed as an integrated and organic whole. Meaningful connections are made across subject areas and between main-lesson themes.

The class teacher chooses material, presentation and activities to suit the requirements of the curriculum and the needs of the specific class. Considerable care is given to preparation. Following a daily review process, the class teacher makes adjustments to the lesson plan as needed. It is the aim of the class teacher to make each lesson an artistic whole in which the parts relate to the whole; and the whole is permeated with rhythm, structure and purpose, as opposed to being a mere chain of events, however purposeful each link may be. This artistic approach is thought to have a beneficial effect on the children's learning.

The main-lesson incorporates activities and content which address the children's intellectual-cognitive, aesthetic-affective and practical modes of learning.

Each lesson is structured to contain a range of the following activities:

* First part – a morning verse, recitation of poetry, singing, musical instrumental work, mental arithmetic and recall of previous material.
* Second part – presentation of new material and discussion.
* Third part – individual working, narrative, practice of basic skills.

Assessment and learning outcomes

The assessment of learning through the main-lesson programme is an ongoing process as the teacher endeavours to draw up a detailed profile, or child study, of each pupil, which conveys a picture of the child's learning and behaviour in the practical, emotional and cognitive realms, while seeking to understand and develop each child's skills, capacities and faculties (see Chapter 4, Evaluation and Assessment).

Assignments are ongoing and arise out of work covered or introduced in classroom presentations. Projects, essays, tests and artistic/practical tasks indicate the range of assignments which are given.

In the course of the main-lesson the pupils' work is assessed in a variety of modes and recorded and used to build up individual pupil profiles, known as School Reports. This information is included in the personal profile and used to define points of progression, intervention strategies or appropriate remedial support.

Records that are kept are shared with subject teachers, parents and, from the Middle School upwards, with pupils.[2]

The teachers plan their main-lessons and define their aims and expected learning outcomes. This is done individually and shared with the team of other class and subject teachers in regular weekly teachers' meetings.

Rhythm in learning

The Steiner-Waldorf approach sees rhythm as a vital element in learning.

The school day and the school year are structured in an organic way, which establishes a healthy balance of experience between concentration and relaxation, mental and practical work, movement and rest, listening and participating, looking and doing. Each lesson should contain a balance between the engagement of the child's thinking, their feeling and their willing. Each day has its own structured rhythm, as does each lesson.

Rhythm enables repetition to occur with renewed interest. By changing activities regularly, interest and attention can be maintained as well as being physiologically stimulating. The teacher can plan a variety of activities to suit the attention span of a given class and can vary this spontaneously according to need.

Such rhythms are flexible and can be directed by the teacher in response to the needs of the children, e.g. Monday morning has a different quality to Friday morning. These factors actively play into lesson planning.

The celebration of the seasonal festivals gives the whole school year a balance and a sense of continuity as well as helping to form a strong community experience.

Forgetting and remembering

The learning process itself benefits from a rhythmical approach.

Steiner-Waldorf differentiates between skills needing regular practice (foreign languages, music, maths, spelling, etc.) and the introduction of new content. New experiences or teaching content are often best introduced after a period during which the assimilation of previously taught material can occur. Acquiring new skills and practising them until they become ability are two different processes requiring different rhythms

Following a period of concentration on a given topic, say three or four weeks, this is then dropped and allowed to rest before being explicitly raised to consciousness again later. Experience shows a significant 'settling' effect, during which knowledge becomes faculty. This can be recalled at a later stage and built upon in a subsequent main-lesson. The 're-membering' or re-integrating of personal experience into a wider context is an important part of the learning process.

The nature of memory itself undergoes metamorphosis, evolving from situational, reflex memory to abstract memory. Steiner-Waldorf draws strongly on these different memory types. Situational memory is strengthened by healthy routine in the younger classes, rhythmical memory is cultivated by such oral work as learning multiplication tables, number bonds, poems, proverbs, songs and foreign language vocabulary by heart. Active recall is a major skill practised daily in most lessons, as is the remembering and reviewing of complex shared situations. Good memory is based on the individual forming a strong bond of identification to his/her experiences. This is best achieved by engaging the pupils' interest and stimulating their feeling response. The other key to memory is context. All knowledge needs to be bedded in a context meaningful to the pupil. Imaginative teaching is crucial in the sense that pupils are enabled to imagine or form mental pictures in relation to what is being taught. Lack of tension is also a help to active memory, and the teacher attempts to create a mood of relaxed awareness in the class.

Learning in stages

In the main-lesson programme, and in the subject lessons where appropriate, three broad phases of learning can be identified. Stage one generally takes place over one day – the first day. Stage two usually occurs on the next day – the second day. The third stage, or phase, may take place over the following days, weeks or, in some cases, years, since the guiding aim of the third stage is to explore and consider concepts that are not fixed and finished, but fluid and alive. By focusing on concepts that are unfinished and organic, the pupils have the time and the space to make them their own through a process of digestion, assimilation and growth. In this manner, the lesson content can be understood by the individual in a differentiated and meaningful way. The teaching is thus transformed into learning.

Stage one

The teacher presents new material or guides the children to specific learning experiences. The children receive the new content, they experience it and then, at the end of the lesson, it is hoped that they will let it sink from focused consciousness to the deeper layers of memory. Teaching content that is too abstract may prove 'indigestible'; and teaching that is too unstructured or chaotic may not have sufficiently engaged the pupils' attention – as is the case in boring, tedious lessons.

Stage two

On the second day, after 'sleeping on' the previous day's content, the children are called upon to remember what was previously presented. In a process of discussion, recall and 'weighing up', the pupils are now invited to express creatively individualised and differentiated learning outcomes. The content is now owned by the pupils and has been transformed. On a feeling level, a process of judgement-forming has taken place.

It is felt that the literal process of sleep is an essential part of learning. Clearly the brain processes sensory information in significant ways during REM and phases of deep sleep. On the following day such experiences often have a far more integrated character.

Stage three

As the children move through the Lower School years, towards the development of analytical, causative thinking capacities, this third stage becomes more important as a consciously-sought element in the lesson. In this stage there is a further development of understanding towards the conceptual realm. Through a guided synthesis of different experiences, judgements and perspectives, the pupils are led towards the identification of a concept, or a scientific law. The seeds of the first stage have now developed and metamorphosed through a process of experiencing, forgetting, creative remembering and individual expression towards the flowering of concepts which are lively, mobile and founded in reality. Living concepts, introduced pictorially to younger children, are revisited as the children grow up. The inner structure of the curriculum facilitates this spiral learning by building on earlier experiences.

Whole class teaching

The Steiner-Waldorf approach is centred around whole class teaching. The teacher is a focus for the learning experience. This form is complemented by group work, differentiation into ability groups for maths, reading, etc. However, such differentiation always goes from the whole class to groups which are then re-integrated back into the whole class.

A class of mixed ability children is a model for community. The task of the class teacher is to foster social awareness and cohesion within the class group. This process is enhanced by the long-term continuity offered by the class teacher.

There is much emphasis on children learning from and with each other, learning to appreciate each other's gifts and developing an understanding of each other's limitations and weaknesses.

The cultivation of such social awareness, empathy and the daily experience of individual and group problems being tackled constructively helps prepare pupils for life (see Social Skills curriculum).

Pictorial and imaginative language

Throughout the primary years (age six to twelve), the pictorial element is preferred to abstract terminology. Imaginative concepts have the capacity to grow with the child's changing understanding of the world. The teacher uses imagery wherever appropriate in speaking to the children. Young children up to the age of eight or nine require concrete images that evoke strong sensory impressions on the imagination:

> *Hot, salty tears ran down Cinderella's cheeks, making streaks like rain on dusty windows, dripping from her chin and making dark, damp patches on her grey dress.*

Children progress from an imaginative, picture consciousness to more abstract intellectual thought processes. The transition occurs after the age of ten when the ability to think in abstract, and later causal, terms begins to emerge. From this age until puberty, language changes in character from literal to a more metaphoric and moral tone in description. Simile, metaphor and comparison create images in which physical detail is transformed into evocative mood:

> *The north wind cut like a fish gutter's knife. The sea swelled darkly, fraying the wave crests like torn flags. His cheeks aglow with youthful enthusiasm, the young James Cook gripped the rail of the Whitby collier with pride and daring.*

In adolescence, imagery must build on the layers of language to create a level of symbolic meaning:

> *In an image that would later be faked by the photographic department of Pravda (Truth), Lenin climbed onto the giant hulk of a locomotive derailed in the shunting yards of Finlandia Station. Unlike later icons, Lenin did not stand with feet firmly apart,*

left shoulder forward, chest proudly inflated, jowl jutting, the lapels of his greatcoat flapping in the biting wind. He was in fact hunched forward, feet unsteady on the icy metal, cheeks white, eyes dark and bloodshot, the famous beard wispy, his lips cracked. Someone had thrust a straggly bunch of red carnations into his hands. As he tried to clear his head and address the group of ragged railwaymen below, he absent-mindedly plucked the heads off the flowers one by one.

The pictorial element is not only relevant for stories. Instructions and directions in classroom contexts can often be given in pictorial form.

We should educate children so that all their concepts are capable of growth, that their concepts and will impulses are really alive. This is not easy. But an artistic education succeeds in doing it. And the children have a different feeling when we offer them living concepts instead of dead ones, for they unconsciously know that what is given them grows with them, just as arms grow with the body.[3]

RUDOLF STEINER

The place of textbooks

The teaching in a Steiner-Waldorf school comes essentially through the teacher and not via text books. The teacher chooses the material and presentation to suit the particular group of children. This is the case in all subjects.

Imaginative, oral and practical presentations of lesson material, thoroughly prepared by the teacher, engender interest and enhance the authority of the teacher in the eyes of the children.

The fundamental mode of delivery for lesson content is the immediate and direct interface between pupils and teacher, with the latter supported by appropriate materials and resources, including prepared work sheets, texts, vocabulary lists, maps, diagrams, etc.

Reference books, such as dictionaries and atlases, are made use of as appropriate, but always in support of the teacher's main presentation.

Likewise, assignments and projects arising out of the lesson theme require that the pupils develop competence in a range of reading techniques and manual information-retrieval skills by the time they reach age twelve (Class 6).

The authority of the teacher

In the Early Years period, the presence of inner authority working through the teacher's gestures, speech, actions and mood allows the young child to imbibe a living example of authority, the essence of which may be emulated in later years. The inner attitude of the teacher is reinforced by strong rhythms and routines which quieten behaviour.

In the Lower School period, children need clear guidance and boundaries. It is the role of the class teacher to provide these and to exemplify models of conduct. This authority manifests in the presentation of lesson material and in the whole social and pedagogical life of the class.

In adolescence the emphasis on authority as a pedagogical gesture shifts to the teacher as an authority in a given subject field. Based on his or her own integrity and search for truth, the teacher can lead the young person towards enthusiastic enquiry into what is true. The focus now moves to the development of independent judgement based on sound observation.

Together these three broad approaches, or aspects, of authority – imitation, guidance and respect for expertise – provide a setting in which ethical individualism and individual morality may flourish.

Discipline

Early Years

Young children imitate. It is in their nature to do so. The young child is sensitive to the environment in all its aspects – the material and the human – the physical, emotional and spiritual.

In order to cultivate discipline in the early years, it is incumbent on teachers and parents to create a healthy environment for a child to imitate. Children unconsciously respond to the moods created by adults. The extent to which conscious activity has structured this environment in a meaningful – as opposed to a haphazard – way is important. Children notice whether adults are sincere in their gestures, speech and general bearing. Adult relationships are observed, and children have a deep need to know that the world is good. Educators and parents have a responsibility to strive towards an honest morality. In many life situations this may be the only 'good' available – yet it is the most important. Time and again this has been demonstrated in times of war and social disaster: love is the absolute essential in Early Years education.

By consciously working with rhythm – daily, weekly and the yearly cycle through the seasons and the festivals – and using rhythmical repetition as a pedagogical tool, the teacher promotes and provides discipline for the young child.

Lower School

In the Lower School, rhythm, form, boundaries and teacher-authority unite to provide a meaningful structure within which the children are held and nurtured.

Well-prepared lessons, employing a suitable range of teaching strategies, foster a mood of positive discipline. When pupils are inspired and encouraged to develop specific skills and capacities, while working at a suitable pace and level, conditions are present in which good discipline can flourish.

The teacher's quest for self-development and professional excellence provides an important role model for pupils.

When authoritative guidance inspires the teaching, independence is conferred on the child and conditions are laid down for the development of self-discipline in later years.

The approach to discipline seeks to follow what may be called an 'artistic' approach. In presenting lesson material, setting of tasks and assignments, the teacher has the responsibility to create and inspire structure in classroom management and classroom life. In consciously providing a space, the teacher offers freedom. In this creative space there is room for dynamic interplay between absorption and assimilation, guidance and discovery, teaching and learning.

Upper School

In the Upper School classes, the process of cultivating and developing discipline continues and the focus now shifts towards conscious self-discipline, taking responsibility for one's actions and accepting the consequences of one's behaviour. When infringements occur, students are guided to understand the full consequences of their actions and given the opportunity to redress the harm done. Exclusion is very much a last resort since dialogue is crucial and youngsters need to come to terms with their responsibilities within the context of the social group. Alienation through rejection or humiliation can only make matters worse.

Young people clearly need to test the boundaries they are given and they should be given every opportunity to do this in a positive and constructive way. They also need to learn how to discuss such matters and in particular to understand complex situations from a variety of perspectives.

Rules and their application

Rules and codes of conduct are designed to promote care and respect for the people and objects in the child's environment.

Social harmony, health and safety and a positive, creative learning environment are the guiding motives of school rules. Rules and codes of conduct should be clear, transparent and comprehensible to teachers, parents and pupils, in principle and in detail. Rules and the consequences deriving from their infringement should be age-appropriate.

Where infringements do occur, the incidents are looked at on a case by case basis. The emphasis is on the deed that has been done and attention is given to making good what has been harmed.

Sanctions are not applied in an automatic, 'fixed penalty' manner. Rather, individuals and individual situations are considered and appropriate sanctions and consequences are applied.

Codes of behaviour are regularly reviewed in the weekly staff meeting and are discussed with older pupils and parents.

4

Evaluation and Assessment

> *Assessment is clear seeing, rich understanding, respectful application.*[1]

Assessment, in this sense, is implicit in the whole Waldorf approach. Steiner-Waldorf schools aim for the development of the child to take place holistically, in the round; assessment is therefore a means of gaining knowledge of, insight into and understanding for the child. The more accurate and comprehensive the observations, the richer the understanding and the better staff are able to support and promote positive development.

Good practice occurs when the self-reflective teacher assesses his or her own teaching and its results for the children, and shares their evaluation with colleagues on a regular basis. Thus individual insights are tested collegially and flow back into the classroom. Where this happens, the outcome of assessment is that meaningful help is offered and new developmental opportunities are created. Good assessment can lead to transformation in both teaching and learning.

Assessment serves two essential functions: supporting learning (assessment *for* learning) and providing evidence of attainment in order to monitor the quality of education and the children's response (assessment *of* learning). Assessment *for* learning identifies areas that need attention, helps in setting appropriate tasks for the pupil, focuses on improvement, and is most concerned with the progress of individual pupils with their particular strengths and weaknesses. It can be considered 'formative'.

Assessment *of* learning is usually aimed at providing quantifiable data; it is retrospective to a learning process and is related to a pre-determined set of achievements, for example through external tests or examinations, summing up a course of study or period of instruction. It can be considered 'summative'.

Both types of assessment have their place but either applied inappropriately can be limiting: formative assessment if it is overly intrusive or insufficiently personalised; summative assessment by encouraging a 'closed mindset', avoidance of activities that seem difficult or that require practice, and fixation on 'token' or grade, rather than effort and progress.[2]

Any form of assessment depends upon the curriculum that underpins it and the Steiner-Waldorf curriculum naturally takes formative assessment as its core focus, alongside 'ipsative assessment', to which it closely relates and which is the evaluation of the progress of an individual pupil in their own terms, against a personal starting point[3] (for example, instead of 'I ran faster than x today', 'I ran faster than yesterday'). Formative assessment is an expression of the essential ethos of the kindergarten or class teacher, who provides long-term continuity for the child's development. Each teacher works on the assumption that the child before them possesses greater reserves of potential than can reveal themselves in the present. A child's entire biography is a path of progressive individualisation and realisation of potential. This potential expresses itself in the way a child works through key developmental stages, and how a child learns and encounters the difficulties which life presents. Observing this developmental path, and responding to it, is the prime objective of ipsative and formative assessment.

Summative assessments, which include standardised or 'normative' assessments, such as tests for 'reading age', act as staging posts along the path of the development of a young person. Their role becomes more prominent as the time for external examinations draws nearer. Ideally, of course, these would be an acknowledgement of achievement related to a wide multi-layered curriculum and of the resulting enthusiasms, strengths and cumulative effort of the individual young person. In that sense, assessment of learning could become a springboard for life-long learning. Unfortunately, very few exam systems get close to providing that and 'swot up and forget afterwards' remains commonplace in most. Proposals such as those for various types of diploma, along with assessment made continually over time, are attempts to establish means to identify and give credit to a wider range of attainment. In spite of frequent calls from organisations like the Campaign for British Industry[4] for more emphasis on personal, creative and co-operative skills for school leavers, the trend from the political side of education remains uneasy with concepts like 'soft skills', and uncomprehending of the concept of person-centred assessment. Sweeping pronouncements about educational quality, and over-simplified truisms appealing to competition and intellectual survival of the fittest, rule the day. The failure of the resulting policies, however, can hide itself behind continuous and continually more rapid reform and reorganisation.

While excessive and excessively bureaucratic assessment stifles teacher initiative and intuition and turns results and therefore pupils into the 'fodder' of education as a system, too little assessment carries the danger of subjectivity and arbitrariness. It is the duty of every school to find ways to acknowledge and celebrate the active work, human contribution and broad accomplishments of its students and to set them on a path of what the psychologist Abram Maslow called self-actualisation and self-transcendence.[5]

This can be represented in the following way:

* Ipsative level – biographical – development (a picture of the emerging 'I' of the young person)
* Formative level – exploratory/individualising (qualitative and related to an aesthetic feeling for the craft of learning)
* Summative level – summing up progress made over a period of time (consolidating and comparing according to criteria)
* Normative level – comparison based on typical cohort (quantative) – (measurable/objective/'physical')

Each level informs the others:

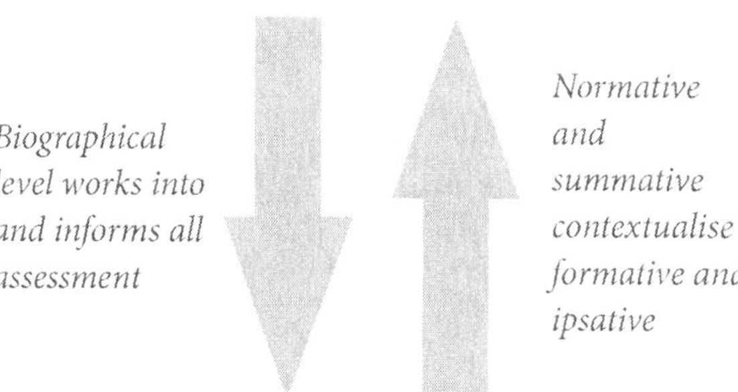
Biographical level works into and informs all assessment
Normative and summative contextualise formative and ipsative

Record-keeping

Not all assessment can, or should, be recorded. Record-keeping should support and inform teaching, not divert attention from the reality of working with young learners towards exercises in paperwork. Where records are made, they consist of two types. The first are ongoing observations made by the teacher on a daily or weekly basis, which include attendance and punctuality, completion of classroom or homework tasks given, grades given (where appropriate), behavioural evaluation, unusual occurrences (untypical behaviour, domestic or social crises, illness and injury) and the child's level of participation in lessons. Such records may be kept in a variety of forms, electronic and otherwise, but always with due diligence in the recognition that this is sensitive data. Depending on need and the nature of what is being recorded, records may be narrative/descriptive, in list form, or summarised as symbols with or without notes.

On a monthly or termly basis records are kept on each child's progress in subject-specific skills, numeracy, literacy, gross and fine motor co-ordination and social skills. Guidelines for attainment levels in language, literacy and numeracy in the form of checklists are included in the subject curricula in the later chapters of this book and some schools have amended and developed these further.

Formal records are also expected to be kept in the pupil's file. They should include:

* Early Year's Foundations Stage developmental records (profile)
* Summaries of child studies done in the teachers' meetings
* School doctor's reports
* Learning support reports
* Results of screening, or other normative tests
* Record of pupils 'settling-in' periods
* Notes on disciplinary situations and outcomes and reviews
* Pastoral care reports
* Copies of termly, annual reports, student profiles
* Copies of documentation from previous schools, as relevant

It is essential that schools have a clear policy and procedures for maintaining records, including having access to such records.

Annual or other regular formal reports are written for the parents (see below). In some schools Student Profiles are written (see below).

Monitoring and tracking progress[6]

As discussed above, class teachers regularly monitor and record children's progress in literacy, numeracy, co-ordination and social skills using checklists, records and screening.

Teachers plan their lessons and record children's performance. These plans are shared and integrated into the whole school curriculum through the regular teachers' meetings. Children's ongoing work is evaluated and reflected to the children and used as a guide to lesson planning, as well as for determining whether there is need for extra support, additional work or other intervention.

School reports

A summary of teachers' evaluations is given to parents in the form of an annual school report, which is often personalised by the teacher in style and design. This document normally includes:

* Characterisation of the student as a whole person, highlighting their strengths and weaknesses
* Evaluation of participation (attention and engagement), progress and ability in the various subjects (including comprehension, verbal and written attainments), age-appropriate ability to work independently, social behaviour (listening, working with others, co-operations and leadership), activity (presentation of work, tidiness, completed tasks), level of involvement and affective-aesthetic response
* Brief summary of the curriculum for the year
* Record of attainments in all subjects
* Indication of how the student might improve and how the parent might be able to support that improvement
* For younger children, a part of the report may be addressed personally to them, offering praise, guidance and challenges for the coming year
* Older pupils at some schools may receive Student Profiles for each subject and bi-annual reports
* Students graduating from Steiner-Waldorf schools may receive a detailed Leaver's Report, sometimes called a Record of Achievement, alongside a European Portfolio Certificate, where relevant

Student Profiles

In some Upper Schools (ages fourteen to nineteen), Student Profiles are written at the end of each main-lesson block for each arts/crafts/life skills course and termly for ongoing subjects. These profiles summarise both formative and summative aspects and include some element of student self-evaluation. As well as a description of the course and outline of its objectives, there usually follow two sections: one covering behaviour and engagement and the other covering subject-specific attainments. Judgement according to these criteria may be given descriptively or through a grade, depending upon the age of the students or other considerations. Some schools make use of versions of the 'taxonomy of learning domains' developed by psychologist Benjamin Bloom[7]. Each subject requires its own specific 'success criteria', which older pupils may have had some hand in designing, collectively or individually. The Profile concludes with a summary by the teacher highlighting possible areas of future development.

A fully-fledged system of pupil profiling thus includes the entire range of student (holistic) assessment recorded in the most appropriate way and with regard for data security. Such a profile would include:

* Child's name, date of birth, family details and contacts, essential medical information (including serious allergies)
* Photograph
* Significant relationships (including important pets, depending on age)

* Items child might wish to add about themselves, e.g. 'I'm the best tree climber in the class'; things important to child, similar to a one-page profile[8]
* Annual or periodic records, including:
    * Achievements, challenges, important events in the life of the child
    * Examples of best work (photographs or copies of free writing/maths/painting/book page – some chosen by pupils, as appropriate)
* Formative profile, including:
    * Records of key observations such as pencil grip (e.g. before and after photo) and student response as appropriate, bench-marked against success criteria and/or the individual pupil's (ipsative) progress
* A moderated view of expectations across time carried out with the assistance of advisers or visiting colleagues (generational cohorts)
* Evaluation based on curriculum checklists for this age/class and records of any tests conducted at the conclusion of a lesson block (as appropriate)
* Results of any normative screening: reading age, standardised attainments, etc. as relevant

Leaving certificates

In addition to usual public examinations and alongside Student Profiles or the Portfolio Certificate, some Steiner-Waldorf schools are adopting alternative forms for accrediting the upper school curriculum. One of these is the Secondary School Certificate developed by colleagues in the Federation of Rudolf Steiner Schools in New Zealand. This certificate is fully accredited and is equivalent with the National Certificate of Educational Achievement of the New Zealand Qualification Authority. This qualification has three levels corresponding to UK Levels 1, 2 and 3 (GCSE, AS and A Level). Through the Lisbon Recognition Convention, Level 3 provides access to the university admissions systems in other countries that are signatories, including, with few exceptions, all of those within the European Union.

Class and child studies

Class studies are formatted reviews of the progress, challenges and diversity of a whole group of children, involving characterisation, examination of sample work across the ability range and narrative examples of response to the curriculum and subject areas. These enable the teaching team as a whole to 'look through the window of a classroom' over a period of time and for colleagues to refine their expectations and maintain standards. Class studies can be especially helpful at nodal points, e.g. end of Classes 3, 6 and 8, after a new teacher has taken on the class, or if there is a consensus among subject teachers that a class is in need of a specific focus of attention. Class studies can also focus on different aspects such as levels of attainment or social dynamics. Major reviews are carried out for a class entering the Upper School.

Child studies take the form of development reviews of children who will be shortly entering the main school from kindergarten, along with any new applicants. These reviews are informed by the early years' profile and, where possible, by a school doctor. Other types of child study are usually conducted for students in need of special consideration, e.g. those with learning or behavioural difficulties, exceptional qualities, or who typify a condition. These studies involve all the teachers who teach the child and may involve specialists such as a school doctor or therapist. Parental involvement and support is important and their knowledge of the child helps to give a more complete picture.

Observations are made of physical constitution, movement, behaviour in class and outside (home), results of any tests done, artistic work, social interaction with other children and adults, work habits, home circumstances, school and homework, willingness, participation, the child's relation to different subjects and school activities. Staff members involved exercise their imagination in trying the build a picture of the best qualities and potential of the student.

These child studies are often shared by the whole teachers' group. Sometimes it is enough that the heightened awareness of a particular child has a beneficial effect on the child, though usually the study leads to some action and always requires regular follow-up.

5

Leadership and Management

The founding of the first Waldorf School came at a time of social depression and crisis in Germany following the World War of 1914–1918. The principles of leadership and management in Steiner-Waldorf schools represent Steiner's contribution to social and political reconstruction, which he saw as vital in the wake of the cataclysm of world conflict. This was a time of political change, emergent modernism and innovation alongside movements for social reconstruction. These are reflected in the curriculum and methodology as well as the social and organisational aspects of Steiner-Waldorf schools and continue to inform the educational movement that has grown from it.

Steiner's ideas for political reconstruction gained some influence but were finally swamped in the storms that gathered in the wake of the armistice and Treaty of Versailles. Central to Steiner's notion of a well-ordered society was that it corresponded to three principle physical and psychological systems of human beings which we described previously: 'head', or nerve-sense/cognition; 'heart' or respiration-circulation/feeling; and 'hands', metabolic-limb/volition. He called this a 'threefold social order', but always stressed that although the threefold model might aid our understanding of the dynamics and interactions of social life, the threefold social order itself would need to be applied to the governance of a whole state, and could not be realised within individual institutions.

Nonetheless, the core idea of differentiating fields of governance based on the threefold motto of the French Revolution ('freedom, equality and fraternity') in order to establish a more humane, human-scale social life is one of the ways in which Steiner-Waldorf schools attempt to unite the explicit curriculum (what is taught) with the implicit curriculum (the context, or ethos of the organisation and management as lived experience). Steiner described the main areas of social life as those of economics, rights and politics, and culture and the expression of spirit. Each of these three primary realms co-exists in mutual interdependence. But each realm has a basic functioning principle: in spiritual-cultural life this is freedom and innovation; in the sphere of rights and politics, equality and justice; in economic life, association, or mutuality. When a functioning principle is applied to its appropriate sphere, it enables healthy social interaction, enhancing what the philosopher Edmund Husserl called our life-world.[1] Applied in an inappropriate way, these principles lead to social imbalance and conflict. For example, unrestrained freedom applied in economic activity leads to greater inequality through exploitation and destroys environments. Equality, forced onto productive culture undermines creativity leading to denial of individual expression and enforced uniformity ('socialist-realism' under Stalin, or 'fascist art', for example). Where justice and equality are absent or weakened in political or institutional life, the loss of respect for human rights leads to all manner of oppression.[2]

Thus, since education is an activity within the cultural life of a community, Steiner's primary concern was to ensure that the curriculum and educational approach should be in the hands of educators rather than politicians or commercial interests. In his view education should both be free of economic and political influence and be freely accessible:

> *A healthy relation exists between school and society only when society is kept constantly supplied with the new and individual potentials of people whose education has allowed them to develop unhampered. This can only be realised if the schools and the whole educational system are placed on a footing of self-administration within the social organism. The government and the economy must receive people educated by the independent spiritual-cultural life; they must not have the power to prescribe according to their own wants how these people are to be educated.*[3]

Steiner further argued that the demands of what he called 'self-administration' would ensure that a free cultural institution like a school would be closer to reality. Real social renewal requires that society takes the risk that an education system which is independent and based on ongoing research into the nature of humanity as a learning species, would produce free-thinking individuals of initiative. To this end he argued for a complete disassociation of education from government bureaucracy and industry:

> *The place and function of educators within society should depend solely upon the authority of those engaged in that activity. The administration of the educational institutions, the organisation of courses of instruction and their goals should be entirely in the hands of people who are simultaneously either teaching or otherwise productively engaged in cultural life. In each case, such people would divide their time between actual teaching (or some other form of cultural productivity) and administrative control of the educational system.*[4]

That said, Steiner also spoke of the need to work with productive compromise: no school can exist in isolation and the elitism of minority-interests was to be avoided. For him the social task could only be achieved within and for the society in which it is placed. For example, he struck a deal with the local education authorities guaranteeing pupil attainments at key stages. The real role for Waldorf education is as an active part of the cultural landscape, taking part, representing its view of child development, yet not relinquishing its identity.

School as a republic

At the founding of the first Waldorf School, Steiner pointed out that, given the need to find a healthy balance between the ideals of Waldorf education and the need to be flexible –'to conform to what lies far from our ideals',[5] it would be necessary for everyone to:

> *use their full strength from the beginning. Therefore, we will organise the school not bureaucratically, but collegially, and will administer it in a republican way. In a true teachers' republic we will not have the comfort of receiving directions from a head teacher; rather we must bring our own contributions towards the solution of problems and take full responsibility for what we have to do. Each one of us must be completely responsible.*[6]

Each school finds its own way to work with this principle of collegial, or associative, leadership. Practically all schools beyond the pioneering stage work with the delegation principle, which sees individuals or groups given responsibility for specific areas of decision-making or management within overall agreed aims.

All Steiner-Waldorf schools are not-for-profit organisations, usually with a Board of Trustees, or School Governance Team (sometimes called the Council of Management). Trustees delegate day-to-day management for the education to the staff Collegiate (or College of Teachers). The Collegiate usually comprises all staff on permanent contracts, i.e. those carrying prime responsibility for the education, and appoints a Chair and other officers as required through a process of delegation. The Collegiate carries the educational ethos, or pedagogical governance, of the school and work areas are delegated to individual members of it so that what is ordinarily thought of as the role of a head teacher is carried collegially, in a republican manner. From this there flows a form of organisation not dissimilar to that to which 'distributed leadership' inclines.[7] In terms of leadership, however, the approach is opposite to one that depends upon a single head teacher, or principal, from whom leadership is devolved or distributed. In a collegial system, leadership rests in the responsibility of each individual and specific leadership tasks are allocated through collegially-determined remits among its members, thus helping to ensure that decision-making is owned by those involved in its implementation.

For this to be possible, the Collegiate must work in accord with the trustees on matters of planning, policy and monitoring of quality. The Board of Trustees has overall responsibility for the school as a public institution. Their chief role is to support and monitor the work of the whole school. This includes finance, legal and contractual matters, buildings, maintenance, administration, materials, health and safety, insurance, etc. The Collegiate, on the other hand, is primarily responsible for teaching, educational research and curriculum development, staffing and staff development, admission of children, pastoral care, the timetable, celebration of festivals and the general cultural life of the school.

Schools usually have administrative staff in a variety of support and management roles. Such administrators are usually part of, or at least work in close liaison with, the Collegiate. The intermediate role of management is thus closely integrated with the core educational task of the school.

A typical school structure might look like this:[8]

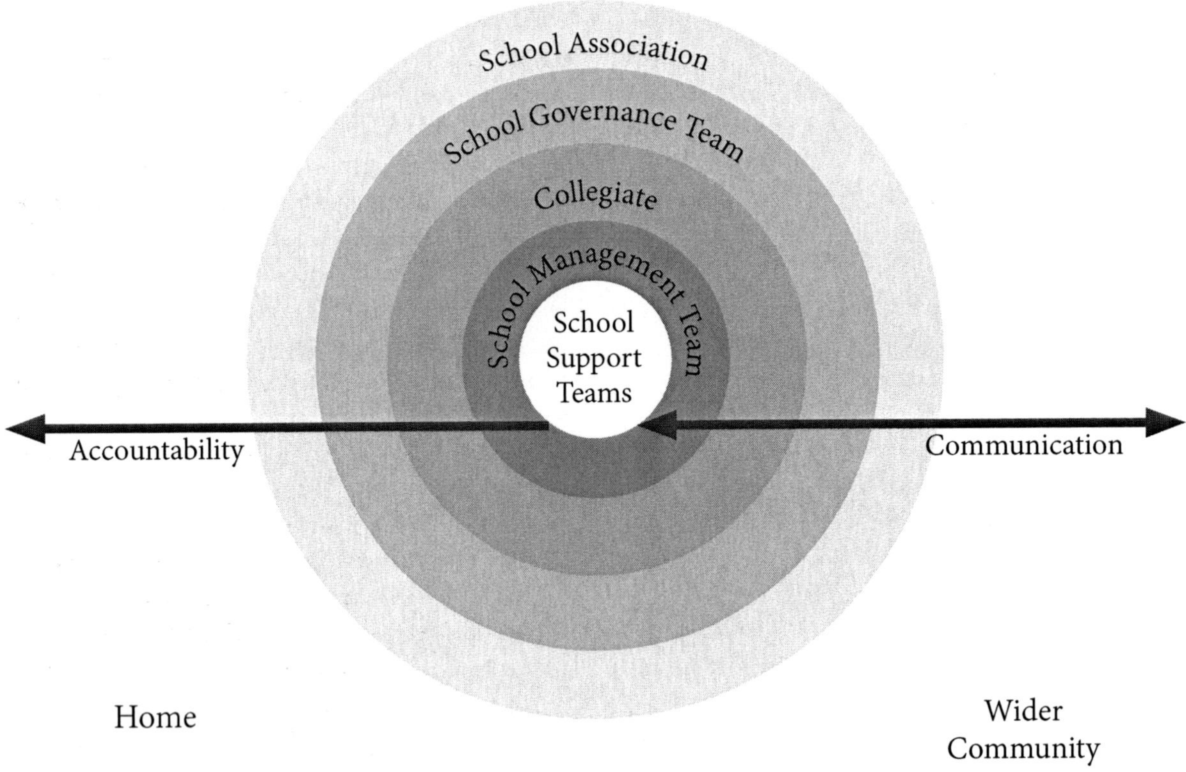

Although there are many variants of this, the principle layers of the organisational 'onion', in line with UK charity law, are:

* School Association – membership (sometimes the entire school community)
* School Governance Team – trustees, or governing body
* Collegiate and School Management Team
* School Support Teams – all the many activities supported by the structure of the school in order to sustain its core work, which usually include the voluntary work of parents and friends of the school, as well as responsibility teams consisting of staff members

This serves to underline the essential collaboration between parents and teachers in a Steiner-Waldorf school, which is needed to support the development of the children. The educative effects of this community aspect of school cannot be over-estimated and children too can become *de facto* associates in the school enterprise, if not *de jure* members of the school's Association.

Some schools have discrete PTFAs, which

provide a forum for parent-teacher discussion and opportunities for consultation, exchange and dialogue for whole school issues or educational themes. In addition, parent evenings are held, at least once a term for each class, at which the teachers can present aspects of the work currently being undertaken by the class. Matters of concern can be discussed and support for the children can be generated. Steiner-Waldorf schools have a policy of home visits in recognition of the importance of the home situation in the child's development. Most schools enable regular access to teachers through parent surgeries and appointment times.

The life of the whole school community is enlivened by the celebration of seasonal festivals, occasions at which parents and friends can often participate, and much effort is devoted to informing parents through outreach materials, open days, 'school for parents', induction courses, parent handbooks, newsletters and school magazines. Access to information and transparency of organisational structures help to answer people's questions. When communication breaks down, or individuals are not able to resolve outstanding issues, schools have mediation, concern procedures and formal grievance procedures (usually outlined on the school's website). In addition, UK Steiner-Waldorf Schools' Fellowship members follow a detailed Code of Practice which outlines basic procedures and describes best practice in a whole range of areas within the life of a school community.

School improvement, quality care and development

The life and purpose of a school is sustained by continually revisiting, renewing or revising its educational programme and methodology. In this, the nature of childhood, which is one of rapid change and development, needs to be matched by the school as an institution. Processes of planning and review, research and reflection, and ongoing child study and mentoring are paramount to this, but to be fruitful and fit-for-childhood these need to be infused by creativity, a spirit of 'play' and rooted in classroom experience.

As Steiner put it in Ilkley, the meeting of teaching staff should be a

> *living adult education – a permanent training academy… for the reason that every practical experience gained by the teacher in school becomes, in turn, part of his own education. And he who derives such self-education for himself from his teaching work, gaining on the one hand a profound psychological insight into the practical side of the education and on the other into different qualities, characters and temperaments of the children, will always be finding something new, for himself and for the whole faculty. All the experience and knowledge acquired from the teaching should be 'put into the pool' at these meetings. In this way the faculty in spirit and soul becomes a whole where each member knows what the other is doing, what experience has taught him and what progress he has made as the result of his teaching with the children in the classroom.*[9]

One could quote many more references[10] from Steiner to show that he considered the practical review of actual lessons, the study of children and classes and the involvement of all teachers in educational research as crucial to the development of quality in education. When Steiner refers to the self-development of the teacher or the group of teachers, this self-development includes learning to do things better. Development without the process of feedback and adaptation, without reference to outcomes and without aims, is no development at all.

Thus the central aim of those responsible for leadership in Waldorf schools is to serve the 'spirit of the school'. That is a spiritual task for the school's management and the inspiration for its leadership. The Imagination or College Meditation[11] which Steiner gave at the founding of the first Waldorf school is the framework through which this activity can be focused.

Whilst each individual is existentially responsible for his or her deeds, institutional responsibility and accountability for quality development in the education rests with the Collegiate. Administrative and organisational responsibility lies with the School Governance Team, Board or its equivalent. The question of formal accountability is an important one. Whilst the individual is responsible for his or her own actions, the Collegiate is collectively responsible for maintaining standards through study, mentoring and professional discourse. The Collegiate is responsible for saying whether the quality of work in the school is good enough. This in turn informs the School Governance Team, whose responsibility it is to be assured that quality development occurs in appropriate ways, and to provide the resources necessary to enable it to happen. Ultimately, accountability comes to rest with them, although they are in turn accountable to the wider school community, either formally via the school Association, or indirectly through their general responsibility as 'company directors'.

The levels of accountability this implies in no way contradicts the autonomy or freedom of the teachers, or indeed of the individual within the sphere of the cultural life. Indeed, this is exactly the kind of administrative responsibility within the free cultural life that Steiner foresaw in his work on the threefold social order.[12] Judgements made about quality in education should be made by educators engaged with the work of Steiner-Waldorf education. Children and young people, their parents and guardians, can form judgements from their own personal perspective, but such judgements certainly cannot be made theoretically, by officials with no knowledge of schooling.

Whether quality development takes place or not, and how it takes place, is a question that links to the legal-rights sphere of social life, connecting as it does with contractual agreements, employment law and the imperatives of fairness, transparency and a respect for the individual. Here too is where regulation has its place. In the UK, schools receive regulatory inspection and standards conform to these legal requirements, ideally by teams of inspectors who understand the basics of Waldorf education but who are also independent of the schools and professionally objective.

6

Early Years Care and Education

Children enter the kindergarten between the ages of three and six. Before this age, baby or parent and child groups and playgroups/nurseries are provided for younger children. Group sizes vary. Traditionally, five morning sessions per week are offered, each session lasting for approximately four to four and a half hours. Children take up provision according to age and need. Afternoon care is often available if required. Increasingly, provision is being made for longer hours, with nurseries and all-day kindergartens.

Cognitive, social, emotional and physical skills are accorded equal value and many different competencies are developed. Activities reflect the concerns, interests and developmental stages of the child and the carefully structured environment is designed to foster both personal and social learning. The curriculum is adapted to the child.

Teaching is by example rather than by direct instruction and is integrated rather than subject-based. In recognition of its vital role in early education, children are given time to play.

Emphasis is given to regular patterns of activities both within the day and over each week. A cyclical pattern is reflected in themes of work related to seasons of the year.

The nature of the early years

Physical, emotional and cognitive development are subtly and inextricably linked. This view underpins and informs the Early Years curriculum which is tailored to meet the child's changing needs during each phase.

The formative period (birth to seven) is seen as the period of greatest physical growth and development. Structures in the brain are being refined and elaborated, and young children's primary mode of learning is through doing and experiencing – they 'think' with their entire physical being.

The nature of this early learning should be self-motivated, allowing children to come to know the world in the way most appropriate to their age – through active feeling, touching, exploring and imitating; in other words, through doing. Only when new capabilities appear, around the seventh year, is the child physically, emotionally and intellectually ready for formal instruction. Through experiential, self-motivated physical activity, the small child 'grasps' the world in order to understand it – an essential prerequisite for the later activity of grasping the world through concepts. Children are encouraged to master physical skills before abstract intellectual ones.

Aims and objectives

Providing opportunities for children to be active in meaningful imitation

Imitation is acknowledged as the prime means of children's learning. The child learns for life from life (the acquisition of the mother tongue for example, takes place largely through imitation) and children model their behaviour on what happens around them. Adult activities stimulate direct responses in the young child, and educators carry out their daily tasks in such a way as to be worthy of imitation.

The kindergarten is a community of 'doers' supported through meaningful work, for example by baking bread. The children are welcome, but not required, to help. The activity of the teacher may inspire the children to become independently active, finding their own learning situations in play. Children perceive and register everything the adults do – it isn't only *what* one does in front of the young child, but also *how* one does it. Teachers are conscious of their own moral influence upon the child and of the development of good habits through imitation. One would expect to see a range of suitable activities for imitation taking place in the kindergarten; these might include domestic tasks such as baking, cooking, cleaning, toy-making, gardening, etc. – all activities with a social, practical, moral and educational basis.

Working with rhythm and repetition

Children need the reassurance of continuity and regular events to mark the year, week and day. Seasonal activities celebrate the cycles of the year – autumn in kindergarten might be a time for threshing and grinding, and spring a time for planting. A 'seasonal area' in the room or wider environment reflects the changing natural world, as do the themes of songs, stories and poems. In addition, each week has its own regular rhythm of recurring activities, such as baking day, painting day or gardening day.

Every day also has its own smaller rhythms which support the day's activities. These daily rhythms help the child to feel secure and to know what to expect. A tidy up song, for example, might signal the end of one activity and the beginning of another. The day is structured so that there is a varied pace – with periods of contraction and expansion – providing a balance between times of activity and times of rest. In practice, this might mean that creative play would be followed by a more concentrated ring-time, or energetic outdoor activity by a quiet story. There is a rhythmic alternation between the child's time (creative play, outside time) and the teacher's time (ring-time, story), the teacher's time being comparatively short at this age. Working with rhythm helps children to live with change, to find their place in the world, and to begin to understand the past, present and future. It provides a very real foundation for the understanding of time – what has gone before and what will follow – and helps children to relate to the natural and the human world. Attention to rhythm promotes healthy development and leads to a balanced life later.

Repetition also plays a key role in establishing continuity, good habits and in the healthy development of memory. Children's memories are strengthened by recurring experiences; and daily, weekly and yearly events in kindergarten are remembered and often eagerly anticipated a second time around. Stories are told not just once, but many times: repetition brings the opportunity for children to familiarise themselves with the material and to deepen their relationship to it.

Personal, social, emotional and moral development

Children learn, through their creative play and through their daily social activities, to interact with each other. In kindergarten they learn to share, to work together, and to co-operate. They know and trust their teachers and are able to establish effective relationships with other children and adults. Teachers and children care for and respect each other.

Much emphasis is placed on caring for the environment – both inside and out. Wooden toys, for example, can be polished and mended, unlike their plastic counterparts. Where possible, gardening and composting activities introduce children to the idea of ecology and form an important part of the curriculum.

There are moments of reverence each day, and teachers lovingly create opportunities for children to experience joy, awe and wonder. Kindness is practised by teachers and encouraged in the children. Festivals provide rich cultural and religious experiences for the child. Traditional fairy tales and nature stories address the feeling realm and gradually awaken a fine moral sense for knowing right from wrong. The teacher sets the example and has certain expectations of the children.

Providing an integrated learning experience

The learning experience of children under seven should be integrated and not compartmentalised. Young children need to experience the relevance of their world before they separate themselves from it and begin to analyse it in a detached way. Consequently, learning in kindergarten is integrated rather than subject based. Mathematics and use of mathematical language, for example, might take place at the cooking table, where food is prepared (thinly sliced carrots make wonderful natural circles and have the added virtue of being able to be eaten later in soup!) and concepts such as addition and subtraction (or more or less), weight, measure, quantity and shape are grasped in a practical manner as part of daily life. Meal times offer an opportunity for the moral, social and mathematical to work together as children engage in place-setting, serving and the sharing of food which has been prepared earlier for everyone to eat.

Through movement games, children recognise and recreate patterns – in, out, alternate, in front of, behind. Natural objects such as acorns, pine cones, conkers and shells are sorted, ordered and counted, as part of spontaneous play. Children in Waldorf kindergartens are directly involved in mathematical experience and use mathematical language in a natural way which is usually embedded in a social and moral context. Learning experiences for the young child are not separated from the business of daily living: learning gains meaning by its relevance to life.

As indicated above, a similar approach is taken to the teaching of language and literacy. Children develop competence in talking, listening and in the ability to use words with confidence they speak freely and learn to listen to others. Good speech and the development of aural skills are promoted. Concentration is on the oral tradition and the children listen to many wonderful stories – which belong to the literary heritage of the culture of childhood.

A well told story creates an appreciation for the human voice and the beauty and rhythms of language. It also helps to extend vocabulary and to aid the development of a good memory. Children leave kindergarten with a rich and varied repertoire of songs, stories and poems; this might also include verses in French or German. Much of this learning will have taken place in the integrated way described – although story time is always a very special event.

Children engage in many activities, such as sewing, which develop hand to eye co-ordination, manual dexterity and orientation (useful preparation for reading print from left to right). Children also discuss their own drawings and take great delight in telling stories by 'reading' their pictures. This activity promotes the development of verbal skills and frees the narrative from the printed text, thus encouraging children to use their own words. Many children also act out or perform puppet shows and develop dramatic skills through working with narrative and dialogue. Painting and drawing help with balance and symmetry and most five year-olds are able to write their own name. Children experience the musicality of language and its social aspects through playing ring games and doing eurythmy, a form of movement which works with language and music.

The combination of these activities cultivates a love of language, promotes fluency and allows children time to become really familiar with the spoken word – the best preparation and foundation for the subsequent development of literacy. Use of language also affects cognitive development as well chosen words and good syntax support clear thinking.

Encouraging learning through creative play and supporting physical development

Children are able to exercise and consolidate their ability to understand and to think through their play. Creative play supports physical, emotional and social development and allows children to learn through investigation, exploration and discovery. It also gives scope for the use of imagination – an essential aspect of human intelligence. Play encourages the child to become inventive and adaptable, and to work with initiative and flair. In addition it develops and strengthens concentration.

Studies[1] show that children who score highest in socio-dramatic play also demonstrate the greatest gains in a number of cognitive areas such as higher intellectual competence, longer attention span, and more innovation and imagination. Good players also show more empathy toward others, less aggression, and in general more social and emotional adjustment. Time and space is given to creative play and a selection of suitable objects, for instance cloths, shells, logs, domestic toys and dolls, is provided in order to support a variety of play situations.

Encouraging children to know and love the world

As mentioned in the section on rhythm and repetition, children develop a good relationship to the natural world. They learn to value its gifts and to understand its processes and patterns of change. Domestic tasks provide opportunities for elementary experiences in science and nature. Children make toys from sheep's wool, wood, felt, cotton and other natural materials. Family participation is encouraged and teachers, working with parents, create 'birthday stories' which are based on the child's personal biography and are told at special ceremonies to which families are invited.

People in the community who practise a particular craft, or who have special skills, are often invited to visit the kindergarten. Outdoors plays a strong role, and in some cases children spend much of the day outside playing or gardening, in the park or woodland, or are taken on local walks.

Providing a safe child-friendly environment

The kindergarten should be a warm and welcoming place, an artistically-shaped free space which serves as the setting for what the day's impulse brings. This 'impulse' is a mixture of child-motivated play experiences and teacher-structured activities. There are few 'finished' toys, which allows imaginative use. Furniture is small-scale and child-friendly and, as mentioned, the day is structured so as to provide the child with periods of activity and periods of rest. Groups are usually of a mixed age range; older children, who are familiar with the rhythm of the particular kindergarten, are able to help the younger members of the group to feel secure.

Working with parents

Waldorf teachers are committed to establishing good relationships with parents and to the process of developing parenting skills. The importance of a happy, smooth transition from home to school is recognised, teachers working closely with parents to achieve this end. The majority of kindergartens hold parent and child sessions and meet with the family before the child enters kindergarten. Teachers promote and emphasise the importance of close partnerships with parents holding the child at the centre. Links are also created with parents through a range of social and school-based events and activities. Close liaison between parent and teacher is encouraged and the child's developmental steps are shared.

An example of a kindergarten session

Perhaps the best way to exemplify the integration of the above educational aims is to describe a typical kindergarten morning session. This example, of course, only highlights one range of activities. Normally each day of the week would have its own main focus and these vary with the changing seasons.

The kindergarten staff spend hours in their kindergarten both before the children arrive in the morning and after they have gone. There are activities and materials to prepare, of course, but more importantly there has to be the right mood in the place. The staff often meet in the morning to say a verse together before going to their rooms to be there when the children arrive.

As the children begin to arrive, the kindergarten leader is already busy so that the children, having hung up their coats and changed their shoes, can be given a homely welcome. At first there may be a period of free play with small groups of children choosing their area, perhaps getting the dolls up and dressed, building with small logs or driving a bus made from an upturned chair. The adults are usually engaged in some task, such as preparing the dough if it is baking day, or the soup for lunch. There is conversation and some of the children may prefer to be around the adults, as children traditionally have been, watching, 'helping', while adults work, asking questions and so on. These informal moments are vital, not least in a world in which everyone is often so busy. During this time children also have the opportunity to do a domestic, handicraft or artistic activity alongside the adult or on their own. There is no deliberate effort to teach the children in any formal sense. The conscious activity of the teacher is imitated by the children.

The adults initiate the next phase by beginning to clear the things away and the children join in helping each tool or object to find its place on shelf or in basket. The forces of imitation are strongest at this age and can be most easily directed when the adults perform their tasks in a conscious and careful way, repeating the gestures of each action in a rhythmical and natural way. Children can learn to do quite complex practical tasks, even involving sharp or awkward tools or equipment, if they see them regularly performed with love and care.

Tidying up is an important task and it is done in such a way that it does not occur to the children that this is something which spoils their fun or is a tedious chore. Once things have been put back in their places, the children gather for ring-time, during which traditional songs are sung, and rhythmical verses spoken and acted out. Sometimes the eurythmist or foreign language teacher may visit and contribute to the circle's activities. These activities help focus the children's attention and especially strengthen their linguistic skills. Listening and clear articulation can be exercised through this kind of rhythmical recitation. Afterwards, the children go to the toilet and wash their hands. Some of the older ones who are first back help lay and set the table with placemats, cutlery and perhaps a vase of flowers. Bread is cut and everyone gathers to say a grace and sing some seasonal songs.

Following the morning snack, some of the children help clear up while others get ready for the outdoors, where they could play in the garden or sandpit, work in the vegetable patch or clear the leaves alongside the adults, or engage in a craft activity. A walk to the park could also be a possibility. On their return, the children change, wash and come together for story time, where the teacher tells a folk, nature or fairy tale or performs a puppet show. By then the parents are waiting outside to collect the children. Some kindergartens include afternoon sessions as well. In this case lunch is eaten, followed by a rest and then further periods of play.

Each day of the week has its own artistic or handicraft activity, such as a baking day. While most kindergartens offer watercolour painting and drawing with wax crayons, or beeswax modelling and eurythmy, the handicrafts vary according to the facilities or the particular skills of the adults concerned. In all these activities the children learn by example, finding their way in to the experiences at their own pace. In this way the children learn to explore and be creative whilst acquiring a love of work. This manifests itself in an increasing mood of self-reliance and calm industriousness when the children are engaged. The same mood is carried over into creative play. A strong and lively rhythm helps give the children a deep sense of security.

7

A Horizontal Curriculum

I myself have witnessed in the Waldorf School how the teacher and his class have become a unity and by this I do not mean the sum total of pupils plus teacher. This wholeness is the matrix out of which the development of the children can grow. According to each teacher's individuality, outer forms of teaching may vary enormously in the different classes, and yet the fundamental qualities are retained. In a Waldorf school outer forms do not follow set patterns, so that it is quite possible for one teacher to teach his class of nine year olds well while another, who takes a completely different line, may be an equally good teacher. In this way we plan the curriculum for each year in accordance with the nature of the growing child. As long as the teacher feels in harmony with the underlying principles and with the methods employed, he must be given freedom in his work instead of being tied to fixed standards. No matter whether he happens to be teaching a Class 1 or a Class 8, he should feel part of the whole school so that already in Class 1 he will lay the foundations for what will find a certain completion in Class 8.[1]

RUDOLF STEINER

'Horizontal curriculum' is the term used to refer to the various subjects that are taught to children in any one class – that is, children of the same age. The 'vertical curriculum' in Part II of this book shows how each individual subject develops from year to year and from the youngest age groups to the oldest. The horizontal curriculum shows us the integration of the various subjects in meeting the age groups' needs in interdisciplinary ways. It also enables us to give typical developmental pictures of the children in the different age groups. The vertical curriculum shows us the spiral nature of the path of learning, in which new skills are built on existing skills and topics can be revisited from new and age-appropriate perspectives.

What neither of these forms of presentation can easily show is the 'diagonal curriculum', which would reveal cross-links between different skills and abilities at different ages. It would show, for example, the relationship between knitting in the first two classes and mathematical skills in the Middle and Upper School, or between folk tales and fables in Classes 1 and 2 and ecology in the Upper School, or indeed between grammar in the Middle School and the ability to form judgements in life after school! The diagonal curriculum is just as essential to the educational tasks of Waldorf education as the other two dimensions. It has to be said that this third curriculum still needs to be thoroughly researched, though there are many references to it within the curriculum descriptions given in this book.

Each teacher adapts the curriculum to meet the needs of the children. Therefore it is important to bear in mind that in the main-lesson blocks and subject lessons mentioned below, qualitative differences of approach are as important as the actual lesson content. These variations keep the content in tune with the spiritual, psychological and physical stage of development the children have reached. Every teacher at a Steiner-Waldorf school has a duty to shape the curriculum or, better still, to recreate it anew to suit every situation.

The following sections constitute guidelines based on typical good practice. They give an overview and summary of the teaching content and methodology for each age range. The classes are grouped into three sections, Classes 1 to 3, Classes 4 to 6 and Classes 7 and 8, since these stages mark significant developmental stages and distinctive teaching approaches. For reasons of space, the choice of examples is of necessity selective.

The Lower School: Classes 1 to 3

Class 1 (age six to seven)

Developmental profile

The seventh year sees the commencement of 'formal' schooling in the Steiner-Waldorf method. During the first seven years, the young child learns to be at home in the physical body, developing an orientation in space and acquiring the initial, fundamental developmental capacities of uprightness, speech and thought. The content of the child's whole environment is the learning context; the child 'imitates' the people and the agencies that are in his/her environment. This imitating gesture serves to imprint on the child's will the content and the quality of what is learnt. In the nursery or kindergarten, experiential learning, discovery through creative play and intensive social interaction with peers and teachers constitute the main educational themes. Awareness of the complexities of the mother tongue and number is acquired through informal play and social interaction. These is not taught didactically.

Around the seventh year the child completes the process of forming the second dentition sufficiently for forces that have been concentrated on growth and physical upbuilding to become active in developing the facility for independent, representational, pictorial thinking. 'Formal' methods of teaching – in literacy, numeracy and other disciplines – are introduced. The child is still in a mood of dreamy wholeness, more able to bring broad awareness than focused concentration to learning settings. Much learning is continued through activity and imitation through which the child receives an image, internalises it, recalls it, and generalises it into a concept which can be applied, e.g. the letter 'R' or times 'x'. What was experienced practically, though not conceptually, in the pre-school years, is raised to a feeling relationship through mental picturing. The child's holistic experience of the world is nourished by archetypal pictures such as those reflected in fairy tales and well thought out nature stories.

Aims and objectives

In this year the children make the important transition from the kindergarten to school where they begin formal learning. The children are led by their teacher to a first experience of the forms, sounds and sequencing of letters and number symbols by using pictures, rhymes and stories.

The children learn to recognise and memorise these with lots of practice involving movement, verses, drawing and writing. During this first year the class acquires the good habits of classroom life and work, which will form the basis of their time together in the Lower School and indeed for all subsequent learning at school. Cultivating reverence for nature, care for the environment, respect for others, interest in the world and a feeling of confidence in their teachers – these are the moral aims for Class 1 and the following classes. The teachers aim to lead the children into becoming a socially cohesive group who care for and listen to each other.

Class 2 (age seven to eight)

Developmental profile

The eight-year-old child continues to reside in a largely self-created psychological landscape, which derives from the child's faculty for developing individualised thought-pictures from the realms of their inner life. The events and experiences of the outside world are filtered through the child's imagination and rearranged to accord with the child's homogenous world-picture. Children show greater alertness in noting what happens around them at this age. The mood of wholeness differentiates into contrasts such as a deeper, more conscious feeling for the religious element alongside a tempting awareness of the mischievous.

The curriculum content for this age serves to cultivate in the child a sense for the breadth and richness of the language of the feelings and emotions.

Cognitively the child continues to be at home in a learning context where pictorial thought content is to the fore. Concepts are best understood meaningfully when they are mobile and organic in quality. The pupils continue to familiarise themselves with the fundamentals of numeracy and literacy, while in gross and fine motor movements – whether through skipping, catching and throwing a ball, or knitting, crocheting or flute-playing – they develop a repertoire of skills and competencies that were initially introduced in Class 1. Thus the intellect is allowed to awaken through the artistic approach.

In Class 2 pupils, the adult teeth continue to push through, laterality and dominance are firmly established and it is during this year that specific learning needs and difficulties are observable. The range of abilities within a class becomes clearly discernible. Much of the confidence and sense of belonging which Class 2 pupils exude is clearly due to the fact that the child is building on the foundations laid in Class 1.

Aims and objectives

The initial experiences of the first year are deepened and enhanced in Class 2. This time is used primarily for practising and developing all the new skills from the previous year. Whereas in Class 1 a lot of energy goes into forming the class into a social cohesive group where children are supported by the wholeness that they experience, in Class 2 a mood of contrast or polarisation often surfaces, which can be observed in the way children relate to each other. To help the children go through this stage they are told stories where contrasting human qualities and characteristics are found portrayed by holy people and saints in legends and by animals in the fables. This class needs strong leadership from the teachers through consistency of approach and through the power of imagination. The children derive direction and form from the images they are given.

Class 3 (age eight to nine)

Developmental profile

Class 3 in the Steiner-Waldorf curriculum is the equivalent point of entry into Key Stage Two in the English National Curriculum guidelines. In Class 3 the pupils enter their tenth year. At this point, noticeable physiological, psychological and cognitive changes take place in the child. These changes, referred to as the ninth/tenth-year threshold, may begin as early as 8.5 years or as late as 9.5 years and may last from between six months and one year.

The child develops a firmer, more balanced gait; speech sounds are increasingly formed in the middle of the mouth and articulated more directly and the child focuses on the 'middle distance'. The child's constitution is noticeably stronger. The heart increases in size and is capable of receiving a larger volume of blood and a new breath/blood pulse ratio is established in the region of one breath to four pulses. Growth begins to focus more on the limbs and metabolism and there is a growth in the breadth of the trunk. In some children this developmental phase is marked by symptoms including weariness, tummy and head pains, nausea, dizziness, a variable appetite, asthma, eczema and disturbed sleep patterns.

Steiner talks about a metamorphosis in the child's feeling life. At seven years, there is a metamorphosis in the child's thinking. In Class 3, the child experiences a duality in perceiving the world, in his or her feeling. A process begins to unfold through which the child experiences with increasing strength, a sense of objectivity, alongside growing subjectivity. Subjective inner experience and objective world reality stand at odds within the child's soul. Questioning, doubt, aloneness and a dawning tendency to criticise are emergent features in the child's psychological landscape.

Sometimes a little earlier, sometimes a little later, but for most children a very significant step in self-awareness occurs during this year. It is experienced as an awareness of being separate from the surroundings both human and physical, and of a distinction between an inner and an outer world. Contrasting emotions of the sense of loss of the previous unity with the world and a sense of wonder at seeing the world in a new way often lead to confusion and insecurity. These can be expressed in marked changes of behaviour that vary considerably according to temperament and personality.

The images of the Old Testament, its laws and guidance foster inner security during the unsettled period and the main-lesson blocks on farming, building, etc. help the children to engage in a new relationship with their surroundings.

Aims and objectives

As the Class 3 children become more aware of themselves and the physical environment in which they live, a new interest in the practical, material world emerges. After practising their literacy and numeracy skills in Class 2 they can now apply these in a wide range of everyday situations which require measuring or weighing, solving simple problems and the writing of simple formal letters.

By involving the whole class in the experience of working together in building, farming and other examples of work projects, the class teacher helps to transform the initial feeling of separateness from the physical world into a feeling of responsibility for it. It is important for the teachers to lay down clear guidelines for behaviour and to give the children confidence in the authority of the teachers, not only the class teacher. The children should have a strong sense of the social unity of the class, an experience of 'we'.

Curriculum in Classes 1 to 3

The Steiner-Waldorf curriculum usually begins with a subject unknown in other schools. This is 'form drawing' or 'dynamic drawing'. Basic straight and curved lines and shapes are made and drawn by the children, preferably making the shapes with their whole body to begin with (walking, running, sweeping movements of the arms and hands) and later using crayons or pencils on paper. Having been experienced in movement, these shapes and rhythms are then brought to rest by drawing them on paper. All this requires the children to make purposeful, concentrated efforts in movement, a medium ideally suited to them. The shapes have no outer meaning, neither do they depict anything in particular, rather they make the dynamic of movement and shape visible in space. The children learn to experience, feel (with their fingers, for example) and understand the inherent quality and nature of different shapes and movements. Experiencing the inner nature of something through movement is one of the basic themes in Classes 1 to 3. Form drawing is also an excellent preliminary exercise to writing. In Classes 2 and 3 such exercises stimulate the activity of forming mental pictures, an activity which both engages the will and stimulates the feelings. In a sense the life of feeling is used as an organ of perception. The child *feels* the balance, proportion, symmetry, integration and character of the forms and the dynamic movements they embody.

In English language lessons the children are introduced to the letters of the alphabet. Initially the aim is to lead the children to experience the qualities of the spoken sounds and sentence melody, whilst the shape, name and meaning of the capital letters of the alphabet are taught. By allowing the shape of a capital letter to emerge from a picture that stands for the character of the sound, the children can develop their own relationship to the individual letters and later to the whole activity of writing. Consonants are evolved out of pictograms, vowels out of interjections and expressions of feeling. The process proceeds from pictorial representation of the letters to formal writing, with the children initially copying examples written by the teacher and later through dictation. The exploration of the relationship of sound and symbol includes the use of emergent writing. From capital letters the children proceed to lower case cursive handwriting, usually in Class 2.

The content of written work is related to main-lesson themes and the children's own experiences. As a general guideline, about a third of writing is composed by the children, the other two thirds comprising texts prepared by the teacher and copied from the board or dictated by the teacher. By Class 3 the children write longer, more complex compositions. Instruction and practice in formal letters, diaries and description of nature moods supplement this. Neat legible handwriting is encouraged.

Reading proceeds from writing and in Class 1 the children read familiar texts which the teacher has written on the board and which they themselves have written in their exercise books. An integrated combination of whole word, phonic and contextual methods is used to develop reading, though with an emphasis on whole sentences/whole phrases. Reading books are not normally used until Class 2. A differentiated approach to reading is used including whole class reading, child to child and child to adult reading and supported with regular practice in the recognition of auditory, visual and kinesthetic patterns. Spelling is based on a whole language approach reinforced by contextual, phonic and kinesthetic methods. By Class 3 reading progresses to a differentiation of material for different purposes, including understanding instructions and tasks, finding information and reading timetables. Reading aloud is practised with an awareness of content and punctuation. Children are directed to a wide range of reading material according to ability.

Oral work plays an important role throughout the classes with equal emphasis on both speaking and listening. Good skills at both are prerequisites for the development of all literacy skills. As well as the daily recitation of poetry and verses, many of which are designed as speech exercises to strengthen pronunciation and articulation, the children are encouraged to describe their experiences and recall the stories they have heard. The teacher's own language serves as a model for the use and form of spoken language. This emphasis on oral work provides a basis for the subsequent understanding of grammatical structures and punctuation as well as exemplifying the linguistic expression of emotional qualities such as surprise, curiosity, denial, enthusiasm, willing affirmation and so on.

The work on writing, reading and speaking and listening in the first two classes provides a basis for introducing children to a systematic exploration of grammatical qualities in Class 3, starting with nouns, verbs, adjectives and adverbs. The aim is not only to make conscious principles that have hitherto been learned pragmatically but to school the child's thinking and awareness of the real relationships which grammar and syntax express and define.

Foreign language lessons are as important as those focusing on the mother tongue. From Class 1 onwards the children learn two foreign languages by the direct method of listening and speaking. Writing and grammar are not touched on during Classes 1 to 3. The children are immersed in these languages by means of poems, stories and fairy tales and dialogue, all learned by heart and enacted in context. Through the other languages they experience a different way of describing things, a different way of looking at things, a different way of approaching the world. This is one of the most important prerequisites for a lively ability to form concepts and also for achieving a more universal view of the world that encompasses more than one perspective, in that it broadens the one-sided orientation of the mother tongue. During the first three years the children acquire orally an extensive vocabulary of everyday things and situations and a practical usage of most of the main grammatical structures of the language. In the succeeding years the children will draw on this reservoir of oral language and experience as they begin to learn to become literate in the foreign language.

The stories told in this phase are those which describe 'the child's path down to the earth'. In Class 1 the oneness of humankind, animals, nature and the heavens is experienced in an archetypal way in traditional fairy tales and local folklore. Stories are also chosen which portray the cycles of the natural world and especially the seasonal changes. In Class 2 differentiation between these kingdoms begins to be demonstrated through fables and legends. In Class 3 the human being's responsibility towards the earth and God is shown in the creation stories of Genesis and other Old Testament material. (This applies chiefly to schools in countries with a European tradition. Steiner-Waldorf schools where Buddhist, Hindu, Islamic, Hebrew or other cultures predominate choose other suitable material.) The essential elements in these myths are the creation of the heavens and earth, the plant and animal kingdoms, the divine origin of humankind: the tasting of the Tree of Knowledge, the origin of human community and the laws which govern it.

In Class 3, through the themes of farming and house-building, the children's journey is brought literally down to earth. They carry out practical farming and building activities. The actual topics chosen depend on the locality so that, for example, in coastal regions fishing may feature in the lessons. Such practical activities, tailored to the children's age and capabilities contain long-term pedagogical elements that prepare them for later insight into economics and ecology. Learning how natural raw materials are transformed into products, which serve real needs in the world, sows the seeds for a real experience of mutuality and service.

Arithmetic also involves movement. In Class 1 the children experience the totality and the individuality of numbers. Whole numbers are introduced with emphasis on their archetypal character – one means unity, two is a duality and so on, using pictures familiar to the child's world (the sun, parts of the body, petals of flowers, etc.). Then come the four basic arithmetical operations and their different qualities, always going first from the whole to the parts. The symbols are introduced in a pictorial way. Rhythmical counting, recitation of tables, number bonds up to twenty and mental arithmetic are all practised intensively in the early years. This gives the children an experience of movement in mental activity, which complements the way the letters of the alphabet are introduced.

By Class 2 there is a shift of emphasis from manual operation to mental computation and the exploration of various forms of appropriate notation and algorithm and their application to problem solving. In Class 3 measurement moves from the oral realm, which is comparative, qualitative and contextual (this is bigger, there are more here etc.) to the use of formal units. Starting with traditional measures based on body proportions, the children are introduced to standard units of linear, liquid, weight, time, money and music measurement and notation.

In painting with watercolours the inner qualities of a colour are explored. What feelings does this colour generate? What soul qualities are linked to the three primary colours: blue, yellow and red? The aim of these painting lessons is not to copy external objects or make illustrations but to experience and 'listen' to the inner language of colours. The children illustrate their main-lesson books with pencils and crayons, an activity which unites the dynamic of line drawing with the mood and feeling expressed by the colours. In this way the children bring their powers of imagination to what they have perceived with their senses.

While in painting the 'sounds' of the colours are explored, in the music lessons during the first three years of school the inner 'colours' or character of the notes are explored. In these first school years, however, it is important that the children do not yet focus on musical moods that are as yet unfamiliar to their experience, such as those connected with the musical scales or the tonalities of major and minor. Their inner life is not yet mature or differentiated enough to empathise with such qualities. At this age the children still need to experience the tones and the space they fill in a free way, for example through the pentatonic mode. The music they play with their simple wooden flutes, recorder, child's harp or lyre is initially related to the songs they have learnt. This can perhaps be compared with the way they learn to write, by beginning with what they already know by heart.

There is an emphasis on active listening through singing, often accompanied with movement and gesture in response to melody. Through Class 2 the children expand their range of tunes, and individuals take the step to small solo parts within the context of the class as a choir. In Class 3 the transition is made to music that relates to a keynote or diatonic perspective, when the children meet with an early 'grammar' or 'spelling' (notation) of music. The recorder is an instrument that shapes and differentiates the stream of the breath. Bowed instruments bring in a new important element. With the recorder both hands are involved in shaping the stream of air. With a bowed instrument the right hand wields the bow, the left hand selects the notes and the listening ear makes sure that the result is in tune. An almost craft-like skill is needed for this, but it remains within the realm of feelings and sensations in the soul. It leads to a sense for the qualitative shaping of time.

Eurythmy lessons provide the link between space and time: the sounds of speech and the sounds of music are made visible through movement in space. This art helps the children harmonise their actions through the balance between the alert perception of the senses and bodily movement by filling both with feeling. Eurythmy helps the children become aware of the qualities of the spatial dimension in an artistic way.

During the first three years at school the children are led gently through movement to an experience of their own bodily orientation and mobility within their surrounding space. Traditional movement and ring games are learnt and practised, which develop skills and co-ordination as well as having a strong social component. The transition to more formal gymnastic exercises comes in the third year. The harmonious movement sequences already practised become more target-oriented.

Handwork lessons are also aimed at training manual skills. All children learn to knit and sew and use basic handicraft tools (scissors, craft knives, adhesives, string, etc.) and work with a range of materials. The children produce useful articles such as recorder cases, potholders, shopping nets and so on. This schooling of fine motor skills, co-ordination combined with the artistic and practical element provides a sound basis for the subsequent basis of practical intelligence.

Summary of Classes 1 to 3

The first three years of school can perhaps best be described as helping the children find their way into the world while taking into account their basic need to experience the 'inner side' of nature, language and music. The children also acquire a range of basic skills. It is important for the children to gain a sense of respect and reverence for what they learn about as well as for the people whose skills they admire. Then, in addition to learning to feel at home in the world, they will strengthen their desire to be good at things, which is an important stimulus to self-activity in learning. This feeling of wanting to be good at things forms the basis for the children's love for the authority of their teachers.

In their pre-school years the children had a strong urge to move; their movement was space-oriented and directed into exploring the world around them. In the early school years new developmental forces have to be taken into account, which seek to find an orientation in the qualities of their inner life. A start is made in achieving an interplay between external activity and inner reflection. In this sense it is the teacher's task to help the children acquire a healthy balance between the inner and outer worlds, between taking in and taking part, in bringing the child's own individuality into the right relationship to her own body and environment. This process of finding a healthy balance between the inner experience and the bodily organism is what Steiner referred to as teaching the children to breathe[2] the breath being the archetype of inner-outer exchange. The metaphor also infers that the exchange is not fixed but rhythmical, with breathing in, a transformation of substance and breathing out.

The Lower School: Classes 4 to 6

Class 4 (age nine to ten)

Developmental profile

In Classes 4 and 5 when the pupils are ten and eleven years old, the mid-way point of the class teacher years is reached. The transition from early childhood is complete, the transition towards puberty has not yet begun. This centre-point of the class teaching period coincides with the middle of the second seven-year period of life, and is referred to in Steiner-Waldorf pedagogy as the 'heart of childhood'.

The self-activity of the child brings about a harmonising of the relationship of the breathing to the blood circulation.

Confidence in their new state is expressed in a quality of vigour and an eagerness to look at and learn about the world. A start is made on natural science with a phenomenological study of the animal kingdom in relation to the human being from a morphological point of view. Also a thorough study of the local surrounding and developing the process of map-making.

Aims and objectives

The aim of Class 4 is first and foremost to channel positively the powerful energy which ten year-olds bring to the classroom. Pupils need to be challenged and stretched in every possible aspect of their work. 'Work, work and lots of it' is the best motto for Class 4.

The teachers aim to meet, through imaginatively presented lessons, the growing interest of the children in more concrete areas of knowledge and to provide them with opportunities for more independence in their work. Individually the children need to find a new relationship to their work, to their peers and teachers. The narrative content of the lessons aims to respond by offering stories in which a multiplicity of personalities contributes to the social whole (e.g. stories of the Norse Gods) and in which darkness and evil become more concrete. The children should begin to identify individual 'badness' in contrast to social or communal 'goodness'. The children should form a sense of where they are in relation to their environment, in both a social and geographical sense.

Class 5 (age ten to eleven)

Developmental profile

At this age the child attains a certain ease and grace of movement intrinsic to the age. Movement that is co-ordinated, balanced and harmonious is a key-note of the developmental phase. Psychologically, the 'I'/world differentiation develops, the individual 'will' element begins to grow, the awareness of 'self' strengthens and socially, a powerful group dynamic can surface within a class, although the individual ego is very much a fledgling. Cognitively, children are more able to understand questions and phenomena in a realistic and reasoning manner. The pictorial element in thought processes remains an important element in the child's consciousness, although the understanding and formulation of concepts are beginning to depend less on the development of individualised images and thought pictures and more on the development of a faculty for comprehending clear, matter-of-fact, sense-free concepts.

Out of the growing memory powers, the sense for time has developed. Memory allows for looking back and planning the future and, combined with deepening feeling, for the emergence of conscience and responsibility.

This age is a time of rapidly flowering capacities. The child experiences a growth in length; sustained physical effort is within his or her group. Musically, a child has the capacity to master a musical instrument. In the basic skills of numeracy, literacy and linguistics pupils exhibit the emergence of independent creativity founded on a confident group of the basic rules, processes and structures.

Intellectually and morally the child is ready for new challenges. Foundations for the basic skills in numeracy and literacy have been set down by the tenth year. Elementary notions of personal responsibility and a faculty for understanding 'right and wrong' in a 'reasoning' spirit may be grasped from this age.

This year marks the pivotal point between childhood and puberty and for a short moment each child is poised at the crest of the wave, marking the end of the first part of their school years. They reach standards of work hitherto never dreamed of. They identify totally with their work, they spend time embellishing it, bringing it closer to perfection. They are often proud of their work, whereas in Class 4 they could easily be dismissive about it.

Towards the end of this year the teacher will begin to experience her pupils' emergent intellectual faculties, ready to be used more consciously. They bring with them a new detachment and their accompanying critical standpoint. The harmony is lost, to be found again at the end of the Upper School years.

Aims and objectives

In this year the aim is to make the transition from myth to history and its emphasis on the individual. The children should develop a greater consciousness of the interrelatedness of life and environment – particularly through the study of botany. There will be an emphasis on the original Olympian ideal in which group distinctions are subservient to the greater whole and in which qualities such as beauty are as valued as speed and distance. The children should be encouraged to strengthen their memory by learning such things as vocabulary and by visualising spaces through the use of maps.

Class 6 (age eleven to twelve)

Developmental profile

Class 6 in the Steiner-Waldorf school is the equivalent point of entry into Key Stage Three in the English National Curriculum guidelines. In the mainstream this age constitutes the first year in secondary education. There is a clear difference in methodology between the Steiner-Waldorf curriculum and the English National Curriculum as regards the age that it is appropriate for pupils to be introduced to the conscious development of deductive thinking, logical thought processes and analytical-critical faculties. In Steiner's pedagogical indications there is common ground with the work of Piaget, Vygotsky and others, in the understanding that abstract thinking, or 'formal operations', begins around the thirteenth year, and not in Key Stage One.

Generally, the child's growth begins to express itself in the skeleton. The limbs begin to lengthen; the child develops a tendency for awkward, angular movements. The twelve year old experiences the strength of gravity through the skeleton. The physical change is accompanied by the first experience of causation in the thinking realm, while psychologically, the child enters a phase which may be characterised as the 'changeling' period. The twelve year old witnesses what may be described as the death of childhood and the birth-pangs of the individual.

In the final third of the second seven-year period, the child begins to anticipate adolescence. In the various curriculum topics indicated – sequential, recorded history, the geography of Europe, formal geometry, business maths, phenomenological science, gardening, woodwork and organised games – the child's changing physical, psychological and cognitive make-up is acknowledged and tended.

Aims and objectives

At this age the teacher aims to work with the children's growing orientation towards the outer world. Their dawning critical faculties should be directed towards observing the natural world from a scientific standpoint and their increasing interest in social relationships should provide many opportunities for the children to take responsibility for their own class community. The aim is to forge a new social relationship between each other and their teacher.

As new capacities for thinking emerge, the children can be led to understand causal relationships at work in the world. The children's awareness should be directed towards the world they will live and work in as adults. The pupils should be challenged and are capable of high standards in their school work.

Curriculum in Classes 4 to 6

In Classes 4 and 5, when the pupils are ten and eleven years old, they enter a period that can justifiably be called the heart of childhood. They have left early childhood behind them but have not yet entered puberty. The intensification of self-consciousness, which began during the ninth year, continues into Class 4 and the teacher increasingly experiences the power of the group of young individualities emerging in the class. Each child appears as a strong personality with distinctive gifts, talents and challenges but this is still essentially childlike in its manifestation. The children still respond well to imaginative stories and well-formed rhythms in teaching. The teaching needs to be challenging and lively if it is to engage the strengthening will of the children. Physiologically the self-activity of the child strives to bring about a harmonisation of the relationship of the breathing to the blood circulation.

At the latest by Class 4 the children enter into a psychological situation that differs from that of the preceding three years. Their relationship to nature and to their fellow human beings has become more distant. The 'world of which they are a part' has become 'the world that is around them'. As Steiner put it:

> *The time after the completed ninth year is particularly important because it is a significant turning point in the children's lives. Questions dart into their consciousness, you could say whole heaps of questions, all of which relate to differentiating on the feeling level between themselves and their environment, also between themselves and their teacher ... These questions need not necessarily be expressed, but they are there. In their feeling life the children question whether the teacher is skilful in the way he leads his life, above all whether the teacher has a firm foothold in life, whether he knows what he wants; above all they have a sure sense of the overall situation of the teacher's soul.*[3]

Having lived hitherto in a totality of space and time, the children now want to begin to structure this totality in their thinking. They do this by differentiating both in space and in time. 'Before' and 'after' are more strongly felt and also related to one another and this reflects the child's growing ability to form independent mental images and recall them at will. Cognitively, the children are more able to understand questions and phenomena in a realistic and reasoning way, though the pictorial element in thinking remains important. Combined with greater capacity for empathetic feeling, this new clarity of thinking enables the cultivation of notions of personal responsibility and reasoned sense of right and wrong.

Around the age of eleven, the child attains a certain ease and grace of movement which is co-ordinated, balanced and harmonious. By Class 6 (age eleven to twelve) the children begin to undergo significant physical change commensurate with the onset of puberty. Growth usually begins to express itself in the skeleton, which becomes longer and heavier, leading to a tendency to awkward and angular movements.

These important physical changes are accompanied by a growing interest in the factual and sense perceptible world on the one hand and a psychological turbulence on the other. By about the twelfth year (Class 6) the moment will have arrived when the children no longer merely ask about causes, but actively look for them or actually create them in order to observe what effect they have. This applies equally to social relationships.

The trust shown up until now by children towards their teachers is now put to the test through challenging, silly and sometimes sharply critical behaviour. Peer values become increasingly significant in children's development, leading often to clearly distinguishable roles within the group, including leaders, bullies, victims, jokers, those who are deemed 'cool' and those who are marginalised.

The teachers must establish a new relationship to the class, one which can deal with the mood swings of the children and which can assert a new 'lawful' authority. Rules and parameters with clear consequences are essential at this age, though the teacher will also need to be able to defuse tension with humour.

In language lessons (both mother tongue and foreign) a new consciousness needs to be awakened for different linguistic qualities.

> *Before their ninth year children have an entirely emotional relationship to language. However, they would be unable to develop an awareness of themselves if we did not bring an element of thought into language. That is why it is so important to bring in the thought element by means of grammatical rules, sensibly taught, mainly in the mother tongue but then also perhaps in a foreign language. However, the language must be learnt before the rules are introduced.*[4]

For foreign languages, writing and reading in those languages must precede this.

The verb tenses bring an experience and understanding of how time is expressed in language. In English lessons the children learn about how the various parts of speech express different qualities and this responds to their increasing variety of inner experience. Declension, sentence structure, punctuation, prepositions etc. help articulate different standpoints and varying relationships, while distinguishing between direct and indirect speech or active and passive modes defines the speaker's own position (Class 5). In Class 6 comes the added facet of reality to be gained through using the subjunctive mode to indicate the difference between wish, intention and fact. Exercises in writing business letters brings in a further aspect of the real world and cultivates a sense for appropriate use of language in different contexts. The corresponding phase in foreign languages involves conversation exercises on situations in everyday life.

Music lessons now also involve the 'grammar of music'. Linked to what is going on in arithmetic lessons in which fractions are introduced in Class 4, note lengths and time value are now added to the notation begun in Class 3. The intrinsic laws of music are not studied theoretically but by playing music. The relationship of the subsidiary keys to the main key leads to the discovery of the cadenza. In keeping with the need to link everything to the level of the children's emotional development the difference between major and minor is practised by using the major and minor third (this refers particularly to Class 6). In keeping with this, singing and playing in unison now leads to rounds in several parts and then to simple polyphony.

Eurythmy lessons must be seen in connection with language and music. In speech eurythmy the various grammatical forms are practised while in tone eurythmy the scales and (in Class 6) the major and minor moods are worked on. Stepping in different rhythms and beats links to arithmetic through the values of the notes, while moving in geometrical forms supports the introduction of geometry that begins in Classes 5 and 6.

In the arithmetic lessons of Class 1 the unit was taken as the basis from which to experience the different numbers. Now, in Class 4, a similar principle comes into play again. The unit, the totality, splits up, but the parts have a regulated relationship with the whole through fractions. In the music lessons analogous discoveries are made. Fractions not only depict a 'spatial' differentiation but can also be comprehended in a dynamic and temporal way. Via decimals (Class 5) the path leads towards a preparation for logical, causal thinking, to percentages and thus to the first mathematical discovery of causes.

Form drawing now gains a strongly constructive component in intertwining, interlacing ribbon motifs, particularly in Celtic knotwork and patterns. Beauty now combines with accuracy. Attentiveness and alertness are required. In Class 5 form drawing includes freehand geometrical drawing, initially without compasses or ruler. Having done form drawing for four years, the children have gained a thorough sense of the circle, the straight line and the angle. These components are now taken separately and drawn as accurately as possible. Only once hand and eye have had enough practice is compass geometry introduced in Class 5 to draw shapes and in Class 6 to construct geometric forms.

Cause and effect can be experienced in the observation of the play of light and shadow in chiaroscuro or black-and-white shaded drawing. In Class 6 this subject complements painting with watercolours. As with free-hand geometry, the children search for and feel exactly how a shadow falls before shading it in charcoal.

Thus geometry emerges out of form drawing, and drawing with charcoal emerges from painting with watercolours. In each case the process is one of continuity. In the same way the practical experience of nature and human work in farming and building lessons is now extended and differentiated both spatially and temporally. Local studies lead on to geography and history on the one hand, and to nature studies on the other. From Class 6 onwards the latter also involves the practical aspect of gardening.

In local studies (Class 4) the children learn about the geography and above all the economic situation of their immediate surroundings. They discover how much depends on the type of soil and the lie of the land and learn what influences have been brought to bear during the course of history. The children also learn to make the transition from pictorial drawing to symbolic representation in map-making. When regional geography begins in Class 5, the whole country is studied, including its geographical and economic relationships with other countries. Finally a brief view of the whole world is given. Even at this age it is very important to go into the social aspects of geography both with regard to how the different peoples live together and with regard to caring responsibly for the environment.

Astronomy also appears on the horizon! At this stage the approach is phenomenological, i.e. the children study what they can actually observe with their own eyes, especially the relationship between the earth and sun but also including the phases of the lunar cycle and visible constellations. Now the children come to understand that what they observe in the sky has a direct influence on the climate and vegetation all over the earth.

In the language lessons, mother tongue and foreign, the children have been writing business letters in the former and practising conversation in the latter. The same principle is brought to bear in geography, where, on the one hand, they study how human beings live together and, on the other, experience how we are all economically interdependent. In English the children learn how to write accurate descriptions of what they observe, as well as imaginative accounts of historical episodes they have heard about. In both the mother tongue and foreign languages there is an emphasis on accuracy of meaning through the correct use of words and declensions.

In nature study the animal kingdom is taken first because of its closeness to the human being. This aspect is emphasised through a comparison between the human being and various animal types. From an anatomical point of view, the human being is generalised and unspecialised, whereas each animal species has specific, one-sided anatomically based skills that have often developed at the cost of others, e.g. one particular sense, specialised locomotion and so on, involving specific organs (eyes, nose, teeth, limbs, etc.). The children learn about animals grouped by their chief characteristics in this regard, such as species with powerful metabolic systems (herbivores), animals that hunt and use their claws, strength and teeth (carnivores such as the big cats), animals with highly developed visual abilities (birds of prey) and so on. Human beings potentially have all these capacities, but each remains in balance with all the others, so that they can be seen as both synthesis and archetype of the whole animal kingdom. The children discover that *humans have what animals are*. We have technology and culture whereas they have specialised anatomy.

In plant studies the evolutionary path from lower to higher plants relates to the developmental stages of the child and young person. The sequence of plant forms growing ever more differentiated and expressive provides a visible image of the children's psychological development as more and more capacities develop. The children are shown how plants relate to the earth and sun, how they change during the course of the year and, in broad outlines, how they are distributed over the whole globe. In a manner comprehensible to children (but not in a childish manner!) the two important themes of evolution and ecology are thus present as an inner thread running through biology from the start. In nature studies in Class 6 the children enter for the first time the world of mineralogy in a block period devoted to this subject.

In the history lessons the children step out of the immediate present and imagine time processes in a concrete way with the help of vivid images from the past. The time for this falls between the eleventh and twelfth years. Psychologically the children are ready to move from myth and legend to history and biography. In Class 5, history involves giving the children historical images of Asian and Middle Eastern peoples i.e. the culture of Ancient India, China, Ancient Persia, Mesopotamia, Egypt and Greece. The culture of these early civilisations is characterised through story material. With Greece myth becomes history. In Class 6 they are introduced to Roman history and the Middle Ages. They learn about cultural changes throughout history, e.g. what changes were brought about for Europe through contact with Islam. Here again the aspect of causality is taken into account. Europe lagged far behind the Orient. Then, thanks in part to contact with Islam and the East, new technological and industrial progress developed in European towns, particularly in Italy. The monastic settlements and the growth of urban cultures as well as the early influence of technology such as water wheels, building techniques, advancements in navigation and shipbuilding are important themes. The end of feudalism can, for example, be graphically characterised by events such as the Battle of Agincourt, which revealed a microcosm of social change.

Physics also begins in Class 6, and with it comes an experience of causality. The lessons are not yet concerned with the theories and hypotheses of physics: rather the children are helped to experience the basic phenomena of acoustics, optics, heat, magnetism and static electricity. Mechanics is held over for Class 7. Two of the reasons for this are as follows. Mechanics requires the study of gravity (unless you remain entirely in the neutral realm of theory), and it provides opportunities for the children to experience this force consciously. As the pupils enter puberty, they become 'ready for the earth.'[5] The growth associated with puberty has the effect of literally burdening the youngster with a new sense of physical weight. They have a need to explore the new strength that comes with this muscle and bone growth though they often lack an orientation both in their movements and in their emotional instability. They can be helped by discovering how the force of gravity can be employed in mechanics and made serviceable in life.

The second reason that mechanics is deferred until age thirteen is that it provides examples for the application of physical law to technology, the consequences of which one can see most clearly in the industrial developments during the nineteenth century. Practical applications of mechanical principles are the central theme. It is impossible to stress too strongly the importance of letting experience precede knowledge.

The practical subjects within the curriculum are now also expanded and differentiated. Gardening enables the child to encounter the consequences of work in a practical and necessary sphere of life. By providing opportunities to observe plant growth, gardening affords experiences of how time relates to space.

Three-dimensional space is now explored in handwork. The children knit gloves and socks on five needles and sew stuffed animals that require them to have a clear idea of the animal's shape when they design and cut out the pattern (the cause and effect aspect can also be seen here). The skills learned in cross-stitch are developed further to include the embroidery of interlacing ribbon motifs, such as those learned in form drawing.

'Soft' handwork is now joined by 'hard' craftwork, which is pursued by boys and girls alike. Working with wood provides a wonderful experience of what 'expertise' really means. Together, wood and tool are a unit when handled expertly. The skills of sawing, carving, rasping and filing are practised. In textile handwork, with the exception of leather, the resistance offered by the material is slight. Wood provides a considerably greater challenge so that form can be created by the practical activity of exercising expertise.

Gym lessons provide a similar theme. The movement games are now replaced by various kinds of running game, such as relay races, which have a specific aim. Achieving this is the challenge. The same goes for apparatus work, which begins now, as well as athletics and swimming. In each case the children have to learn to move using the appropriate technique in the given medium.

The themes chosen for the narrative content of the lessons during these three years help the children experience their own psychological and spiritual steps in development, through examples which span the transition from myth and legend to history.

Summary of Classes 4 to 6

During this period of development, in which the children begin to distance themselves from their surroundings, it is extremely important that their connection with the world be strengthened and renewed by means of direct and differentiated experience supported by understanding. To work in the world means to understand the world. The new subjects introduced during this phase make this possible. In working out of an understanding that has a moral foundation, the children learn to work in service for the sake of the world. Turning towards the world in this way can also be described as loving it in an active and concrete way. Class 6 marks an important transition in the class teacher period. With the onset of puberty the children are ready to develop a causal understanding of the world, yet given the emotional and subjective nature of their experience, it is important that this causal aspect be clothed in imaginative and pictorial language.

The Lower School: Classes 7 and 8

Class 7 (age twelve to thirteen)

Developmental profile

In Class 7 the pupils turn thirteen and become teenagers. Two fundamental gestures characterise this phase of life: an outer, active principle and the stirring of a dynamic, inner, psychological state. An appetite for knowledge of, and about, world phenomena, mingles with a budding capacity for reflection and the first promptings of self-reflection. In this picture of emerging forces, the physical changes which establish sexual identity and capacity begin to manifest more clearly. The physical changes tend to be somewhat in advance of the psychological development. While a feeling and yearning for independence and solitude may be experienced, a certain anxiety, emotional sensitivity and embarrassment can run alongside. Sporadic bursts of energy and an appetite for expanding outer horizons vie with periods of lethargic heaviness and subdued introspection.

Generally, there are significant differences in the manner in which boys and girls face up to and deal with the challenges of this age. Curriculum themes which mirror the pupils' outer exploration of the world and the inner journey include: the journeys of exploration in history, the focus on mood and style in English, the areas of combustion and mechanics in chemistry and physics and the health, nutrition and hygiene main lesson block.

Aims and objectives

Teachers should provide adolescents with new perspectives, particularly by directing their attention into the world. Pupils should be encouraged to take initiative and to appreciate ideas which have an abstract and logical character. They should be encouraged to challenge attitudes and assumptions which formerly they accepted on authority and be shown how to formulate their own points of view as well as accepting that others may see the world differently. The teacher should increasingly appeal to the individual judgement of the children and should lead them gradually to the exercise of social responsibility within the context of their class community. At this age it is important for the class to experience themselves both as world citizens but also as individuals who have social responsibilities.

Class 8 (age thirteen to fourteen)

Developmental profile

Class 8, during which the pupils pass their fourteenth birthday, signals the end of the class teacher period. Historically, this used to be the school-leaving age for many pupils and the entry point for an apprenticeship in a trade or craft. As such, Class 8 was seen as a 'rounding off' of the child's schooling. With the establishment of Upper Schools and the raising of the school-leaving age throughout Europe over the last fifty years, it is no longer the case that children leave school at 14.

However, Class 8 today continues to represent a certain 'completion' of a picture of the world and humanity's place within it.

At fourteen, the pupils are in the midst of adolescence; bodily and psychological changes are well under way, so that in general, the young person seems more robust and the tenderness of the previous two years has lessened somewhat. Growth in height and sexual development are clearly established, with the onset of the 'breaking voice' in boys and the establishing of the menstrual cycle in girls. At this age, the world of ideas begins to take on meaning for the young adolescent and the critical faculties of the fourteen year old are noticeably sharper. Parts of the accepted framework – particular rules for example – are subject to questioning scrutiny. Counter-balancing this critical tendency is the emergence of a reasoning or 'reasonable' side in the child.

The emergence of an independent life of feeling enters the 'labour and delivery' phase and the emotional turbulence which may attend this birth presents an important challenge to parents and teachers – how to accompany this birth or beginning of the emancipation of an individualised and independent inner life of thinking, feeling and intention without either being overwhelmed or swamped by the waves and tides of emotions, while being able to recognise that the state of crisis is part of a development.

While girls may spend much time and energy discussing and sharing their feelings and the social and emotional aspects of life in small, cohesive groups, boys generally tend to respond rather differently to the hormonal and soul changes. Seemingly rather behind their female counterparts in terms of social behaviour and emotional maturity, boys can appear uncommunicative, emotionally illiterate and tend towards the brash or the sullen. Regardless of the outer manifestations, both genders now stand before new and unknown vistas with sharpening minds, tender hearts and limbs that struggle to reach an accommodation with gravity. By the end of this class, the pupils are already searching for new authorities and role models.

Aims and objectives

Children should be led to bring together all that they have learnt into a meaningful world-picture in which the human being as a striving ethical individual has central significance.

Independence of working should be brought to a certain culmination in the Class 8 projects in which each pupil chooses a theme, researches it throughout the year and then makes a public presentation. The pupils should be prepared for the different style of teaching they will encounter in the Upper School.

Curriculum in Classes 7 to 8

The children have now reached a critical period in their development that may be experienced negatively as a crisis and is often described as such in many publications on puberty. It is important, however, for educators to treat this challenge more as an opportunity than a crisis. Between the ages of twelve and fourteen, the pupils have indeed come into quite a new relationship with the world. Physically they undergo a second change of shape, often growing much taller, but their 'inner shape' also changes noticeably. Hitherto, habit and upbringing have governed their behaviour more than their own choices and inclinations. Now their soul life erupts into the world outside them.

The human being works his way through via the breathing system and the circulatory system right into the part where the muscles are attached to the bones. He works right to the edge of being human and at puberty breaks out into the outside world. Not until this moment does he arrive fully in the outside world.[6]

Steiner's choice of words here shows the drama of this situation. Often the sheer force of the children's inner tumult shocks those around them so much that they forget that the children are equally shocked. But the children do not want their alarm, which is very deep and disturbing, to be noticed by those around them. They don't want to reveal their individuality in this 'new territory' until they have gained some sense of security. Until they have achieved this they hide in many ways behind masks and 'difficult' behaviour.

The pedagogical task for the middle of childhood is to understand that the children enter in their own time into the rhythm of a past that can be thought and a future that can be sensed.[7]

There is even something of an existential feel about this future that can be sensed. The young people feel they are both solitary and a part of humanity as a whole. Sexual maturity makes this even clearer. Having become fully a part of the human race in their ability to reproduce, they also long for an extension of their own individual responsibility towards the world. Steiner described this as follows:

One of the principles in the Waldorf School is to educate young people so that, on the one hand, they can bring to the fore in the right way the whole of their human potential, and, on the other hand, what they need to enable them to take their proper place in the world.[8]

What is referred to as a 'lack of discipline' or descriptions of the pupils 'just hanging around' can also be seen as a sign that these young people are searching to find their way within a new psychological situation and thus also within the new sense they have of the physical world.

In addition to the changes of physical and psychological 'shape', there is now also a change in the young people's consciousness. Conceptual thinking comes more to the fore as they endeavour to make links between isolated phenomena and thus leave their isolation behind them to take hold of a new totality. Whatever they experience must be transformed into original thinking, otherwise it will make them insensitive and merely a prey to sensationalism. At this age, it is not models and/or the data of specialist science they need, but the basic attitude of scientific work, which is: *thinking integrates the world of phenomena.*

Chemistry, a new subject introduced in Class 7, provides the right kinds of challenges and opportunities in the above sense. Here the young people get to know the world of substances and explore their characteristics. In addition, what they perceive can be used to form concepts, thus bringing them into the research process and helping them meet the world anew in a deeper way. Reality is not contained in an abstract concept but in thoughtful observation which does not look exclusively either at the one-sided concept or at the perception, but sees how the two are linked together.

Inorganic chemistry offers impressive possibilities for dramatic experiments that illustrate this. The main-lesson block often begins with fire and the process of combustion (an experience the youngsters are well acquainted with!), and proceeds via the burning of limestone to acids, alkalis and metals. The historical and cultural aspects of the various technologies are always included in the lessons.

Chemistry in Class 8 turns to other questions. Organic processes in nature are more complicated and therefore much harder to understand. The human being, in whom all these processes take place, is the starting point and focus for these lessons. Understanding organic life processes, the creation and metamorphosis of substances, requires an active, imaginative kind of thinking to conceive of such processes. Concepts need to be formed that also relate to a sense of responsibility.

As with inorganic chemistry, physics in Class 7 has an equally 'dead' emphasis: mechanics. There are two aspects of this. On the one hand, the subject fits in well with the youngsters' search for practical ways of changing the world such as can be found and are applied in industry and transport. On the other hand, by practising and 'playing' with mechanical experiments they can become acquainted with the systematic work required by the scientific method while also enabling them to bring order into their own steps in thinking. Physics in Class 8 shows how mechanics extends into and helps to explain the other areas of physics (e.g. steam engine, Morse telegraphy, hydrostatics and hydraulics). Fixed concepts and reductionism are still avoided. But a beginning is made in using quantitative formulae based on the mechanics learnt in Class 7, such as the 'golden rule of mechanics', calculating the speed of sound, calculating pressure etc. Here we encounter an interesting paradox. As increasingly accurate observations are made with the help of measuring instruments – a process in which our direct experience withdraws from the phenomena – so, on the other hand, the human being becomes newly involved in a practical way by making apparatus, instruments and machines on the basis of the laws of physics. Decisive industrial changes take place as a result, which in turn lead to grave social consequences. As direct experience of nature fades, this is replaced by a working knowledge of the laws of physics, which forms the basis for an interventionist approach. This stage in consciousness reflects the profound shift in human consciousness from pre-industrial societies to the modern condition in which nature loses its identity as being and becomes an objective world described by the pronoun 'it' rather than 'thou'.

In Class 6, geography presented an overview of the globe as a whole. Now the focus is on individual parts of the world not yet dealt with in detail. The cultural aspects of unfamiliar regions provide a focus for understanding the relationship of human society to its geographical circumstances. The way individual cultures arise as the result of geographical context provides the pupils with examples of individuation at the cultural level as they themselves begin to become more aware of their own cultural identity. Directing the lessons towards cultural phenomena draws the youngsters' attention away from egotistical everyday concerns of gratifying needs towards more objective examples of lifestyles as exemplified by the cultural forms of other peoples, and especially non-European or Western orientated societies.

Biology is similar in this respect. Steiner suggested that Class 7 was the last chance to introduce the subjects of health and nutrition while the children are still relatively less self-preoccupied than they will be in the depths of puberty, and can experience the nature of the human being in a general way. These days, Class 7-age pupils are well into puberty and therefore it is a question whether the aspects of human biology usually dealt with in Class 7 shouldn't appear earlier in the curriculum. Nevertheless, if the topic *is* taken in Class 7, the teacher will have to accommodate the increased self-consciousness of the students.

Gardening has a role to play here in that it teaches about food plants and the worldwide origins of food resources. Class 8 then turns to the human form as such. In the anatomy main-lesson the skeleton is studied in detail, including the mechanics of bones and muscles, and comparisons are made with animal skeletons. Eye and ear are here seen as instruments serving the inner being of the individual.

The discovery of the human being is often preceded by history lessons in Class 7, when the (re) discovery by Europeans, of new continents, and the discovery by non-Europeans of the strange forces emanating from Europe, is a major topic. Another aspect of this whole theme, is the discovery of natural laws, and the discovery of laws in art. The beginnings of scientific thinking in the Renaissance, as well as the emergence of a new individual self-consciousness that began when long-held views of the world and of faith came under scrutiny, are clearly comparable to the developmental situation of youngsters as puberty begins.

By studying the rise of industry, the industrial revolution and the human being as the shaper of social order right up to the present time, the youngsters in Class 8 are led not out of but further *into* the real world. In studying cultural history they can experience how the world can be transformed by human beings; they can investigate the causes of events and thus more and more become citizens of the world.

The Renaissance discovery of the vanishing point in painting and architecture where everything meets or from which everything emanates is now the foundation for the themes in painting and drawing. Exercises in perspective and studies of works by the great masters Brunellesci, Massaccio, Piero della Francesca and non-vanishing point perspective (Van Eyck), lend more substance to art studies. Here the excitement of the discovery can be conveyed through biographical anecdote. The pupils are not yet mature enough to grasp the deeper levels of meaning that concerned the great artists of the Renaissance. This will be the theme of Upper School art studies. Having arrived at this structure in drawing they now have to begin imbuing it with new life. Once the elements of structure, perspective and composition have been introduced, colour can be reintroduced to express the feeling and mood element to painting.

English language studies in Class 7 could be a way of preparing for this. One subject, among many other parts of speech dealt with, is 'interjections' which are, after all, simply expressions of feelings and sensations given direct expression in language. During this period young people tend to become inarticulate in the presence of adults, yet they develop fluency in the rich vocabulary of teenage jargon. Both phenomena are aspects of the search for their own individual ways of expressing themselves and such stylistic exercises can be a great help.

Solo and chorus recitation of poetry and prose must be strongly cultivated. In Class 8, when the students are searching to find their own new language, a new beginning can be made in working with the various types of clause and with texts that characterise them. Lively interest can be generated by exercises in which sentence structures are sought to suit the different temperaments. As the pupils begin to notice the sanguine, melancholic, choleric and phlegmatic temperaments they begin to see each other in a new light, and often with considerable insight. The transition can then be made to stylistic studies and exercises, with particular attention to the special qualities of epic, lyric and dramatic poetry, whereby metaphor, simile, etc. are given individual attention.

Drama is a most important theme of this biographical period. It should involve not only the reading or reciting of ballads but also a larger theatrical project, the Class 8 play. One of the important aspects of this is getting the youngsters working together in a social way on a work of art involving language.

Similar considerations apply to foreign language lessons. Exercises in writing reports and stories can relate to geography and social history, i.e. themes of a universal nature.

> *What I have said with regard to the characteristics of languages means that it is necessary – if we want to educate in a generally human but not specialised way – that we should take what comes out of the genius of a particular language regarding human nature and balance this by means of another language.*[9]

The interest of the pupils can be focused on other peoples all over the world and this can help them develop an understanding of those who are different.

Once again astronomy can be related to geography and history. The pupils can be shown the Copernican view of the world and discuss how the view of the heavens changes in different parts of the world. The point of departure is practical, *perceived* astronomy, rather than theory. Practical navigation can be taught, thus linking the exploits of early voyages of discovery, with astronomy and orientation.

As with physics in Class 8, formulae now also begin to appear in mathematics. A start is made with algebra and equations, perhaps using interest percentages (Class 6) as a point of departure. Then the pupils have an analytical experience of perspective in mathematics when they learn about square roots. The realm of negative numbers is also entered for the first time. Learning how to gain an overview of things can also be schooled through practical business calculation, e.g. in book-keeping, the basic principles of which can be introduced in Classes 6 and 7.

In geometry, theoretical proofs are practised in connection with the congruence of triangles using all kinds of definitions according to angles, triangles and quadrilaterals with inscribed or perimeter circles and also through the different proofs for the Theorem of Pythagoras (including the use of square roots) that links up with these. By repeating and constantly practising the proofs, the pupils can develop their capacity for forming judgements. Constructions in perspective provide the link with history and drawing, just as the construction of the Golden Mean in Class 8 allows for a link to be made with anatomy through anatomical proportions.

Forming exact judgements and concepts in geometry is less difficult than in music. The youngsters need to find their orientation in this realm that expresses soul qualities. As before, listening is every bit as important as solo playing and making music and singing with others. Like eurythmy, as we shall see, music at this age is important socially and therapeutically because it helps the youngsters form links with others and extricate themselves from the loneliness that is beginning to take a grip on them. Music lessons can introduce them to various composers and styles and also help them develop an understanding of composition.

Eurythmy is connected with this. Ballads and humorous pieces are worked on. Speech eurythmy also supports language studies by cultivating artistic interpretation, while tone eurythmy adds to and accompanies music studies. As mentioned above, doing eurythmy in a group allows for the practice and development of social skills. At a period when they can be shy, self conscious and awkward, the youngsters are helped by discovering that the formal principles of eurythmy can articulate their experience of dynamic space as well as providing an artistic medium for the expression of soul moods.

The Class 8 play has already been mentioned in connection with English studies. This is intended to be much more comprehensive than the short plays and scenes that have been worked on from Class 1 onwards in the main-lesson and foreign languages. This play for the first time allows the children to shape their emotions while still under the protective mask of a role in a play. This can be stimulating and motivating. In addition everything they have learned and worked on in the Lower School can be drawn on: making the scenery (painting and carpentry), sewing the costumes (handwork), making the posters (drawing), choreography (eurythmy, music).

In the description of handwork in Classes 1 to 3 we have already mentioned practical skill. Now we become increasingly concerned to combine this practical usefulness with a sense for the aesthetic, whilst relating natural materials to their environmental context. For example the youngsters might make shoes and then embellish them artistically to suit both purpose and wearer. Use of the sewing machine is practised so that in the coming years complicated pieces such as shirts, blouses, trousers, skirts and dresses can be made. Here design, function, material and technical skill are brought into a relationship with aesthetics and individual expression.

Just as handwork in Classes 7 and 8 gains an element of the artistic, so do crafts and woodwork. Useful objects of artistic design are made. The design takes account of both function and aesthetic appearance. Salad servers, candle holders, postcard stands etc. are made in woodwork. To make toys with moving parts you need a basic understanding of mechanics, enough not only to allow you to understand how something works but to be able to design it in the first place.

Two qualities are particularly important at this age, namely self-restraint and self-motivation. Things that prevent us from participating in the world, e.g. laziness, antipathy or fear, are tackled for the first time in subjects such as gardening. The weather itself provides a challenge because of its unreliability. Difficult procedures requiring patience and skill, such as transplanting, are learnt. If possible the whole gardening year should be experienced, from sowing, planting, cultivating (watering, hoeing, weeding) to harvesting, and then even selling the produce. A sense of responsibility is needed to sustain all this. The same goes for the care of shrubs and trees because in addition to immediate results it also requires foresight over many years.

History is mainly concerned with experiencing and understanding the past (although in Class 8 the future can also be allowed to appear). Gardening, on the other hand, is a responsibility directed to the future.

Gym and sport lessons provide the aspect of self-restraint and self-motivation that leads to clear experiences of self. Apparatus work and springing in all its many varieties, provide plenty of choice.

Perseverance and stamina are schooled by more intensive running exercises. Ball games provide an important social balance to the more solitary disciplines. Once puberty begins a distinction is made between the sexes for the first time. Training is directed to developing strength for the boys and elasticity for the girls.

In Class 8 a year-long project is also undertaken by each pupil. Subjects and methods are many and varied. The aim is for the youngsters to produce and document work showing their own formulations and graphic solutions, their own craft skills or musical progress. The element of self-restraint and self-motivation can be particularly strong here. At a time when it is often difficult to 'reach' individual pupils, a project provides opportunities to enter into relationships with them based on an area of common interest. This enables teachers to continue an on-going relationship genuinely wanted by the pupils.

Summary of Classes 7 to 8

The overriding theme is working with the world's laws by conversing with them and, in doing so, finding one's own voice. Students should experience how knowledge makes one capable of forming appropriate judgements and how forming judgements leads to new questions. The students should be led to bring together what they have learned into a meaningful world picture in which the human being as a striving ethical being has central significance. The students should also reach a degree of independent working that enables them to approach the Upper School equipped for a more subject specialist approach to learning which requires more initiative and independent working skills.

Even though at the founding of the original Waldorf school, the pupils left school after Class 8, Steiner's comment below is equally relevant when the students go on to the Upper School.

> *When you discharge a child from school you should have laid the foundations for him or her to be no longer tied to the body with every fibre of the soul; in thinking, feeling and will he must have become independent of the body.*[10]

The Upper School: Classes 9 to 12

Rather than provide developmental profiles for each Upper School class, we will describe educational aims for each age group. This seems more appropriate given the increasing individual differentiation that occurs during adolescence. Nevertheless one can identify an overall progression through the years of the Upper School that can be characterised as follows.

The Class 9 student (fifteen years old) has reached a point in his or her development when the inner life of feeling in its search for independence can take extreme forms. Steiner once characterised the feeling life of the fifteen year old as akin to having been 'spat out' of the spiritual world. That means a radical distancing of the individual not only from the sense of being embedded in a secure world of certainties provided by family as much as by childhood innocence, but also from what that individual has learned. It requires the inner equivalent of re-learning how to walk, talk and think.

Thinking, feeling and willing as activities are often entirely at odds with each other. This can manifest in great clarity of intellectual argument and total inability to act out the consequences of those ideas; fierce assertion of emotional independence (don't tell me what to do, think or feel!) with an almost childlike dependency and need for emotional comfort.

On the other hand there is a strong will to engage in life, which needs equally strong ideals as orientation. The Class 9 age student seeks and welcomes clarity of explanation, sympathetic understanding from the adults around them and much open-hearted humour, the balm which smooths and makes bearable the inconsistencies of life. We can summarise the situation of the student on entry to the Upper School as follows:

* The awakening of a stringent logic and thinking potential that requires distance from one's own self and other people
* The search for balance between intellectuality and the realm of passion and urge-driven will.
* The experience of the emergence of a higher ideal humanity
* The search for a new harmony with the world, but one that should not be gained at the loss of the new-found and still tentative identity and personal freedom

The Class 10 age student (sixteen years old) often appears after the summer holidays as different in marked ways. The often tumultuous nature of Class 9 has given way to a desire to know outer facts, information and details, which requires of them a new intellectual focus. Previously students have mostly been satisfied to know how it is, now they wish to know *how we know* how it is. In other words they seek not only information but insight. Thus behind every question of *what*, is the question of *how*, of origins. How have things come to be as they are? Above all the students want to know how facts relate to *them* personally.

At this age young people experience their 'I' strongly in harsh judgements of sympathy and antipathy, especially the conventional world of parents, authorities, routines and rules. The facades of 'bourgeois' existence need to be torn down to expose what lies naked behind them. They can be rigorous in their pursuit of perceived injustice. Class 9 students are rarely quite so ready to fight and argue and yet the individual is never so prone to being hurt as at this age. Dialogue with adults acquires a sharper, more existential tone. It is no longer merely an intellectual sport, as in Class 9. Now it is for real.

Class 10 students become in many ways the modern equivalent of medieval knights or warriors. They adopt many elaborate rituals in their behaviour, their clothing becomes their armour. Depending on fashion, this can be quite literal with the tendency to leather, chains, pins, studs, insignia, motor-cycle helmets, heavy boots, layers of clothing etc. These warriors are, however, not graced with the arts of chivalry. There is often a sense of imprisonment in their own inner lives, with a corresponding urge to break out. There is deep pain to endure and slow-healing wounds to bear. The clothing is not only protective armour, it is camouflage, disguise and mask. There is a heightened consciousness, a kind of double awareness that the adolescent is quite aware of what he does, how it appears and just how transparent the disguise is.

The sheer unbridgeable gulf between appearance and reality is often experienced as truly tragic. This age is highly prone to suicide and other lesser acts of self-destruction. They seek groups in which to hide among those who feel the same way, speak the same language, enjoy the same irony, who understand each other. If Class 9 was still lit by the remaining glow of the class teacher period, by Class 10 the light has entirely faded. This is one of the most decisive points in the whole maturation process. The individual has arrived and is in grave danger of diffusing. The temptation to flight in inner or outer 'emigration' is strong, to run away from the world of challenges, to hang onto childhood's certainties, to blot out the light of day.

Two powerful new forces, that of burgeoning sexuality and that of physical power, now further destabilise inner uncertainty. These tendencies have been there for a long time, for some individuals since Class 7. Yet in Class 10 most students have arrived at a certain low point in their overall development. Anthroposophical psychology recognises the significant 'Rubicon' experience of the child in his or her ninth year. This is taken account of in many ways through the curriculum. A further significant Rubicon challenge occurs in the sixteenth year, in Class 10. The students are confronted with a significant threshold experience in their inner development. Those who successfully negotiate the transition over this threshold will have taken a major step in the individuation process. Those who don't, run the risk of falling prey to their own unredeemed soul forces. Much adult behaviour that we deem anti-social and immature is a reflection of these unredeemed adolescent forces perpetuated into adult life in often pathological ways. In men this generally takes outwardly threatening forms, in expressions of power. In women, it often takes the form of dependency and self-denial, even self-destruction. The gender differences have many cross-overs.

The question of the 16 year old is 'who am I?'; it will find an answer when the individual discovers that who I am is not solely determined by what I have inherited and what has happened to me in my life so far, but also by something that has to do with *me*? The Class 10 student can begin to explore new territory using the new powers of judgement that can be developed during this year.

Life begins at 17. This popular conception certainly highlights the fact that this age marks a significant new beginning. If the interest of the Class 9 student is strongly directed outwards into the world, and the interest of the Class 10 student is strongly focused internally, the Class 11 student's interest is a synthesis of both these directions, namely in insight. The young person at this age wishes to understand the inner principles that determine not only the human being's inner life and configurations but also those of the wider world. It is a question of finding the balance between inner and outer.

This balance is especially critical in social life. Social conscience awakens with the ability to empathise with the other person. What has previously been acutely experienced within one's own soul can be recognised in the other. Deeper dimensions to life now begin to reveal themselves. The young person has to find an inner orientation between appearance and reality, between what is said and what is meant. Above all the seventeen year old is called upon to find his or her own way, to make personal and binding decisions, to consider the full consequences of their actions. Polarities in life have to be resolved, have to find a higher synthesis to a new oneness. The choices to be made highlight that most characteristic experience of this age-doubt. Throughout the curriculum, the question of polarities requires an inner engagement from the student.

The student in Class 12 seeks an overview in which to reconcile two opposing forces that have become increasingly apparent through all he or she has learned, namely the tension between increased individualisation and ever growing global consciousness. These two trends will have become apparent through studies of science, the humanities and through practical experience. The curriculum has led the students to find inner and outer connections and correspondences between important phenomena in the world. Hopefully they have learned how to make an inner personal connection to that which they have learned. Now the question is turned round. The question is no longer how does the world affect *me* in my life, but how can I influence the world? This question needs to be asked in very concrete terms, in terms of economics, in social and personal life, in politics or in science. Am I a pawn or a King, a performer or a spectator? Where is my position in the world?

School has to become a place in which the student can find his or her own place in the world and actively cultivate it. The students should at last have the opportunity to define, create and live their own learning space, not alone but in partnership with fellow students and teachers. The emphasis should be on self-determination of objectives and pathways towards those objectives. This level of independence will be denied most individuals once they have left school for many years of further professional training or career-building. Perhaps some will never again have such freedom and at the same time such youthful geniality, untrammelled by life's responsibilities. It is a moment when students can give back to their education freely of themselves. It is fatal to the cultivation of true individuality if this twelfth school year is determined by the wishes of teachers or parents, or indeed society at large in the form of examinations and the like.

Gaining an overview is a last chance to remain a generalist before plunging into the specialisation that profession and university life entails. A balance between independent working, choosing themes and projects which express a personal interest and seeking the linking, integrating overview between all fields of knowledge and experience is the challenge the eighteen year old demands. Recognising, even at this relatively young age, something of one's individual destiny is the corollary of recognising the global aspects of the destiny of humankind. Ultimately the Class 12 student wants a useful answer to the question, can the world be changed and am I worthy of being an instrument of change?

Learning to form judgements

The periods leading up to and following puberty (Steiner's own phrase *erdenreife* means 'being ready for the earth') tend to make one want to look at puberty as a separate phase in itself. The nature of puberty has to be understood in the context of what goes before and comes after it. It makes itself known in advance both psychologically and physically, culminates in an obvious physiological process that is often felt to be quite dramatic, and then continues to have after-effects. These after-effects are not limited by the achievement of biological maturity (which has already passed its culmination as soon as the capacity to reproduce has been attained) but include the process of psychological maturation that goes hand in hand with it.

Steiner summarised this process as a 'new, third birth', the birth of the independent body of soul forces (the sentient body) in the individual. The first birth is the one we normally regard as such, the beginning of the path of life. The second is when the organic development reaches a culmination at the change of teeth, when the forces hitherto used to build the body become free to form and structure memory and imagination.

Prior to this 'third birth', feelings were the source of the child's inner life, but from now on they reach a new stage of independence. An individual's inner life confronts the outer world in a relationship that still has to find a form. Among other things, this relationship is created by the capacity to form judgements. The content of all lessons should respond to this need by challenging it and by providing a context in which the individual can develop his or her faculties. This means that the task of education is to provide learning opportunities in which objective laws that are accessible to thought can be experienced and made conscious. Real judgement can only be based on recognition of the true nature of phenomena.

This also provides a basis for doing things that are recognised to be necessary even if the personal part of one's feelings doesn't feel like it. This is where duty as a voluntary act can be discovered, together with responsibility for one's own actions. Adopting one's own standpoint becomes important, as does finding one's *own voice*, both of which lead to having one's own opinions. Once the first stages of this process have been achieved both physically and psychologically, and when the often tumultuous phase has died down, the young person achieves a new plateau of development.

By the end of the sixteenth year the crisis or transition of puberty can be regarded as completed. Bodily proportions reach a new harmony. There is a greater inclination for serious work. On the other hand there is also a danger of becoming eccentric:

> *In all modesty, the young person assumes that he has a significant part to play in saving humanity, and plans his life accordingly.*[11]

Teachers can help in such cases by setting an example of how judgements are formed. The youngsters must learn how to handle judgements in an appropriate way. It is clear that they are feeling and seeking for 'ideals', in their own selves as well as in others and in the world.

What they find in their search rarely comes up to expectation, and their comments are all too plain and often merciless. They can easily become sceptical. The science the teacher presents must be seen to have been successful in the steps it has taken towards knowledge. Pessimism about knowledge is not good for young people's psychological state at this age, though what they themselves say often expresses it. When they do this they are actually challenging the adult world to 'show me that this is not so'. There is an entirely objective tragic element in young people of this age, for only rarely do they find others living in the way they seek to live, namely as self-determining adults.

School is no longer acceptable if it is felt to be running *alongside* rather than *within* real life. It must offer possibilities that lead to surefootedness in the here and now. The pupils will detect anything speculative or masquerading as reality. Their search for authenticity and truth is a more concrete version of their search for an unattainable ideal. It is the teachers' task to provide positive experiences in this search. If they fail, the young people will not find a foundation for their existence which can give them firmness and direction. They will remain empty, standing without a foothold in the stream of time. Adolescents who find only inadequate answers among their teachers and the adults around them may, later in life, struggle to overcome selfishness and insecurity. As adults themselves, they may be unable to find the altruism and confidence a healthy society needs.

Values: meeting real needs

An education that takes its orientation from life questions of this kind can never be value-free. When the children were younger it was the task of the teacher to assess and choose what he or she told the children. Now the teacher must let the youngsters experience the teacher as a person with real questions. What encourages and develops the young people now are not results but rather the processes of the teachers' own self-education. Those teachers will be successful who can lay aside their own ingrained attitudes and remain 'life-long learners' themselves.

The third seven-year period does not end with Class 12 or even Class 13. The urge to enter professional or other specialist training makes itself felt. Aims become clearer. Faced with external influences such as the pressure to gain places in higher education or the possibility of unemployment, young people may become restless and gradually lose the will to learn. The challenges of public examinations can, in their one-sidedness, lame initiative and narrow the scope of interest.

The real needs of modern society for people of initiative, energy, flexibility, creativity and social competence, demand that Upper School students learn to learn, learn to work, learn to transfer skills from one realm to another, develop problem-solving abilities, be creative and above all have a fine sense of social responsibility.

For this reason many Steiner-Waldorf schools have developed integrated Upper School programmes offering a variety of practical training in such fields as carpentry, environmental studies, electronics, metalwork, design and clothing, catering, child care and so on, alongside the usual range of subjects. There is an emphasis on project work and this is combined with a range of practical work experience opportunities. Such activities cultivate transferable skills in learning through making, team work and social competence. School in this sense becomes a real preparation for life if it provides opportunities for individuals to become free personalities capable of recognising and accepting the tasks life presents them with and whose soul faculties of thinking, feeling and willing are integrated by the activity of their 'I'.

In countries such as the UK, where the public examination system permeates the whole Upper School, or even into the Middle School, the question of life skills and developing real engagement and motivation is often subsumed by the narrowing effect of exams on the young person's horizon. Such schools work hard to find the right balance, not least in the consciousness of the students, who too often see the exams as the 'real' task. The challenge to awaken genuine ideals should not be underestimated. The real task of a Waldorf Upper School is to work with adolescents in such a way that they can ask: what do I need to do to be useful in society? rather than asking: what do I need to do to get what I want?

There are several aspects to this task. The young people must:

a) become familiar with the world and the tasks it sets them;
b) develop a range of skills that equip the individual to be creative and adaptable in fields beyond what they have specifically learned;
c) discover their own individuality;
d) develop powers of judgement and discernment;
e) develop a moral and ethical will based on insight.

Prepared in this way, young people will be able to contribute freely and responsibly as self-dependent individuals to the society and the times in which they find themselves, learning to take part in shaping the future.

Educational competence

Steiner-Waldorf education aims to combine schooling the intellect with caring for imaginative qualities and character building. Therefore artistic and practical activities are seen as being of equal value to the provision of knowledge. Each of these fields of experience should be integrated. Education is not solely a matter of intellectual training: it is a holistic process. Nor should education be restricted to specialist knowledge but should seek to engage the whole human being. Both pupils and teachers can regard themselves as 'successful' if they succeed in developing intellect, a rich emotional life and will in equal measure and if they bring about a feeling for freedom, equality and fraternity. People will then not reject the challenges life offers, nor will resignation be their reaction to crisis. Instead they will help to find meaning and seek and follow new ways. Shaping every lesson will be an 'art of education' which presupposes a creative teacher who is him or herself continuously in the process of developing. Education in this sense means teaching the right subject in the right way at the right time.

If the teachers succeed in working with and understanding the laws of human development, then they will become capable of 'reading' the human being. The various physiological and psychological phenomena that occur as a young person matures need to be linked with the overall human being. Comparison can be made to the plant whose totality can only be observed in the whole sequence of its life cycle. When a person has learnt to read the human being well enough to be able to base their educational actions on this insight, thus helping young people in the whole of their being, then he or she can be said to have gained educational competence. They can take on full responsibility for education in school. The curriculum is then no longer merely a syllabus to be ticked off item by item, for the curriculum then arises out of the conditions necessary for development at each specific stage.

Class 9

In history, attention returns to the period spanning the fifteenth to the twentieth centuries. The aim is to make the pupils acquainted with the leading ideas of this period. Great ideas and ideals bring about new developments (the French Revolution, the American Wars of Independence and Constitution, the Russian Revolution). Ideas can also be powerful instruments of evil, as the history of the Third Reich demonstrates. These exemplify the problems young people themselves have at the Class 9 stage: that the journey from ideal to realisation presupposes a perception of reality, that violence and failure can be a consequence of moral rigour and fanatical idealism.

The last 'blank spots' disappear from the European map of the world, and consciousness begins to encompass the whole globe. This history main-lesson is intended to awaken the youngsters' interest in the world. They also need to understand the historical forces that come to expression in the current global situation. At the start of a new millennium, the end of the Cold War and its proxy conflicts in Asia and Africa as well as the lingering forces of disintegration that followed the end of Colonialism have left a complex world, one in which the young person needs to find an orientation. The globalisation of both the world economy and communications systems is creating a new phase in world history, one for which the students have a keen interest. Their increasing familiarity with electronic media and in particular the internet needs to be put in a global context.

Important aspects of human invention and discovery are treated in physics, including the steam engine, locomotive, combustion engine, electric motor, light bulb, telephone, calculator, television, laser and computer (some of these may be dealt with in Class 8). The pupils in Class 9 come to grips with the rationally planned technology of the nineteenth and twentieth centuries. Many of these technologies have revolutionised people's mobility and ability to communicate. The relationship between the machines themselves and the kind of consciousness that accompanies their use is an important topic. The impact such inventions had on everyday life is important, as is their replacement through even more modern tools and systems. The post-industrial age is the world the students are growing into and this needs to be put into perspective.

It is also important for the pupils to get to know the individuals whose ideas and intentions led to specific inventions. Through such examples they can grasp technology as human thought which has become actual reality. A glance into the workshop of these thought processes and into the biography of the inventors provides the pupils with pictures that can rouse their enthusiasm while as yet avoiding the moral implications and cultural pessimism of today.

In mathematics, equations right up to probability calculations take centre stage. This provides good practice in formal, logical thinking. All kinds of quadratic equations and surface and volume calculations are done.

In geometry, Platonic solids with plane surfaces provide the opportunity to make inner pictures of processes before drawing them. The manner of depiction is chiefly that of diagonal section with vertical parallel projection which is easy to construct and easy to see spatially. Conic sections now also make their appearance. This is new as compared with Class 8. Ellipse, parabola and hyperbola are developed using dynamic exercises.

In biology, the subject begun in Class 8 in human biology continues: the human skeletal and muscular system and the sense organs, i.e. those systems by means of which human beings experience themselves in physical existence. Carrying on from Class 8, the pupils can now be led much further into the shape and functions of the bones. Taking hold of these and overcoming gravity with them is what young people are unconsciously occupied with the whole time. The whole theme of uprightness has a central place at this age. This complements the experience of the sense organs. These enable the young person to reach out beyond his or her own body, which is often experienced as being 'too small'.

In geography in the Upper School an understanding of the earth as a whole entity begins in Class 9 with the study of the earth's mineral crust. The students' newly awakened but as yet disorderly personality forces and the growing capacity to form judgements are directed towards geological phenomena. A thorough understanding of the physical ground on which our existence is built with its tectonic and geomorphological processes can provide orientation and a sense that the structure of the landscape is the result of largely subterranean dynamic forces. The contrast between imperceptible yet inexorable processes of erosion and the dynamic of volcanic activity offer the students a picture of extreme forms of change. The levelling and up-building process of sedimentation offers a stabilising middle between these two poles. The extremes of forces and time scales are polarities which mirror the young person's way of experiencing the world.

In chemistry, the way substances come into being is studied: combustion processes, results of carbonisation, the decomposition of organic matter leading to the formation of humus, how fossil fuels are formed and metabolic processes in plants. Distillation allows the pupils to experience how substances evaporate and then become tangible once again, a process of clarification and purification like those they are experiencing inwardly at this time.

The study of art becomes a subject in its own right in the Upper School, and is very important for Class 9. It provides a balance for the inorganic, lifeless worlds of physics and chemistry with their strict laws, showing the pupils a different world, one in which human beings are free to create their own order. Getting to know great paintings and sculptures will awaken their enjoyment of art and teach them that it is a realm in which human beings can experience freedom. In European schools, the origins of the Western tradition are explored from Ancient Egypt, through Greece to Rome and Early Christian art leading to the Middle Ages and the dawn of the Italian Renaissance. The main theme is, art as a reflection of changing human consciousness.

Drawing is now exclusively chiaroscuro, black-and-white (possibly also lino cutting and printing), which mirrors the polarity in which Class 9 pupils find themselves. By dealing with this polarity consciously in shaping their work they experience what their soul now needs. Particularly important are the exploration of the transition from dark to light and the crucial transitional 'grey areas' of life.

English studies also involve two main elements.[12] One main-lesson period is concerned with the origins and history of drama and theatre. From sacred beginnings both tragedy and comedy have their spiritual aspects. The transition from sacred to secular and profane is an important one to experience at this age. Drama should have both a theoretical, historical aspect and of course be a practical skill to be learned, in drama workshops and plays. Shakespeare is a high point of this study. Key elements in studying Shakespeare are on the one hand his theatre and the structure of his dramas but on the other the quality of the language. Shakespeare's leading characters provide studies in personality of the highest order. In wrestling with Shakespearean language the students discover the many levels of subtlety and meaning in the images and metaphors, which open them to the whole meta-level of language and human thought. In this they are able to make an inner connection to the spirit of language and thus consciously re-form a connection to spirituality which puberty has clouded or even separated them from entirely.

Humour is another theme. The subject of humour enables the pupils to stand back a little from their situation and see things from a variety of different perspectives. This involves an exploratory study of human nature and psychology. It also reduces to a bearable level the sharpness of criticism and self-knowledge. Laughter is an individual's way of beginning to cope with what happens to one. The varying emotions of empathy, compassion and weeping, laughing *at* and laughing *with*, can also be discussed from a social and psychological point of view. When these soul qualities are stimulated in an aesthetic way, Class 9 pupils can experience the all-pervading tension of polarities and the possibilities of resolution and redemption.

Finding their own voice requires practice, as do

the practical skills of literacy. Book reports, study skills, essays, use of syntax and style all help the students master their written and oral skills and find a new conscious relationship to language. The process of distancing oneself from one's cultural environment also involves the mother tongue. This can lead to an 'in'-language or slang amongst young people in which expressions taken from other less-than-obvious lexical sources are often preferred. The shock effect of such language on adults is very much part of the process.

This tendency to become estranged from one's own inherited language can come as a bonus for foreign languages. The pupils get to know ways of thinking and expression that are not customary in their own language, and they enjoy being able to step back from things by this means. Texts for reading can be biographies of inventors, engineers, artists and other great personalities of the era with which the history lessons are concerned. In admiring individuals who have gone ahead of their fellow human beings along the path towards conquering the earth, the young people gain a degree of maturity in their own ideals and aims. Learning about the issues facing other cultures also helps broaden adolescents' perspectives. Indeed in our times the need to understand the other person, the foreigner, the refugee from another culture, gives the teaching of foreign languages a special significance. The entire cultural aspect of modern language teaching is very important at an age when youngsters are especially drawn into their own folk soul element, adopt more strongly their local regional accent, and begin to identify with the 'laddish' tendencies that come to expression in the adolescent culture that is often anchored in local prejudices, support of the local football team and so on.

Grammar is repeated systematically in a broad overview, and elements the pupils have been practising, open the way for new possibilities of comprehension. The path in foreign language learning has moved from immersion and imitation, through usage and learning by heart and has now led to the need to understand. Thus a systematic review of all aspects of grammar in Class 9 is very much from the aspect of consciously working with rules, structures, comparison of idiom and so on. This is the age when a grammar textbook becomes a useful tool in teaching. Earlier, such textbooks are more useful as points of reference and reminders of things already learned. Now the systematic, tabulated, abstract structure of a good textbook really comes into its own. As in the English lessons a balance of humour, biographies, everyday useful usage and exactness of expression is needed. It is crucial that language lessons remain at heart experiences of orality in language. Literature and grammar both serve the primary aim of providing resources to support the students speaking and communicating in the foreign language. This is a major challenge for teacher and student alike but one that is amply rewarding when successful, and tedious when not.

Music lessons take their departure from a similar viewpoint. By getting to know the biographies of great musicians the pupils begin to develop an interest in their immortal compositions. It is a good idea to place two great composers side by side e.g. Mozart and Beethoven, or Handel and Bach for Baroque music. Listening to the works of the great composers can lead to discovering the differences between the Baroque and Classical styles. In working through such compositions, either vocally or instrumentally, the pupils are guided to discover not only new depths of feeling but also the 'grammar of music's language', to hear and show how keys modulate, and thus to understand the metamorphosis from the Baroque to Classical style.

The youngsters are willing to understand anything to do with metamorphosis, and if this is coupled with art, it can help them find clarity in their own 'rebuilding process'. From Class 9 onwards the pupils sing in the Upper School choir and/or play in the Upper School orchestra.

In eurythmy, through poems and musical compositions from the twentieth century and contemporary artists, Class 9 pupils are led into movement and choreography in a thoughtful and businesslike way. The students should become conscious of the formal elements in eurythmy, learn how to choreograph appropriate forms for the different styles of music or poetry, for the grammatical and linguistic elements, for the different keys and so on. There should also be the opportunity to experience other forms of dance, including both formal ballroom dancing, Latin styles, jive, line dance, folk and morris dancing as well as contemporary dance. In all this the youngsters must be fully aware of the artistic element, and a good leavening of humour should also be included. For eurythmy to really engage the students there must be regular opportunity to see professional performances as well as being motivated by regularly seeing Classes 11 and 12 students performing to a high standing. The students should be able to experience that other people take eurythmy seriously.

Gardening in Class 9 can either take the form of a long main-lesson or project block (work experience on the land, landscaping, laying paths and building flights of steps, putting up fencing etc.) or lead to a practical period of agricultural or forestry work. For two to three weeks the pupils live with farming families and share whatever work is going on in farmyard and field. Apart from many other new things, they experience nature as the element that shapes each day and the whole of life. The tasks depend on the locality and opportunities available to the school. The important element is the encounter with real physical hard work and the necessary practical wisdom of tools, the work and safety procedures and the teamwork that accompany such activities. The economics of farming are an important topic too, not least in revealing the true value of work and stewardship of the environment.

In carpentry and joinery, simple joints are studied and applied. In dressmaking, the pupils make their own patterns and then sew skirts, jackets, etc. Copper beating and basket-making lead to similar objects by very different means of manufacture, e.g. bowls or vases on the one hand and baskets of all sorts on the other. An inner space is created from the outside by hard work. In all these crafts, the student learns to experience the nature of the material, how it is won, processed and worked. The economic and ecological aspects of craftwork should always be integrated into the practical work and especially the link between landscape, raw material and work process. Above all, objects should be produced that meet a real need in the world and not merely be a demonstration of practice pieces. The same is true for information technology. All pupils should learn basic word processing and use this for practical purposes such as the presentation of work, designing and laying out magazine pages and so on.

Pupils who do not participate in the full academic programme for some reason are offered alternative lessons of a practical and social nature. Such students should be given the opportunity to develop a specialist interest with specific responsibilities within the school. This may include helping in the kindergarten, kitchens, maintenance department, school theatre and so on. Whatever programme the school is able to offer, it is important that the students experience that their work is valued and that they are increasingly to take responsibility for it.

Educational aims for Class 9

By the end of Class 9 the students should begin to:

* show self-motivated interest in the world around them; acquire knowledge about what interests them through independent gathering of information and facts;
* show structure in their thinking and be able to make logical, causal deductions; move from judgement based on feeling (Class 8) to judgement based on observation and understanding. Apply analytical processes to an overall nexus and discover the underlying principles;
* know how to make the transition from idea to ideal, and from ideal to applied practice and move from discovery (Classes 7 and 8) to creation and invention. Engage their will in the realm of ideals;
* appreciate technology as the 'fifth kingdom', the kingdom of culture, created by the human being; discover in technology the *thought become worldly reality;*
* understand the transitions between polarities in many different realms of life and especially the arts;
* understand that art and science reflect historical changes in cultural consciousness and that artists and scientists have world views that are expressed in their work;
* learn to work and be able to learn through work. Have hands-on experience of as many areas of practical life as possible;
* be able to work in a team and to solve problems together.

Class 10

How does a Class 10 differ from a Class 9? Personalities become more individualised through the work. Steps need to be taken so that the pupils' own activity helps them find themselves. Clarity of thought and an increasing ability to form judgements should help pupils extricate themselves from the unstable nature of the forces of emotional sympathy and antipathy. Hence the effort to come to grips analytically with laws that can be understood through thought.

Steiner's curriculum suggestions for biology were:

> *To make the human being as a single entity comprehensible ... The physical human being with his organs and organic functions in connection with soul and spirit.*[13]

The point of departure is morphology, from which a physiological and psychosomatic consideration of the organs can follow step by step. This could include a comparison of the brain and nervous system with a study of the heart and circulation. The brain's relationship to perception, thought and memory provides a basis for discussing consciousness and moral aspects of conscience. The relationship of the heart and circulation system to emotional experience is important. In this way the young people come into contact with a part of themselves where there is interplay of those developmental processes to which they are so intensely exposed at this age.

In geography the holistic view now expands to include the earth's mantle of water and air and also the climatic zones and further spheres including the earth's core and the outer spheres, together with their varied interactions and movements. In this way we continue to build a foundation for an understanding of the biosphere and ecology. The aim is to enable the pupils to become more aware of the earth as a living organism that reacts with the utmost sensitivity to interference in its rhythms and cycles.

In gardening, cultivation and propagation now come to the fore. If gardening as such is given in Class 10, then the mysteries of grafting are taught. But just as in Class 9, where a practical period in agriculture can take the place of gardening, so can Class 10 have a practical forestry period. This period need not necessarily be regarded as an alternative; it can equally well be complementary to gardening, deepening understanding. It is also important at this age that the students have direct experience of work in a variety of professions. A period of practical work experience may replace the forestry practical.

The history main-lesson brings to the fore an aspect that is obviously linked to geography: human and cultural evolution governed by the earth and the landscape. This is an opportunity to explore human prehistory, from the emergence of modern *homo sapiens* and the Paleolithic Revolution around 40,000 years before the present. This can include a study of the high culture of Ice Age art, followed by the Mesolithic period of transition at the end of the last Ice Age. The development of agriculture and the founding of the first permanent settlements shows not only a major shift in the economy of prehistoric peoples but a fundamental shift in human consciousness. From there, the establishment of the urban civilisations, with their theocracies, temples, use of writing, bureaucracies, laws and hierarchical social structures, can be described. Significant developments in technology as well as the consequences of urbanisation, such as the transference of diseases from animals to humans can also be discussed. The main focus of these studies should be a comparison of the specific ways the various cultures reflected their natural geographical circumstances, and the ways in which complex human societies were structured. The links between human beings and the earth are experienced, as is the evolution of the human being who increasingly becomes an individual emerging from the group, be it clan, tribe or nation.

The English main-lesson has similar aspects to the history in handling the transition from myth to literature, from pre-literate cultural forms such as myth, saga, and religious ritual to the origins of literature with its shift from collective to individual experience. Another theme combines linguistics with poetic diction and aesthetics, in which both the origin and structure of language are explored.

The study of art has so far involved mainly the visual arts. Now poetry and language as an art, is added thus shifting the emphasis from art in space to art in time. The formal laws of poetry – rhythm, sound, and image – are investigated and practised in epic, lyric and dramatic examples (the 'poetry and metre' main-lesson). A second main-lesson can be devoted to a continuation of the study of painting with a discussion of art to the north of the Alps (from Dürer, Holbein, Grünewald, van Eyck to Rembrandt). Overall, formal composition and principles of shaping a picture come to the fore, to correspond with Class 10 pupils' need to grasp things with their understanding. In practical art, painting is reintroduced with colour exercises designed to develop a vocabulary of colour and then developed into motifs in which atmosphere and mood can be expressed. Print-making can also be fruitfully explored at this age. The logic involved in planning pictures or designs that may need to be drawn in mirror form, or in which a composite picture is built up using several plates or blocks, challenges the students' powers of thinking as well as the precision involved in the work. Print-making can be applied in a range of media.

Eurythmy supports poetry and the use of language through the use of suitable examples in which the group moves as a whole. The pupils should work out their own eurythmy forms.

In foreign languages humour also comes into its own. It is fun to get the point through a direct understanding of the language (without translation). A study of humorous texts, jokes and idiomatic expression can broaden the adolescents' social, psychological and cultural horizons. The pupils also begin to develop a feeling for style. Unabridged literature is increasingly used. The use of grammar as a tool can be appreciated through the pupils' enjoyment of clear thinking. Comparative studies of grammar using English and the foreign languages can heighten awareness of how the spirit of language expresses itself through the genius of the different folk souls. The history of the development of the various languages can enhance this insight into the changing consciousness which underlies language evolution. Being able to present arguments for and against various propositions in the foreign language calls for the ability to think in that language.

In music lessons the endeavour is to give the pupils a foundation on which they can develop a genuine appreciation of music. Examples are practised in choir work and a chamber orchestra. Harmony is explored through musical examples. Main-lessons in mathematics, physics, chemistry, geometry and surveying have similar points of departure. In physics the formative principle is particularly obvious. Nowhere else are the laws of nature so obvious or clearly followed as in classical mechanics. The pupils can proceed from experiment to observation and on to the laws, the formula and the calculation without loss of clarity. Clarity in observing, logic in drawing conclusions, the ability to relate cause to effect, and analytical thinking are all schooled.

One of the aims for Class 10 is to enter into practical life. The use of the right angle has wide-ranging application in Class 10. The relationship of the perpendicular to the horizontal provides a conceptual framework for many practical tasks involving both accurate observation and common sense judgement. In surveying, the right angle forms the framework for the theoretical calculations, as it does in technical drawing. In woodwork, as in most constructions, it provides the concepts of plumb, square and true. In dressmaking and tailoring all individual patterns relate to the rectangular shape of the woven cloth. Even in throwing a pot on a wheel, the process of centring the clay requires an awareness of the perpendicular in relation to the horizontal plane of the plate. In metalwork the forging of iron and the work at the anvil in transforming the metal through the rhythmical application of the hammer, into a range of shapes requires the exact application of force and knowledge of the material.

The surveying main-lesson provides a wonderful opportunity to come to grips with the earth – or a tiny part of it – by measuring and drawing it. After this one or two-week practical period, the pupils know this 'tiny part' like the back of their hand! Surveying requires three levels of measurement, common sense estimation, ground measurement using rods, chains and tape measures, and theoretical calculations based on the readings taken with theodolite and measures. All three systems require to be integrated in order to create a three-dimensional understanding that will be expressed in a series of section drawings. Having applied these technical skills to geography, they know exactly what is there and have also learnt how to work with accuracy. The main content of the first mathematics main-lesson in Class 10 is trigonometry, which is applied in surveying. The cosine also belongs to physics when calculations are needed.

Further work on mathematical laws is given by rhythmical calculations, raising to higher powers and logarithms. In Class 10 mathematics should be related to practical matters of everyday life. The realm of irrational numbers and incommensurability, from which the law of the Golden Mean can be derived, points to a different type of formative law applicable to the human being, and is more appropriate for Class 11.

In chemistry the pupils work on the polarities of acid and alkali and on the crystallisation of salts. This main-lesson is directly related to the geometry main-lesson in which the regular and semi-regular solids and their laws of symmetry are worked out and drawn.

In technology the transition from raw material to processed material to product is explored, for example in the path from fibre via thread to textile. This principle applies also to wood, where the whole timber cycle from tree planting and cultivation, to felling, sawing, drying, planing etc. comes to a culmination in joinery in Class 10. As in surveying and the other practical subjects, the objects the students make correct the pupils simply by being objective proof of what they have done. It is important that useful objects are made. In addition many other technical applications in practical life can be discussed, e.g. the gears of a bicycle, how the toilet flush works, vehicle maintenance and information technology. Class 10 is the best point to explore the technology of recycling in which the cycle from raw material to finished product begins again.

Information technology is a part of technology that needs responsible discussion of how these things affect the human being. Understanding what information is, how it is (and has been) stored, and the social aspects of access belongs to this theme. A brief history of the recorded word and mathematical calculations is a part of this. The basic principles of how a computer works are described. On the basis of what they have learnt in physics and mathematics, it is useful for Class 10 pupils to work with the basic building blocks of circuits to produce adding machines in which the principle of computer hardware can be learned.

A practical period in first aid fits in with the pupils' need to be engaged in meaningful, practical activities. Inner confidence grows when you can react on the spur of the moment and know what is the right thing to do.

Educational aims for Class 10

The students should begin to:

* achieve objectivity and clarity in thinking; draw conclusions logically and causally; be able to form common sense judgements as well as formulating concepts;
* recognise natural laws using analytical thinking; apply conceptual tools to practical situations;
* understand how complex processes come about by studying their origins and basic principles;
* work with accuracy and apply what they have learned to respond to the practical needs of those around them;
* take increasing responsibility for their own work and behaviour, and be able to make and follow through choices based on their own insight; form their opinions and be able to explain and justify them.

Class 11

An overview of the subjects suggested by the curriculum for Class 11 shows that the themes of going beyond the sense perceptible, finding the inner balance between polarities, 'processes' and 'renewal' are common to all the content given in the different subjects. If Class 9 was concerned with expanding horizons, Class 10 with seeing where things come from, Class 11 is about gaining insight.

Themes of this kind come into the mathematics lessons, e.g. in analytical geometry, in the concepts of infinity and counter space and in the integration of geometry with algebra and arithmetic with geometry. The laws of Euclidean geometry are integrated into projective geometry. By considering the 'infinitely distant elements' (point at infinity, line at infinity, plane at infinity) the pupils learn to learn to think about infinity. In the study of vibrations, the content of Class 10's trigonometry is brought into movement, creating a base for understanding wave theory as the background to all varieties of wireless data transmission in the Class 11 physics block. Spherical trigonometry extends and enhances planar trigonometry. As with many subjects in Class 11, subjects experienced and worked on separately are combined: links begin to appear.

Similar aspects show up in biology where the study of cells and microscopy is the subject, as well as in the study of ecology. Here any insights into microscopically-small elements are always complemented by views of the macroscopically-large biosphere. The pupils probably already know this process of 'turning inside out' from their projective geometry work.

In chemistry the task is to provide a general overview by looking at the individual character of the elements in the way the chemical substances interact. The periodic system can also be dealt with in this connection. It is presented not as a pre-existing principle of order but as a particular conceptual model that opens the way to describing various laws and relationships.

Similar aspects can be found in physics. In Class 10 the observable forces of mechanics were the focus of study. In Class 11 we move on to electromagnetic fields, radiation and radioactivity and the theories on the nature of matter. Seen logically as separate systems these appear to be contradictory, yet which also point to the unimaginable realm of reality. Physics and chemistry can now be seen as a coherent unit.

The cycles and processes of progression and renewal are also themes in the history lessons, which are now concerned with the heritage from antiquity that contributed to the development and spread of Christianity and Islam. Questions about the meaning of life and of suffering as depicted, for example, in the Parzival epic can be found again not only in the cultural history of the Middle Ages (which is discussed in Class 11) but also in the pupils' own inner mood. The essential elements in this history main-lesson are antitheses as well as processes in the struggle to overcome them. One can see such polarities in the conflicts between Pope and Emperor, Church and State, Christianity and Islam, monarch and barons, peasant and lord, town and country etc.

Literature asks questions of the individual and society in ways that often challenge the existing, conventional world view. Great literature is always in some sense prophetic and original, though it rarely provides answers. Rather it stimulates the reader to go beyond himself or herself. It opens the soul to *extraordinary* experience. This is exactly what the young person in Class 11 needs.

The late medieval text of Wolfram von Eschenbach's *Parzifal* is a text, though only accessible through translation, which takes the reader on a journey through individual failure, pain and inflicted hurt, lost opportunity, guilt and disintegration, and leads to atonement and redemption. It is a unique story of a quest for selfhood which matches the adolescent's inner path. Precisely because it is formally based in an unfamiliar cultural context, the psychological archetypes portrayed stand out.

The themes alluded to in the Parzifal myth can be taken up in nineteenth and twentieth century literature. The questions of the imagination, the individual between nature and nurture, the source of the artistic and the sublime and the threat of materialism are themes which the Romantic period brought to expression. This period in art and literature strikes a chord in the souls of young people of Class 11-age. The biographies of Blake, Shelley, Coleridge, Clare, Hawthorne and Keats are of great interest in this respect.

In foreign languages, great poets and playwrights also take the foreground. Themes from the English lessons can also be taken up in a suitable form, and perhaps the class will perform a play in one of the foreign languages.

There are two aspects to consider in the geography main-lesson in Class 11. On the one hand the pupils can now be led beyond the bounds of what they have so far been able to imagine. This can be served by going back over older traditions of cartography and letting them calculate and draw various projections of the globe. (Astronomy is sometimes given as a separate main-lesson. Again, this goes beyond the bounds of what can be imagined for the earth.) On the other hand, the youngsters in Class 11 begin to search for their own psychological and social position, their 'inner home'. This can be helped by a study of geography from the point of view of world economics. This makes them aware of yet another 'mantle' that humanity as a whole creates for itself. As cultural and economic creatures, human beings shape space and develop an ever increasing awareness of this space. Global economic relations and the principles underlying them can equally reveal blind, egotistical and exploitative forces as well as the concept of mutuality, ecological consciousness and co-operation.

Technology lessons have the theme of 'energy and matter'. The various means of energy production (solid fuel generators, nuclear generators, water and wind generators, solar energy) are thought through in detail and the consequences of irresponsible energy production discussed. The inalienable need for the world in which we live to continue, is nowhere more obvious than in the realm of energy production. Links with physics, chemistry and ecology are obvious. The 'matter' element of technology is taken up in the topics such as the study of paper manufacture and processing, including everything to do with the paper industry (including the media that use print) and also the recycling question.

The step from Class 10 to Class 11 in information technology comes in, going into processes that can no longer be detected with the senses. The relation between cause and effect that was discussed in Class 10 by following work processes step-by-step is now directed to situations that can only be understood in thought. Observations in electrostatics take place in a realm that is not sense-perceptible but has to be imagined. Semi-conductors and their technologies provide the background in physics and technology.

Art lessons also bring links into the foreground. Similarities and dissimilarities in the different arts lead to a confrontation between painting and sculpture on the one hand with music and poetry on the other. Opposite concepts such as Apollonian/Dionysian qualities or stylistic trends such as Impressionist/Expressionist become motifs for consideration of the underlying role of art in expressing the struggle for human consciousness and truth. This exploration can be made in an interdisciplinary way by relating developments in literature, the visual arts and music.

In sculpture and modelling as well as in eurythmy the students endeavour to express attitudes or moods of soul (question, answer, conversation, joy, sorrow, anxiety) in gestures of the human body. The body as the mirror of the soul, is discovered through gesture. The task is to try to discover the objective in the realm of the subjective.

In the eurythmy lessons these explorations involve practising examples of Apollonian and Dionysian moods in poetry and music, discussing stylistic characteristics and encouraging the pupils to form judgements. Poetry and music should combine to form a single element. The way children live in their own movement was lost at puberty. Now it can be won back at a new level and formed into gestures and movements that express each youngster's own identity.

A period of practical social work can form an important culmination for Class 11. For three weeks the pupils work in hospitals, clinics, homes or schools for the disabled. This opportunity enables them to experience others whose needs are greater than their own. It can also show them how they as individuals can bring a ray of light into the gloom of another person's life, though it is often the case that those receiving the care have in fact far more to offer. A new level of social perception can be developed. One of the most fundamental qualities learned through such work is tolerance, both of the weakness and failings of others but more importantly for one's own limitations. Long-term developmental possibilities can arise from such experiences.

Educational Aims for Class 11

By the end of Class 11 the students should begin to:

* attain objectivity in their feelings and thus increasing capacity to form judgements of taste, style and social tact;
* bring mobility into their thinking, which goes beyond the logical causality of their thinking in Class 10 and can now synthesise and correlate different factors within a holistic view. This also means being able to think about infinite and non-sense-perceptible phenomena;
* have a self-directed sense of social responsibility;
* be able to correlate and integrate related phenomena in a more holistic understanding.

Class 12

The inner question of eighteen and nineteen year olds differs from that of a seventeen year old. They want to know: how can I, as an individual human being, make an impact on social, economic, technical or political affairs? What is my place in the world?

The curriculum for Class 12 brings together what has developed over the twelve years of school. It is intended to integrate, within an overall picture, the most important aspect of Steiner-Waldorf education, the evolving nature of the human being and humanity's place in the world.

In biology all the knowledge and skills built up over the years are brought together in an overview.

In this, biology has a special position in relation to the inorganic sciences. There are usually two biology main-lessons in this final year at school: botany of the higher plants, and zoology of the whole animal kingdom culminating in a view of the human being. On their journey through the Lower and Upper School the pupils have travelled a path that began with the familiar human being and went step by step into the kingdoms of nature as far as the mineral kingdom. In the later part of the Upper School the opposite path is travelled, from the simplest forms of life through the kingdoms of nature to the human being. This enables the idea of development as a motif for life to be discovered.

Geography also leads to a uniting overview. The pupils are on the brink of adult maturity and they naturally turn their attention to the current world situation and their personal future. They are ready to take another look at some of the questions of rights that have been touched on in earlier years, including those arising in the context of other subjects. The centrepiece of the lessons might be the cultural diversity of humanity, its races, cultures and socio-political realities. In this way the themes of Classes 7 and 8 are taken further, this time leading to an understanding of the cultural, spiritual forces that have shaped the earth . One could call this a 'cultural mantle' of the earth.

In a similar way the pupils in Class 12 should grasp the individual styles of speech and thought in the foreign languages they are learning, and get to know the important cultural impulses expressed in those languages, especially through original literature. This brings about a fundamental, qualitative understanding for the contribution each culture brings to world history, and in consequence also leads to a better understanding of the pupils' own culture and language.

One of the aims of the music lessons is to recognise, understand and describe the intrinsic language of twentieth century music. The pupils will need to form their own judgement as regards contemporary music. The range of different types of music in our time reflects the present situation of humanity, as expressed by many different individualities and cultural streams.

English lessons provide an opportunity to experience examples of contemporary literature in the English language and also translations of world literature. Central to this exploration is the aspect of how literature reflects changing individual and cultural consciousness. Classics of world literature can be taken which exemplify both the universal and the personal/cultural experience of our times.

Steiner's curriculum suggestions offer something for history that corresponds with the suggestions for geography. The pupils work towards achieving a qualitative understanding of the inner structure and periodic evolution of cultures. This asks questions such as: What characterised the Greco-Roman age? How did the Middle Ages differ from modern times? How are historical periods defined? Can one find the same stages of cultural evolution in geographical regions, such as the Far East in comparison to Europe? It is important in this main-lesson to show how historical events are an external aspect of internal processes of evolution.

This leads to an awareness of one's own point of view and also to the knowledge that by his or her own good or bad deeds, every individual makes history. In seeing how individuals can influence their own surroundings, one becomes aware of the individual responsibility. History teaching in Class 12, complemented by sociology, undergoes a change of viewpoint. Earlier in the school the structure has been chronological. Now different perspectives, processes and themes are studied that span large periods of time. This change of position enables the pupils to gain some understanding of the philosophy and methods of history as a science.

Social studies should now lead to political education in a way that is not merely theoretical. Given the general distrust young people have today in the world of politics, it is important to stress the necessity of awakening an active interest in political processes. One point of departure can be group work on various situations (e.g. a high court case, collective wage bargaining, putting a bill before parliament), and also excursions to visit political institutions and where possible have the opportunity to speak with politicians about their work and ideals. The material to be covered includes the development of the state, law and economy from the French Revolution up to the end of the twentieth century. One can study, for example, the development of citizens' rights and human rights. The East-West and the North-South conflicts are analysed. By taking examples and studying them in more depth, the pupils gain an overall picture of human civilisation and culture. (These studies can also take the form of specialist lessons beginning in Class 9, outside of the main-lesson structure.)

By introducing and discussing various models of chemical procedure, the chemistry main-lesson endeavours to lead on from the traditional analytical approach to a more process-oriented form of chemistry in which metamorphosis is central through, for example, phenomenological and qualitative study of the different kinds of protein. The pupils learn to observe and understand qualitative aspects alongside the measurable quantitative ones. Biochemistry is particularly important, and provides opportunity to present chemistry as something that can bring healing to humanity instead of poisoning the environment.

Technology can either continue on from the results of the chemistry lessons with an emphasis on chemical technology, or take further the computer technology begun in Class 11. For the former, one example would be the study of plastics, their manufacture and use in industry, or laboratory work on the problems of pollution, removal of waste, recycling of waste etc. If a practical period in industry is arranged in Class 12, it can be followed with discussions on health in the workplace. In connection with this, new technologies can be investigated and tested for efficiency. If the emphasis is on computer technology, the pupils write programs that must be usable in industrial situations. This allows them to experience how the human being is not the slave of the machine but the spirit who shapes it.

As with chemistry, physics is also treated phenomenologically. Having entered the non-sense-perceptible realms of physics in Class 11, the pupils in Class 12 now investigate new paths in the realm of optics. The applicability of quantum theory to the microcosm and of the theory of relativity to the macrocosm are combined in relation to human experience. Beginning with the sense of sight and by bringing thought to bear on the known facts concerning light, an attempt is made to find a relationship to the real nature of light. Parallel with this, art lessons can involve working through Goethe's *Theory of Colour* through painting. The question of one's standpoint becomes central. The questions that arise include the unique position of the human being in the world.

In both painting and modelling, art lessons also provide the opportunity for working with that part of the human body that most clearly expresses the individual: the head. Painting, modelling or sculpting in stone, the pupils give *their* head an unmistakable shape and facial expression. Such work can lead to questions such as: is the human body an expression of soul and spirit?

A similar direction is followed in eurythmy. Here the task is to find a suitable form for the basic gesture in a piece of music or a poem, so that the depiction as a whole demonstrates the inner characteristics and quality of the work of art. In a eurythmy performance for the school community the young people are to show that they can express their own personality through movement and gesture.

In Class 11 in analytical geometry the path taken was from geometry as a depiction to geometry as an algebraic calculation. Now, in Class 12 mathematics, the class goes in the opposite direction. Through analysis the pupils begin with pure calculation and move towards an experience of integral and differential calculus. By learning the concept of 'differential quotient' the pupils come to understand a new dimension in mathematics. In addition to being able to apply this, the pupils should also understand and experience it. Only when this has happened can the drawing be added to the calculation. By deriving the form from the equation and the equation from the form we endeavour to generate an inner activity in the pupils as well as an understanding of what is qualitative in mathematics. This is essential for an understanding of applied physics. In this connection one can also show that equations of the same type can be applied in all kinds of different ways in applied physics: in optics, electricity, mechanics, space travel. By coming to understand the basics of integral calculus the pupils will recognise that in the realm of higher mathematics one mathematical process can correspond to an opposite one which opens up a yet further level of mathematical comprehensibility of the world.

Depending on what was done in Class 11, there can be a second projective geometry main-lesson, built either on perspective or on spherical geometry. If taken in this way, projective geometry would lead to an understanding of the application of perspective drawing in the architecture main-lesson and on the art trip. Spherical geometry can lead more towards astronomy or more towards the earth.

Another possibility for a second mathematics main-lesson would be to combine mathematics, botany, astronomy, embryology and geometry in an overall panorama, in a study of the principles of form. This depends very much on the general stage of maturity of the class.

During the industrial practical period in Class 12 the pupils are concerned with an entirely different concept of 'tolerance' from the one they met during their social practical period in Class 11. In industry the 'tolerance' met with might concern the exactitude of machine tooling in the production process of a metalworking industrial factory. During this practical period in industry (several weeks), the pupils have many different experiences to do with the work, with the people they are working with and, also, with themselves. The purpose of this practical period is to get to know economic and industrial life 'from the bottom up'. The pupils experience what it means to work with others towards a common industrial goal. They learn about the opportunities and problems of our modern world with its division of labour. They can observe how a mistake in one part of the process affects the whole production process. They may also have the opportunity to learn how to use an industrial machine accurately, how to check materials and carry out other controls. By their own experience they learn how much strength it takes to make a space between the polarities of work and leisure for conscious, creative mental work. This practical period thus fulfils many different educational tasks. An alternative to the industrial practical would be a work placement in a business or part of the service industry. The heart of such projects is to experience the moral aspect of work and serving the needs of others.

The Class 12 play demonstrates the responsibility of each for the whole and shows how efforts towards a common goal can bring about more than can be imagined by taking the sum of individual capacities. For the last time the class experiences its potential as a whole in putting on a big play, an opera, a musical, a cabaret, etc. Speech, gestures, music, singing (possibly eurythmy), direction, scenery, lighting, making the programme and posters – all this has to be managed, in addition to putting on several performances, perhaps with double casting.

Some Steiner-Waldorf schools round off the twelve years with major individual projects. Each pupil takes on a year-long project consisting of a practical/artistic theme and a theoretical theme (encompassing several subjects). This is worked on throughout the year, in addition to normal school work, with the help of a tutor or project supervisor. The practical results of these projects are displayed in an exhibition or performed during an afternoon or evening performance. The pupils speak in public to the theoretical parts and this is followed by a discussion. Giving these presentations in appropriate form is another aspect of Class 12's work.

In keeping with the element of Class 12 work that calls for a combination of many viewpoints and subjects, the main theme in art is architecture as the universal art, in which all the arts can work together to form a comprehensive work of art. An important theme in Class 12 is to philosophise about art and aesthetics. A history of philosophy and a comparative study of world religions can offer an overview of mankind's spiritual endeavours.

The work in Class 12, representing twelve years of Steiner-Waldorf education, is intended to contribute to the aim of getting to know the human being in the sense formulated by Rudolf Steiner in 1920:

> *Knowing the world, the human being finds himself, and knowing himself, he finds the world revealed to him.*

Educational aims for Class 12

By the end of Class 12 the students should be able to:

* have an integrated view of the nature of the human being, human society and nature;
* articulate, explain and relate their own views on a wide range of topics which concern them;
* show a good degree of social competence;
* show interest in questions of human destiny;
* recognise and be able to characterise qualities through sensory observation and reviewing the facts;
* move from the parts to a perception of what is whole in practical, social and conceptual contexts;
* show the inner mobility of thought to move forwards and backwards within a process so as to be able to understand the whole and be able to articulate the idea behind the process;
* begin to make connections and inner links between phenomena which express the activity of the underlying formative, creative principles in the world and thus reveal the interplay between spirit, visible form and matter;
* understand the distinction between causal, analytical observations and teleological ones;
* consider the relationship between law, necessity, freedom and responsibility;
* think for themselves, and act out of their own insight whilst carrying responsibility for their actions.

Part II:
A Vertical Curriculum

8

Introduction

It is necessary to re-state that Steiner-Waldorf education lives in a process of constant renewal in terms of both content and method. Therefore every teacher is called upon to carry on educational research based on what he or she perceives to be either the developmental stage reached by the pupils in a particular class or changes in the world as time moves on. This was the sense in which Steiner gave his educational advice and curriculum suggestions to the teachers of the original Waldorf School in Stuttgart. These can be found in the lectures known as *The Foundations of Human Experience* (formerly *Study of Man)* and in the subsequent course of lectures *Practical Advice to Teachers*, as well as in *Discussions with Teachers and Three Lectures on the Curriculum*. The other main source for Steiner's indications on the teaching comes from the meetings he regularly held with the teachers and which are recorded in the *Conferences With Teachers.*[1]

He counted on the teachers' educational imagination, on their responsibility towards the developing individualities of the pupils and on their unconditional commitment to whatever is educationally necessary.

> *Certain pedagogical ways are followed by us at the Waldorf School, but we also have the greatest possible freedom ... Our whole curriculum is determined according to what is spiritually necessary, but on the other hand the teachers have the greatest possible freedom to do what they consider to be appropriate.*[2]

An orientation in those 'pedagogical ways' that are determined 'according to what is spiritually necessary' can be discovered in *The Foundations of Human Experience* mentioned above, which remains an inexhaustible source from which educational impulses can be drawn in teachers' meetings and in individual study. On the other hand they arise out of the way the teacher works on the subject matter of the lessons.

> *We must approach the curriculum in such a way that we find ourselves in the position of being able to recreate it within ourselves in any situation, so that we can look at children aged seven, eight, nine or ten and glean from them what we should do in each respective year.*[3]

The following framework curriculum is intended in this sense. If it becomes nothing more than tradition to be followed to the letter, it will depart from what is meant by Steiner-Waldorf education. On the other hand it is also important not to introduce changes in a subjective or arbitrary way, without prior thorough and responsible educational research. What is here presented as a range of possible teaching content is based on good practice that has proven itself and is founded on experience of children.

Checklists

Integrated within the sections covering English, mathematics and foreign language teaching, guidelines are given for checklists to be used by teachers to monitor individual children's attainments. These lists describe what most children of normal ability range will be able to do, understand and repeat at the end of the designated school year. These attainments would constitute a minimum level. Such guidelines are for the teacher's own reference. They are not intended as criteria for implying any kind of success or failure but simply as an orientation for the teacher.

It is perfectly possible for each school and even each teacher to set their own guidelines for attainment if they can justify them. Those presented here can be used as a reference point. All experienced teachers know that individual children can be precocious or late starters. There are many cases of children who have appeared to develop intellectual, literacy or numerical skills slowly but have later distinguished themselves in these and others fields of ability. This point should always be borne in mind before judgements are made. The point about attainment guidelines is not to label this or that child as in some sense deficient but simply to have a benchmark to aim for and with which individual attainments at a given stage can be compared.

We make an important distinction between teaching content and minimum attainments. There are many experiences children should have because they help the child in his or her overall development. There are some things, however, that need to be mastered in order to be able to progress in a particular skill.

In some ways these minimum requirements are not age related; rather they belong to the internal logic of the subject. It is not easy to progress with arithmetic, for example, if the basic knowledge of number bonds and tables is missing or too fragmented to be of much use. If an individual, for whatever reason, has not mastered these basics, he or she will need learning support, remedial strategies or other aids in order to progress in being able to understand and use basic arithmetic. It is in this sense that the guidelines are given.

Curriculum notes by Rudolf Steiner

1. After puberty, it is essential that the practical subjects should become a part of the lessons. People must get to know the meaning of our modern technological age in school, not in the factory.
2. This needs to be counterbalanced by the aesthetic side of education. Impressions of beauty are the only thing that can unite human beings with their childhood and beyond this with eternity. Such impressions are needed to provide not only the courage to step beyond the limitations of knowledge but also to give a content to faith based on experience. Such impressions increase the value of work and justify leisure. Knowledge is something that can lead people towards the divine; will impulses

are always only a germinating seed. Through beauty the picture becomes filled with all the magic of reality, yet it does not make demands in the way the will does.

3. Links with the spirit are severed if beauty is not there to maintain them. Beauty binds the 'I' to the body.[4]

9

Arithmetic and Mathematics

> *Mathematics in the Waldorf School is divided into three stages. In the first stage, which covers the first five classes, mathematics is developed as an activity intimately connected to the life process of the child, and progresses from the internal towards the external. In the second stage, covering Classes 6 to 8, the main emphasis is on the practical ... The ninth year onwards is characterised by a transfer towards a rational point of view.*[1]

Thus writes H. von Baravalle, the first mathematics teacher at the Waldorf School in Stuttgart.

Classes 1 to 5

Here two questions must be answered:

1. How should the first mathematical concepts be tackled?
2. What is the psychological basis on which to build them?

In answer to question one, careful scrutiny shows that the teaching of arithmetical and geometric concepts is connected to the consciousness and activity of the child's movement organism. Counting is inner movement by which outer movement can be observed. E. Schuberth calls this 'the sensory content of mathematics teaching'.[2] The results of Piaget's research on the development of intelligence in children also point in this direction: in the 'concrete operations stage' (twelve or thirteen years old), children still carry out movements when they want to connect one thing to another. Anyway, these movements are connected to the physical objects from which the children can as yet barely free themselves, if at all.

This leads on to question two: if the development of mathematical concepts occurs in the static, concrete phase, our purpose must not be to 'generalise and abstract', but to 'make concrete and look at individual cases'.[3] This defines the means whereby it is possible to avoid confronting children with abstract logical structures, but rather to immerse their whole capacity for experience in mathematics. We can now refer to form drawing where the consciousness necessary for using mathematics is nurtured and practised. This physical experience is a basis and assumption for a healthy immersion in the 'formal operations stage' (Piaget). The rule 'from hand, through heart to head' (which is meant by the child's above-mentioned 'whole capacity for experience') makes it possible for the children to bring their own capacities into play.

> *It is evident that the best, most fruitful questions about concepts and explanations come from pupils who do not pose questions using a quick intellectuality, but a capacity for involved feeling, which allows clarity to come into thinking.*[4]

To this concrete approach in mathematics at primary school level we should add something further which does not depend on the element of movement. This is the quality, one might say the identity, of the individual numbers.

As the accent above is on a quantitative approach to numbers, as the result of a brief pause in movement or even based on the movement itself, we need to place our introduction to qualitative number concepts beside those of quantity. We approach these qualities when we examine many examples where the number in question is really active in the world, as for example the number five in the flowers of a rose. Here we use the child's desire to question what lies behind the world and human creations, that is, to seek what lies behind the phenomena. The nuclear scientist W. Heitler referred to this when he said in a lecture:

> *One directs one's attention to qualitative phenomena, to characteristics which have something to do with the totality of the objects observed.*

Steiner recommended taking this as the starting point for an introduction to number concepts:

> *We have gradually come to the point in the course of civilisation where we can work with numbers in a synthetic manner. We have a unity, a second unity, a third unity and we struggle while counting in an additive manner to join the one to the other, so that one lies beside the other when we count. One can become convinced that children do not bring an inner understanding towards this. Primitive human beings did not develop counting in this way. Counting began from unity. Two was not an external repetition of unity but it lay within unity. One gave us two, and two is contained in the one. One, divided, gave us three, and three is contained within one. If we wrote the number 1, translated into modern terms, one could not get away from the 1, for instance to 2. It was an inner organic picture where two came out of unity and this two was contained in the one, likewise three and so on. Unity encompassed everything and the numbers were organic divisions of unity.*[5]

This 'real' way of looking at numbers leads on to written numbers, to symbols. It is not a picture like that which should be used for introducing letters, but pictures of number qualities. The picture belongs to the being of the number, not to the outer symbolic form. At this point we indicate a further point of this 'quality-oriented' teaching: today, especially, when we face the results of a quantitative world view in ecological catastrophe and destruction, it is increasingly important to make a beginning of this kind in teaching mathematics.

By beginning with the concrete qualities of number and by working with the properties of movement in counting and calculating, children develop a kind of intelligence which seeks and finds the way to reality.

This brings us to the second stage: the approach to mathematics teaching mentioned earlier. Here we must deal with the practical use of calculation.

If calculating has been practised thoroughly enough during the first stage in the manner indicated, then applied calculation also gets a qualitative colouring. The forces of intelligence which are served by business mathematics as well as percentages and interest, are not 'value-free', but can retain a colouring for balanced testing and judging. The human significance of what is thought out can and should be made clear. In this connection one should point to the suggestion by Steiner that elements of bookkeeping should also be taken up in mathematics lessons. To see what the general idea behind such an indication is, one should ask what skills may be developed through bookkeeping. There you will see how above all a moral method of trading can be decisively supported by these means.

All these themes can lead us on to other educational aims: inner mobility leads to imaginative ability in solving mathematical problems.

Through the experience of number qualities the children experience trust and security: Number, world and human being belong together.

The children can experience further security through the correctness of solutions to problems By this means they win some independence.

> *For this reason mathematics is an activity suited to freeing children from the fetters of authority even if, at first, they depend on the help of the teacher.*[6]

A final educational aim which should not be undervalued and which is connected with the latter is calculation. Calculation is not possible without regular practice, which also makes it an excellent medium for schooling the will.

An explicit presentation of the third stage will be given under the heading Classes 9 to 12 and is therefore omitted here.

Geometry as part of mathematics teaching begins in Classes 5 and 6 and is taught in separate main-lessons. One of the principal intentions in this subject is to develop and nurture the ability to visualise space.

The controlled security of directed movement and the estimation of proportions and relationships, practised in freehand geometry, is well prepared for by form drawing in Classes 1 to 4.

The establishment of skills, knowledge and techniques partly in connection with subjects is taught with increasing complexity related to age.

* Pupils should gradually learn to discover, to grasp mentally and to apply geometrical properties, and the practical, drawn, solutions representing them.
* Work with geometric drawing instruments should lead to clear and exact construction.
* Patience, care and precision should be developed, as well as independent creative work through enjoyment of drawing.

Classes 1 to 3

The dynamics of will activity should be internalised by the experience of countability. Motivation should be awakened through pictorial description of number qualities. This dual aspect is important: on the one hand it educates the bodily senses through experience of movement, unfolding of movement possibilities (both coarse and fine), and co-ordination exercises. On the other hand internalising of the expressed activities in soul activity (i.e. calculation). Here the main medium for achieving this is the use of pictures. Through pictures, children can grasp internally what is intended. Pure symbolic, logical presentation can never achieve this. (Nevertheless one should always be conscious that calculation is aiming at a picture-less world, in contrast to the introduction of letters of the alphabet.) In order to be able to handle quantitative numbers freely, an inner numerical space needs to be created, in which one learns to move, rhythmically at first, with varied number patterns. This is achieved, amongst other means, by a memory developed by learning the times-tables through rhythmic movement e.g. through clapping, passing bean bags or skipping. It appears important initially to approach actual calculation as concretely and visually as possible and to keep in mind the principle 'from the whole to the parts'. This means that the right connection between analytical and synthetic thinking is produced. Work with the temperaments should be formed in the sense given in the 4th discussion in *Discussions with Teachers*.[7] At the end of Class 3 the pupils should have a confident grasp and clear view of numbers up to at least 1,020. This does not mean just the quantity or extent but equally the quality of the numbers.

Class 1

In mathematics lessons the approach is analytical in the sense of the reference by Steiner given above. Starting with the number 1 as unity, numbers (symbols) from 1 to 10 should be produced in a qualitative manner (see above), which are contained as manifold in unity. With written numbers one can begin with Roman numerals which are less abstract than the Arabic.[8] Alternatively, the Arabic numbers can be introduced in pictures as with the letters of the alphabet.

- Counting up to 110
- Learning up to the 7 times table by heart and through rhythmical practice
- Introducing the four rules using numbers up to 20 and also in written form (in notation, the sum is written first: 7 is 3 + 4)
- Number riddles
- First exercises in mental arithmetic

Class 2

- Further practice in mental arithmetic
- Extension of counting and practice of the four rules using numbers up to 100
- Practice in combined calculation
- Initial consideration of number connections 'Kingly' numbers and 'beggar' numbers (primes)
- Up to the 12 times table by heart
- Representation of tables in drawing
- Written analytically and synthetically practised calculations
- Calculations should be reversed (3 + 4 = 7)

Class 3

- Mental arithmetic
- Sums using numbers up to 1,020 or 1,100
- Written addition and subtraction using several places (place value)
- Written multiplication using two place values
- Written division using units as divisor
- Up to 15 times tables; 10 times table up to 900
- Square numbers by heart as a sequence
- Weights and measures (practical subject) and calculations with simple practical problems

Numeracy checklist for Classes 1 to 3

Most children within the normal range of ability will be able to:

Number

1 have working knowledge of four processes and their symbols + - x ÷ (including processes in verbal and written sentence form)

1 appreciate number qualities 1–12

1 understand Roman numerals 1–X and Arabic numerals 1–100

1 count from 1–100

1 know number bonds up to 10

1/2 understand difference between odd and even numbers

1-3 have work knowledge of the multiplication tables 1–12

1/3 apply simple mental arithmetic in narrative form using above listed skills

2 know number bonds up to 20

2/3 recognise, analyse and count to numbers up to 1,000

2/3 work with tables as division (24 shared between 6 is 4)

2/3 know patterns in multiplication tables 10, 9, 5, 4, 11

2/3 use place value to four places (ten, H, T and U)

2/3 carry numbers across columns e.g.

19 74
+2 x2

3 be able to recite tables 1 – 12 in chorus and individually

Form Drawing

1/2 draw straight line, curves, linear forms, symmetry on vertical axis

1-3 draw common geometric forms freehand

3/4 draw symmetrical reflections: about horizontal and diagonal axis

Measurement

2/3 use money for simple bills and calculating change

3 tell time using hours, half hours, quarter hours on 12 hour clock

3 calculate simple practical sums, e.g. how many milk bottles in a crate holding six by six, bricks in a wall, floor boards, etc.

3 calculate simple sums in measurement of length, capacity and weight

Classes 4 and 5

Upon reaching their ninth year, children make a decisive change. Their close relationship to the world around them becomes different and more remote. The earlier harmony between outer and inner worlds is fundamentally broken.

This transformation in their soul is reflected in the mathematics curriculum when in Class 4 the children begin to work with broken numbers (fractions). By this means they meet something in the teaching content which they have also experienced in themselves.

It is not essential for the children to be able to manage fractions swiftly. It is much more important that they can experience these 'external' fractions very strongly. In connection with this, the historical development of fraction calculations in Egypt can give the teacher interesting and significant teaching ideas. In order to do general justice to the subject of fractions it is recommended to use the following three methods as an introduction: To proceed from the whole to the parts, from the parts to the whole, and to establish the principle of equivalence. After this the four rules are practised with fractions, the same with simplifying, expansion and division of the denominator into prime factors.

After this, decimal fractions follow as a practical application. Once the divisibility border is crossed the children can discover the practicality of calculations in Class 5.

The aim according to Steiner is as follows: 'in Class 5 we want to continue with fractions and decimals and to give the children everything which will allow them to calculate freely with whole and fractional numbers.'[9]

In Class 4 form drawing is led into elementary geometry. Here one can begin again with the basic linear polarity of circle and straight line. In order that the pupils get as intensive an image as possible of these forms, it is recommended that they do not initially use compasses and ruler, but draw free-hand.

Although we deal with the most basic elements in the first geometry lessons, it is important to let the pupils feel something of that dimension which is connected with existential questions over and above the practical and utilitarian. This is made far easier if the beauty of form and strongly regulated connections of geometry are felt in addition to the working rules and methods.

In connection with stories from ancient Egypt in the history lessons, the Pythagorean rope can be introduced as a first introduction to Pythagoras' Theorem.

Class 4

- Mental arithmetic
- Practice of written calculations using higher numbers
- Introduction to fractions: experience of a fraction as part of a whole. From part to whole, similar fractions and different fractions. Transfer of improper fractions into mixed numbers and the reverse
- Introduction to decimal fractions
- Revision: the four rules and written multiplication and division with several place values
- Freehand form drawing leads into geometrical drawing. Circle, square, triangle, isosceles and right angled triangle. Division of circle into 4, 5, 6, 8, 12 equal parts. This is done by organised guess work. Colouring and imagination will bring out different patterns

Class 5

- Constant practice in mental arithmetic
- Revision: the four rules with natural numbers
- Combinations of the four rules
- Calculations with fractions: expansion and reduction of equivalents (division into prime factors)
- Illustration and comparison of fractions. Calculation with decimals. Consolidation of fractions methods
- Table of place values, rhythmically, through movement, and qualitatively introduced
- Introduction of the relationship of decimals to place values
- Measurements using decimals
- Recognition of connections between decimal numbers and decimal fractions

The main new task for Class 5 is learning to use a pair of compasses with accuracy, though some teachers prefer to wait until the beginning of Class 6. The forms previously drawn in Class 4 can now be accurately constructed. Children will naturally colour these flower-like forms, and thus make an obvious link with the botany main-lesson in Class 5.

A set square and ruler can also be used to draw accurate parallel lines.

* Starting with the construction of a circle, discovery of the main geometrical figures: triangle, hexagon, square, rhombus, parallelogram, octagon
* Division and joints on 24-point circle
* Construction of perpendicular bisector, angle bisection, perpendicular bisector, angle bisection, perpendiculars
* Construction of different triangles; equilateral, isosceles, scalene, right angled
* The various angles; acute, obtuse, reflex.
* Circles touching a triangle; inside (incircle) and outside (circumcircle)
* Pythagoras' Theorem; visually using knotted string. (Egyptians used this to construct their pyramids). Grains covering an area, theorem drawn using Roman tiles (Isosceles triangle)
* Tessellation (tiling) involving accurate construction of parallel lines
* Exact construction of pentagon/pentagram

Numeracy Checklist for Class 4 to 5

Most children within the normal range of ability will be able to:

Number

4 carry out all four processes of number confidently

4 read and understand numbers up to six figures

4 know the multiplication tables up to 12 out of sequence

4 do long multiplication with numbers up to 122 as multiplier

4 find factors of a given number

4 identify prime numbers less than 100

4/5 answer more complex mental arithmetic questions involving a mix of processes (e.g. The 12.38 train to Reading takes 18 minutes but left 14 minutes late, when did it arrive? or I doubled a number and added 8 and got 32, what was the number?)

4/5 do long division including making use of remainder and estimating approximate answers.

4/5 find Lowest Common Multiple or Highest Common Factors

5 use all four processes with fractions including mixed numbers and improper fractions

5 understand how to use decimal notation, decimal fractions and interchange of decimal with common fractions

5 carry out four processes with decimals

5 use long division and multiplication using the decimal point

apply the Rule of Three (if, then, therefore) to practical problems

Measurement

4 record information such as height, weight, volume, etc.

5 work with metric measurement including estimation

5 work with aspects of time including 24 hour clock
5/6 calculate average speeds

Geometry

5 draw freehand archetypal geometric shapes: different kinds of triangle, rectangle, quadrilaterals, polygons and circles
5 divide circles into 17, 16 or 20 parts, deriving regular figures like pentagon and hexagon from them[10]

Classes 6 to 8

So far, concept-building about method given pictorially has been rooted in an approach to the child's soul. Now, after the twelfth year, children can increasingly create order out of what has been gained with the strength of their ability to experience internal logic. This step is exemplified in algebra: it leads from the activity of calculating to observation of the processes and from there to the discovery of general relationships.

> *The purpose of an algebraic formula, of 'calculating with letters of the alphabet', is to express the formal, intelligible processes. This is a general step forward in the development of the child as only the method is formulated: By this means the transfer from an imagination-bound thinking to a conceptual thinking is facilitated ... The process: the delineation of a concrete problem (interest), the solution of the problem, the evidence of the validity of the solution method, and finally the applicability of the discovered rule. All this would be experienced by the children in many situations.*[11]

As the children approach puberty, their feeling life expands in all ways. Mathematics can offer an important support in this stage of life. Their own subjective opinions and ideas are not required! Mathematics attracts their attention not only to the numerical material but especially to their own thinking. If the pupils manage to become confident and secure with mathematical laws, they learn self-confidence. When this is achieved the young people are on the way to the most important aim in mathematics teaching: that of gaining trust in thinking.

However, this thinking can now connect itself in a one-sided selfish way to its mentor, the human ego, and this leads to egoism. It is essential to link thinking to world interests in practical and necessary life situations. It is, however, important that the attempts to solve problems do not lead to resignation with the 'I can't do that' attitude, because mathematics lessons then achieve exactly what they should not. Instead of enjoyment and confidence, they create boredom and despair. There is hardly any other subject which is so equated to scholarly ability and intelligence as mathematics. To 'give up' here or to have problems means to give up generally, and simply to be 'stupid'.

For this reason, mixed ability classes make particular demands on the teacher as regards method or possibly even remedial measures. During the class-teacher stage, what the pupils have to do must be differentiated although all of them must deal with the basic mathematical questions. Work with practical problems offers a rich fund of activities for the pupils and can even be formed into a life skill, which might open various avenues to the real world of work. Working by means of mathematical exercises to make thinking energetic fosters an active connection to these areas. The practical activities bring the pupils towards life and reality and also to a description of basic connections.

Calculation is an education of the will in the area of thinking. For this reason practice lessons are added to the main-lessons from about Class 6 onwards.

The precision and beauty of geometrical figures are the teachers who will lead them to greater awareness. What has been experienced through amazement in geometry in Class 5 should be worked on in thinking in Classes 6, 7 and 8. Geometrical rules are sought and formulated. The pupils must also experience geometrical proofs adequately. It is important for them as they develop their individual forms of speech and expression that they can experience something like this, which is quite free of emotion and concerns itself purely with what ought to be. In Class 8 one can use the new subject of conic sections to approach the problem of infinity as one did before with parallels. Infinity is still not defined specifically.

Geometry

* Geometrical proof of sums of angles of triangle: using cut outs, protractors
* Proof of above using calculations
* Accurate construction of angles using compasses, bisecting angles
* Construction of triangles from description
* Congruent triangles; the four principle cases for congruency
* Translations; movement properties of triangles and quadrilaterals; crown transformations, triangles in the same segment of a circle (colouring enhances this). Thales' Theorem
* Leaf forms from triangles, circle
* Caustic curves, envelopes of a cardioid
* Congruent shapes, construction of similar angles, complementary, supplementary and other angles
* Construction of triangles, with altitudes, and angle and side bisectors

Class 6

* Continuing with mental arithmetic
* Revision: calculation with natural numbers, positive fractions and decimals
* Unitary method, with direct and inverse proportion
* Percentages
* Application of percentages to business: interest, discount, exchange, profit and loss, VAT, general introduction to the use of formulae by means of simple interest
* Block graphs and pictograms

Class 7

* Continuing practise in mental arithmetic
* Revision: the four rules in natural and positive rational numbers
* Basic bookkeeping
* Introduction to negative integers (through debt calculation)
* The four rules with negative numbers
* Extension to cover all rationals
* The four rules with rationals and their connections.
* Introduction of brackets
* Recurring decimals, later on the value of π. Full understanding and comparison of decimal places and significant figures

* Compound interest
* Simple statistical data rendered in graphical form and deductions therefrom

Algebra

* Simple equations, including brackets, fractions and negative numbers. Their practical application to solving problems
* Making and transforming formulae
* Powers and roots of numbers. The exact evaluation of square roots
* Ratio and proportion
* Calculation of the areas of figures bounded by straight lines and circular arcs
* Types of quadrilateral and their symmetries, leading to simple set theory

Geometry

* Areas of geometrical shapes through construction and calculation
* Area of circle, and using this to calculate the value of π, by cutting the circle into pieces
* Pythagoras; theorem; area proof
* Shapes and stretches of simple shapes
* Tangents to circles
* Further transformations of pentagons. Construction of decagon and polygons
* Perspective drawing. (Can be linked with modern history main-lesson)

Class 8

Revision

* Fractions
* Squares and roots
* Equations
* Practical problems

Algebra

* The commutative, associative and distributive laws in algebra. The factors of the difference between the squares and the application of this to practical problems
* Volumes of rectangular blocks, pyramids, prisms, cylinders and cones. Density and weight of solid objects
* Simultaneous linear equations and problems
* The dissolution of complex brackets in algebraic expressions
* A brief look at balance sheets and mortgages
* Number systems. Binary arithmetic
* Further statistical work including mean, mode and median
* Graphs of more complicated curves. The solution of simultaneous equations by graphs

Geometry

* Locus of line and plane
* Locus and conics defined geometrically
* Enlargements, rotation, reflection of shapes
* Angle properties of circle (angles in the same circle, intersecting chords)
* Construction of five regular Platonic solids. Orthogonal view of them
* Exact spatial perspective drawing including the golden section
* Discussion of general triangle sides and altitude formulae as part of the development of the investigation of Pythagoras' Theorem
* Optional: Internal and external angles of a polygon
* Similar figures especially triangles

Numeracy Checklist for Classes 6 to 8

Most children within the normal range of ability will be able to:

Number

- 6 convert percentages to fractions and vice versa
- 6 estimate results by rounding off number prior to accurate calculation
- 6 business maths: balance sheets: profit and loss, discount, commission, VAT and book-keeping, bank accounts
- 6 work out averages including speed
- 6 read co-ordinates (e.g. for map reading)
- 6 use letters in formula
- 7 know powers of numbers
- 7 work out ratio and scale
- 7 use algebra as a general solution to specific problems
- 7 use negative and positive integers
- 7/8 know how to work with square roots
- 7/8 calculate compound interest, mortgage rates, income tax
- 6/7 make time and speed calculations
- 7/8 calculate mechanical advantage in simple machines, e.g. pulleys, levers

Data

- 6 present information via pictograms: use pie charts, bar charts, linear graphs (foreign currency exchange)
- 7 use algebraic graphs

Geometry

- 6 make precise use of compasses, ruler, set squares to draw constructions of major geometric figures
- 6 make use of freehand perspective
- 6/7 use protractor
- 6/7 draw translations, reflections, rotations
- 6/7 know Pythagoras Theorem and its applications
- 7 use instruments to draw linear perspective
- 7 know properties of triangles, parallel lines and intersecting lines
- 7 know and apply formulae for area of regular geometric forms, including triangle, circle, parallelogram, derivation and use of
- 7/8 calculate areas of irregular forms

Classes 9 to 12

The central point of mathematical activity is problem solving. The important thing is learning how to solve problems, not what the answer is. With this as the focus, school mathematics builds on both bases of mathematics: inspiration (induction) as a beginning and logical conclusion (deduction) at a later stage in the mathematical activity.

The most important aim will be to develop the ability of the pupils to think with a wide range of approaches until they get to the logical conclusion, and to give them confidence in themselves and in their thinking.

Another justified aim is to prepare the pupils to apply calculation methods to everyday life and also to give them the foundation for further education.

It is nevertheless valuable for the principal aim to give problems in many new contexts: It is more important than the division into subject areas, such as algebra, functions, etc. to pose questions in various heuristic ways in order to 'unravel' a problem.

The pupils may rehearse their ability to guess, to test variations in an investigation and practise making theories. In order to find a clue for the solution one can simplify the problem; likewise, it helps to make analogies or to generalise the question in order to get an idea of the recurrent theme.

If there is a large proportion of creative problem solving, mathematics can have enormous value for the pupils' development in this period. They are given the opportunity to observe their thinking in a variety of ways: seeking points of departure, choosing examples or counter examples, systematically running an investigation and proving the results. They learn to analyse and to judge conditions.

The artistic educational quality of Steiner-Waldorf education is especially evident in mathematics. One can create a fruitful dialogue with the pupils as well as between them. The curriculum indicates the aims and teaching content and curriculum questions, but how the lessons are formed is independent of the required knowledge of the pupils. In this regard it is an advantage if the teacher gradually forms a collection of problems tailored to a particular class.

It is important that pupils are allowed to make inner conquests of general value. They get most value from results which they guessed at first and were then able to prove.

As thinking is an expression of our ego activity, mathematics affords quite special opportunities for the pupils' inner development and self-knowledge.

In geometry, which can be taught as a separate subject within the framework of mathematics, the following applies in these classes:

* The pupils should practise methods of construction in 3D space
* The pupils should learn to think in processes; they should break through to, and release, habits of thinking and habits of understanding, and thereby bring more openness and mobility into their thinking
* The representation of spatial reality such as orthographic and other projections and perspective, are practised and investigated for their applications

Class 9

Class 9 often begins with the introduction of combinations or probability. These are both areas which offer pupils good experience and practical skills in formal logical thinking, without having been especially prepared for it in the Lower School.

The study of equations, which is extended and deepened, offers a good field of work for their growing formal abilities through its transparent methods of solution. In addition, there are all kinds of series which lead the pupils into deeper study.

A further study of triangles with this new approach offers a medium for experience in simple proofs, whereby things already learnt are brought into use (e.g. congruence rules from Class 8). The method is analytical, growing from the concrete to the general, from the geometrical construction to the proof. In geometry, work on the conic sections, which may be begun earlier and can be extended later on, offers a variety of construction methods, to create mobile ideas, which are also worked out by rigorous method. In the construction of one of the principal curves (ellipse, hyperbola, parabola), the subject of infinity which has been latent since Class 6, reappears more clearly. At the same time exercises should lead the pupils to a clear experience of the 3 dimensions. One can begin with the cube which visibly represents dimensionality. From this the most varied solids can be developed. Exercises are given to transform these in stages so that the pupils learn to picture them in a fluid way.

Oblique plan views are used to represent these.

The pupils should get to know the personalities whose thoughts they are using, through biographies or mathematicians (e.g. Pascal, Fermat).

Periodic excursions into irrationals and incommensurables with their polarities prepare for the unification of arithmetic and geometry in analytical geometry in Class 11.

At the appropriate moment the calculator can also be introduced.

The wealth of possible content does not permit a comprehensive tackling of subjects. The important thing for Class 9 is the 'how'. It depends on bringing to life concrete representative examples of general rules.

Algebra

Revision of:

* Natural numbers, integers and rationals
* Divisibility rules, HCF and LCM
* Primes and the question of how many there are
* Calculation with four rules of polynomials and fractions
* Squares and roots
* Irrationals and the new subject of the domain of real numbers
* Direct and indirect proportion in connection with practical life (percentages and interest)

Algebra:

* Linear equations in 2 and 3 unknowns
* Depending on the class ability: quadratic equations (can be done in Class 10)

Combinations:

* Permutations
* Variation
* Optional: basic elements of probability stemming from questions using combinations
* Elements of number theory (bases, particularly base 2 in consideration of computers)

Binomial theorem:

* Binomial coefficients
* Pascal's triangle
* Calculation with squares and roots, a look at the cube root
* Tricks for simplifying calculation without electronic aids based on the binomial theorem

Algorithmic calculations:

* Continued fractions and their use for simplifying fractions
* Converging fraction series for the golden section (see irrationals)
* Optional: the Euclidean algorithm for HCF and LCM with practical examples

Incommensurability in arithmetic and geometry:

* Extension of the number domain to include irrationals
* Extension of number series to include continued fraction approximations of roots
* Perhaps: root 1 to root 25 by continued fractions and their number series
* Squares and root 2
* Equilateral triangles and root 3
* Regular pentagon and root 5
* Derive the formula for pentagon sides and diagonals

Geometry

* Revision of work with angle types
* Alternate segment theorem
* Using the triangle to revise congruence; similarity, proportional division
* Using parallels; the four main centres of a triangle and the Euler line
* The forms of Pythagoras' Theorem, extension of the theorem
* Revision and deepening of area calculation (triangle, right angle, square, rhombus, parallelogram, trapezium, deltoid, area transformation)
* Investigation of the circle (circumference, area, π)
* Volumes of solids (cube, cuboid, prism, pyramid, cylinder, cone, sphere)
* Conics approached from locus as well as other curves (Cassini, Descartes)
* (Could also be done in Class 10)
* A variety of plane solids or bodies usually through a main-lesson on descriptive geometry
* Diagonals
* Platonic and Archimedean solids
* Training in symmetries based on the simple Platonic solids cube, octahedron, tetrahedron, dodecahedron, icosahedron, and their duals
* Training in visualisation of spaces by exercises in picturing to help drawing tasks, as well as separate description of spatial connections and construction methods
* Design of a simple alphabetic typeface
* Optional: the constant division of the golden section (application in architecture, nature and human beings) is also recommended for Class 10

Class 10

The pupils should be guided 'from knowledge to insight' (R. Steiner). This means a completely new approach for the teaching method.

Trigonometry offers a wide field of activity for this. In the angle functions the pupils discover a completely new structure of relationships and also the practical use which can be got from this. The application of mathematical calculations should be experienced. This is possible through the parallel offered by physics (sine wave in statics, parabolas for projectiles), as well as the so-called 'surveying' project, which allows ideas to be shown in practice, where the pupils measure and draw a small ground area. Precision is learnt; the problems – not the teacher – correct the youngster.

Similarly, in another main-lesson the pupils learn the special meaning of the normal technical projections. The various possibilities for creating pictures can be seen as the start for this. In continuation of perspective, spatial projection and some elements of projective geometry are worked through in drawing.

For arithmetic a final area is logarithms as the summit and final stage of this development.

Calculators are now used more frequently.

In algebra, quadratic equations are now dealt with, if not done already, and the various solution methods and formulae are developed.

Mathematics in Class 10 should have a strongly practical character. One can therefore take up the bookkeeping begun in Class 7, and move on to double-entry bookkeeping.

The pupils become more aware of commercial processes and the way businesses develop, which means that they can now reflect on these things. They will notice the aspect of interdependence, and the implications of social responsibility become evident.[12]

As for Class 9, there is more material than can be dealt with here:

Algebra

Quadratic equations:

* The quadratic expansion
* Development and use of the general formula
* Development and proof of Vieta's root formula (principle points on a quadratic graph)
* Development of the general quadratic equation
* The significance of determinants
* Optional: linear and quadratic inequalities

Powers with whole and rational indices, logarithms:

* Revision of methods with natural number indices
* Series with index of 2 or 3
* Extension of the index domain over rationals, integers and real numbers
* Development of logarithms and creation of a table base 2.3.10
* Calculation with logarithmic tables (briefly, for practice in use of tables)
* Commutativity, associativity, distributivity
* Rules of logarithms
* Solution of exponential equations
* Solution of logarithmic equations
* The logarithmic and exponential curves (first contact with functions)
* Optional: logarithmic scales in science, Archimedean spirals, logarithmic spirals (morphological examples from nature, evolutes). The biography of Euler

Number series (or possibly in Class 11):

* First contact with series, especially monotones, e.g. arithmetic, geometric, exponential, the Lukas and Fibonacci series
* Application to calculation of interest and various means

Plane trigonometry

(with application in the Surveying project, see Chapter 24)

* Revision of similar triangles and proportional division by parallels and its extension to the image through concentric similar shapes
* Angle measuring systems: degrees, gradients, radians
* Sine, cosine, tangent (cotangent)
* Solution of basic exercises in a right triangle and extension to include plane figures and solids
* Angle functions in circle of unity radius
* Use of angle functions in the general triangle by dividing into two right triangles
* Derivation of cosine rule (recognition of the special case of Pythagoras' Theorem)
* Use of these techniques for calculation in surveying
* Development of the sine rule
* Development of the trigonometrical area formula
* Graphical representation of angle functions

Descriptive geometry

Description of plane solids by various means:

* Representation of solids
* Exercises in interpenetration of solids
* Curvilinear solids
* Shadow construction

* The boundary case of an infinite point in shadow construction
* Transformation of a dodecahedron into an icosa-hedron; stages of interpenetration
* Screws, snails, spirals
* Technical drawing: designs and details of pupils' own carpentry

Geometrical work on circle and line

* Proof of the construction of the golden section
* Construction of the golden section
* Perhaps: the golden section in the human being (Dürer, Le Corbusier). See Class 9

Elements of projective geometry

* The question of parallelism and the infinite point on a straight line
* Optional: The circle as the curve of division; tackling problems of technology
* Periodic experience applied in mechanics in industry (e.g. linkages, drive machinery)
* Running a bank account book and diary
* Balance sheets and household budgeting
* Recording of a complete project
* Optional: double-entry bookkeeping project

Class 11

The areas of geometry and algebra which were dealt with separately until now are brought together in analytical geometry. It will become clear to the pupils how geometrical forms have their counterpart in equations and how new geometrical forms can be defined by equations. Straight lines are dealt with as the track of a movement and functions elaborated. Vectors will also be formally established following their introduction in physics in Class 10. How far vectors are taken depends on the teacher's assessment of the maturity of the class.

The laws of Euclidean geometry are raised to a new stage in projective geometry. Infinity should be grasped by working through the 'elements of infinity' (infinite point, line and plane). Through this the pupils acquire an extension of their thought space.

In a study of oscillation, trigonometry from Class 10 is brought into motion giving a basis for the wave theory background of radio communication (physics Class 11).

With spherical trigonometry the student can experience an enhancement of plane trigonometry. Like analytical geometry, this gives a connection between arithmetic and geometry. As in many areas, Class 11 sees how earlier separate areas of study come together: connections should be formed.

A new stage in thinking meets the pupils as they work with series towards the sum of an infinite series. In percentages, a new process is discovered as steps tend towards zero. Calculation of 'half lives' provides a link with atomic physics in Class 11, and this leads on to topical questions.

Again geometry should be explored in a separate main-lesson (timetable permitting) and the teacher can choose a selection of topics from the available range according to class ability.

Series and sequences

* Introduction to finite and infinite arithmetic and geometric series and sequences (if not done in Class 10)
* Development of next term and sum of terms formula and applications in science and industry

* Perhaps: draw connections between part formula of higher order arithmetic series and binomial coefficients
* Achieve a clear limiting value and find out sum
* Graphic examples of geometric series
* Development of the compound interest formula as a special case of geometric series: application to a variety of problems from nature and business (half lives, growth patterns, etc.)
* Discovery of e

Functions

(or in Class 12)

* Leibniz's idea of functions
* Domain and range
* Graphs of functions
* First inverse functions

Algebra and analytical geometry

* Historical context
* Introduction to Cartesian and polar co-ordinates and their connection
* Point, distance and line in the above systems
* Linear equations in their various forms and their plane graphs using co-ordinates
* Application of calculation to geometrical problems (intersection of two lines, calculation of special points in a triangle)
* Introduction to vectors from physics I (if not done in Class 10)
* Discovery of the circle formula
* Investigation of positional relationship between circle and line (chord, tangent, external line; polar)
* Discovery of basis for the tangent equation and recognition of the significance of the determinant. By this means acquaintance with:
* Complex numbers as solutions to quadratic equations
* Optional: intersection angles of circle and line, separation into linear factors, discovery of formulae for ellipse, hyperbola, parabola, especially their tangents or asymptotes (can also be done in Class 12)

All solutions should be done both by calculation and graph!

Oscillations

(mathematical basis for electricity main-lesson in Class 11)

* Revision of unity circle, gradients, radians
* Description of angle functions in Cartesian terms and also graphically
* Physical oscillations approached from mechanics point of view
* Perhaps: representation using polar co-ordinates, mathematical formulation of physical quantities (amplitude, frequency, wavelength, period, phase, frequency modulation, oscillation). Include the addition theorem, also algebraic formula of waves. Application: calculation and representation of 3-phase current

Selected approach to projective geometry or spherical geometry depending the class's stage of maturity (possibly in Class 12).

Projective geometry

* Infinite elements
* Concept of duality
* Desargues' Theorem
* Pascal's Theorem
* Basic harmonic figures, harmonic reflections

Spherical geometry

* Pole and polar planes of the sphere, introduction to non-Euclidean geometry on a sphere
* The 'parallel axiom'
* Graphical representation of great circles and small circles on a sphere
* Spherical bi-angles
* Calculation of the surface area and volume of a sphere
* Construction of a spherical triangle by means of 3 defined dimensions (congruence rules); angle sum in a spherical triangle
* Construction of tangents in the triangle points on a sphere

Mathematical geography

* Calculation of great circle angle, great circle distance and course angle
* Development of the sine rule of spherical geometry
* Optional: the cosine rule of spherical geometry
* Geographically derived measurements (metre, nautical mile, knot)
* Polar triangle

Mathematical astronomy

* Graphical representation of horizontal system and stellar position in space
* The equatorial system (RA declination)
* Perhaps: construction of a nautical sextant; the sun in the course of the year; calculation of time (local, time zone, sidereal; calculation of the calendar, the Platonic year, lunar and solar rhythms
* Algebra of switches; the concept of 'or' and 'and' can be shown with switches in parallel and series
* Set theory
* Mathematical logic

Optional: Boolean algebra (introduction of information technology (can be done in other classes).

Class 12

This class should take an important further step from what was achieved in Class 11. Just as Class 11 moved in analytical geometry from visual into algebraic, the reverse is done in Class 12. In calculus the pupils should move from the purely numerical into an experience of differentiation and integration. Limits of series should be grasped as the representatives of an endless process. The pupils should understand this new dimension of mathematics by working with the concept of the 'difference quotient': the quotients of two difference series which both tend towards zero produces something completely new. This should not be merely applied but should be grasped thoroughly and experienced. In calculus the equations should be made so translucent 'that one gets a feeling for what is what in equations'[13]. Only then should the sensually visible graphical form of the calculation be shown. Find the form from the equation, recognise the form of the equation. In this way one nurtures inner activity in the pupils and also an understanding for the functional connections as well as the qualitative in mathematics, which is after all indispensable for a true understanding of current physics. In this connection it is also possible to show that functions of this type can be used decisively in applied physics; in optics, electricity, mechanics and motion. Quality and quantity part company.

While working through the basic rules of integrals, the pupils should recognise that there is also a mathematical method (differentiation), a polarity in higher mathematics which permits the mathematical grasp of the world to reach a new level.

Depending on what was done in Class 11, projective geometry can be built up from the central projection (perspective), or spherical geometry worked through. Projective geometry can be worked through in such a way that it opens a link to understanding applications in bird's eye perspective, and perspective drawing in the architecture main-lesson on a possible art trip. Spherical geometry can be approached from a more representational or analytical angle, and tend more towards astronomy or to the earth (also in the context of descriptive geometry).

A further possibility for a second mathematics main-lesson consists of bringing together the sciences of mathematics, botany, astronomy, embryology and geometry in a great picture. Attempting this would, however, depend very much on the maturity of the class.

Infinitesimals

* Revision of function concepts, building on the number continuum (independence of real numbers)
* A look at the turn of the eighteenth century with the historical development of infinitesimal calculations through Newton and Leibniz
* Extension of the connections between function and graph by means of elementary functions

Calculus

* Development of difference quotients
* Discovery of differential quotients
* Working through the rules of differentiation of polynomials, reciprocal functions, root functions and angle functions
* Derivatives as increasing functions and their expression in the concepts of speed and acceleration
* Product, quotient and chain rules
* Optional: derivatives as inverse functions
* The connection between the initial function and its derivative shown graphically
* Discussion of curves for polynomials of order 2, 3, 4, and reciprocal functions
* Application in various areas of work including technology
* The function of e, natural logarithms (possible extension of current knowledge of these)
* Definition of function terms from characteristics of their graphs
* Maxima and minima with exercises from industry, optics (Fermat's principle)

Integrals

* Derivatives and the return to the original function as opposite mathematical processes
* Development of integrals for polynomials
* Integrals functions as a function of the upper limit of a particular integral
* The concept of original functions and 'indefinite integrals'
* Flow fields
* Several integral rules (basic integrals)
* Principal rules of differential and integral calculation
* Areas bounded by curves in a plane and other applications
* Optional: solids of rotation

Geometry

(see also Class 11)

Projective and affine geometry, constructive and analytical:

* Illustration of point and line
* Invariant elements
* Illustration of cones (analytical, only in elementary position relative to co-ordinates)
* Invariants
* Introduction to group theory elements as seen in the illustrations
* View of the development of mathematics based on the history of its important personalities (Felix Klein, David Hilbert, George Boole, Moritz Cantor *et al*)
* Optional: synthesis of mathematics, astronomy, botany, embryology, and geometry. Complex numbers. Probability and statistics (if not done in Class 9)
* Laplace and non-Laplace distribution
* Addition and multiplication rule
* Binomial distribution
* Hypothesis testing

10

Art Studies*

Painting, drawing, form drawing, graphics, modelling and sculpture

Art exists for it own sake though its very character makes it fundamentally educative. As they learn to understand the physical world and its laws, human beings grow in capability. When they do art, on the other hand, they grow in creative freedom that is not aimed at any particular purpose. Art can of course have an illustrative function in support of other activities, or it may serve a dialectical purpose and both of these purposes have their place in the curriculum. However, art is essentially taught for its own sake. When practising artistic activities, children experience their own soul realm. This feeling of being caught up in the soul realm should take place in every lesson, and that is why art is never something that takes place separately from the lessons. Steiner formulated the educational task of art teaching as follows:

> *Children need art – both the fine arts and poetry and music. And there is a way of being actively engaged in both sorts that is suitable for children in their school years. If you are a teacher you should not talk too much about one or another art form being 'useful' for the training of certain human faculties. After all art exists for its own sake. Teachers should love art so much that they do not want this experience to be lost to children. They will then see how the children grow through their experiences in art. It is art that awakens their intelligence to full life.*
>
> *A sense of duty develops if children can use their urge for action to gain control over matter in a free and artistic way. It is the teacher's artistic sensibility that brings soul into the school. They bring a happy mood into the children's seriousness and dignity into their joy. With our intellect we merely comprehend nature; it takes artistic feeling to experience it. If children are taught to comprehend things in a living way they become 'able' people, whereas children who engage in art learn to be creative people. In the first case they are merely applying their abilities; in the second case they grow through this very application. However clumsily a child models or paints, this activity awakens inner soul forces. When children engage in music or poetry they feel their inner nature uplifted to the*

*For the study of art history and aesthetics, please see Chapter 26, Study of Art and Aesthetics.

ideal plane. They acquire a second level of humanity alongside the first.

None of this is achieved if art is taken as a separate, unrelated subject and not as an organic part of the whole of education. For all the child's education and instruction should form a whole. Knowledge, culture and training in practical skills should all lead to a need for art, just as artistic sensitivity should reach into the realms of learning, observation and the acquisition of skills.[1]

Painting: Classes 1 to 8

From Class 1 to Class 8 painting is integrated into the main-lesson and is thus the domain of the class teacher. We distinguish between painting or drawing as depiction or illustration (using wax blocks, wax or oil chalks and later coloured pencils, in main-lesson books for example) and painting with watercolour paints. The former accompanies all subjects and is a regular part of classroom working in support of the themes of the lessons. Painting with watercolours, on the other hand, usually takes place once a week during a main-lesson.

Painting with watercolours provides the class teacher with a further opportunity for getting to know the children's soul constitution in even more detail. Different temperaments and constitutions reveal themselves through what and how the children paint.

Steiner based his indications for a painting curriculum on Goethe's *Theory of Colour* and this approach forms an important part of Steiner-Waldorf initial teacher training[2]. The children should experience the objective, psychological (sometimes referred to as moral) impression that is called into being when they perceive a colour. In their fluid, transparent nature, watercolour paints are an excellent medium for this. An additional possibility for making these discoveries is provided by painting straight on to damp paper, i.e. wet-on-wet. In this medium, the colours can more freely move and blend. The following general guidelines may be of help:

1. In painting lessons, an artistic approach should be practised at all levels. The techniques of painting with watercolours, from wet-on-wet to veil painting, must be practised thoroughly so that they can be handled to a high standard.
2. The purely artistic work with the paint itself should not be overlaid or detracted from by expecting the children to create a 'picture' of something specific. We begin to paint with children in a way that is very similar to abstract painting. Painting like this 'out of the colour' must be done in a manner that is psychologically concrete for the children. The tasks that are set should relate the affective qualities of the colours themselves to definite psychological qualities, such as moods which could be described, for example as quiet and retiring, strong and bold, cold and hard, warm and expansive. The outer form is an expression of an inner experience. The teacher prepares these experiences by telling 'painting stories' that bring the colours to life before they are used.

You must let the forms arise out of the colours. You can talk with the children in the world of colours. Think how stimulating it would be if you could reach a level of understanding with the children at which you could say: Look at this coquettish mauve with this cheeky bit of red peeping over its shoulder; and all of it is standing there against the background of a humble blue. You must make it quite objective – this is what works in a way that shapes the soul – so that the colours themselves also do something. Once you think out of the colours you can work with each other in fifty different ways. You must get the children to live within the colour by saying something like: what if the red looks out through the blue! This must be created by the children.[3]

When the children have explored and experienced the colours in this way sufficiently intensely and for a long enough time, we can move on to finding shapes out of the colours, shapes of minerals (mountains, stones), the atmosphere (clouds, sunsets, sky moods), plants and animals, whereby the awareness of the primary qualities of the colours themselves continue to be constantly strengthened. The external form must arise out of the inner experience of the colour. The temptation to be led astray by the wish to produce something aesthetic and illustrative should not be underestimated! It is not that this natural wish on the part of the children should be resisted but rather that *they* be challenged to be true to the nature of the colours.

In Classes 7 and 8 the wet-on-wet technique is joined by an entirely different element. This is veil painting. The way of working is much more differentiated and requires patience and observation. The method requires a palette on which colours can be mixed, time to observe how the picture is developing, and a well-practised technique of applying the paint.

With wet-on-wet the process is strongly sympathetic in that the child is drawn into the inner activity and dialogue of the colours as it happens. They can go with the experience as it unfolds. The process is more important than the outcome. Looking at the paintings the next day is more like an 'antipathetic' process in that the children can stand back and see what happened, can see the outcome. With veil painting the sympathetic and the antipathetic come together, and this 'breathing process' is led not by the teacher but by the pupil.

'Art is a daughter of freedom', said Schiller in his *Letters on the Aesthetic Education of Man*. The pupils should experience this in painting lessons by creating for themselves the conditions freedom needs.

Figurative painting or drawing accompanies all subjects, usually in the form of a picture drawn by the teacher on the blackboard. The starting point for figurative drawing is always the coloured surface and not the outline. Outlines and contours arise in nature for the most part where surfaces of different colours meet. Illustrations in main-lesson books, pictures relating to nature studies or later on geography, and also accurate and aesthetically pleasing depictions of experiments in physics and chemistry, all require continuous practice and further development of drawing techniques to meet the needs of the subject.

Class 1

Painting lessons in Class 1 contribute to a schooling of the senses that nourishes the soul of the child. When a colour is perceived by the senses, a non-sensory element is also at work, so the perception of colour leads on beyond these limits and into a world of objective, moral qualities. In Class 1 the aim is to get to know and characterise the 'movements of soul' awakened by colours. The children get to know these movements of soul through the act of painting; they learn to characterise them when the pictures are discussed after the painting day:

> *The children gain flexible inner images, flexible feelings and flexible actions of will from these experiences of colour. Everything in their soul becomes more flexible…*[4]

It is important to create a quiet, unhurried mood in the painting lessons. The children also need time to establish all the practical work habits to do with preparing for the painting lesson and clearing up afterwards.

Colour stories introduce the exercises and personify the colours in their character and interactions. 'Yellow is a bright cheerful character who spreads out into the world; everywhere he goes he brightens things up. One day he comes across blue, who is sitting there quietly…' Perhaps most effectively such colour stories can accompany the actual painting process so that dialogue between the colours can occur. It also provides an imaginative way of offering the children technical guidance while they are painting; to a child who is hesitant with the yellow encouraging words can be offered along the lines of 'yellows want to shine right across the paper, right up to the edge and beyond', or to a child who is more in a hurry, 'blue is very strong but it doesn't want to be too strong and take the shine off yellow'. Such images can be a help to children, not to mention the colours themselves. Colour pictures can be used in age-appropriate ways throughout the Lower School as an imaginative yet objective approach.

Whether the teacher paints with the children or demonstrates beforehand, or indeed does not paint at all but merely describes the process in words, is a matter of pedagogical judgement. All three options will be appropriate in different situations. With simple colour exercises the teacher can stick a piece of soaked paper onto the blackboard and paint in front of them. If the painting doesn't take too long, it will hold long enough before drying and peeling off. This has the advantage of visibility. Its main advantage is to demonstrate the use of the brush, which children can learn far better through imitation than by following verbal instructions.

Once a range of basic colour exercises have introduced the colours and the techniques of painting, paintings can be done which relate to the narrative content of the lessons, fairy tales, legends, fables and myths. This goes for all classes from Class 1 upwards. Initially it is more a question of reflecting the mood of a story, a dark forest, the golden colour of Rapunzel's hair, the prince's cloak, but gradually the paintings can become more figurative, showing plant or animal forms and later human figures. Always one strives to let the figures arise out of the colour itself, rather than being illustrative or defined by outlines. No attempt is made until Class 4 or 5 to impose any form of perspective, except in the most elementary way, with trees growing upward out of the earth, etc. though the children should be free to portray the images however they feel them to be. The watercolours lend themselves to nature moods though no attempt should be made to impose any form of naturalism. The colours should be appropriate to the mood in a way more akin to expressionist paintings, say in the landscape and plant paintings of Nolde, or even the more formalist abstraction of Klee's watercolours. This progression goes for the first four classes and will not be repeated in the succeeding descriptions.

* Start with the polarities yellow/blue and get to know the colour 'tones' that have much or little tension (yellow/green)
* Paint with the primary colours yellow, red and blue

* The colour surfaces are chosen freely by the children after the teacher has told them a 'colour story'
* Extend the palette by adding the three mixed colours
* Thoroughly ground in the technique of wet-on-wet painting including the necessary preparation (wetting the paper and fixing it to the board)
* Paint on coloured paper, or first paint a wash in one colour and, when the paper has absorbed it fully, apply a second colour
* Fairy tale moods

Class 2

In keeping with the theme for Class 2 (see 'Horizontal Curriculum'), the children can practise balancing what is missing, creating symmetry, or duality. The aim is to activate the souls of the children in this direction. It is important that the teacher should not let the 'colour stories' become subjective or arbitrary but that he should be guided by the colours themselves. This is the only way the children can learn to participate in the life of the colour harmonies.

* Exercises that aim to let the children experience colour harmonies that are:
  * characteristic (red and yellow, yellow and blue, blue and red, orange and green, green and violet, violet and orange)
  * complementary (red and green, yellow and violet, orange and blue)
  * characterless (yellow and orange, orange and red, red and violet, violet and blue, yellow and green, blue and green)
* Exchange exercises: for example the middle colour is changed into its complementary colour while the surrounding colours remain. Then the surrounding colours are changed while the middle colour remains. This is done with the children's actual pictures, i.e. the individual picture is the object of the exercise. This can be done in a sequence of exercises

Class 3

The emphasis in Class 3 is on the 'grand act of creation' of the world (Genesis) and the small-scale shaping of the world through farming and house building. Painting lessons can take up this theme. The children investigate not only the creation of a picture by means of colours, but also how the mixed colours themselves come into being.

* How the primary colours yellow, blue and red arise out of light and dark
* Intensification to the plus and minus sides of the colour circle
* How the mixed colours of green, orange and violet arise
* The seven days of creation as a painting exercise in colour, starting from the creation of the light, the polarity of light and dark, the creation of above and below, the earth and the waters, proceeding to the plants and animals
* Finally a human figure, becoming two can emerge as a whole form out of the colours

Class 4

Up to the beginning of Class 4 the children have been painting with watercolours to make colour harmonies and 'colour stories' in a free way. Now, by being linked with animal studies or the stories of the main-lesson (Norse mythology, for example), the exercises are now introduced in a way that enables the colours to come together in shapes that depict the essence of the subject figuratively. Painting in 'blobs of colour' requires strong concentration from the children. Form must be found from colour, and colour from the theme of the day.

* Let animal forms arise out of colours
* Painting linked to nature studies, trees, simple landscapes with hills and mountains and sky, patterns of fields in a range of browns, greens and yellow, simple generalised shapes of buildings such as a castle or large church, a farm house or barn
* Figurative themes related to the story part of the main-lesson (Norse mythology), e.g. Nifelheim, the World Ash Tree, the Dark Kingdom of Hel, Ragnarok, Viking ships with sails, etc.
* Painting on coloured paper creates new and wider possibilities for creating colour harmonies and colour moods

Class 5

The ever-changing colour processes in nature reveal the forces at work in the plant: sun forces and earth forces, light and darkness. An initial painting exercise can be linked to these polar opposite effects.[5]

As mentioned above, painting can echo or take up the themes of the main-lessons. Let it be said once more that it is not a question of painting illustrations but of letting the colours of nature find their own forms. In this way the painting lessons can provide a qualitative deepening of themes that come up in the main-lesson. At the same time themes from plant studies can provide an opportunity to take what has been seen and heard into their painting lessons as well.

* Develop plant moods from green and yellow
* Contrast 'rose red' and 'lily white' with the pink-white of water lilies. Find the qualitative difference between 'moss green' and 'birch green'
* From now on the children can begin to work with more subtle differentiations and nuances of colour
* Rather than observing the wonderful coincidences of a watercolour picture when the results of the lesson are observed and discussed, we now look more at the way the children have consciously sought to discover and consciously create colour differences
* Maps can be painted showing the qualitative differences between coastline and ocean, river forms, mountains and plains etc.
* Images from mythology can be taken

Class 6

As with other subjects, painting too needs to take into account the children's twelfth year and the various characteristic psychological developments it brings. Steiner's curriculum suggestions regarding art point to 'projection and shadows'. The pupils should gain a clear idea of how shadows come about and they should make appropriate observations of this. There are various ways of approaching chiaroscuro and the study of shadows. Here are two:

1. One possibility is to leave colour on one side and work solely with charcoal or chalk. This would mean that from Class 6 onwards painting is replaced by drawing (see 'Drawing in Class 6')

2. Another possibility is to keep on with painting and tackle the questions by means of painting exercises (see following content suggestions)
   * Obtain grey and black from the three primary colours and the mixed colours. This is a long process in painting that needs building up in stages
   * The grey or black of shadows obtained through using colours can be tried out in themes from plant studies (trees) or mineralogy. If the shadow aspect has been studied through tree studies in drawing, these can be transformed into colour
   * Paint themes from the main-lessons such as geology or history

Class 7

A new technique, veil painting, requires the pupils to practise patience (waiting until the paper, or a layer of paint, has dried) and endurance; they cannot simply set to and get on with it. The colours, too, do not provide the elementary satisfaction of the Early Years period, for they have to be applied very delicately and are very pale. This technique provides many new possibilities for achieving differentiations and depths of colour. The theme of 'perspective' in drawing lessons is taken up through painting in this way.

Painting can also be expanded in another way in connection with geography. If 'Asia' is on the programme in Class 7, then the pupils can practise painting with ink. Chinese brushwork requires so much concentration and self-control that it is therapeutic not only for individual children but also for the sloppiness of the teenage years in general. As regards self-discipline, it could be a good predecessor for veil painting.

* Veil painting with watercolour paints
* Practise with a single colour initially
* Conscious application of perspective by means of colour
* Observe what a colour requires of one in a painterly composition
* Ink drawing and painting in connection with geography lessons
* Work with ink brush and pen
* Proper preparation of the paper
* Inner preparation of the painter for work with the brush

Class 8

Veil painting continues and the technique is perfected. The children might try to carry out the same task once in wet-on-wet and once by the veil technique. The aim of such exercises is to develop the pupils' ability to judge and to strengthen their understanding of painting as an art. What does it mean to work *with* the colours in a particular technique and on a particular theme, or *against* them and thus also against the theme. In this way necessity, opposition and freedom can be practised artistically.

These exercises, that go hand-in-hand with the students' search for themselves, can be strengthened even further in a way suggested by Steiner:

> *If I were teaching thirteen to fourteen year olds who had never done any painting before, I would then get them to look at Dürer's Melancolia. I would show them the wonderful distribution of light and shadow: the light by the window, the way the light is distributed on the polyhedron and the sphere. In fact, making Melancolia one's starting*

point is really a very good idea indeed! Get them to metamorphose the black and white into imaginative colourings.[6]

Such exercises can reveal the possibilities and appropriate ways of painting. They provide not only a continuation but also for the moment a conclusion of what we began in Class 1 as a path of painting, aiming at discovering the inner qualities of colours, and their moral effect.

* Continue with veil painting. Nature studies emerge entirely from colours, using various techniques
* Metamorphosis exercises going from wet-on-wet to veiling and vice versa
* Transformation of chiaroscuro, or black-and-white compositions into colourful imaginations, e.g. Dürer's *Melancolia*, or *St Jerome in his Study* (also in Class 9, if painting lessons are given)
* Similar exercises could be done with Franz Marc's pencil sketches alternating with his colourful animal studies

Painting: Classes 9 to 12

The psychological changes in puberty described below in connection with drawing in Classes 9 to 11 can be observed and described with much greater differentiation in Class 10 as psychological processes. The youngsters are endeavouring to emerge from their isolation. They are searching for friendships and want to enter into relationships with other human beings. In the process, sympathies and antipathies are often vehement and radical, so the teacher is faced with a wide range of tasks: the tendency to see everything in black and white needs to acquire other, richer nuances of colouring. The youngsters' newly-awakened interest in other human beings and their environment needs to be intensified and supported, otherwise there is a danger of this deteriorating into too great an interest in one's own personal affairs and feelings. The young people seek help from the subjects they are taught as well as from their teachers in maintaining this 'forward direction'. They want to experience enthusiasm and develop the will to change as they seek for their own orientation.

Occupying themselves with living, changing colours is thus not only appropriate but also necessary for the psychological situation in which sixteen to seventeen year olds find themselves.

With chiaroscuro or black-and-white drawing there is often only a single correct way that obliges you to use a particular artistic solution. With colours the situation is entirely different. The inexhaustible profusion of colour variations has a liberating effect and also helps the soul find orientation. Finding such orientation on the basis of new discoveries in the act of painting can help activate the young person's will. Drawing can lead to an experience of 'reaching a conclusion', a 'death process' or a 'passion mood'. But with painting all is redemption, release, renewal and 'resurrection'; this remains unspoken in the lessons but can be felt deeply and existentially. The purpose and importance of art as such is not something that stops at the school gates. It is relevant equally for art teacher and for the pupils working with art:

What is important in art can be clearly stated: it is not its purpose to embody something supersensible but to transform what exists and is perceptible. Reality is not intended to sink to the level of a means of expression. No. Reality must remain as it is in all its independence. But it must be given a new form, a form in which it satisfies us ... This is

> *not 'the idea in the form of a sense-perceptible manifestation'; it is 'a sense-perceptible manifestation in the form of an idea'.*[7]

What would the consequence be if young people were not enabled to experience these picture-forming powers of resurrection? There would be deep and all-embracing resignation and helplessness that would seek release in disorientation or else in aggression and destructive violence. In this context art lessons, and among these painting in particular, have an essentially social component that has existential implications for individuals in society.

> *The image-less legacy of the Old Testament, 'Thou shalt not make graven images', has come down to us from ancient times. Human beings now need to turn back from such purely abstract laws and enter once more, now purposefully, into an ability of the soul to make pictures. Only through pictures, through imaginations, will social life be able to establish itself in the right way.*[8]

In the present chapter the following subject/class grouping is taken as the basis:

Class 9:	—	Drawing	—
Class 10:	Painting	Drawing	Modelling/sculpture
Class 11:	Painting	Drawing	Modelling/sculpture
Class 12:	Painting	—	Modelling/sculpture

The general aims are:

* Awaken from black/white to the experience of colours
* Experience painting as an expression of subtle psychological feelings about the world and human beings
* Discover painting as an aid to achieving a more subtle and varied view of the world
* Discover in painting how to ask after the purpose and meaning of art
* Call up, cultivate and practise image-creating powers to make them available in achieving 'realistic imaginations' and 'future-oriented, concrete imaginations'

Classes 10 to 12

The time has come to experience the difference between watercolour and oil painting techniques (the possibilities of creating and mixing colours, and the various brush techniques).

The pupils should learn independently to assess these techniques as to their suitability for the purpose in hand.

Painting experiences from the Lower School are refreshed. Colours are now more consciously used because their nature and expressive possibilities have been understood. The students should learn to search for appropriate expressions of specific experiences by means of colour and form. They should acquire a feeling for the expressive content of the colours. Individuals should gradually discover a personal style based on an objective understanding of the techniques learned.

Reflection is for the most part done during art lessons, while the pupils' work is discussed during painting lessons. The purpose is to help recognise the connection between content and form, the effect of the means used, the 'readability' of a statement, and the power of its message.

Increasingly the pupils themselves should choose the problems they want to work on and the medium they want to use. The teacher's role is to help them overcome difficulties in decision-making. The advice will refer to themes, techniques, design and how to organise the work. The pupils should also be given the opportunity to embark on larger-scale projects and work on these in the way they think best. The project selected should be used to increase concentration and depth rather than be a superficial occupation involving all kinds of different partial tasks.

* Basic exercises for coming to grips with the individual nature of colours
* Contrast colour harmonies (warm/cold, major/minor etc.), also chords with three colours
* More wide-ranging exercises based on Goethe's colour theory. Application of Goethe's theory of harmony and disharmony
* Contrasting themes shaped entirely out of colour experiences
* Nature and landscape moods; metamorphosis of black/white (etchings by, for example, Dürer, Rembrandt, Munch, et al) into colour imaginations
* The development of colour imaginations for a motif as a basis for unfolding a free painterly imagination
* Tree and flower studies (e.g. trees in sunshine, storm, and rain etc.)
* Translation of specific moods into colour and form: joy/sorrow, adagio/allegro *et al*
* The human head and face in various forms
* Free imitation of historical art schools, e.g. Impressionists, Expressionists, Modernists, Cubists, Surrealists, etc.

Materials and techniques

* Oil paints, oil brushes on prepared paper or canvas
* Observing brush techniques and the structure that results in painting with oils
* Unconstrained painting using the veil technique or other liquid paints
* Watercolour painting
* Exploration of other appropriate painting materials

Form drawing, drawing and graphics: Classes 1 to 8

Drawing lessons are very different from painting lessons. A form that has been drawn is always a result, something that has come to rest or, put more bluntly, something 'dead', i.e. at the end of a process. The drawing lessons are, however, not primarily concerned with the result but with the process, the skill involved and the feelings that arise while the activity is going on. These feelings are connected with the form; they are triggered by the form and shaped by it. As with painting, this is the moral realm of forms.

The children are initially not expected to draw some external object; they are to experience a quality of movement. This kind of drawing (which leads to free-hand geometry in Class 5) is called form drawing in Steiner-Waldorf schools.

In the early years of school the children are shown how to draw simple forms and form transformations and experience their qualities. This helps to develop a lively inward ability to comprehend forms. From this the children and later the young people learn to understand the form gestures that come towards them in things created by nature as well as by human beings.

This is important for their further development. When young people experience the form gestures of what they meet in nature (in landscapes, plants, animals etc.), in art, and in other artifacts made by human beings, they gain a rich and realistic relationship with the world. Ordinary looking, not filled with powers capable of creating shapes, can only comprehend what has been finalised, what has become petrified in its final form, what is dead. Such looking confines human awareness to what is dead in the world. Looking that is creative leads the human being beyond the surface of what has become and takes him down into the inner life of things.[9]

Kandinsky, an experienced artist who nevertheless continued to make his researches with regard to the line, formulated the above thus:

If a line drawn in a picture is freed from having to denote something specific and can therefore function as something specific itself, then its inner sound is not weakened by any subsidiary role, so it can exert its full strength.[10]

So initially the purpose of form drawing is to awaken the children's sense of form. This is needed and used when they learn to write and read. Form drawing is a preparation for techniques that belong to our civilisation.

If children have learnt to orientate by means of movement in the classroom as well as on paper, this can help later with spatial problems that might arise for those who are dyslexic. Such children derive a good deal of help from the therapeutic possibilities of form drawing.

Steiner had this therapeutic aspect in mind as well when he encouraged the teachers to find and develop forms that would have a helping, liberating effect in cases where a child is completely dominated by a particular temperament. Awareness of space is called up and stimulated by shapes that are a part of the spatial experience, such as symmetry, movement and counter-movement, repetition, enhancement. For children who have something extremely one-sided in their nature, an important aim is to learn to orientate and move properly in space. In fact, however, today's civilisation contains so much that is destabilising and disorientating that form drawing as a school subject has a generally therapeutic function to fulfil for all children.

A branch of form drawing developed in work with special needs children is called dynamic drawing. This also seeks to release health-giving powers by utilising the enlivening, awakening element of searching for primeval forms and form gestures.

Teachers and therapists need to be clear about the psychological effects of the different shapes and forms, i.e. they must develop the ability to know which forms work more on the will, which work more on the feeling life and which have an effect on the capacity to make mental images.

When geometry begins in Class 5, form drawing is absorbed into geometric drawing. By Class 6 the children have reached 'the age of causality', which calls for real accuracy in their drawing. At the same time they also embark on a new kind of artistic drawing, namely drawing with charcoal. This is initially more akin to painting, and its content is chiefly the contrasts of chiaroscuro. In keeping with the children's psychological situation, this drawing leads on entirely logically to projection and shadows. Before these are constructed geometrically in the older classes, 'feeling shadows' and 'looking for shadows' is handled entirely artistically. Having passed through perspective drawing in Class 7, drawing lessons in Class 8 end with studies on light and shade in connection with perspective. These studies can either involve drawing geometrical solids arranged like a kind of still life, or the children can copy woodcuts or etchings by the old masters, who also practised these themes, using them to develop their techniques. Exercises and encouragement of this kind lead on to the lessons in the Upper School.

Class 1

Straight lines and curves are the starting points for form drawing. This begins with the discovery that the line is a path along which one can move. Children should experience the characteristic difference between straight lines and curves through drawing them, after having explored their character through whole bodily movement in space. The definite direction of the straight line requires concentration and the will to be guided by thinking. The dynamic, meandering curved line with no specific direction leaves room for individual variations; the will is guided by feeling. Once children have become confident in line drawing, symmetrical form and form completion are the main elements in Class 1.

Form drawing forms a preparation for the introduction of writing.

A form drawing main-lesson often precedes the introduction of writing.[11] Straight and curved lines are practised in alternation, in different sizes and in a variety of forms. By this means these basic forms, needed during Class 1, are developed.

* Exercises with vertical, horizontal and diagonal lines, with angles (acute and obtuse), star shapes, triangles, squares and other regular-sided shapes
* Exercises with convex and concave curves, waves, circles, ellipses, spirals, lemniscates and so on
* Continuous patterns and sequences as a preparation for cursive writing

Class 2

Form drawing – as a branch of 'pictorial learning' (Steiner) – aims to cultivate inner perception in a way that will enable thinking to develop without slipping into an intellectual mode. One way of practising this inner perception is to give the children one half of a symmetrical form and let them find and complete the corresponding half themselves. To do this they have to be inwardly active, and must feel that the pattern they have been given is something 'unfinished'. So the aim is to complete, to make perfect in their imagination (and of course also on paper) something that is as yet incomplete or imperfect.

* Exercises around a vertical central axis (which can also be there only in the imagination) mirroring curved and straight and curved forms. Symmetry and reflections
* Then a similar exercise with a horizontal axis; form transformations: making straight-lined forms into curved ones, or vice versa, also with mixtures
* Exercises around a diagonal axis; later also using two perpendicular axes (either vertical/ horizontal, or two diagonals)
* Borders around pages of written work or illustrations
* Running and rhythmical forms

Class 3

Having practised the axial symmetries, the children can now work on free 'asymmetrical' symmetries. This helps them develop a sense of style, for now they have to discover appropriate corresponding shapes in a free way. These exercises are also suitable for cultivating a capacity to imagine spaces inwardly. This helps prepare qualitatively for geometrical drawing. The sense of form is developed through more complex symmetries and cross-over patterns. These elements are fundamental to design, balance and coherence of shapes and to a sense of contrasting form. The patterns learned can be applied to illustrating (e.g. letting for title pages) and to handwork (e.g. embroidery).

* More complex running forms and rhythmic patterns
* Spirals and forms which overlap, coil and intertwine
* Mirrored forms and reflections in vertical and horizontal format
* Forms based on triangles, squares, pentagons, etc.
* Four-fold symmetries, i.e. forms combining horizontal, vertical and diametrical symmetries
* A corresponding outer form must be sought for an inner form, and vice versa. Variations: if the inner form is angular, find a 'curved answer', and vice versa
* Practising differentiations in this way inside a circle, whereby the shape of the circle must be included as a part of the exercise
* Practising 'balanced' forms

Class 4

Spatial imagination continues to be practised and taken further, leading to a summary at a higher level of what has been practised so far. A lot of consciousness is needed when lines cross each other at different angles. This promotes concentration.

The story material in Class 4 (Norse mythology) provides material for form drawing in the shape of intertwining ornamental motifs (engravings on brooches and bracelets; decorations on weapons, helmets, the prows of ships; Celtic, Carolingian and Langobardic intertwining, boarder and knotwork motifs). A new feature at cross-over points is to make them look plaited by showing where the strands go under and over each other. In connection with this, nautical knots can also be practised and then drawn

Class 5

In Class 5, form drawing leads to elementary geometrical drawing. Once again the starting point can be the polarities of straight line and curve. To enable the pupils to gain an intense experience of these, it is good to begin with free-hand drawings without compasses or ruler.

> *Although we are still only at the very beginning of geometry, it is important to give the pupils a sense of the dimension of geometry that goes beyond practical applications and leads to the solution of the ultimate riddles of the world and life. This is easiest done by letting them appreciate not only the laws that govern geometry but also the beauty of its forms and their strictly regulated mutual dependence.*[12]

See the geometry suggestions for Class 5 in Chapter 9, Arithmetic and Mathematics.

Class 6

Having reached their twelfth year and begun the growth spurt including that of muscles and sinews that accompanies puberty, the children now gain a new relationship with gravity. This leads to a new field in drawing. In Class 4 the intertwining ornamentation already called for an awareness of space in drawing. This is now expanded to include flat surfaces in chiaroscuro. We now embark on the conflict between light and darkness, dissolution and densification, height and depth, lightness and heaviness. This world of contrasts is a more existential experience than that of linear forms. However, the children's work with light and dark is not done in an abstract way. In projection and shadow studies it links up with a scientific subject, i.e. physics. The pupils must gain an exact understanding of how the lit surfaces of a solid relate to its shadow. It is the shadows that feel their way out into space and allow the solid body to appear on the flat paper. The question of cause and effect that comes to the fore at this age and even becomes a problem needing attention, is thus also central in drawing lessons.

* Free drawing exercises with charcoal, shaping a surface with light and dark using various shading techniques
* Sphere, cylinder, cone and cube are drawn as spatial solids. Various sources of light and the way these change the shadows are taken into account. Shadows falling on the wall, on the floor and across angled surfaces. A combination of solids casting shadows (shadow still life), whereby shadows also falls on to other solids

Class 7

Light and shadow exercises are continued in Class 7. Perspective drawing now means that these can be constructed more accurately. Perspective and exercises involving the vanishing point are what the pupils need at this age, in an inward sense. They are looking for their own, unmistakable standpoint. How often do they love to flee into their own inner vanishing point! There is something mysterious about this point: on the one hand it is the most minute, most intimate thing imaginable, and on the other it contains a new beginning and infinite possibilities within it. These drawing lessons aim to research this point in ever new ways, while of course also introducing the laws of graphic, spatial construction.

* Projection and shadow studies: interpenetration of solids (a cylindrical or edged rod piercing a sphere, a cone piercing a cube, a cube piercing a sphere, and so on). Special attention is paid to the surfaces of intersection and to the shadows cast on to varying backgrounds (plane, angled, concave or convex surfaces).
* Perspective: central perspective, bird's (vertical) or frog's (horizontal) eye view, drawings with more than one vanishing point. The distribution of light and shadow must always be observed
* Studies involving actual objects such as a building or an interior space

Class 8

Class 4 saw a summary and integration of all that had been learnt in form drawing. In Class 8 the second phase of drawing lessons culminates and is brought together in geometry, projection studies and perspective: 'Combining technique with beauty' (Steiner) signifies a 'redemption' of geometrical and perspective laws through art. The functional aspect is evaluated aesthetically and depicted accordingly. For fourteen to fifteen year olds it is difficult to form aesthetic judgements because of the labile nature of their subjective feelings. Something is accepted as valid only if it is right and true. So in drawing, too, it is important to apply the laws of graphics correctly, not only in free compositions but also in studies of the old masters like Dürer or Leonardo. These themes continue in the Upper School, when the techniques are perfected, e.g. in etching.

* Time can be spent on preparatory studies for copying Dürer's *Melancolia*. Details of the picture are worked on freely, such as the sphere, the polyhedron, the tools and instruments. The garments are also studied, as are nature (day, night, land, sea, sky, earth), architecture and animals etc.
* The beginnings of the laws of proportion. The golden mean as a secret of composition. Finally Dürer's etching is copied
* In connection with nature studies, Rembrandt's etchings of trees and landscapes can be studied and copied

Form drawing, drawing and graphics: Classes 9 to 11

In the Upper School, painting and drawing are given their own timetabled lessons, usually in rotating blocks parallel to other arts and crafts. They are now also taught by specialist teachers, rather than the class teacher.

In the Lower School, artistic activity was embedded within other subjects, and similarly individual pupils were more a part of the class community as a whole so that the element of individual giftedness was less of an issue. For Class 9 pupils this can become somewhat critical, for now they are not only thrown back more on to their own resources, but they also have to experience that the imaginative powers of childhood have decreased. Having earlier been full of ideas and originality, they now find that they increasingly need a 'key' with which to regain access to those faculties. Thus it is not possible simply to continue with what was done in the Lower School.

The students in the Upper School now need to develop an awareness of the complementary roles of arts and crafts, the cultivation of the aesthetic for its own sake as an expression of inner feelings and the transformation of materials to produce artifacts which meet real and practical requirements in the world. The integration of these two aspects is important since art is based on the practical mastery of materials and techniques and making artifacts without concern for the aesthetic element is mere functionalism. The third element in this integration is that of schooling accurate observation. This is particularly important as a basis for balanced judgement.

When inherited capacities (childhood imagination and creativity) begin to fade, space for something new becomes available. Art lessons should take this into account and make use of it. If this is done, the youngsters feel the wind of change that they are seeking psychologically, and then art lessons can gain a contemporary, modern, existential significance for them.

One example of how these three elements can be integrated is in black and white shaded drawing which depends upon accurate observation as well as an understanding of the laws governing light and shadow. The techniques to be mastered have a strong element of craftsman-like skill and the medium itself gives full expression to the psychological qualities of light and dark and their infinite transitions.

Another example is the designing and painting of posters. Here the pupils can experiment with modes of expression using colour and form in response to a practical need. They school their sense of how image and text work together and should become confident at selecting the most sparing and therefore effective means. Posters for events in the life of the school (plays, summer festivals, bazaars, etc.) are designed and made. Many techniques can be learned and employed, such as collages, printing using stencils, monotype, coloured linocuts, offset lithography, silk screen and so on, depending on the art department's resources. Computer graphics also have a role to play, though it makes sense to have explored the medium using manual techniques first.

The following courses can be offered from Class 9 upwards with a progression over several blocks through Classes 9 to 12. Once the students have had basic instruction in the various techniques in Classes 9 and 10, they can apply these skills to project work throughout the Upper School.

Black and white shaded drawing: Classes 9 to 10

The main aim is the schooling of the perception of artistic and natural forms by bringing will activity into sense perception as well as developing a sense for the artistic possibilities of light and dark.

The pupils should be able to apply techniques and their own artistic experience independently in artistic processes. They should be able to carry out independently the making of a pre-sketch, sketch and the finished drawing as a process.

- Abstract basic exercises to learn about the expressive possibilities of light and dark
- Create a balanced surface in all exercises
- Movement directions (e.g. rising/falling), movement and counter-movement (e.g. raying outwards/pushing inwards)
- Where to place the emphasis in the distribution of the components on the surface
- Different ways of shaping surfaces either with continuous, soft transitions of light into dark grey or with clear, clean borders through edges (without outlines); the result should be a rich spectrum of light, silvery greys via many intermediate stages to dark grey; hatching, diagonal shading etc.
- The pupils should recognise the various shading techniques in the graphic work of masters (such as Dürer, Rembrandt or Blake) so as to be able to use them later on themselves

The pupils should gain basic insights into spatial relationships and be able to make these visible in three-dimensional sketches and models.

Tasks that arise out of the above exercises:

- Exercises for studying basic shapes: sphere, cube, pyramid, cylinder, polyhedrons, pentagon, dodecahedron, etc.
- Elements of flat and curved surfaces should be studied and drawn in light and dark
- Drawing of shadows from solids
- Freely combining various solids to form compositions
- Organic and cubic shapes, various light effects in landscape moods
- Drawing from nature during excursions. Utilising the sketches in free compositions
- Depiction of a simple interior space with a

light source and corresponding shadows. Or drawing of the human skull

* Building up a drawing from small elements using the shading technique that makes it possible to observe a slow process of development; building up a drawing from superimposed surfaces using the broad side of the chalk. Use of black chalk or charcoal
* Poster design

Printing

This is usually done in Classes 9 or 10, though more usually 10.

* Using a variety of media to introduce printing on paper or fabrics such as lino-cut, woodcut, block printing, etching, copper plate
* Getting to know the strong tensions between black and white in a print
* Experiencing the possibilities this technique offers for expressing emotions
* Limitations of where this can be applied (e.g. in illustrations)

* Exercises in making lino-cuts: relationship between the intended picture and the way the means are used (material and non-material such as rhythm, contrast, proportion)
* Function of the hand drawing, e.g. as pre-sketch, sketch, study, or as an independent means of artistic expression
* Aspects of style and important masters of (examples from various periods)
* Origin and development of graphic printing as a medium for reproduction and as an artistic medium.
* Use of the tools, techniques and materials of the media practised
* Exercises in etching: from sketch to finished print of a landscape, beginning with a mood and leading to a figurative landscape
* Copperplate etching, use of etching needle and etching press
* Handling etching inks
* Use computer graphics for layout purposes in connection with tasks such as producing theatre programmes, student magazines, presentation of project work
* Design posters

Clay modelling and sculpture: Classes 4 to 8

Wherever appropriate during Classes 1 to 3 the class teacher will let the children model with clay, wax or plasticine. From their ninth year on, modelling can begin as a complement to form drawing. The starting point might be elementary experiences of the sphere and the pyramid. Modelling is developed from the interplay of the hands, which together form an inner space. It is not a matter of adding bits of clay or plasticine here and there but of working with the whole lump, a given amount that can be changed and shaped. Pressure and counter-pressure shape the form of the surfaces. In drawing, corrections are made by 'the will working through the eye' (Steiner); in modelling it is the hand that feels the surfaces, thus becoming a kind of organ of perception and formation. Modelling can add depth to form drawing and also to other main-lesson subjects from which it derives inspiration.

In modelling the underlying principle is that of the metamorphosis of form. That which is given, the material, is transformed through the activity of the soul in a process that reflects the inner metamorphosis that comes to expression through child development. In modelling we are working particularly with the formative forces at work within the nature of the developing child. In the process of modelling itself, the senses of form, movement and touch are especially active. In looking at the work, either in progress or at the completion of a project, the child's powers of 'seeing' are activated in a particularly intensive way.

Seeing in this sense means not merely literally using the eyes, though this is in itself no easy achievement, given the tendency to 'see' what we want to see rather than what is there. When observing form we perceive the form *activity* that the clay actually expresses. This includes its inner movement (frozen in the outer shape) such as direction, expansion or contraction, but also balance, symmetry, sense of gravity or levity and sense of life or lifelessness. The children learn to understand the vocabulary of form and how to read it. This also requires a verbal vocabulary to describe it, and developing this is also part of the task.

When the children are fully engaged in the task of modelling, they are usually quiet, concentrated, breathing deeply and unaware of their surroundings. This mood is sometimes difficult to achieve. Creating the right mood is important if the children are to connect to their own formative forces. If they are unable to do so, this manifests in lack of concentration, superficial forms and a tendency to fragment the piece. Respect for the material itself helps, which comes from exploring its properties. The lesson may begin with simple exercises to familiarise the children once more with the clay or modelling material. Equally important, however is a clear picture of the task in hand. Rather than show the children pictures of what they are to model, giving a verbal description or even asking the children to act out the mood or form they are to model is a great help. This need not take long but is a major help in engaging their self-activity. When working figuratively or abstractly, it is important that the children have a strong feeling for what the form is going to express.

Objectively describing what has been modelled is an equally important part of the lessons. The children need a certain distance from their own work, perhaps even waiting until the next lesson. Their judgement of form needs to be carefully schooled through accurate observation and description, which encourages them to 'slip into' the form and describe what is 'happening'; is it sleeping or resting? Is it slowly swelling? Is it reaching out in a certain direction? Is it striving upwards but leaving most of its volume behind? Is it withdrawing? Is it just a hollow shell with no more activity within, shaped not by inner activity but outer forces, like erosion? Such conversations can be held with children using age-appropriate terminology quite soon in modelling lessons, once the children have good experience of the main elements of form. Especially important is an awareness of the relationship of forms to their surroundings and particularly the way forms respond to each other. This can be done quite simply by placing two forms in different relationships to each other and asking the children to describe what they are saying to each other.

Class 4

* Simple solids such as sphere, pyramid, cube, modelled with hollow of the hands
* In support of the animal main-lesson, beginning with a sphere, make animal forms (sleeping cat, resting deer, cow lying down, etc.)

Class 5

* In the plant main-lesson, beginning with a sphere or egg-shape, make buds, fruits and other plant forms. These need not be naturalistic; the important thing is to sense a growth movement that forms the unformed material
* Human figures can be made, at first standing then sitting. Figures that work with the whole form as an entity, with arms and legs unarticulated (e.g. wrapped in a cloak, crib figures etc.) are easier for the children before dealing with the static problems of legs. Later the arms can move away from the body and the legs can take up a stance

Class 6

* In connection with the geography main-lesson, mould the shapes of various types of mountain: granite, chalk and sharp-contoured shapes that resemble crystal forms. Caves and waterfalls with boulders can be modelled
* Work with figures can proceed to include groups, mother and child, farmer and horse, figures wrestling etc. Keep the detail of faces, hands, feet, clothing, etc. to a minimum

Class 7

* In connection with projection and shadow studies, or with geometry, solids such as the cone, the cube, the pentagon, dodecahedron, etc. can be modelled. The latter in particular can be obtained from the sphere by using the flat of both hands
* Starting from the sphere or a geometrical form, a sequence of form transformations can be undertaken
* In figurative forms, explore gesture and movement, starting from figures turning, bending, pointing, reaching, again leaving facial expression minimal

Class 8

Studies linked to the temperaments can be taken up in modelling:

* Studies of earthy dryness (melancholic), fiery flames (choleric), watery softness (phlegmatic), and airy evaporation (sanguine). These can be done abstractly and figuratively
* Studies in dramatic gesture; adult protecting child, dancing, sleeping, lovers embracing, using whole body language gestures which have first to be acted out before being modelled

Clay modelling and sculpture: Classes 9 to 12

Once again the important thing is to develop the manual dexterity needed to work appropriately with various materials, but also to become submerged in artistic activity that is free of any specific 'purpose'. The creative process as such is experienced consciously. The youngsters are offered a realm in which step by step they can experience the intrinsic laws of art and at the same time the freedom of their own expression. Modelling lessons can help mould and differentiate the pupils' life of feeling while at the same time stimulating their enjoyment of being creative.

Modelling proceeds through wood and stone carving to sculpture proper.

Classes 9 and 10

The pupils should once again re-experience the basic elements of modelling, volume, surface, transitions between planes, line or edge and point. The main aims are:

* Recognising and being able to describe the different qualities of modelled shapes
* Becoming conscious through observation of the movement of surfaces.
* Experiencing shapes from inside and from outside This is a new realm of experience for the pupils They must learn to distinguish between organic and inorganic shapes
* Becoming competent in the manual skills and techniques involved

Experiment with the basic elements of modelling using clay to make reliefs, e.g.:

* Compositions arising out of a flat surface
* Compositions arising from concave and convex surfaces
* Curved and angular shapes
* Compositions from surfaces that turn in on themselves
* Endeavours to find a holistic composition within a specified form language

The pupils learn to experience the reality of the space around them. Possibly a negative cast of the relief is made in plaster of Paris, and then a new positive cast is made from this negative.

* Make masks from a clay base, from the relief form to a complete three-dimensional figure
* Sphere (a form at rest within itself)
* Model a complete figure that not only looks satisfactory from every angle but also constitutes a plastic whole. As with the relief, the starting point as a rule is a basic geometrical form. These basic forms can be developed into animal figures. Perhaps suitable motifs from history of art lessons are taken up

Techniques

* Working with clay, either a single lump or using the building up technique used in ceramics (e.g. coil technique)
* The technique of applying plaster of Paris
* Taking a cast in plaster of Paris
* Casting with lead, silicon or synthetic resin
* Various techniques of mask making including paper and fabric
* Woodcarving. Following clay model, repeat the form by carving in wood. Relief forms are a suitable starting point. Geometric and organic forms are possible
* Stone carving can be introduced using a soft stone such as chalk or tuff

Class 11

Once the basic elements of modelling have been practised in Class 10, Class 11 can move on to studying the movement of form on the one hand and the psychological expressiveness of form on the other. Stone and woodcarving lead on to monumental sculpture.

The modelled 'form as an expression of movement':

* Form movement as a shift of mass
* Transition from static geometric forms to dynamic movement

* The surface turned in on itself as an expression of movement
* A series of shapes showing stages of a movement, e.g. a falling drop, a growth form, etc.)
* Form transformations: variation/metamorphosis (also possible in Class 12)
* Transformation of an organic movement into an artistic form

The modelled 'form as a expression of soul':

* Suitable modelled expressions are sought for various soul gestures
* Contrasting feelings (e.g. sorrow/joy) are depicted
* Conversation between two forms
* Abstract forms can be taken further to become concrete and figurative
* Model the human head in three dimensions (e.g. working from inside a hollow form to create the form from within)

The expressiveness of the human form can be studied. Suitable ideas are brought in from art history (medieval sculpture, e.g. the portal figures in Chartres, Expressionist sculptures, e.g. Barlach, Kollwitz, abstract sculptures, e.g. Arp, Bill, Moore).

Exercises may include:

* Facial proportions as bearers of expression
* One-sidedness of specific features, e.g. grimace, caricature, animal-like face
* Character studies based on the head
* Physiognomy as a mirror of human moods
* Self-portraits
* Contrast opposite types of head and face: man/woman, old/young, beautiful/ugly, laughing/crying, etc.

Techniques

* Initial designs are usually worked on through sketching, then usually worked in clay; later other materials are used
* Plaster of Paris techniques
* Woodcarving
* Working with other materials (depending on what the school can offer)

Class 12

The pupils should achieve some degree of maturity and independence in their work with modelling and carving; they should develop the ability to work freely with the forms they have discovered.

* Transformation of naturalistic forms into an artistic whole; simplification; stylisation
* Combining separate form elements in a whole work, e.g. incorporating copper and wood, glass and wood or metal, stone and metal (in jewellery and brooches)
* Making use of all experience gained; first attempt at using sculptural techniques on a larger work
* Working out individual possibilities of expression

The theme for the year could be: sculpture as an expression of spiritual intention. The important thing is that the students choose a motif or theme that expressed their own artistic aspirations. They should undertake a major artistic project for the year, working through an entire process from initial sketches and studies, through models in wax or clay to a finished exhibited piece in a material, or combination of materials, of their choice. Such a piece should be accompanied by a description of the theme, the process and reflections on the outcome.

Techniques

* Modelling in clay
* Woodcarving
* Stone sculpture

If possible, depending on what the school can offer, other sculptural techniques can be used, e.g. casting in bronze.

11

Chemistry

Popular science books, including those for children, frequently introduce models of atoms and molecules that bear little resemblance to contemporary understanding of 'sub-atomic' and particle behaviour. The crude, billiard ball picture of chemical processes is both inaccurate and at odds with a phenomenological approach to the subject.

The Steiner-Waldorf curriculum for chemistry, as for other subjects, aims to give a developmental and adaptive picture to children and young people, based on clear observation and open-ended questioning. In this way, pupils follow some of the key steps taken during the history of the physical sciences and can learn to appreciate the intricacies and the power of practical applications of the subject. The chemistry curriculum is informed by the principles that inform the other subjects, encouraging lateral and creative thinking across the whole curriculum. By fostering imagination from early years onwards and working from this towards close study of observable phenomena, the pupils are well-prepared for atomic theory and, the sphere of life science, genetics and Darwinian evolution, which will normally be studied in depth in Class 11.

Kindergarten to Class 6

In popular understanding, the word 'chemistry' implies crystals, powders and liquids in bottles. If the study of chemistry is not to isolate children from the living world, then it must be deeply integrated into the life science curriculum from the beginning and not used during this phase of childhood to train them into current materialistic/reductionist explanations. All the considerations given to the place of the life sciences therefore apply to the chemistry curriculum. The whole curriculum, from kindergarten onwards, supports the approach to chemistry that will come to focus in Class 7.

In Class 6, within the geology main-lesson, limestone, silica, chalk and coal illustrate the way in which what is dead and mineral can arise from life. Living organisms shed enough materials in growing and dying that they can be responsible for substantial geological strata. It is only relatively recently that science has acknowledged the living origins of such deposits and it is an important counterbalance to the prevailing view that a dead mineral world is the foundation of life (evolved from a 'primeval soup'), to see that dead matter can arise *from* life through excretion and death.

Class 7

Now chemistry becomes a subject in its own right. The approach should be phenomenological, with the emphasis on accurate description and the children's own experiences, rather than those mediated entirely by measurement. It is also important to maintain the widest possible connections with world processes, in nature and in the human being. The study of combustion, for example, will include observations of the burning qualities of different materials, descriptions of the power of a forest fire, the nature of biological respiration and the ritual/sacrificial use of fire in different cultures and legends.

The imaginative and pictorial faculties engaged here provide a deeper basis for a conceptual understanding of the roles of oxygen, carbon dioxide and energy as well as the role of the plant world over the whole earth.

Biographies of scientists such as Priestley and Lavoisier show how science is set in an historical context and how determined and creative individuals pursued their fascination with the phenomena.

The technical applications (welding, smelting, fire extinguishers) then take their place within much wider moral, social and environmental perspectives.

Combustion

- The burning of all kinds of dead material (e.g. straw, cotton, pine needles, spores, alcohol, gas)
- The role of air in fire – forest, bush and oil fires, firestorms and chimney effects
- The generation of oxygen from pondweed and mineral sources
- The combustion of sulphur, carbon and phosphorus (volcanoes, charcoal burning and fireflies)
- The role of oxygen and carbon dioxide in human, animal and plant
- Smoke and ash, acid and base
- Indicators, using red cabbage, beetroot, litmus
- The chemistry of the candle

Salts

- Limestone and marble, origins and chemistry. Natural formations, caves and cliffs, flora of chalk soils
- The lime kiln and the lime cycle (limestone-quicklime-slaked lime-chalk). Cement and mortar
- The reaction of concentrated hydrochloric acid and solid sodium hydroxide to illustrate the power of the acid/base polarity in forming salts. Practical applications (e.g. toothpaste, the farmer's use of lime)

Metals

- The chemistry and the cultural/historical/technical significance of those metals that can be obtained from the earth, naturally or by reduction of the ore with charcoal (e.g. iron, copper, lead, mercury, tin, silver, gold)
- Smelting of iron – historical links with charcoal burning

Class 8

The thinking ability at this age is ready for more conceptualisation and children are increasingly interested in technical applications. The choice of plant and food chemistry for Class 8 introduces quite complex chemistry, while maintaining the wider picture of the plant world, human diet, agriculture and food technology as well as relationships with other main-lessons. Simple experiments which involve measurement and testing are more appropriate now.

The general theme is how metabolism and the food chain involve a direct relationship with nature and the seasons, although the ripening process can be halted (e.g. pickling), slowed (e.g. storage), or accelerated (e.g. cheese). Food production also involves separating out and purifying what was in the natural environment. The food products may still retain some of their connection with these origins until they finally become isolated into chemical substances (e.g. starch powder, vitamins). The need for cooking rather than eating food raw needs to be examined along with the highly processed food habits of the Western world. Issues of health and diet arise.

* The process that changes grain to flour, various cereals and milling techniques
* The properties of dough, the role of gluten
* Breadmaking (practical). Sourdough and yeast breads
* Extraction of starch from flour, potatoes or rice. The qualities of starch, testing with iodine
* Glucose as the primary product of the plant/sun relationship. Other sugars in nature. Testing for sugar (Benedict's or Fehling's solutions)
* Sources of sugar (historical and cultural). The effect of sugars on the teeth and the diet. Blood sugar and diabetes
* Glucose extraction from sugar beet and its manufacture from acid and starch
* Fermentation (practical) and decay
* Germination of seeds – starch/glucose
* The roles of starch, protein and yeast in breadmaking
* Protein in milk, eggs, fish, beans, meat, feathers and fur
* The qualities of fats and oils, their relationship to water and fire. Their origins in plant and animal
* Milk – raw, pasteurised, 'long life'
* Cheese and yoghurt (practical)
* Soap manufacture
* Cellulose in plant and insect. Its role in human diet. Paper manufacture and recycling (practical)
* Leather and tanning
* Biographies (e.g. Pasteur, Lavoisier, Priestley)

Classes 9 to 12

(see also Chapter 19, Life Sciences and Chapter 23, Physics)

Following a developmental theme, adolescents in Class 9 are in a process in which the forces of their childhood which leant on the adult world now thrust them towards stark questions of identity. The accompanying emotional upheavals are sometimes cause, sometimes effect, but they are the horse which the rider must learn to master and take responsibility for. Through Class 10 the rider gathers the thinking powers that make some sense of the conflicts that are met inwardly and outwardly until the qualities of the steed are more familiar and the explorations have more self-discipline. In Class 11 skill in this regard reaches a high point, while in Class 12 the individual begins to take stock of the past and lay plans for the future.

The chemistry curriculum accompanies this development. In Class 9, the substances formed in the living plant and the substances created in its decay are followed up in technological processes – for example, through the oil industry. For the pupils in Class 10, the conceptual clarity required to study and analyse mineral substances, meets their new thinking ability, while in Class 11 they are ready to compare contrasting models of how matter is currently understood and to see how the atomic model has arisen historically. In Class 12, the environmental and social issues that have accompanied all these studies are examined in their relationship to the human being and the whole earth. At the same time unusual substances and reactions highlight some of the lesser known features of matter, in mineral substance and in the living world.

Class 9

On the basis of the work done in Class 8, a more comprehensive and detailed study of the plant world brings Class 9 to focus on the principles of plant chemistry and the manufacturing and technical processes that have arisen from it.

Although much of the work would conventionally be called 'organic chemistry', the approach is to follow the transformations of substance (e.g. sugar-ethanol-ethanoic acid-ester) within the plant rather than examine substance in isolation as would be the case with a systematic study of an homologous series. Likewise, the use of formulae and equations is an unnecessary abstraction. Where pupils in a particular class show real interest, then it would be much better to use structural formula.

Many of the technical processes may have been examined in Class 8 (e.g. paper, ethanol), but these should be extended to highlight the principles (e.g. cellophane, esters). There needs to be a focus on the oil refinery and its attendant processes as the basis for Western material progress (from fuels to medicines, plastics and pesticides).

The theme of plant decay and decomposition to coal and oil, followed by analysis into individual molecules, needs to continue down to elements such as nitrogen, phosphorus, chlorine and hydrogen, as well as sulphur and carbon with their allotropic properties.

Class 9 needs to engage in individual practical work to test themselves with the hazards of apparatus and chemicals. Young people of this age should be encouraged to explore, to trust their senses and their thinking (though safety and health considerations are, of course, vital). Although they need to structure their observations, ideas and records, following a rigid scientific procedure with controlled experiments, testable hypotheses and exact measurements should not be allowed to dominate the mood of an investigation. The key elements of the scientific process of investigation can be distilled from the reflections that creative and enthusiastic teaching can demand from them. The more disciplined scientific training in method and thinking needed for Classes 11 and 12 is built up through Class 10.

* Photosynthesis and respiration as processes of oxidation and reduction
* The chemistry of sugars, starch, cellulose, alcohols, acids and esters both within the plant and in technological applications (e.g. cellulose, soap, artificial flavours. Explosives: sugar, starch, guncotton)
* Enzymes. Fermentation. Aerobic and anaerobic respiration
* Alcohol abuse. Addiction
* Carbon and nitrogen cycles
* The chemistry of oxygen and carbon dioxide. Air pollution. Ozone
* Destructive distillation of wood and coal

* Factional distillation of oil
* Exploration and drilling for oil, refining and catalytic cracking, products of oil refining
* The chemistry of hydrocarbons and its everyday application (e.g. plastics, refrigerants)
* The chemistry of hydrogen
* The ecological and environmental consequences of the use of hydrocarbon derivatives (e.g. carbon dioxide, pesticides)
* Our personal, local and global responsibility for their use. Alternatives. Recycling
* The chemistry of non-metals (e.g. sulphur, chlorine)
* Biographies (e.g. Alfred Nobel and those not told in Class 8)

Class 10

Class 10 have gained sufficient control over their thinking to grasp concepts and work with them in following processes and in practical work to follow procedures. They seek clarity and are ready to take on the discipline of measurement through precision instruments – weighing and volumetric calculations. By way of contrast, projective geometry brings another kind of precision and quite a different perspective on crystalline form.

The mineral world provides rich opportunities to focus Class 10 on these considerations. Acid-base polarity in the forming of salts leads to practical work whose principles can be followed in living organisms as well as in the human being. The reduction of ores and the chemistry of metals leads to the Reactivity Series and the Periodic Table, laying the basis for the atomic theory in Class 11.

* Mineral forms
  * geology and geography
  * geometry and symmetry
* The origin and history of common salt
* Crystallising, dissolving and melting
* The biological significance of solutions (e.g. osmosis, plasmolysis)
* The thermal decomposition of salts (e.g. calcium carbonate)
* The formation of salts from acid and base (the lime cycle, cement)
* Acid-base polarity in the living world (e.g. breathing, the digestive system). Indicators and titration. Insoluble salts
* Analytic chemistry: tests for acid radicals and metal ions
* Electrolysis of a molten salt (e.g. lead bromide)
* Industrial applications (e.g. electroplating) and historical discoveries (e.g. sodium, aluminium etc.)
* Chemistry and technology of metals, particularly those discovered by electrolysis
* The Reactivity Series

Class 11

At this age, the pupils' thinking ability can firmly grasp the clarity of a model while holding a perspective which can challenge it as well as consider other possibilities.

Quantitative chemical laws should be introduced and the historical discoveries which led to the Periodic Table. This should be presented as only *one* way in which a coherent picture of the chemical elements can be summarised.

This is the age at which the atomic theory can be taught in detail. Although only a small number of students are likely to be considering chemistry as a science to specialise in, when the approach is historical with attention to biographies and to the moral, social and environmental implications of the use of nuclear fission, the whole class can be engaged.

Contemporary research indicating the intimate electromagnetic relationship between water and chemicals could be included alongside some discussion of the biography of Samuel Hahnemann and homeopathy. The emphasis throughout, however, should be on scientific methodology and the nature of 'proof': formulating a question based on observation; forming a rational conjecture (hypothesis); making predictions based on this; testing the predictions through experiment; analysing results (deduction). This could be contrasted with mathematical modelling, where existing evidence is used to make predictions on the balance of probability (also argument from analogy). A contrast can be drawn between complex living processes, which can permit only limited observational intervention, and the relative transparency of experiments in chemistry (organism and test tube).

Such discussion would be harder in Class 10 and probably impossible without vehement polarisation and adversarial argument in Class 9!

The mood should always be entirely positive towards a science that is ready to develop new ideas, remaining open-minded towards all phenomena and grounded in clear thinking and exact observation. It is unfortunate that science is usually presented as synonymous with technology and that its current ideas, from 'big bang' to Darwinian evolution, are to be believed as if they are absolute truth. This is not a healthy point of view for the future of science.

* Establishing the concepts of element, compound, mixture and the basic laws of chemical combinations
* An historical and practical approach to:
    * Laws of conservation of mass, constant and multiple proportions
    * Relative atomic mass, the use of formulae and equations
    * Gas laws
    * Avogadro's number
    * The Periodic Table
    * Radioactivity, the atomic theory and the Manhattan Project (along with the Physics main-lesson)
    * The moral, social economic and environmental effects of nuclear power
    * Homeopathic and/or other models of the interaction of matter and life
    * Biographies (e.g. Dalton, Lavoisier, Mendeleev, Curie, Bohr, Rutherford, Oppenheimer)

Class 12

As in other areas, Class 12 needs the opportunity to have an overview of the subject. Such an approach would survey the origins and historical development of contemporary atomic theory already worked with in Class 1, look at the global effect of chemical technology (economic, social, environmental) and consider the effects of a range of chemical substances on the human organism.

The exploration of unusual chemical reactions gives a practical side to studies at this level and keeps alive the sense of the unknown in such phenomena.

* From Greek ideas of the atom and the elements and those represented by Dalton, Bohr and modern Quantum physics
* The impact of petroleum products on twentieth century, building on Class 9 and looking to

the future of transport and renewable energy sources

* Enzymes, hormones and other biosecretions and their relationship to bodily processes
* Poisons – curare, mushrooms, cyanide
* Addictive substances and their relationship to consciousness
* Impact of chemicals on the environment (e.g. nitrates, hormones, pesticides)
* Carbon as the physical/chemical vehicle of life. (Concepts such as allotropy, an homologous series, polymerisation, the benzene ring)
* Unusual reactions, e.g.:
    * Belousov-Zhabotinsky (BZ) reaction (spatial forms from a chemical reaction)
    * Nitrogen iodide (unusual explosive)
    * Phosgene (luminous spontaneous combustion)
    * Iodine 'clock' (time reaction)
    * Sequence reactions (colour changes and gaseous emissions)

12

Crafts

> *The more we take into account... that intellect develops from the movements of the limbs, from dexterity and skills, the better it will be.*[1]

This motto stands above not only the craft curriculum, but the curriculum generally. Learning through doing and learning through making are twin aspects of the same fundamental attitude to education that permeates the Waldorf curriculum. Thinking and understanding arise out of activity and movement, indeed living thinking is internalised movement. In view of the fact that modern life has deprived children of so many opportunities to imitate and practise meaningful movement through the activities of the hands, education has to compensate if children are to develop in a healthy way. Practical work harmonises the child's soul faculties and thinking, feeling and willing, just as stories work down into the life processes and bodily rhythms in an equally harmonising way.

Obviously the craft and handwork curriculum has a crucial role to play in this experience of learning through doing. The Crafts Council is well aware of this vast constituency of makers which it serves and represents. But, in addition, it saw an urgent need to examine the central learning role played by making – not only in learning the skills to overcome the well-documented famine of competent makers, but also in learning life skills – in schools, higher education and through adult life. It realised that the contribution was only incompletely recognised – and its potential even more rarely appreciated.

As a recent report by the Crafts Council concludes:

> *Making is a creative process that develops skills and competence by engaging with ideas and materials. Knowledge and understanding acquired through 'learning by doing' allows young people to enjoy a sense of achievement which will sustain a life-long interest in the made world.*
>
> *Creative and practical skills, developed in education, can provide valuable experiences which will support the national economy and improve the quality of everyday life.*[2]

This however is an area of the Waldorf curriculum that has remained limited, conservative and traditional in its approach. Innovation has been limited, especially in the UK. The crafts have been preserved in a niche which appears to many students as increasingly isolated from their interest in modern technology.

In many European countries (with the resources to support it) the craft curriculum has been extended to include full apprenticeship programmes in a range of subjects. Many schools[3] have moved practical subjects and the crafts lower down into the school, so that children in puberty, from the age of 12 and 13 onwards, can begin their 'earth maturing' their engagement with the world of matter, materials, practical human needs and the development of skills at an age when they really need it. There is no doubt that this trend was anticipated and encouraged by Steiner himself. The famous comment in lecture 7 of the Torquay Course, about the wish to include a shoemaker on the staff, comes to mind: 'Nevertheless we do try to make children into practical workers.' In the Oxford course, Steiner also indicated that practical work presently being done at the Waldorf school in Classes 5 or 6 should in future be done by pupils in Class 3.

These innovations are important as they mark real attempts to meet the developing needs of today's children. Naturally a sixteen year old will be more competent than a thirteen year old, so many craft teachers prefer to teach older pupils. But perhaps the thirteen year old has a greater need for the experience. Nor is it a question of either/or: both need it. Unless pupils have practised a craft to a certain level of competence over several years, the creativity and self-directed activity we strive for will hardly be achieved. If we want the students to make real things that serve real needs in the world, they will need to have the time in the timetable to do so. Merely sampling a range of crafts is a form of consumerism!

Furthermore, practical activities need to be integrated into the whole curriculum and not compart-mentalised into specialist lessons. That means, each craft or handwork activity needs to be experienced within a context, related to the rest of life. This also has to occur in age-appropriate ways. That means progressing from play to work, from picture to ideal, from archetypal gesture, through craft to technology. Of course, the various hand skills need to be taught in regular lessons and blocks, the challenge is how those activities can integrate with the rest of the curriculum and how they can make the transition into modern technology and work with synthetic materials.

The increase in learning and behavioural difficulties among children has many causes but can certainly be seen as a symptom of a lack of integration, perhaps even a disintegration of the soul forces of thinking and willing. What comes from the head cannot be carried out by the hand, and what the limbs learn through meaningful activity, does not translate into con-ceptualisation and understanding. Learning through doing is a mode of learning that 'ascends' from the limbs to the head. Reflection and analysis of what the hands have made, brings consciousness into the intelligence of the limbs.

Mediating between these two realms is the affective realm of feeling. On the one hand, sentient experience of the materials and processes provides a rich basis for a differentiated life of feeling. On the other, the aesthetic-artistic experience transforms those feelings into the basis for sound judgement. This is a rhythmic process of exchange.

Classes 1 to 8

Handwork lessons are more than a means of promoting dexterity and skill. Through rhythmically repeated movements and exercises while working on tasks suited to the age of the children, the hands – expressing the middle realm of the human being – help to bring about both a strengthening of the will and of the capacity for logical thinking; the transition between these is the cultivation of the feeling life. J. Piaget stated that schooling intricate manual skills was essential for the development of intelligence. He said that the mental operations we carry out only function properly – i.e. bring about real thoughts rather than combinations of words – when they are prepared by physical actions. According to him, mental operations of logic (amongst which are: reaching conclusions, forming judgements, and comprehension) are nothing other than the result of taking actions into the mind and co-ordinating them there. This approach has been borne out by research done by Prof Matti Bergstrom of Helsinki University.[4] Everyday language still uses physical expressions to describe mental operations, e.g. 'to grasp something', 'to take up the thread', 'to get one's thoughts tangled up'. Mention should be made at this point of the difference between an intellectual education as opposed to a training of the intelligence.

The intellect focuses on grasping facts. Acting in accordance with indications or outside guidance is intellectual action. The intellect seeks to conform with what already exists or is known.

Intelligence, by contrast, is not directed to finished things. It understands what is in movement or still in a state of becoming. In keeping with this, intelligence is formed through 'activity', through movement and manual dexterity.

> *If we let the children do things in handwork or crafts that are meaningful, we shall do more for the spirit than if we let them do things that are generally believed to be spiritual.*[5]

> *The faculty of judgment is indeed essentially enhanced by this activity of the hands. It is least developed through mere logical excercises. Logical excercises actually do very little for the development of the faculty of judging, of forming opinions.*[6]

In handwork and crafts, the formative qualities of above/below, heavy/light, light/dark, inside/outside form the basis of the work for children of all ages. All the tasks are performed by both boys and girls. They are not done for their own sake but in order to develop the capacities of the children. They should always have a practical purpose and awaken a social awareness for the work of other people.

Respect for the source of the material and the final handling of worn, used and spent artefacts are, in addition, the first stages towards individual responsibility for the environment and resourcefulness. This means that the preliminary skills for craftwork are best integrated throughout the curriculum.

It is precisely in the encounter with the material world that we can appropriately meet a world of 'process'. In our overly sanitised society children need to play with and explore basic materials and processes; likewise adolescents need an appropriate challenge, one that will help to equip them with essential skills to manage the practical affairs of life and to develop a moral sense of responsibility for the environment; both the natural and human.

A curriculum of activities in association with main-lessons as well as the formal handwork for children within the Lower School as well as pupils in the Upper School, can be developed where a school consciously opens up to the potential of its environment. Many of the necessary materials can be responsibly obtained from their primary source within the school grounds or nearby locality.

Although many of the crafts have their formal lessons, the crafts are integrated throughout the curriculum. The children encounter a material such as wool, in the kindergarten, where they learn its tactile, scented qualities. They collect it from fences and hedges, use it to make gnomes and stuffed cushions. In the Lower School they learn to learn and learn about sheep farming. They may experiment with plant dyes in the Middle School. In history and geography lessons they learn the economic aspects of the wool industry. By the time they start weaving and textile technology in the Upper School, they already have a very broad understanding of wool, its qualities and origins. This example can be extended to wood and timber, plant fibre, clay, metal and other natural materials.

Quite apart from the formal handwork curriculum, the children in the Lower School should have many opportunities to work with their hands in many different lessons, using whatever materials are to hand, especially natural materials such as wood, plant fibre, leaves, bark, clay, water, material, paper, curd and so on.

Craft work is not as specifically related to age groups after the age of twelve or thirteen as other subjects, though the way it is taught is. There is great variation in schools as to when the various crafts are introduced. The important issues are as follows:

* There is a progression from materials taken from the animal kingdom, through the plant kingdom to the mineral kingdom
* Learning the sequence from naturally occurring objects and materials to processed material (e.g. planed wooden planks, or paper)
* The progression from using the hands to handtools to machines
* Teaching the subject in age-appropriate ways

Handwork

Class 1

The task in Class 1 is to make the transition from play to work in a playful and artistic way. The children initially learn by imitating the teacher. Boys and girls learn to knit on two needles. On the one hand, knitting trains awareness and dexterity of both hands and, on the other, it awakens and promotes the children's mental powers through the transformation by which a one-dimensional element, the thread becomes a two-dimensional fabric which has a three-dimensional function. The children should begin to develop a sense for practical design and for suitable colours and simple shapes.

* Teasing wool into thread by hand
* Felting wool
* Making knitting needles using dowelling rods, sanding and waxing
* Knitting using plain and edge stitches: gnomes, balls, recorder bags, small dolls and animals, potholders etc. often starting with white cotton

before moving on to wool, in primary colours
* Embroidering woollen objects with silk thread using straight and diagonal lines
* Cords for handles or skipping ropes, using cotton or parcel string, and the handles made of wood
* Willow whistle made out of a green stick
* Subsidiary work: form drawing, designing small knitted objects, tearing tissue paper for making transparencies, etc. often in connection with the seasons, festivals and main-lessons, making a wooden drop spindle, free form nest basket using grasses, etc.

Class 2

Once both hands have practised knitting plain and purl sufficiently, crocheting can begin. The emphasis in the activity is on the dominant hand and even the dominant side of the body. Alternating between chain stitch and doubles can have a harmonising effect on the individual child's temperament.

* Finger knitting, French knitting, making and using a knitting nancy
* Knitting: purl
* Crocheting using chain stitch and doubles to make: nets for balls, bags for recorders, small bags etc. Also crocheting round potholders
* Plaiting threads to make bands and cords
* Start dolls which can be made with a simple flat construction
* Clothes for dolls can be knitted or felted
* Stitching of seams with overstitch or running stitch
* Subsidiary work: as in Class 1, including as preparation for house building, felting pieces to make tent structures

Class 3

The first garments are made to be worn. Beginning with the head, caps are knitted or crocheted. The techniques learnt can be used elsewhere. There is plenty of room for the children's imagination in making glove puppets. Form drawing is practised thoroughly from Class 1 to Class 3 in order to further the children's formative capacities.

* Knitting/crocheting hats, jumpers, scarves
* Knitting or crocheting, glove puppets
* Embroidering with silk to enhance the shape and reflect the use of the object
* Consolidate basic stitches and stitching
* Practising the techniques learnt
* Subsidiary work: build Classes 1 and 2. Rural crafts including wattle and daub, hurdle making, clay oven, etc.

Class 4

There is a particular exercise that is very helpful at this stage of the children's development: cross-stitch. With its symmetry, and supported by colour and form, cross-stitch helps children to gain confidence and inner firmness in this initial phase of their becoming independent. An understanding of a meaningful design to suit the purpose of the object begins to awaken.

The crossing work is enhanced by plaiting and braiding techniques.

* Use of scissors, needles, pins and thimbles
* Cross-stitch, sewing by hand
* To their own design the children can make embroidered and sewn pincushions or book covers, recorder bags, shoulder bags, etc.
* More complex plaits, cords and strong ropes
* Felt animals stuff with wool

* Construct a simple pit forge, burning charcoal, to make a simple poker

Class 5

At this age the children have a new need for harmony; they seem to rest within themselves. A new technique to learn, that fits in with this, is round knitting on five needles. Over the next two years it is the turn of hands and feet to receive garments, and the children make their own designs called for by the use of the object.

* Knitting on five needles: socks, mittens, gloves
* Use felting technique to make garments
* Consolidation of stitching skills
* Whittling wood

Class 6

To suit the psychological stage the children have reached leading up to puberty, it can be helpful to make three-dimensional objects either based on the human or animal form, or garments for people: soft dolls or animals (to their own design and pattern). The important aspects are the processes of turning inside out (which corresponds to the children's first attempts to show their inner being externally), of stuffing and shaping.

The increase in size and heaviness of the children directs their attention to their feet. So now they can make slippers, designing the colouring to suit the function.

* Human or animal forms in a pattern design, sewing the parts together
* Making slippers with a felted upper on leather sole (see woodwork curriculum)
* Macramé, fishing nets, shopping nets, friendship bands
* Tie-dyeing

Class 7

As the children approach physical maturity an awareness of body shape can be channelled into clothing; shorts, blouses, smocks, waistcoats can be made. Pupils should design their own garments. Knowledge of the materials is broadened and recorded.

* Leatherwork, belts, pouches
* Slippers, sandals or moccasins including working out the shape of shoes and making the pattern
* Various methods can be used, using materials such as cloth, leather or plaited threads, etc.
* If possible, a shoemaker can be asked to help, and a visit to a shoemaker's workshop arranged
* Hand-sewing simple garments, shirts, waistcoats, bags, rucksacks etc.
* Hand-looms can be made and simple weaving techniques learned
* Using green wood and scrap wood, constructing a shaving horse and pole lathe (related to mechanics main-lesson)

Class 8

With puberty or 'earth maturity' the pupils gain an inwardly experienced understanding of cause and effect, and the need to understand how mechanical things work. So now they can begin to used the treadle sewing machine. To use this properly they need to understand its structure and function. Using this machine gives ample opportunity to practise the co-ordination of foot rhythm (will), hand skill (feeling), and attentiveness (thinking). Knowledge of the materials is deepened and formal records are kept (folder, notes in a project book etc.), with an emphasis on the different qualities and use of the various materials to enhance awareness to differentiation. Care and maintenance of materials is also important e.g. washing, ironing, dry cleaning, differences between natural and synthetics (related to hygiene and nutrition main-lessons).

* Using the sewing machine to do double seams, oversewing, hemming
* Machine sewing household linen, aprons, gym shorts, pyjamas, boy's shirts
* Costumes for plays
* Constructing a clay bread oven
* Cooking and bread making
* Building a Cretan windmill with cloth sail.
* Building a coracle, tepee, etc.

Classes 9 to 12

Handwork lessons in the Upper School build on what the pupils have learnt during the Lower School, especially as regards handling textiles. In basketmaking and dressmaking they practise two skills that increasingly call on them to make their own designs but also to be more and more accurate, learning how to make the transition from soft, pliable stuffs to hard, spiky canes. They are helped in three ways:

* Their manual movements must be appropriate and skilful
* Imagination and individual taste are developed as they design the object to be made
* Finally, every work sequence must be properly thought through. Mobility in thinking and the ability to make a mental picture of something are practised, and can be checked and corrected when the result becomes reality. The students should learn to evaluate what they have made in terms of appropriate use of material and technique, form and function and aesthetics

It is important that the pupils learn the origin and production processes of the materials they use, where possible learning the skills involved.

The crafts practised are those that use wool, thread, material, cane or paper (cardboard). Even the simplest objects made are intended for daily use. The link between the object being made and ordinary human life should be obvious as the children work. The lessons should provide insights into the properties of the materials used and the techniques needed, into the connections between function, material and form, and into the links between human being, machine, production, commerce and industry, and the environment.

Working practically and theoretically with the different materials will help the youngsters to school their faculties of thinking technically and to become more aware of life processes in nature; it will help them learn to invent, plan and organise processes and to develop an appropriately critical attitude as consumers. Such work will also play a part in developing their personality, in furthering their technical education and deciding what profession or occupation to aim for later on.

Learning through doing and learning from having done is essentially a moral process, in that the will to do better is motivated and this motivation is not egotistical but objective. The pupil feels the need to make a better basket, better in the sense that it serves a real need and in that form relates harmoniously to material and function.

From Class 9 onwards, craft studies usually take the form of blocks of lessons. They vary depending on the location and preferences of the school.

The aim of all the subjects is:

* Accuracy in planning, carrying out and checking the work
* Meeting a real need

Two main directions are followed:

* Design should be functional and pleasing to the senses
* The technical workmanship should involve the most economical procedures using the most appropriate materials

Class 9

Basketmaking

Traditional basketmaking is also taught in Class 8. The basic skills can be learned in Class 8. In Class 9 the emphasis is on design, different materials and individual creativity. In keeping with the youngsters' stage of development (their growth is for the most part complete), they now need some inner firmness (upright posture and steadiness). Shaping a basket in the right height and breadth can help with this. The sense of touch is also experienced.

In Class 8 willow cultivation and processing is done in preparation for basket making.

* Getting to know the origin and preparation of the materials and use of tools
  * Making some of the basic parts:
  * Weaving the base, the uprights and the final border, following the specific instructions of the teacher
  * Free construction of a basket in which the types of weaving are chosen by the youngsters to suit the purpose and the aesthetic design
* Exercises in imagining the finished work:
  * Making sketches of the planned work.
  * Describing a piece of work when finished.
  * Writing a self-evaluation of the process and finished product

Class 10

Dressmaking

The pupils experience the need to make accurate calculations and to work with accuracy. They recognise certain laws of number and measure and develop an understanding for the work and skill of others (e.g. those who have hitherto made their clothes for them). Differentiating between made-to-measure and off-the-peg garments. If possible, a visit to a factory should be made. Dressmaking is fruitfully related to costumes and drama productions.

* Measuring for a garment (getting to know their own proportions)
* Drawing the pattern; altering the pattern
* Selecting the material: quality, weave, structure
* Cutting out, marking, tacking, trying on, sewing
* Finishing: fastenings, seams, trimmings, neck openings
* Getting to know the electric sewing machine
* Buttonholing by hand or with the machine

Appropriate design:

* Fitting, colour, colour gradations
* Sewing one or more garments

Textile Technology

It is good for pupils to get to know all the phases humanity has gone through in textile making, from ancient times right up to industrialisation. In the Lower School, children have learned drop spinning and basic thread work. In spinning, the important aspect is the co-ordination of hand and foot, so this needs much practice.

* Preparation of material (wool or silk) from cleaning to dyeing
* Study of materials
* Individual design

Spinning fibres with spindle or spinning wheel:

* Getting the spinning wheel ready
* Spinning yarn for weaving
* Getting to know the characteristics of various wools and silks
* Various kinds of design
* Deciding yarn thickness to suit the job in hand

The development of the spinning wheel up to the spinning machine. Visits to museums or a spinning factory.

Batik

(painting on silk or other forms of textile design)
Free artistic work should always take into account the ultimate purpose. It is important to have a comprehensive, exact and qualitative picture of the person or environment for whom a piece of work is intended, e.g. temperament, age, style. Pattern, colour, shape, technique are chosen accordingly.

* Preparing the material
* Selecting the colours
* Planning and describing the work phases
* Various techniques
* Design
* Producing the squares, scarves, cushions, tablecloths, curtains or garments, etc.

Classes 11 and 12

Weaving

Weaving combines handwork and technology, so the youngsters should be given some insight into the historical development of weaving. Depending on the capacity of the pupils, the spread of techniques should be as broad as possible, from delicate squares or scarves via larger garments (also cushion covers, tablecloths, mats, etc.) to the design of rough linen work. (Weaving is also possible in Class 10 – see Technology if the emphasis is on 'Bookbinding and Cardboard Work'.)

Elements of weaving:

* How warp and weft work together
* The basic techniques of weaving
* Getting to know different types of loom
* Designing a piece of weaving

Calculating:

* Length of the warp
* Number of threads in the warp
* The amount of yarn that will be needed

Working at the loom:

* Setting up the warp
* Setting the frames
* Using two or four shaft looms
* Making a woven piece of work

Possible: visit to a handweaving shop

Cardboard work and bookbinding

Following the making of paper in Classes 7, 8 or 9 and practical tasks cutting and stapling sheets and card to make exercise books, the students move on to bookbinding itself in Classes 11 or 12. In Class 10 printing is often introduced, including the use of hand-made paper. Getting to know the new materials and noticing their characteristics requires attentive senses and sure judgement (characteristics such as: tone, colour, texture, smell, elasticity, firmness). The precise technique of bookbinding, with its strict sequence of moves, schools disciplined thought and action. It is possible to consider every step of a sequence forwards and backwards, checking and improving. The next step cannot take place before the previous one has been done properly. The work itself shows the pupils the sequence of tasks that have to be carried out.

Cardboard work:

* Handling the materials: paper, cardboard, textiles, leather (as a covering), adhesives. (In Class 10 the students can bind main-lesson books using heat binding techniques and pre-cutting paper and card with the guillotine)
* Carrying out the different tasks introduces the pupils to the various tools, apparatuses and machines (presses, cutters)
* Partly copying and partly designing their own work, the pupils make: picture frames, blotters, folders, little boxes, photo albums

Bookbinding:

'From the flat board to the finished book' (ideally with gilt edges)

* Folding proof-sheets or writing paper
* Sewing for paper binding
* Hardcover binding
* Half leather, patent leather or parchment bindings

The content of the book decides what bindings, binding materials and cover designs are used. Various materials are studied.

Craftwork

In Classes 1–3, children are handling natural wooden twigs and branches which they find. These can be combined to make simple creative toys, or arrangements on the nature table, or to make furniture for dolls or gnomes. Introduction to basic tools suitable for children of this age, e.g. knife for handcarving, saw, drill and bit, hammer, rasp, etc.

Classes 4 and 5

* Using bark and twigs (with suggestive shapes) make twig figures, fabulous animals, gnomes, sheep with shepherd, bark boats and so on
* Making simple utensils such as stirrer, whisk, small spoon, paper knife, etc.
* Simple log constructions e.g. climbing frames, flower bed borders, edges, etc.

From Class 5

* Begin studying trees and different timbers
* Use of hand axe to make tent pegs, etc.
* Use of adze to shape timber, make dugouts
* Splitting and chopping to make firewood and kindling
* Make hollowed out bird boxes out of large logs

Class 6

In the craft lessons we take up something the children learnt earlier; what has been prepared beforehand now works on into the future. Thus craft work refers back to the very first lesson in school when straight and curved lines were drawn. Both are present in the background of the articles made by the children. For example a wooden spoon has a straight handle and a rounded (and concave/convex) bowl. The children work inwards from the outside; filing and chiselling always mean you have to work inwards towards the shape. Long movements (e.g. planing, sawing, cutting) relate to the straight line. Short movements (e.g. chiselling or carving by hand) relate to the curve.

Useful objects and toys are made.

* Making objects in daily use such as cooking spoons, palette scrapers, stirrers, flour shovels, darning eggs, mallets, wood hammers, garden dibbers etc.
* Toys, e.g. hopping bunnies, waddling ducks, pecking birds, bears on a seesaw, etc. Making toys requires that the characteristic movement has to be understood, and also calls for skill and an understanding of mechanics. This can begin very simply, e.g. seesaw or eccentric wheels etc. In Class 7 such effects can be improved on, with the children giving free reign to their imagination
* Safe handling of tools and appropriate treatment of materials is aimed for (e.g. correct cutting methods)

Class 7

Physics in Class 7 brings a first introduction to mechanics. The children now want to apply what they have learnt. For example the pendulum, the crank, the lever, the seesaw, etc. used in making moving toys can now be applied to cranes, mills, propellers etc. With animal toys, more care will be taken to make them move in a realistic way. Some carpentry is also now introduced, e.g. use of the mortice chisel, bowsaw etc. Making usable items featuring a hollow (e.g. a bowl) is an important aspect at this age. In addition to the confident use of the necessary tools, the youngsters also learn to shape the inner and outer form properly.

* The class might undertake a larger communal project for the Kindergarten or a bazaar, such as a farm with barn and animals, or a village with houses, towers, a well
* Carving bowls
* The toys can look much more effective if they are well painted
* Nutcrackers, boxes with lids, pen holders, etc. can follow next
* Greenwood work

Class 8

The pupils learn to plan the best sequence of operations in the production of an item, such as:

* Greenwood turning on a pole lathe
* Making a besom
* Making a picture frame
* Making gardening implements, etc., making and putting handles on tools

More can be expected of them with regard to both manual skill and design. They should combining good design with a good fit and accurate work.

Proper carpentry work can begin even before the technology subjects of the Upper School such as planing. Simple carpentry projects, e.g. shelving, storage boxes are good; larger projects can also be undertaken, possible as communal tasks, e.g. a large seesaw, go-carts, skate-board ramps. Another possibility is making proper nesting boxes for birds, or feeding tables for birds.

Let the pupils choose. They could decide to combine wood with metal (e.g. wooden plinth for copper bowl).

Classes 9 to 12

Craft lessons in the Upper School build on the skills learnt in the Lower School. Now the motto is: 'Every lesson must be a lesson for life'. The tasks set should not only continue to promote the pupils' development but also be meaningful for society at large. Steiner was insistent that crafts and technology should be based on meeting real needs in the world and *not* an artificial process of preparing exercise pieces. He also expected all teaching to be a preparation for life. Steiner did not make many specific suggestions regarding craft work in the Upper School, but he did emphasise in connection with technological studies that many practical tasks should not be tackled too late in life, i.e. they should be practised between the ages of fifteen and eighteen.

In the Lower School, craft lessons served to help the children grow into the world. Now the time has come for them to learn how to meet the challenges of the world. In this they are educated not only by the teacher, who functions like a master craftsman with his apprentices, but also by the materials, the tools and the tasks they are set.

Wood is now not so much something that stimulates the imagination but rather a material challenging one's technical skills. It is something that is alive and has grown, and it poses technical problems. The pupils find themselves caught between their own wishes as to what they want to make and the specific characteristics and limitations presented by the wood. Bringing these two into harmony is helped by the classical methods of joinery. Through good design and accuracy in working the pupils learn both how wood functions and the techniques needed to work with it.

Carpentry and joinery

Class 9

By making bookshelves, boxes with lids, step-ups, tool boxes, etc., the pupils practise work that requires accurate measurement. They check the quality of their own work. The finality of procedures involving the disposal of wood shavings is an important educational experience. Regular practice of specific procedures (e.g. planing, sawing) strengthens the will.

* Study and care of tools
* Knowledge of the different woods, their characteristics and uses
* Gaining confidence in sawing, planing, chiselling for the simpler joints
* Accuracy in surface treatment and the final finish are essential
* Application of these skills to useful tasks
* Forestry work

* Rustic garden furniture
* Discussion of environmental aspects of processing wood.
* Recording of information about techniques and materials

Classes 10 and 11

* Expanding and deepening skills in the techniques learnt now calls for greater precision through practising and becoming independent in sorting out how to tackle a task
* Accurate preparation of wood
* Joints such as tongue and groove, dovetailing, etc. are applied; these require accurate working. Hand-held electric tools are introduced and their proper use learnt
* Making simple pieces of furniture involves artistic aspects as well as constructive ideas. The latter should be split into separate stages that combine together to create a finished piece
* Putting together separately constructed parts, e.g. fitting a door into a frame
* Carving of printing blocks
* Technical drawing in relation to woodwork projects
* Recording skills and techniques learned

Class 12

If there are opportunities to continue joinery into Class 12 (as Steiner suggested), the pupils should design their own furniture to be realised via technical drawings and sketches of details. Artistic design, form and function come together and static requirements are met in aesthetically pleasing ways. The pupils can also make accurate cost estimates.

Depending on the teacher's competence, other tasks can of course be brought into woodwork lessons in the Upper School, e.g. making boats or musical instruments.

Metalwork

Steiner made no suggestion about metalwork. Inflation was rampant in the days when he was working with the teachers of the first Waldorf School (1923) and there would have been no question of introducing this subject. Had there been an opportunity, he would surely have seized it, for he spoke often about metals and on one occasion mused that at least once in a lifetime everyone should experience fiery, molten metal.

The following suggestions are based on experiences gained over the last fifty years. These are so positive that metalwork has meanwhile become an essential ingredient for Upper School pupils at Steiner-Waldorf schools.

All ancient civilisations developed hand-in-hand with the expansion and refinement of obtaining and processing metals. Unlike wood, clay or stone, ores have to undergo a process of transformation before the metal becomes usable. By carrying out the tasks of shaping, heating, smelting, pouring and smithing the youngsters experience those historical processes of development. Pliable copper elicits their own powers of form which have also been brought to bear in other artistic lessons. Iron awakens or promotes the virtues of courage, alertness, and quick, sure seizing of opportunities. Rhythmical hammering is in itself a healing activity.

Copper beating

Class 9

(often started in Class 8 and continued in Class 9) A first metalwork block acquaints the pupils with natural origins and the basic properties of copper, e.g. its divisibility and elasticity. They can then be more aware of what they are doing when shaping it, and they also experience how constant hammering makes it harder, while heating makes it softer and more pliable. Most of the tasks are rhythmical, and this promotes perseverance and concentration. (Rhythm takes the place of strength.)

The techniques learnt are marking out, cutting, hollowing, planishing, riveting and soldering, both soft and hard and the objects made are bracelets, bowls, boxes, candlesticks, bookends, oil lamps etc.

Class 10

A second block takes all the techniques further. The skill of raising the copper in cylindrical, tumbler shapes is added. This makes it possible to manufacture beakers, vases, jugs, watering cans, baking tins, bells, etc. This technique requires much concentration and accurate hammering. Soon the pupils want to carry out their own designs. So they should also learn annealing, hard-soldering, bending and shaping around a form and tin-plating.

Knowledge of how to handle brass, pewter or even aluminium and stainless steel extends the possibilities both of experiencing the metals and of making objects. Closed vessels are preferred, which corresponds to the wish to turn inwards that is typical of youngsters at this age. The students can also learn the techniques of working with copper pipes in plumbing (and could also make copper rods for use in eurythmy).

Iron (wrought iron)

Classes 9 to 11

Whether one introduces copper or iron first is a question of pedagogical research and experience. Some teachers see the application of will needed in hammering iron as an ideal introduction to metalwork these days. Copperwork demands greater delicacy of touch and rhythm and should perhaps follow iron. On the other hand iron may simply require more applied will and strength than Class 9 students have available. Copper is shaped cold (having been annealed). Iron has to be heated. The pupils immediately learn the difference between working with cold or red-hot iron. They experience how the glowing iron responds to the hammer's beat.

The firm stance at the anvil, the proper handling of the various hammers and tongs, the courageous blow accurately aimed, the alertness and quick reactions needed at forge and anvil, all these are profound experiences and important education tools. Basic techniques such as pointing up, stretching, splitting, bending and compressing, after much practice, can be used to make nails, fire-tongs, spits, candlesticks, fire-pokers, decorative hooks and a variety of tools such as knife and chisel, drawknives (for greenwood turning), etc.

Some procedures need two pairs of hands. This brings in the element of collaboration. More responsibility and care are also needed, as working in pairs is more dangerous.

Old tools can be repaired and restored, new

handles made and toolkits made up for use in the developing world.

The pupils will also hear about mining and smelting as well as the industrial production of steel, steel alloys and stainless steel.

Metal casting

Classes 10 to 11

Beautiful and important experiences are provided by casting, which some schools are able to include in their syllabus. It is a profound experience for young people to watch the metal melt in the crucible, and then receive an entirely new form, made by themselves, when they pour it into the mould. Care in shaping the mould is essential for a successful operation. Failures, which are inevitable, have more educational value than anything the teacher can say. The huge delight at success is infectious.

First of all easily melted metals (lead, tin, zinc) are melted in the ladle and poured in a mould. More complicated shape can be attained in moulds and two-part sand moulds. Lost wax casting can be the crowning experience. Then brass and bronze are melted in the furnace. These materials can be won through recycling household scrap. Medals, small figures and all sorts of useful objects, even a small bell, can be produced. Later silver and gold can be used for jewellery making.

All this gives a very practical experience of the link between technology (perhaps visiting a foundry) and art history (bronze sculptures).

Mask making

Mask-making using a range of media provides adolescents with many opportunities for exploration of the human psyche, in association with drama, literature, etc.

Class 9

* Face casting using clay and plaster.
* Transformation of facial gestures to express a wide range of ages, psychological types. In Class 9 this should be more exploratory.

Class 10

* Masks are made more objectively as stage props to represent and express particular characters
* Use of metals and moulds
* Use of wood and leather

Classes 11 and 12

These skills are developed further. Use of masks in other cultures is studied.

Puppetry

Puppetry can be offered as a subject in its own right, or may be offered as an option to students from Classes 9 to 12. With increasing differentiation in the Upper School, students may drop one or other subject, a second foreign language for example, and concentrate on craft work. Puppetry is a very suitable alternative.

Puppetry is an artistic craft. The first task is to create the puppet. Glove puppets are the simplest, needing only a properly formed head and a dress.

Shadow puppets, marionettes and rod puppets pose all kinds of technical problems requiring knowledge of mechanical and optical laws.

So one of the aims of these lessons is to apply artistically what has been learnt in mechanics, optics and technology. Marionettes do not necessarily need strings and frame-jointed limbs. 'Soft' marionettes, i.e. stuffed dolls without legs and with lead-weighted arms, can be manipulated without a cross-frame. For performances to kindergarten children this kind of marionette is preferable.

For proper performances the handler remains invisible (except in the kindergarten, where he or she can be seen by the children). The handler is simply an 'intermediary'. The puppet is the main actor. The glove puppet, the marionette or the shadow puppet 'tells' the puppeteer what to do. The pupils have to learn how to manipulate the different puppets. This is the second aim.

The third aim is social and educational. By remaining invisible through having to stand behind, above or below the puppet, the puppeteer has to make a sacrifice. For some pupils, having to stay out of the limelight is a sacrifice, while for others it is their great chance to perform something through the puppet which they have perhaps not been able to bring themselves to do on the stage. All the handlers are dependent on active help from their co-puppeteers. Handling technically complicated puppets often needs two or more helpers who have to work 'hand-in-hand'. In puppet theatre performances, the interplay between scenery makers, lighters, musicians, speakers and handlers is often more intensive, because it is more intimate and requires a greater degree of mutual empathy and care than real theatre.

Perhaps the most important aim of these lessons is learning to respect what is small.

Sometimes there are opportunities to take a travelling puppet show on the road. This enables the pupils to make a gift to the various homes, special schools or hospitals where they have perhaps been working in their practical social work period. Their social commitment thus gains an extra dimension.

Spanning the four classes of the Upper School, a puppetry course can be designed to take account of the pupils' on-going development.

Class 9: the marionette

More than with any other puppets, manipulating a marionette calls for real artistic ability. The pupils can experience how constant practice rewards them with the ability to breathe life into dead material.

- Getting to know the mechanical laws and analysing the movements of the marionette
- Constructing the various joints
- Moulding heads, hands and feet
- Constructing the cross-frame
- Dressing the marionettes
- Manipulating the marionettes
- Making the scenery and working on the text
- Combined effect of language, light, music and movement of the marionettes

Class 10: shadow puppets

Mechanical and optical laws govern the construction of the puppet and the scenery. The shadow picture should be as clear, sharp and precise as possible. Together with the skill of moving the puppets, another important aspect is combining various elements to create a 'shadow picture' for the scenery.

* Looking for and adapting an appropriate text
* Designing the shadow picture in painting and drawing
* Experiments with coloured and simple shadows
* Construction of the shadow puppets
* Manipulating the puppets
* Designing the scenery and working on the text
* Combined effect of language, light, music and movement of the marionettes

Class 11: glove puppets

Marionette players stand above their puppets; shadow puppet players stand behind theirs. Glove puppet players go down below them. Glove puppets can be especially expressive because of the way they are manipulated from within. Puppeteers need enthusiasm, discipline and also humour if the movements are to be artistic and not merely grotesque.

* The history of puppetry
* The glove puppet as the archetypal form of artistic puppetry
* Modelling or carving heads and hands
* Improvisation exercises
* Handling the puppets
* Making the scenery and working on the text
* Combined effect of language, light, music and movement of the marionettes

Class 12

There are various ways of bringing the puppetry course to an end:

* The experiences gained can provide a basis for putting on a performance (fairy tale, novella, drama, opera)
* If the piece to be performed portrays different levels of experience (this world and the next; daytime/night-time consciousness; archetypal figures, elementals etc.) various types of puppet can be combined
* Special puppets can be developed for special purposes (e.g. performing in homes for people with sensory disabilities)

What is done will arise out of the above possibilities. What has been learnt will then be combined or deepened accordingly. If there is enough time, larger performances can be prepared (e.g. *The Magic Flute*, *Dr Faustus*, *A Christmas Carol* (Dickens), *Momo and the Grey Gentlemen* (M. Ende), etc.).

13

English Language and Literature

Language is our most important means of mutual understanding and is therefore the primary medium of education. It is also a highly significant formative influence in the child's psychological and spiritual development and its cultivation is central to the educational tasks of Steiner-Waldorf education. It is the aim of the curriculum to cultivate language skills and awareness in *all* subjects and teaching settings. Clearly the teaching of the mother tongue has a pivotal role within the whole education.

The spoken and written word

Language has two primary forms within education, the spoken word and the realm of orality and all forms of literacy. It is the task of English lessons to cultivate both. Literacy fits like a glove on the hand of orality. In the pre-school years the emphasis is on language acquisition and is essentially concerned with oral language. With the introduction of writing and reading, a new form of linguistic consciousness emerges. Vital though this is to the developing human being, it needs to be based on spoken language and so the cultivation of oral skills always underpins literacy.

In terms of the emerging child's consciousness, the transition from orality to literacy reflects the historical and cultural transition from pre-literate to literate traditions. Through literacy and the written word, consciousness is significantly re-structured and this factor is important to understand from the point of view of methodology.

One can compare the fundamental differences between the pre-literate and literate mind as follows. Oral consciousness is mythic, whereas literacy tends to a rational and historical sensibility. Situational thinking, exemplified by the riddle, the fable, the parable or the metaphor compares with logical thinking, definitions, categories or syllogisms. Oral thinking involves concrete mental images, as opposed to abstractions. Oral language characterises; literate language structures and defines. Pre-literate thinking is often expressed in the form of collective, communal, contextual memories linked to ritual and situation, whereas literate memory is individual and internalised. Epic, myth, poetry and performed drama are forms of expression which draw strongly on the oral tradition whilst prose belongs to a literate tradition. The oral mind tends to have an experience of self through the context, whilst literature lends itself to self-experience. We can also see this in the distinction between shame and guilt; shame is in the eyes of others; guilt is internal within the soul.

This broad-brush comparison paints two opposing forms of consciousness. Historically, literacy proceeds out of oral traditions and largely replaces them. Yet both qualities are needed to complement each other in the school learning context. As Norman Skillen put it:

> *School is the product and traditional servant of literacy. Its whole ethos – from its typical architecture to its organisational structure and patterns of required behaviour (sitting still, keeping quiet etc.) – is determined by literacy. But if orality is not given its rightful place, the school will not be a wholesome environment for children and literacy will ultimately suffer.*[1]

The task is therefore to cultivate a transformed orality, which, as Skillen concluded in the article quoted above, 'is none other than the power of imagination itself.' Imagination and analytical thinking are two poles of experience that need to be integrated. The cultivation of both the oral and the literate forms of language support this process. Imaginative, holistic thinking are called upon when the child is challenged to participate, to do, to engage in complex situations. Analytical thinking requires that the individual stand back from a situation. Whenever the pupils are engaged in experiential learning, whenever they are challenged to enter the unknown, the realm of the intuitive – be it in mathematics, drama, the arts, crafts or eurythmy, transformed orality will be at work. It is one of the primary tasks of teaching English language and literature to establish a strong culture of orality upon which an equally strong culture of literacy depends.

The nature of language

In the three archetypal stages of early child development – gaining uprightness, learning to speak and the development of thinking – language has a mediating role. From a certain perspective speech is internalised movement and thinking is internalised speech. There is a clear progression from movement and gesture to speech and from speech to thinking. In this inner metamorphosis of movement, language works as a formative force in the developing child's being.

The relationship between movement and gesture, speech and thinking is a key to all aspects of language teaching. At all levels of linguistic experience, from the formation of the sounds, the letters of the alphabet, the rhythm of sentence structure, we find the metamorphosis of movement and gesture into structured form. Movement and gesture translate into figures of speech, metaphor and mobility of thinking. The task of language teaching in the Lower and Middle School is to expand the child's repertoire of linguistic experience through usage. Making this conscious is essentially a task of the Upper School where the stages of this metamorphosis can themselves be explored.

An example of how this might be done would be an exercise such as taking a soliloquy by Macbeth, and analysing the movement of thoughts throughout the passage, observing the rhythms of the syntax, unwrapping the imagery of the analogies and finding the levels of meaning, feeling the effect of the sounds Shakespeare uses in a given phrase and ultimately expressing the whole as movement and gesture on the stage without words.

All these qualities of language are cultivated in the Lower and Middle School. Only after the age of fourteen does it become necessary to make the processes more reflective through analysis. Mediating between these two processes, experiencing and analysing language, is performance, whether through recitation or acting.

Language as a formative process

Initially speech itself structures both the physical organs used in speaking and listening as well as the neural structures that perceive, organise and understand words and sentence structures. This occurs as the child acquires her native language. Subsequently language becomes a medium for the child's soul life. On the one hand, language works to enable the child to express herself and relate to the world, whilst on the other hand it works through its syntax to order and structure thinking, to categorise and conceptualise and thus to enable the child to find meaning. These two elements flow together in narrative structure which enables the child progressively to order her experiences and thus find meaning. Language is our primary mode of representation and is the main medium through which we construct our picture of the world and especially the relationships within it.

Language has a twofold origin. As an expression of thoughts, feelings and intentions, it arises out of the soul as a stream wishing to grasp and communicate with the world. Its other origin gives expression to the universal spirit of language, the Logos, which comes to individualised expression and underlies the structures of the world's various languages. The universal aspect of language enables the human being to gain access to thoughts that can be thought in any language and thus opens the mind to universal concepts. In the process of individuation, language facilitates the progression from an identity based on the family and cultural group the child is born into, through one in which the individual can express his or her own thoughts by finding their own voice, leading ultimately to access to a universal and objective reality. The mother tongue provides the crucial link between these stages.

The close bond between spoken language and the cultural and geographical context within which the child grows up also needs to be nurtured through schooling, particularly before puberty. Local dialect, regional accents and the whole vernacular tradition of nursery rhymes, skipping chants and so on, are important for the child's feeling of belonging to a particular place. This oral element is supplemented by the rich vocabulary of local place names, legends and folklore that are usually authentic to the local linguistic culture. With puberty, children descend more deeply into the physical qualities of their environment and to counter this, language needs to expand beyond the vernacular and seek more universal qualities in the realm of ideas. It is at this stage that young people lose their intuitive connection to the spirit of language and must regain this through conscious work.

As Steiner put it:

> *The speech absorbed by the child through imitation bears the same relationship to the whole human being as do the milk teeth. What human beings possess by way of language ability by the time they have reached puberty ... is something they have achieved, anew, for a second time, just as*

the principle of obtaining teeth has had to be worked at for a second time.[2]

During the pre-school years the archetypal qualities intrinsic to the actual sounds of spoken language work formatively on the child. In the period between seven and fourteen, the child lives linguistically much more in the emotional content of the words, in the moods and feelings they evoke. Words express something of the inner nature of what they describe, albeit clothed in cultural and personal associations After puberty the individual not only has to find his or her own voice (both literally and metaphorically) but has to find access to universal concepts and ideals through language.

In summary we can say that language works formatively at a physiological level in the speech organs and neural apparatus. This process needs time and appropriate models to imitate. At the psychological level language provides a medium for communication. Its syntactical elements help structure thinking and mental representation. The *being* of language reveals something of the inner nature of the world it describes and allows the individual access to universal concepts.

When literacy is introduced, the child's will forces are directed into the cognitive activities associated with mental picturing, representation and memory. To translate the movements of lines in two dimensions on paper into an inner voice which speaks, requires both directed will and imagination. If literacy is to be a living activity leading to living thinking, the imaginative forces of transformed orality must permeate it. The cultivation of orality after the transition to literacy is crucial. It essentially occurs through practising speech, listening, recitation, gesture, drama, debate, discussion – all of which require an inner dynamic and movement. But transformed orality is also cultivated whenever the imagination is engaged consciously and given form and structure. The livelier the interplay of linguistic exchange, the more spacious the 'field' in which language can grow, inviting the individual to move about in it.

Checklists for literacy skills in Classes 1 to 3 are given on p. 187, 4 to 5 on p. 193 and 6, 7 and 8 on p. 199.

Class 1

Speaking and listening

These aspects are emphasised from the children's very first day at school. Following the recitation of a morning verse in chorus, the 'rhythmical part' of the main-lesson begins. Here recitation of poems alternates with short musical exercises (singing, playing the lyre or recorders). The transition from kindergarten child to schoolchild is marked by the way the children can now recite not only nursery rhymes but also longer seasonal poems. Songs and ring games are also included. The main elements of this pattern are maintained for several weeks before any change is introduced.[3]

Stories are told by the teacher from traditional sources including folk tales and nature stories which the children subsequently recall and retell in their own words and may be enacted. Telling fairy tales requires a specific approach. A simple sentence construction and avoidance of dramatic language used by the storyteller helps prevent subjective feelings from coming into play and bringing the fairy tale down into the realm of the child's direct everyday experience, where it loses its validity. Folk tale figures are not to be taken literally but archetypally.

The value of genuine fairy tales for a healthy psychological development of children would require a separate chapter in its own right. What concerns us here is the role of language. Experience has shown that if the class teacher works on story telling with sufficient seriousness, the children's imaginations will be stimulated by the archetypal images rather than the stereotypes suggested by film, cartoon and comic book. These associations soon disappear and the children are ready to listen. They sense that the different language of the fairy tale and the way it is told is something new into which they can grow. They enjoy learning whole sentences and passages word for word by heart.

Teachers consciously prepare such stories by learning the content by heart and choosing language that is clear, artistic, rich in expressive vocabulary and which enhances the meaning of the story. In listening, the children acquire a sense for narrative structure and sense of style. They are able to extend their active vocabulary, learn idioms and phrases through emulation and experience wide variety in the means and form of expression. When the natural rhythms and intonations of the language are consciously used, the children acquire a certainty of feeling for basic punctuation and sentence structure. This provides a basis for the subsequent grasp of the use of commas and full stops. A sense for the different articulation of questions, statements, commands and exclamations is acquired aurally, as well as the distinction between words describing activities, things and attributes. They can also experience the linguistic expression of emotional qualities such as surprise, curiosity, denial, willing affirmation, enthusiasm and so on.

The directness of the oral approach to storytelling (as opposed to reading) stimulates the child's engagement, interest and imagination. This provides an empathetic basis for future reading and appreciation of literature, which depends on the readers' ability to recreate the content of the text in their own imagination in a fluid and uninhibited way. This approach is continued throughout the following years with age-appropriate developments.

Initially, literature in written textual form is in many respects a kind of foreign language for children. This is even more the case for non-literary texts. Being able to feel at home in this strange land requires the child to leave the stepping stones of the individual words and swim in the meaning of the sentence. Beyond that the reader must be able to enter into the imagination of the writer. This faculty is greatly assisted by listening to and emulating quality oral language that stimulates an interest in story and ideas generally and awakens an interest in literature.

The 'story part' of the main-lesson is also an artistic cultivation of language. In a lecture to teachers in Basle Steiner stated that all lessons to do with language should be built up artistically.

> *Children bring their instinct for language to school with them. But it will probably be up to us to shape their feeling for style by the time they reach their ninth year.*[4]

Steiner-Waldorf education attempts to cultivate and encourage the significance of oral linguistic abilities whilst cultivating literacy. Speaking and listening play a key role in the Steiner-Waldorf approach throughout the curriculum. Poetry and verses are recited throughout the curriculum and this begins on day one in Class 1.

To be able to shape and carry through the 'rhythmical part' of the main-lesson which includes the learning and recitation of poetry, the teachers will have had to strengthen their own relationship to lyrical expression as well as practise a suitable way of speaking. Steiner-Waldorf teacher training includes schooling in 'speech formation'. Some schools also have a trained speech teacher who can assist the class teachers in their preparation. When, for example a poem is introduced to the class for the first time it is very important that it should be spoken by heart. The teacher must have familiarised herself with all the nuances of sound, rhythm and other aspects that are special to the poem. Then, by first reciting it to them and then gradually getting them to join in, she will teach them the poem, i.e. will commit it to their memory in an artistic way.

The 'rhythmical part' also includes speech exercises (e.g. tongue twisters) both for the whole class and for individual children, especially when their pronunciation needs to be cultivated and kept under observation. Orientation (e.g. Simon says) and co-ordination exercises also have their place in the 'rhythmical part'. Here the children learn to follow verbal instructions.

The first exercises in repeating what they have heard begin now. The teacher will only tell the next part of the story once the children have repeated what they have heard on the previous day. Initially the children who volunteer have a turn, but eventually every child should be able to stand up in front of the class and retell a part of the story, if necessary with inconspicuous help from the teacher.

Grammar

Grammar is not yet taught at this stage. It is up to the teacher to emphasise sentence structure, be aware of how the sentences are formed and draw attention to striking words or syntax in the text used. Careful cultivation of clear speaking and well-structured sentences creates an 'aural' awareness of language structure.

Writing and reading

The children gradually learn to write throughout the first school year. Reading follows writing on the principle of 'first do then understand'.

> *In seeing to it that the child speaks well we are laying the foundation for correct writing. Running parallel with this telling and retelling of stories we introduce the child to a kind of language of pictorial forms.*[5]

Before the letters are introduced, the children practise form drawing, using sequences of straight and curved lines within a horizontal framework. Out of this follows the introduction of the capital letters through the media of movement, gesture, speech, picture, name and symbol. Consonants are evolved out of pictograms, vowels out of interjections and expressions of feeling.

Writing is a highly complex activity and time taken to establish the skills involved is time well spent. The psychologist F. Kainz described the process as follows:

> *Learning to write during childhood is an intensive process lasting several years that has the effect of retraining the effectiveness of specific neuronal systems. Writing is difficult because it is served by a number of complicated movements. But complicated movements ... can only be carried out successfully if they have been thoroughly practised. This practice is an optical-motor achievement of procedural memory based on a physical substrate. We may imagine that the functional fine tuning brought about by practice leads to most delicate changes in the movement centres of the central nervous system.*[6]

The process proceeds from pictorial representation of the letters to formal writing. This includes exploration of the relationship of sound and symbol through the use of emergent writing.

The shapes of the consonants as capital letters are presented to the children embedded in an artistic drawing made by the teacher with an accompanying story that emphasises the character of the letter. The letter F, for example, may be evolved from a drawing of a fish, and W, perhaps from the shape of the waves. The letter is separated from the pictogram and drawn and practised in its own right. We begin with upper case, then introduce lower case later on in the year, spending more time on it, because lower case can be more difficult as letters are sometimes only distinguished by their orientation: d/b/p/q, m/w, h/y, u/n, etc. It is important to make sure that the letters are written correctly, anti-clockwise, from the top downwards, etc.

A common mistake is to teach every letter of the alphabet with a story and a picture. The alphabet will take all year that way! Once you feel the children have understood the concept – experience (story), picture, letter – then you can teach the remainder of the alphabet more economically.

This approach is used for the consonants. The special nature of the vowels is shown by the way they can appear as interjections expressing emotions. Wonderment can sound like 'ah!', surprise like 'oh!'. Experiences like this at the level of feeling, embedded in a short description and expressed in a picture, pave the way for the discovery of the letters for the vowels. Experiences in eurythmy lessons can be very helpful here. The English vowels and diphthongs are introduced as strong, mutable elements that bond words together.

In English, however, we don't call the letter 'A' *ah*. It rarely makes that sound unless it is accompanied by an 'r' (as in c*ar*t). Although it is important to get the feeling, musical, cosmic quality of the vowels across to the children, it is also much more helpful to concentrate on the short vowel sounds (*a* in *a*pple, *i* in *Indian*, *e* in *e*lephant, *o* in orange, *u* in *u*mbrella). This gives them the tools to read and write simple words.

There should be a clear distinction between the names (and long vowel sounds), for example 'A' for 'Angel', 'E' for 'Eagle', 'I' for 'Icicle', 'O' for 'Opal', 'U' for 'Unicorn'.

In this way the routes that lead to the different letters are enriched and enlivened in a variety of ways. If the synthetic method has been applied for a while, then – once the children have learned a number of letters – a new letter can be derived by an analytical process. This has an enlivening effect. Alternating between synthesis and analysis in this way amounts to more than merely a helpful way of teaching. Steiner advised that both methods are as important for children as waking and sleeping, breathing in and breathing out.[7]

In the early lessons, exercises that serve a conscious command of right and left are also essential. Steiner referred to this as '... letting the children use their own body to become skilful in developing pictorial thinking.'[8] For example one can say to the children; with your right hand quickly touch your left knee, your right ear, etc. In form drawing, mirror images (right/left, above/below) also help orientation in the dimensions of space.

The children learn to read by reading what they have written or what the teacher has written on the board. The first words that the children read and write in school should be of significant content and already be familiar to the children. Sentences of meaningful rather than banal content should be chosen such as, 'The sun gives light to the world'.

Several methods of teaching reading are integrated. These include the whole word or analytic method, the phonetic method and the spelling method. Steiner described this integrated reading method as follows:

> *If the letter forms have been gained through painting-drawing, and if one has gone on to a kind of phonetic (and) or whole word method, which is now appropriate because it leads the child to an appreciation of wholeness, and prevents it from becoming too fixed in details – if all this has been done, there is yet something else... It is this: the single sound by itself, the separate M or P, this too represents a reality. And it is important to see that when a sound is part of a word, it has already entered the external world, already passed into the material and physical world. What we have in our soul are the sounds as such, and these largely depend on the nature of our (humanity's) soul (condition).*[9]

Steiner gave a detailed analysis of the qualities that each of the various reading methods involves in the lecture quoted above. Their transformation and integration through what he called a 'certain pedagogical skill and artistry, which will avoid a too one-sided drill in pronouncing the letters in the conventional way', is the crux of the matter. 'Instead, the child will gain some experience of how the letters came about and this is something which can live within its formative forces, something which is real for the child.' If the children are taught in this way, and assuming as Steiner did in 1923 that the children start at the age of seven,

> *they will be able to read in due course – perhaps a few months after their ninth year. It does not really matter if they cannot read earlier, because they have learnt it in a natural and wholesome way. Depending on the various children's response, this stage may be reached a little earlier.*[10]

To many contemporary educationalists this may seem very late to have learned to read. What is not clear is whether Steiner meant independent reading ability, and at what level. But assuming he meant that children should be able to read text with familiar vocabulary on their own, it is still quite late by conventional standards. One must however see this late start as a conscious extension of orality. Learning in the first three classes does not depend upon literacy skills but on the skills of orality, thus considerable learning in a wide range of topics and areas of experience occurs. Rather than literacy leading the learning process, it complements and supports it.

The fact is, the moment children learn to read is very individual regardless of the methods used. Generally the child will read when she is ready. The systematic and careful introduction of literacy skills benefits all children, but especially those with learning differences. For those who apparently acquire the skill easily the time ad care taken at least enhances their sense that writing and especially reading are something special.

In fact in most Waldorf classes most children can read and understand what they have written by the end of Class 1. Steiner advised that

> *if we proceed rationally in these matters we shall bring it about in the first year that the child can put on paper, in a simple way, anything he may wish to or words that are spoken to him, and he will be able to read simple things.*[11]

By the end of Class 2 they can read and understand printed letters and can use cursive script. Nevertheless, reading and writing are not used as means of access to information or as learning tools. These are skills which are acquired which take their context from the overall context of the lessons. This is a fundamental distinction from learning to read and write *in order to* learn.

Class 2

Speaking and listening

In addition to reciting in chorus, more and more of the children practise speaking poems solo in front of the class. Short poems are enacted or are accompanied by gesture. Those with a strong rhythm and much repetition are especially suitable, such as *The Key of the Kingdom* and *This is the House that Jack Built.* To fit in with the story material of this class, fables can be recited (alternating chorus and solo recitation) or perhaps acted. The children are encouraged to retell the stories they have heard and the experiences they have had. Speech and articulation exercises such as tongue-twisters are practised and the different qualities of oral expressions are explored which emphasise certain elements, e.g. speaking in a fiery or watery way, stressing verbs of action, being aware of descriptive elements and names, in short experiencing the qualities of word types and moods.

Fables, legends, folklore and nature stories concerned mainly with animals and the local environment are the story material for Class 2. In their content these reveal a broad scale of human activity and relate to the natural world. Animal and other fables are about one-sided aspects of moral qualities (greed, cunning, envy, etc.). Legends, and in particular the lives of the Saints look at the other side of human nature, the part where the hero as holy man or woman brings harmony to one-sidedness and by turning towards God gains the strength to serve his or her fellow human beings. There are many examples from a wide range of cultures with the Celtic tradition offering many appropriate stories. The fables of Aesop, Leonardo da Vinci, Lafontaine, Lessing, as well as the animal stories of the Native American traditions also provide important examples. As far as the language is concerned, such legends enable the children to hear and speak in a way that differs greatly from the fairy tale style. The brevity and simplicity of the language of fables initially astonishes the children ('Is that the end already?'). But then they notice they are left with more to think about. The story should be told and retold and listened to several times before a conversation several days later brings this to their attention. The relatively dry tone of the fables is abundantly compensated for in the warm style with which the life and deeds of saints can be told.

Grammar

The children should be made aware in an imaginative way of the character of activity words (verbs), naming words (nouns) and describing words (adjectives and adverbs). 'This should be combined in a simple and obvious way with a talk about the formation of sentences.'[12] Punctuation is taught on the basis of the spoken rhythms which indicate when the sentence starts, finishes or pauses.

Writing

The transition to lower case cursive script is prepared by suitable form drawing exercises, especially running and rhythmical forms. Lower case letters followed by cursive script are introduced with appropriate writing materials. This usually means changing from wax stick crayons in Class 1 to coloured graphite pencils in Class 2. Care and attention is paid to developing a fluid style of handwriting. The children's effort to orientate themselves on the page supports their endeavours to make the page beautiful and gives them an aesthetic interest in their writing. Steiner considered this important since this activity involves the writer more intensely in her work.[13]

The content of written work is related to the main-lesson themes and the children's own experiences. As a general guideline, about a third of writing is composed by the children, the other two thirds comprising texts prepared by the teacher and copied from the board and texts dictated by the teacher. Steiner suggested that the children in Class 2 should be able to write down, 'little descriptions of everything they are told and later what they have learnt about animals, plants, meadows and woods.'[14]

In Class 2 the children should be taught a good beautiful, flowing, cursive script, and their pencil hold and posture regularly checked. The letter formation too should be checked time and time again. The children use fat, soft pencils 2B, 3B or equivalent, which will encourage flow.

Free writing

Compared to mainstream schools, very little free writing is done by the children in Steiner-Waldorf schools. Instead, the children write about the stories they have been having in their main-lesson. By the middle of Class 2, most of the children will be getting keen on writing. A good way to support this is by encouraging them to write letters (at home or in the writing lesson) to the class teacher and to each other. This way the children are using writing as an archetypal form of communication – spelling the words as they think they sound – and the teacher can pick out some of the spelling mistakes and use them as part of the literacy programme. The letters also have to be read, providing valueable reading practise.

One suggestion is to make a letterbox for the classroom. All the letters can be posted in the letterbox and someone's job is to be the postman. The postman sorts out the letters in alphabetical order and delivers them to the appropriate address (desks, i.e. third desk from the front, near the window). The less able spellers can draw pictures for the words they cannot spell (note: this activity can be delayed to Class 3).

Reading

The children continue practising reading with texts they have written themselves or provided by the teacher. A differentiated approach is used including whole class reading, child to adult, child to child and solo reading. There is regular practice in the recognition of auditory, visual and kinaesthetic patterns through teacher-led exercises. Spelling is based on a whole language approach reinforced by contextual, phonic and kinesthetic methods.

In Class 2 the emphasis is on phonics – how spoken sounds are encoded by written letters and letter groups.

Class teachers must have a thorough knowledge of phonics, but need to be flexible about which facts to teach – and to whom. To insist pedantically on teaching every detail to the whole class is a waste of time, since many children will not need it. Other children will need all the detailed teaching and practice they can get.

Phonics

Consonant digraphs:	ng	ch	wh	ck	qu	
Vowel digraphs:	oo	ee				
Vowels + r:	ar	er	or			
2 – letter cons. blends:	tr	gr	gl	cl	st	etc.
Diphthong:	oi	oy				

Doubled consonants: e.g. – fu *nn* y Da *dd* y
Soft c rule: c followed by c, i or y says 'ss'
'Magic' *e* and its effects on the preceding vowel (making it say its name).

Practise listening for a given sound and locating it at the beginning, middle or end of a word

Word building

* Making plurals by adding *s* or (after s, x, ss, zz, ch, sh) *es*
* Adding *-ing* (when it does not involve changing the root word)
* Adding *-ly*

Various activities

* games can be used to practise identifying and locating:
  * the first sound – or digraph – in a word
  * the last sound – or digraph – in a word
  * the vowel within a word

Other games

* Rhyming games
* Alphabet games (incl. alphabetical order)
* Learn to spell some essential irregularly spelled words such as: 'was', 'are', 'have', 'said', 'they'
* Spelling bees; words chosen by the class teacher to conform to patterns already covered
* Substituting letters to make new words

As the second stage in the teaching of reading, many teachers make a reading book for their class. This is best done in the teacher's own handwriting – the children are used to this – it can then be reproduced on a photocopier or risograph. The children can make their own covers and add drawings to go with each story, thus individualising the book.

The book should include stories the children are familiar with such as fables, saint stories, poems, tongue twisters etc. It is important to use reading patterns that have been taught (and learnt!) – ideally getting progressively more difficult. Simple word games are also a good idea. These can go alongside the reading text, for example on the left page and then if the class is asked to read silently the faster readers can then start on the word games. For children who have a difficulty with reading it is a good idea to put one simple summarising sentence on the left hand page for them to read – after the teacher or other better reader has read the right hand page. This is a form of shared reading, which is known to be one of the most effective ways of building the bridge between being *read to* and reading yourself. (Often parents are willing to help with the reading lesson. Please prepare them before hand so they understand about short vowel / long vowel sounds; particular techniques you have used; which children need special encouragement, etc.)

By now the children are *almost* ready for printed books. First however, they need an introduction to printed letters – the 'g' in particular, but also 'a' and 'I'– and the general layout of books: chapters, introduction, index, etc.

At this stage the hardest task for the teacher is to find and choose a good class reader and good reading schemes for individual reading.

High standards of artistic presentation, topic, story quality and age appropriateness are important criteria in the choice of reader. On top of that it is important to find books that are not too difficult and are graded so that the language used is very simple – using mainly phonic words – and gradually gets harder introducing more and more spelling patterns. Some existing Waldorf readers are too difficult and can seriously affect the confidence of less able children. There may be a social reason for a class reader – the children hopefully learn to be patient, help each other, etc. – but it is worth asking oneself what good it does for a group of children with extraordinary different reading abilities and reading styles to read the same book out loud.

Summary: reading in Classes 1 to 2

1. Teach reading via writing – reading (familiar text) from the board and main-lesson books
2. Teacher makes class reader in her or his own handwriting
3. Introduction to printed letters (g, a, l!)
4. Individual reading schemes and class reader if necessary.

Once the children can read, class teachers make every effort to cultivate the habit, by establishing class libraries, by recommending a particular book, by maintaining contact with local public libraries, by presenting the problem at parent evenings, by talking about it with parents.

Children with learning differences

By the end of Class 2, the class teacher should know which children have specific learning differences in literacy, such as forms of dyslexia. Children who appear to be making slow progress or are presenting specific problems may just be slow or late developers. However, by the end of Class 2 it is prudent to have looked at all other possible reasons for the learning difference, such as evidence of physical disability in vision or hearing or fine motor co-ordination. If there is a learning support specialist in the school, it is wise to have the whole class screened. If not, observe and contemplate each child individually and make a list of strengths and weaknesses. The following checklist may be helpful:

- poor balance
- poor co-ordination
- clumsiness
- jerky movements
- difficulty in throwing / catching ball (with one hand)
- mixed dominance
- can't stand / sit straight
- poor pencil hold
- poor letter formation
- unable to write in a straight line on lined (or marked out) paper
- does not place the descending 'tails' of letters below the line
- does not place the ascending 'tails' of letters above the line
- mixes capitals and lower case letters
- reverses/inverts letters and/or numbers (b/d/p/q, u/n, s, 2, 3, 5, 7, 6, 9)
- puts too many (or not enough) legs on the letters n, m
- is bright, but has real difficulty with writing/spelling/reading (or one of them)
- unclear speech
- does not know the days/weeks/months
- has a poor memory

* does not learn what has been taught
* cannot tie her/his shoe laces
* messy appearance, shirt hanging out, laces undone, etc.
* is intuitive
* is imaginative
* looks young (baby face)
* has parents or siblings with SpLD

If three or more of these points are identified, the child may have a special learning difference (SpLD), and may not learn by the same methods as many of the rest of the class. The teacher needs to find out the way the child learns.

It is in any case important to test all the children's dominance, co-ordination, balance, penhold, posture, etc.; as well as letter reversals; and if they have retained what they have been taught (see above), before the end of class two in order to design a literacy programme for Class 3.

Class 3

Speaking and listening

The children take an important step in their development during Class 3. This will become very obvious to the teacher once a good number of them have completed their ninth year and entered their tenth. Steiner pointed to the importance of this step on many occasions:

> *Now the child begins to differentiate more and more between himself and his environment.*[15]

Near the beginning of the main-lesson, simple nature poems now fit in well with the children's feeling for life. The children enjoy reciting descriptive poetry, especially if rhythm and rhyme run smoothly from line to line. They can also cope with longer poems, and humorous ones can be included. Texts composed by the teacher, perhaps in rhymed verse form, can arise out of the practical subjects of this year, house-building; preparing mortar; craft work; farming. Small plays can also be performed which take up some of these themes.[16]

The stories of the Old Testament provide the material for the narrative content of the main-lesson. The creation of the world and of the human being, to whom God gave the earth as a place to work, are subjects that turn the children's attention to created nature. It is up to the teacher to decide what further material following on from the loss of paradise is appropriate, also with regard to the great figures of the Old Testament: Noah, Abraham, Moses, etc. It is essential to retain the lofty distance of the Old Testament stories by means of the powerful language in which they are couched, for that is where they will retain their reality. In this way the children will encounter another new style of language.

There is no real consensus about what stories might replace those of the Old Testament in cultures where these may be deemed inappropriate. Certainly they would have to include the themes of divine creation, a single Godfather as figure of authority, the giver of law, the Fall and loss of innocence, the need for law to structure human society and the concept of obedience.

Retelling orally parts of the content of stories and experiences in and out of school is a consistent part of each day's work and remains so throughout the school in age-appropriate ways which develop narrative skills.

Grammar

Steiner brought entirely new impulses to the subject of grammar, hoping again and again to see them put into practice. Teachers still stuck in the old ways of looking at grammar found it quite difficult to adapt, as is shown in the final teachers' meeting at which Steiner was able to be present. His dissatisfaction after listening in to lessons meant that Steiner-Waldorf education received a legacy of particularly valuable suggestions. One of these is recorded in the meeting of February 6, 1923, when Steiner explained the main reason for wanting a 'living grammar'. The children should learn to link a feeling with everything they name; they 'should get a feeling for what the perfect tense means, or the present tense'. To achieve this one must understand the distinct character of the main parts of speech and realise that we teach grammar not to correct wrong usage, but to awaken the children to the living structure of language. Steiner gave the following example of how grammar should be introduced.

> *We make the children aware of the difference between a statement, a question, and a feeling sentence, if we let the children speak these sentences or sentence part (i.e. clause) in such a way that the feeling sentence is spoken with a different emphasis than a statement, if we show the children how a statement is spoken in a neutral, disinterested way and a feeling sentence... with a nuance of feeling, if we work towards this artistic element in language, and only then, taking this artistic element as our starting point, develop the grammar and syntax.*[17]

This theme keeps reappearing in many variations right up to Class 8 and beyond: develop the whole world of grammatical forms out of the artistic element, with the help of feeling.[18]

By comparing the feeling sentence with the other two types of sentence, the knowledge gained by the children arises entirely from the artistic element: intonation, emphasis, melody all point to the grammatical form.

In a second grammar main-lesson the children are introduced to the three main grammatical elements: noun (naming word), adjective (describing word), verb (doing word). The children should now become aware of their different character. What is new is the task Steiner set in the way the class teacher should prepare for this main-lesson:

> *In what is expressed by nouns we are made aware of our independence as individual human beings. We separate ourselves off from the world outside when we learn to name things by nouns ... When we describe something with an adjective an entirely different element comes into play. By saying: The chair is blue – I am expressing something that links me with the chair. The characteristic I perceive unites me with the chair ... When I use a verb: The man is writing – I not only unite with the entity about whom I am using the verb, but I also do with my ego the activity he is doing with his physical body.*[19]

This is an unusual approach to the task of learning about parts of speech. Steiner justified it by saying:

> *Now that you know about this ... you will speak about nouns, adjectives and verbs with an entirely different inner emphasis than you would if you knew nothing about it.*[20]

The reason is as follows: instead of working towards confining things to a system (that of types of word) you turn your attention to the human being. You ask: What is it that language does in the human being by offering her three main types of word? How do grammatical structures help her to become aware of her position in relation to the outside world? The teacher needs to grasp the distinct fundamental relationship to the world that a noun or a verb expresses. This task that Steiner gave the teachers is, of course, only for them and not for the children. They only experience the entirely different emphasis. The teacher creates a space for the children in which they can experience that in their language, in what they say, there are naming words, describing words and doing words and that each type expresses a different activity.

In Class 3 noun, verb, adjective and adverb are characterised. Basic sentence structure is analysed and the correct use of full stops, commas, capital letters and question marks is taught.

Writing

With the introduction of cursive script, the children's writing begins to become more individual. Great emphasis, however, is placed on neat, well formed and above all, legible writing. The children learn to become aware of the three zones of writing, the parts of the letters that site on, above or below the line (even where no line literally exists). It is also important at this stage for the teacher to draw the child's attention to the position and activity of the hand. At the same time the child has the task of making sure that what is written looks beautiful. Steiner called this 'drawing writing' in which the writer 'pays close attention to his writing' and 'develops a somewhat aesthetic relationship with it'.[21] When they have had sufficient practice the children are taught how to use a school fountain pen. This provides a further opportunity to have another good look at the children's posture while writing, and improving this if necessary. The reason for writing beautifully is to express respect for the person who will be expected to read it by presenting him or her with clear, well formed letters and word-shapes.

The children are encouraged to write longer, more complex compositions based on main-lesson themes and their own experience. Writing also includes instruction and practice in formal letters (thank you letters, requests and inquiries) and diaries as well as simple descriptions of nature moods. Out of the emergent writing of the children the teacher takes up issues of grammar and correct usage, sentence structure, punctuation, spelling, etc. and provides instruction and guidance as opportunity presents itself.

The children are encouraged to read aloud and clear speaking is important for good spelling.

> *The two skills complement one another ... By getting into the habit of listening properly you become inclined to remember the word-shape on the basis of the inner picture.*[22]

Spelling is systematically practised through guided word recognition, word families, similarities and letter combinations, e.g. ee, oo, ou, gh, th, st, sh.

Reading

Reading progresses to the differentiation of reading material and reading for different purposes, i.e. to understand instructions and tasks, to find information or read timetables. Children are encouraged to use reference material and regular reading lessons are introduced. Reading aloud is practised with an awareness of content and punctuation. A wide range of printed texts is made available. As in Class 2, a range of reading techniques is used including whole class reading, group reading, and individual reading, paired reading (child to child, child to adult). Graded reading schemes may be used in Classes 2 and 3 but the emphasis is on 'real' books and quality literature. In terms of text understanding the approach is essentially hermeneutic and contextual.

Checklists for literacy skills in Classes 1 to 3

Most children of normal ability range will be able to do the following.

Writing and reading

1 recognise sounds, shapes and names of all vowels and consonants in capital letters and most of the lower case letters
1 know alphabetical order of letters
1 distinguish vowels from consonants
1 copy sentences accurately
1 write their own first name
1 spell a very few familiar words, such as 'the', 'in', 'to', 'and', and 'so'
1 know that writing is written-down speaking
1 know that some letters represent more than one sound
1 know that every word has at least one vowel
1 know that writing moves from left to right and from top to bottom
1 read and understand what they have written in the classroom
1/2 be acquainted with digraphs 'th', 'ch' and 'sh'
1/2 make plurals by adding s or es
2 recognise, write and read printed letters and cursive script
2 be able to read and spell simple consonant digraphs, vowel digraphs and 2-letter consonant blends
2 be able to read and spell using the soft c rule and magic e rule
2 add –ing or -ly
2 spell using 3-letter blends
2 read, write and spell correctly days of week, months, numbers and other familiar topics and words such as was, were, are, said, their/there, have
2/3 write short descriptions or accounts of recent events or stories
2/3 can read and spell letter combinations in common words
- sh, th, ch, wh, ph, gh
- ee, oo, ei, ea, ai
- ow, ew, aw
- y as vowel and consonant

2/3 read with developing enthusiasm

3 use the soft g rule
3 spell vowel and vowel/consonant digraphs
3 spell simple compound words
3 recognise common homophones
3 write thank-you letters
3 write in well-formed cursive script
3 read aloud texts containing mainly familiar words in context
3 read simple books aloud and silently.

Grammar

2/3 know by hearing when a sentence starts and stops
2/3 know how to use capital letters, full stop, recognise questions

3 recognise and characterise verb, noun, adjective and adverb e.g. an adjective describes a noun, an adverb tells us how we

Speaking and listening

1 recite in chorus
1 speak short verses alone
1 listen to the teacher and other children
1 follow verbal instructions given by teachers in all subjects
1 speak simple speech exercises and tongue twisters in chorus
1 speak multiplication tables in chorus
1 recall main points of story told by the teacher
1 share news with the class

3 recite poem alone
3 recall more complex events and stories
3 give an explanation of what they are doing to an inquirer
3 perform in short plays

Class 4

During the first three classes, literacy skills have tended to be wholly integrated. From Class 4 onwards there is an increasing differentiation of skills practice. As more time tends to be devoted to literacy skills, it is important to maintain the cultivation of spoken language through recitation and speech exercises, reporting and describing, discussing and listening.

Speaking and listening

During Class 3 the children gradually became more detached from their wish to imagine their surroundings through imaginative stories told by their class teacher. Now, in Class 4, they turn much more directly towards nature and the world as it appears to external perception. As well as reciting seasonal nature poems, they now also enjoy poems that tell of human beings who are 'street-wise' or even 'wise' in the loftier sense.[23] Poems relating to the main-lesson topics, such as the study of animals, local geography and history are chosen for recitation.

The main subject for the narrative content of the main-lesson is legends, tales and songs from the Icelandic epic *The Edda*. Speaking and stepping the rhythms of alliterative poetry gives the children the experience that speech carried on the breath can be filled by the rhythm of a slower or faster heartbeat, depending on the content. In speaking alliterative poetry, the will element in speech is strengthened, an experience which enables the children to bring their feeling life into strong connection with their breath and pulse, which has the effect of centring them. The artistic element of the poetic imagery prevents this from being a merely physical activity. Being centred, the children can stand more firmly in life and orientate themselves in relation to their environment.

Narrative content and reading material

Apart from these smaller selections from *The Edda*, the legends of the Norse gods and heroes provide the main story content in Class 4. After the creation story of the Old Testament, the children now enjoy the great creation images from the Norse myths. Their initial question, 'which is true?' is easy to answer. Both are true. Although a high mountain looks different depending on whether you approach it from the south, north, east or west, it remains the same mountain. Considerations like this lay the foundations for a willingness to look at things from several angles.

Should Norse myths be told in all Waldorf schools, or just those within the Northern European cultural orbit? The consensus appears to be yes, but... The myths of the Norse gods do appear to have a universality to them whilst the legends of the Heroes are much more related to the specific folk soul and culture. Perhaps tales of 'local heroes' would be more appropriate here. In the UK, the story of *Beowolf* can be told or read in translation, as can the stories contained in *Harald's Saga*, which recalls the life of Harald Hardrada, a key figure in the events of 1066. The historical background of the Vikings can also be a theme appropriate in this class.

Grammar

Among the many comments he made about how the learning child relates to grammar, Steiner also pointed to a link between grammar and the ego or 'I'. In a talk on language given shortly before the Waldorf School opened in Stuttgart, he said: 'By entering consciously into the structure of language one learns a great deal from the genius of language,' and this, he said, was 'of the greatest importance'. A little further he then added: 'We owe to language in particular much of what we have in our ego, through which we feel we are a personality.'

When appropriate methods were used in the classroom, he continued, the children's ego-feeling is awakened in the right way.

> *If it is wrongly awakened it actually fans the flames of egoism, but if you awaken it in the right way it fans the flames of the will ... for selflessness and for living together with the surrounding world.*[24]

Five years later, in a teachers' meeting on June 19, 1924 he spoke of this again:

> *Working on language in connection with grammar is related to ego-development ... Not that you should ask how to develop the ego from grammar; it is the grammar itself that does that.*[25]

When the children 'consciously live their way into the structure of language', they become aware of the great link that embraces all human beings who share their language with them.

The basic structure of grammar is of course common to all languages. Universal Grammar, or generative grammar is, according to modern linguistic theory since Chomsky, innate and facilitates language acquisition. Raised to consciousness, grammar gives the child an archetypal experience of relationships in the world, as they are expressed by the different parts of speech.

The theme for Class 4 is tenses:

> *It is just this time that one endeavours to call up in the children a clear idea of the tenses and all that comes to expression by changing the form of the verb... A child must clearly feel that she cannot say 'the man ran' when she means 'the man has run'; ... that she acquires a feeling for when to say 'the man stood' and when to say' the man has stood'... Forming language plastically is what we should practise in the mother tongue when the child is about ten years old, a feeling for the plastic formative quality of language.*[26]

In English the children need to become aware of the qualities of the main tenses, past, present and how the future is formed. The forms of modal verbs and auxiliaries, *to do, to be, to have, can, may,* etc., can be learned in connection with the tenses as well as question forms and negatives.

In answer to a question about how to treat the perfect tense in German, Steiner said:

> *I would pull out all the stops in discussing with the children the parallel between the past and the perfect. What is a perfect human being, a perfect table? I would bring out the connection between what is perfect and finished and the perfect tense.*[27]

In English it is clear that we must find equivalent phenomena. The distinctions between the simple past tense and present perfect or past perfect would be examples. The formation of all the tenses, past, present and future, should be taught, including the use of simple and continuous forms.

Prepositions are words indicating direction. Spatial relationship and locality are also themes that belong in Class 4. Initially the literal spatial relationships indicated by *in, on, at, above, beyond,* etc. can be explored. These need to be physically experienced in space and can be pictorially represented, e.g. through a picture of workers in a house, on the roof, at the corner, going into the cellar etc. Other grammatical topics which can be taken include the use of adverbial phrases of time, place and manner, sentence structure and the identification of the main clause. In punctuation the use of question and exclamation marks can be taught as well as the use of the comma.

Writing and reading

Essay writing still chiefly involves recounting accurately in writing what has been heard verbally. Formal letters are also practised, e.g. writing to a farmer, a baker, a jeweller about a possible visit to their business premises by the class. The children also learn to write with a fountain pen, perhaps having first made and used a goose feather quill.

In spelling the children should be learning groups of related words and learning common but difficult words such as *beautiful, experience, create.* They should also be taught to guess the pronunciation and spelling of unfamiliar words. The children are shown how to use a dictionary.

The children write accounts of the stories and experiences they have had in school and in daily life. They write descriptions of animals, scenes from history, their impressions of local landscapes, journeys they have made and so on. Specialised vocabulary and terminology may be provided by the teacher on the board. They may also copy important texts such as sayings and quotations, poems and the texts of songs. Dictation in a range of modes remains an important tool for listening, spelling and word recognition.

Class readers may be used but these are supplemented by access to a wide range of literature in the classroom and in the library.

Class 5

Speaking and listening

Most children enter their eleventh year while they are in Class 5. This can mean a final blossoming of childlike gracefulness and musical mobility before rather more coarse tendencies set in during the time leading up to puberty. The relaxed openness of Class 5 pupils allows the teacher to offer them all kinds of variety in terms of texts for recitation. In addition, their first history main-lesson suggests excerpts from early oriental cultures, such as the Bhagavadgita, the Mahabharata, the Vedas, or Sumerian, Akkadian and Egyptian hymns and prayers.

Such literature coming from so far away both in time and place astonishes the pupils and helps prepare them to be open to other cultures and also respect and appreciate them.

Poems continue to be recited and where appropriate verses in hexameter form can be taken. Prose texts from the Gospels can also be learned by heart and recited. Another field of oral work is word pictures, in which children describe a plant or the mood of a particular landscape.

Narrative content and reading material

Stories and reading material are taken from ancient eastern cultures (Hindu legends of Krishna and Arjuna, the Sumerian legends of Gilgamesh, Egyptian and Greek mythology) up to the time of classical Antiquity, as well as stories from the Celtic tradition. There can be alternation between the teacher telling a story and the class reading in chorus, or exercises in reading aloud and listening. Steiner also suggested describing scenes from history a year before history lessons proper begin. It is up to the teacher to make a selection.

Grammar

There is plenty to work with here in Class 5. Both now and in the near future it is important not to make grammar too technical and full of rules. The emphasis is on usage and the qualities that each grammatical form express. One should first explore the phenomenon before labelling it. Having introduced a terminology, it is important, though, that it is consistent and mutually agreed with the foreign language teachers. Successful foreign language teaching depends to a large extent on the grasp of grammatical phenomena that the children acquire through understanding their own native tongue. Many colleagues prefer the normal grammatical terms to avoid confusion and to make life easier for the teachers of foreign languages. In fact it is very useful if the class teachers first consult with the foreign language teachers on what aspects of grammar need to be emphasised as a support for the foreign languages.

The active and passive voices can now be considered. Attention is paid to the new role played by the subject, which retains its subject-character in an entirely new situation. That the passive voice is willing to leave the doer unnamed is only touched on, without any discussion at this stage.

Another important grammatical phenomenon that belongs in Class 5 is direct speech. When children report what others have said they usually use a lively mix of direct and indirect speech. They should now become aware of what this entails:

> *At this time, try to get the children to report freely in direct speech not only on what they have seen and heard but also on what they have heard and read. Let them report as they would if what they say were within quotation marks. Try to let the children practise distinguishing between telling their own opinion and reporting the opinion of someone else. Then do the same in writing; let the children make a clear distinction between what they themselves think or have seen and what they have heard another*

> *person say. In connection with this you can also try to perfect the use of the punctuation this entails.*[28]

The children must differentiate between their own opinion and the opinion of others. They must pay attention to repeating exactly what the other person has said. Using direct speech correctly provides a foundation for the coming year, when the indirect speech will be studied.

The qualitative difference between the simple and progressive forms should be clearly distinguished with many oral examples e.g. *I drink milk but I am not drinking at the moment.* Negatives and questions forms are also important to discuss and explore. Functional words such as pronouns, conjunctions and the comparison of adverbs and adjectives (a pupil once asked 'isn't there anything better than *best*?') can be discussed. It is always important to draw attention to the qualities that sentences have by including conjunctions or pronouns (do we know who *he* is in the sentence, *he is not here*?) Sentence structure can be ordered around subject and predicate, direct and indirect object (*who did what to whom and how*?). The concept of subject, predicate, direct and indirect object and adverbial phrase can be introduced.

Prepositions can also be introduced which have a temporal quality *(in 5 minutes, at 2.23 a.m., around 7, within the hour, up to midnight* etc.). In punctuation, the use of commas (again!), quotation marks, colons, semi-colons, hyphens and brackets should be introduced (or revised).

Writing and reading

Essay writing in Steiner-Waldorf schools in Classes 5 to 8 contains aspects that differ from what is done in other schools. The main-lessons in these classes (e.g. botany, geometry, geography, acoustics, etc.) provide material that requires clear description (e.g. of experiments) and characterisation. Events such as class outings provide the opportunity for requesting information and making arrangements that can be encompassed in examples of business letters. The aim of all this is to learn how to state intentions and wishes succinctly and with clarity, to strengthen willingness and ability to listen accurately to what is said, and to school alert powers of observation. This helps the children develop the will to make reports that accord with the facts and are not embroidered with arbitrary imaginative detail.

> *You will cultivate the children's idealism in a far better way if you do not approach it in too brutally direct a manner ... If during this period (13th to 15th year) you introduce the children to what is done in real life they will retain their healthy relationship to the idealistic needs of their soul. This will only be extinguished if these needs are senselessly drawn on while the children are still too young.*[29]

This is what Steiner said in connection with writing essays at this age. Descriptive essays on experiences the youngsters have had and subjects that call on their imagination do not come into play until the Upper School when their capacity to form judgements is developing.

Checklists for literacy skills in Classes 4 to 5

Most children of normal ability range will be able to:

Speaking and listening

4 Perform in a play and speak several lines individually, increasing in length by the end of Class 5 and be able to perform on stage before the school community.

Writing and reading

4 know how to use a dictionary
4 write with an ink pen
4 write an accurate account of events or stories heard in class
4 write a formal letter
4 know irregular plurals
4 know more irregular families of spellings
4 know remaining vowel and vowel/consonant digraphs
4 make a reasonable guess at unknown words in a text
4/5 read confidently and independently

5 read aloud fluently with awareness of punctuation including direct speech
5 take down a dictation on a known subject with reasonable accuracy
5 use a dictionary to find unfamiliar words for both spelling and meaning
5 use of common suffixes and prefixes

Grammar

4 use the comma and exclamation and question marks
5 use quotation marks in direct speech, colon and semi-colon, and appropriate use of paragraphs
5 know use and character of all major parts of speech: nouns, verbs, adjectives, adverbs, prepositions (time and space) the articles, conjunctions, interjections
5 use simple and continuous verb forms in all tenses, including present perfect and forms of the future, in questions and negatives and active and passive moods

Class 6

Speaking and listening

'A good strong diet' is needed in Class 6. Ballads, in particular, are likely to satisfy with their dramatic effects. Examples include: *Horatius* (from the *Lays of Ancient Rome*) by Thomas Macaulay, *The Pied Piper of Hamelin* by Robert Browning, *Meg Merrilies* by John Keats, *Sir Patrick Spens*, *John Barleycorn* by Robert Burns, *The Rider at the Gate* by John Masefield, *Schaffhausen* by Brien Masters, *Via Dolorosa* by Brien Masters.

In addition to these, it is good to go on letting the children recite nature poems in keeping with the seasons, traditional and modern ones e.g. *When Icicles Hang by the Wall*, *Love's Labour Lost*, Shakespeare, *The Scarecrow* by Walter de la Mare, *The Snow Storm* by Ralph Waldo Emerson, *Michaelmas Song* by A. C. Harwood, *Spring the Travelling Man* by Winifred Letts, *Winter* by Christina Rossetti, *Sea Fever* by John Masefield and countless others. (The examples given here are only intended to exemplify the range.)

Public speaking and elementary rhetoric can be taught through the presentation of short talks as well as through preparing and delivering exhortations, commands, directives (the pupils are studying Rome!). Steiner was keen that the pupils should experience the power of language to express beauty as well as power.

Narrative content and reading material

According to Karl Stockmeyer's record of what Steiner had to say about this, it would be good to tell scenes from more recent history. In practice most class teachers tell stories from Roman and Medieval history. Longer prose works are suitable for reading.

Grammar

In the original curriculum, Steiner laid great stress on the subjunctive mood (Konjunctiv in German), especially in connection with indirect speech, for which the foundations have been laid with direct speech in Class 5. However, Steiner's real interest in connection with the subjunctive becomes obvious in an example he gave:

> *We now endeavour to give the children a strong stylistic sense of what the subjunctive mood is. As far as possible we should demonstrate this by means of examples to help them distinguish between what can be directly stated and what has to be expressed by means of the subjunctive. A strong feeling for the inner mobility of language must become a part of the children's sense of language.*[30]

The original example given in the passage above had the distinction between the statements, *I'll see to it that my sister learns to walk* (i.e. I'll personally ensure it happens) and *I'm concerned that my little sister learns to walk* (i.e. I expect someone else to see to it). (Ich sorge dafur, dass mein Schwesterchen laufen lerne or Ich sorge dafur, dass mein Schwesterchen laufen lernt). The distinction is not as apparent translated into English. However when we report what someone else has said and cast doubt on the statement, or distance ourselves from it, there is an equivalent shift of focus and identification with the deed. *'I will come'* becomes in indirect speech: *'he said he would come'*. This can also imply: *'he said he would come but I don't believe he will'*.

The third sentence depends on different spoken emphasis (on *said* rather than *would*). This subtle distancing can be experienced by the pupils once they have mastered the technicalities of indirect speech and reporting verbs (such as: *she offered the opinion that; he countered with; they denied strongly; we asserted our rights; he went on to say; she added* etc.). The subjunctive as such, is better dealt with in Class 7 or 8.

In Class 6 one can discuss transitive and intransitive verbs as well as infinite forms. Present perfect can be introduced as an experience or state which began in the past and continues in the present, lasting, with all probability into the foreseeable future e.g. *I have lived in York for seven years (and do not have plans to move away)*.

The difference in meaning between the modal verbs *can, may, should, must, have to, would, ought,* should be (may/can be) explored. This provides excellent opportunity for indirect moral education in relation to necessity, possibility, duty and lawfulness, capacity, desire and wish.

Sentence parsing can be taught in Class 6. The students enjoy this analytical activity, drawing up columns of categories. Relative clauses can be identified as well as adverbial phrases of tune, place, manner, reason etc.

It is also useful (and welcome) at this age to teach abbreviations of all kinds as well as the common symbols used in business letters and on keyboards.

Essay writing

Here what was begun in Class 5 continues. There is now more stress on accurately describing experiments whilst at the same time imaginatively and dramatically retelling scenes from history. The children also write descriptions in connection with nature studies and geography. Spelling continues to be practised.

Class 7

Speaking and listening

In keeping with the pupils' awakening sense of their own personality, it is now important in the lessons that the teacher should begin to reveal something of his or her own personal relationship to lyric poetry, including modern lyric poetry. If some of the pupils are also beginning to have preferences for good poems and poets, these are also included in the lessons as recitation material.

Narrative content and reading material

Texts are chosen which widen the children's horizons with regard to other peoples and cultures. The history main-lessons provide an orientation for text material, especially stories related to the Age of Discovery and the Renaissance. The pupils are encouraged to read around the subjects that relate to the main-lesson and to do some independent research into topics that support the classroom work. They are also encouraged to read widely, both non-fiction and works of literature. Short book summaries which the pupils either give as verbal or written reports help stimulate interest and prompt others in the class to extend their reading.

Grammar

By and large there is considerable flexibility within the curriculum for Classes 7 and 8. Many of the topics here described can be done in either class. As usual in his *Three Lectures on the Curriculum*, Steiner is direct and specific with his advice for this class.

> *One must try to develop in the child, in sentence building, a truly plastic capacity for giving expression to wish, wonder and surprise. The child should form sentences which really do bear an inner relationship to the form of the feeling itself.*[31]

However, Steiner advised against 'mistreating poems or other literature' for this purpose. The children are asked to express 'a wish' or 'something they admire' and then try to formulate this in suitable sentences, 'Then, by comparing the sentence expressing a wish with one expressing wonder, one brings to light the inner formative power in the language and develops it further.'[32]

Grammatically you first draw attention to the difference between a purely indicative statement *'I want ...'* and a subjunctive one *'If only I had ...'*, *'If only I could ...'*, *'If only I were able ...'*, *'If only it would ...'*. You look at how you can intensify the indicative statement by means of adverbs: *'I so very much want ...'*. The interesting auxiliary verbs *'to be able to'*, *'to have to'*, *'to want to'* etc. are brought to the fore. In expressions of astonishment or admiration the contrast between a statement-clause and a feeling-clause initially worked with in the first grammar main-lesson in Class 3 now reappears, but at a much higher level.

There is an educational concern that can be recognised in all this. To wish, to be astonished, to admire – these are expressions of feelings familiar to pupils in Class 7. When such feelings are raised into consciousness in the apparently neutral realm of language, they begin to realise how close wishing is to immoderate or unrealistic desire, or how astonishment and admiration could turn into fascination or being 'carried away'. The full palette of moods and their combinations can be explored in their linguistic expression; wonder and devotion; astonishment with a hint of fear or with scepticism; shock leading to fear or shock leading to humour; urges and desires as opposed to longing; encouragement with a hint of challenge; denial as renunciation or sacrifice or denial as self-defence; resignation with acceptance, or resignation with regret or even ill will. There are many such examples of soul moods which can be explored thus helping the young adolescents to begin to map out the contours of their inner life and given their feelings words.

Understanding sentence structure is important for the same reasons as those just described. The conventions of word order can be almost endlessly modified to imply subtly different meanings.[33] The meta-level of meaning is deeply interesting to pupils at this age. That is to say, they are interested in individualising what they say, finding their own voice and style and also being able to hide behind the mask of language so as not to reveal their own inner feelings.

One can show that in its moods (imperative, indicative, and subjunctive) the sentence expresses the standpoint of bodily-sense immediacy, of balanced inner action, and of ideal, spiritual possibility and potential.

Another aspect of this exploration of the use of language is to explore the realm of metaphor and imagery in which pictures are used to represent other implicit experiences. The progression from concrete experience of words in relation to concepts in the Lower School is transformed into metaphorical meaning. The poetic expression *the moon was a ghostly galleon,* can assume little metaphorical significance if the listener has not first learned to associate concrete images with each of these words, *moon, ghostly, galleon.* The same is true of poetic usage that relies more on the sense impressions of the sound of the words, such as *where the wind's like a whetted knife.* The pupils first have to have been immersed in the aural experience of the pure sounds, especially in eurythmy before the full force of the poetry can be experienced. Expressionist images such as Ted Hughes' line, 'The wind flung a magpie away and a black-backed gull bent like an iron bar slowly', rely for their effectiveness on direct sensory experience of wind, magpies and seagulls as well as the metaphorical power of word sounds and images.

In Classes 7 and 8 such aspects of poetry can be brought to expression through speaking and listening. It is not necessary yet to analyse form and function and aesthetic principles. That should come in the Upper School. At this stage language as a phenomenon needs to be experienced. The other side of this is practising the craft of writing. That means getting punctuation right. It means finding the right formal techniques for different purposes, be they letters to the bank manager, accurate eye-witness accounts of real events, factual summaries, commentaries, notes and so on.

Essay writing

There will be little change as far as essay writing is concerned, but a new aspect can be introduced. In answer to a question in one of his meetings with teachers, Steiner suggested on the spur of the moment:

> *Essays on subjects such as 'the steam engine, a witness to human strength', immediately followed by 'the steam engine, a witness to human weakness'. Give them subjects like this in quick succession.*[34]

Though we would not necessarily take this suggestion literally, the implication is clear. The point is to look at issues of historical or social relevance from contrasting angles, and perhaps even weigh one against the other. The pupils need to work on how to observe existing facts and consider what can be said that directly relates to these. Both in writing and orally the children need to give accurate descriptions of processes, events and other observations. The children should be given guidance on essay writing style. 'Use their mistakes to show them what is correct, also stylistically.'[35] was Steiner's advice.

Class 8

Speaking and listening

On the whole what was suitable for Class 7 continues to be in order for Class 8. The content is best prepared in advance or brought in 'incidentally' while the poem is being learnt, so that the recitation can be effective through the poem's overall artistic form rather than weighed down by questions of meaning. Themes should relate to the other main-lessons such as modern history and should contain a strong biographical and emotional content. Examples include *Survivors*, by Alan Ross, *Ghosts, Fire, Water*, by James Kirkup, *Bayonet Charge*, by Ted Hughes, *I, Too Sing America*, by Langston Hughes.

Narrative content and reading material

This follows the point mentioned above, biographies, historical texts and novels portraying aspects of modern history.

Steiner repeatedly emphasised the suitability of certain works for thirteen to fourteen year olds by Schiller, Herder or Goethe. Of course only brief extracts were suggested. In English one might draw on quality literature from the nineteenth century, Dickens, Melville, Hardy, or passages from non-fiction works such as Darwin's *Voyage of the Beagle*, Thoreau's *The Natural Man*, extracts from *Chief Seattle's Speech*, the opening lines of Jefferson's *Declaration of Independence*, passages from Tom Pain's *Rights of Man*, or Martin Luther King's speeches. When the pupils are carefully introduced to the language of those times without any pressure or hurry, they feel they are being taken seriously. They sense that their thoughts can gain wider dimensions on the basis of these unaccustomed modes of expression and that new fields are becoming accessible to them. They can then approach other prose literature more critically with the powers and skills they have thus developed. The pupils are encouraged to research their own individual interests and this can become a project for the whole year, culminating in a written and verbal presentation.

Class 8 can also now make its first acquaintance with a major drama production. They will of course have performed plays as a class throughout the class teacher period. The difference in Class 8 is the level of 'professionalism' that should be striven for. The way must be paved with a lot of preparation if this is to be a full theatrical experience. It is important for the teacher to first tell the story of the action before getting the children to take different parts and reading the scenes. If a piece of classical drama is chosen, the unaccustomed style of the language will be more easily assimilated in the overall story and the characters are already living in the pupils' imaginations. It is still possible at this age for the class teacher to write or adapt their own play, with parts and themes tailored to the class' needs and abilities. Though perhaps lacking in high literary merit such ventures have the major advantage of being suited to a particular group of pupils. In terms of casting, it is also still appropriate to cast pupils in roles through which they will have a positive challenge to develop aspects of their personality. Giving the leading roles to those most theatrically gifted may lead to a more polished performance but may miss many opportunities for pedagogical development. In the Upper School it is more appropriate to cast plays according to ability in the service of the play. In the Middle School the play serves the cast as a social community.

Grammar

Sentence structure can be analysed from the perspective of style and sample sentences can be written in different styles to emphasise various elements or create a range of moods, e.g. epic, descriptive, lyric, dramatic, questioning, commanding, legal, nonsense, satirical, obscure. Meter, rhythm and rhyme can be studied and applied to the pupil's own poetic efforts.

Conditional sentences and if clauses can be introduced to describe chance situations, expectations, possibilities, theoretical or impossible situations or putting oneself in another person's situation. All of which help the self-preoccupied adolescent to see other perspectives, empathise or even speculate about others. The work in Class 7 on figures of speech such as metaphor, analogy, simile, proverb can be continued and discussed in connection with style. Each of these forms expresses a complex situation in the form of a picture. Qualities familiar in one area of life can shed light on other, apparently unrelated, areas. Apart from deepening a sense for language quality and extending vocabulary at a time when young people are losing their connection to the language, of their environment, such figures of speech open up the meta-levels of ideals and ideas as realities. Of course the abuse of words equally belongs here in the discussion of cliché, jargon, euphemism, slang and swear words. At this age one can discuss the brutal, sexist and racist attitudes that common swear words imply.

Idiomatic speech forms can be studied, using extracts from literature to exemplify them. The richness of phrasal verbs, in particular can be explored (*turn in, turn up, turn on, turn out, turn down*, etc.).

There is another very attractive aspect of language and literature that is also connected with 'interest in other people', one that has not been touched on by many other education writers. Steiner pointed to this in 1922 when he suggested that one might enter into the

> *characteristic, moral images in the style. This can take you a long way. For example look at a reading passage from the point of view of the temperaments. I do not mean the content,*

but the style. You can speak of a melancholic style or a choleric style. Take no notice of the content or even the poetic content and look solely at sentence structure.[36]

This poses a double task for the teacher. First you have to awaken the pupils' sense for the four temperaments by means of simple descriptions or examples. Then it is a matter of finding reading material in which one or other of the temperaments really does show up in the sentence structure. These are to be found, though not easily (Edward Lear's *Limericks* provide some examples). By questioning and testing what are the style elements that make a text phlegmatic, choleric, sanguine or melancholic, the pupils are led to yet another angle from which to look at sentence structure. In our experience this is a relatively unresearched field.

Speaking and listening

The pupils can now be encouraged to research topics and give short talks to the class. The teacher can advise them about sources and literature. Among many other possibilities, the discussions on the temperaments can provide stimulating ideas for essays. Such discussions can take the form of formal debates where a topic is chosen and individuals argue for or against a given position. Such topics should have a close relation to reality, yet leave the pupils open to argue a case they do not necessarily support. This is an aspect of advocacy that has important moral and social functions. The ability to represent someone else's situation or view to the best of your ability is an important skill. Drama exercises are also fertile ground at this age for practising self-expression.

Checklists for literacy skills in Classes 6, 7 and 8

Reading

6 read books in a range of styles and give a verbal summary of the main content

7 give a written summary of a book, highlighting main characters or events in the narrative

7 use books as reference resource for independent study

7 use a thesaurus and etymological dictionary

7 use a bilingual dictionary in French and German (if learned as foreign language)

Writing

6 write a formal business letter or inquiry for information

7 write in different styles including: an account of a scientific experiment, a personal diary, a description evoking a specific mood (early morning in winter, anger or frustration, curiosity about some unresolved situation), a formal letter (e.g. complaint), adventure story, short poem

7 make notes summarising a spoken presentation, following a recall session

7 write an essay on a theme discussion in lesson summarising the main points or highlighting a chosen aspect

Grammar

6 understand the main parts of a sentence: subject, predicate, object, indirect object and adverbial phrase

6 understand different meanings of modal verbs: can, may, should, ought, would

7 use of reported speech
7 use of the conditional forms and If clauses
7/8 be familiar with use and meaning of the following figures of speech: simile, metaphor, image, analogy, proverb, aphorism, euphemism

8 use of subordinate clause, relative clauses
8 be aware of poetic style e.g. characterise lyric, epic, dramatic poetry

9 be aware of the distinction between formal language, idiom, slang, obscenity, jargon

Speaking and listening

6 be able to recite a poem alone
6 give a short talk using notes

7 be able to give a short talk on a prepared topic freely using notes only as a prompt

8 be able to perform in a full length play
8 be able to debate a chosen theme

Classes 9 to 12

There are usually two English language main-lessons in each year from Class 9 to Class 12.

The content of the main-lessons as stated here is not binding. What is more important than sticking to traditionally successful main-lessons would be a clear study of the children in a particular class, on which a choice of new content would be based. The content here suggested has been tried and tested over many years, so any new content would need to be subjected to equally thorough-going investigation.

The few literary suggestions made should be taken as examples only. We have intentionally refrained from setting up a list of recommended literature in order to avoid any mis-understanding that might assume there to be a sanctioned reading plan. There cannot be and must not be an approach to literature to which teachers are expected to adhere. Apart from which, such an approach would anyway need to be varied to suit different cultural contexts. The examples given are based on the Upper School curriculum used in the UK.

Class 9

When the youngsters enter the Upper School, their eight-year orientation towards the personality of their class teacher ends. His or her place is now taken by the specialist teachers whose subjects, material and methods are inter-related and suit the specific age (fifteen) of the youngsters. Teaching is increasingly addressed to the awakening powers of thought and judgement, which call for a stronger training of the intellect and logic. More consciously than hitherto the pupils experience disappointments in relation to the trust they have had up to now in beauty, truth and goodness. They grow irritated with the world around them. In adults as well as themselves they notice a discrepancy between what they say and what they do. Since inwardly they are oriented towards ideals while they search for the truth, they tend to react radically to any inadequacy. On the other hand they are extremely sensitive to any slight, real or imaginary. They suffer as a result of their own inadequacy. While still strangers to themselves they wrestle with questions of sexuality, first love and the violent forces of sympathy and antipathy.

The educational task arising from all this is to strengthen the youngsters in the moral demands they make on the world while at the same time helping them come to terms with reality. English literature main-lessons in Class 9 deal with material, themes and topics that strengthen their youthful powers while at the same time making it possible to talk about these things. The existing and seemingly unbridgeable contrasts in the human world, which can be resolved in both tragical and comical ways, are presented as the task the suffering individual will have to face up to. By working consciously with language in both writing and reading the youngsters are given some means of bringing order into their impulsive, subjective feelings while also being led out of their inner world to the objective world around them. As well as working with themes in literature, the pupils are also given the opportunity to further develop their language skills both verbally and in written form.

First main-lesson

The history of drama from its ancient ritual origins to the development of modern theatre is studied. The main emphasis in early theatre is on Classical Greek drama, including the social, religious aspects and a description of the development of the Greek theatre. Usually at least one full play is studied such as Sophocles' *Antigone*. Medieval drama and in particular the Mystery and Morality plays are discussed including the historical background, the change from sacred to profane contexts through moving performance out of the church into the churchyard and from there onto the streets on pageant carts and the role of the Guilds in taking responsibility for the various scenes. Extracts in original language and modern translation can be taken from Cycles such as the York, Wakefield or Coventry to exemplify the typical range of style, from the highly stylised ritual of the Creation, through the slapstick comedy of Noah, through the pathos of the nativity to the social satire of the Shepherds (particularly Mac the Shepherd in the Wakefield cycle). A highlight of this main-lesson is the flowering of Elizabethan theatre and the life of William Shakespeare. A Shakespeare play would be studied, and scenes from other plays taken as examples. The main-lesson can conclude with a modern play. Obviously actual performance and visiting the theatre is an important complement to such a theme.

Second main-lesson

Their radical views make Class 9 pupils inclined to regard their own standpoint as absolute, which narrows their horizon and perspective. Humorous works can have a loosening, releasing, distancing effect. Laughter is one of the essential psychological activities of the human being, leading to a sense of inner freedom. Examples from epic, dramatic and lyrical works provide an opportunity to discuss humour (comedies, novellas, anecdotes, jokes, etc.). The (often painful) biography of a humorist can be introduced. The aim is not so much to work towards an 'aesthetic of the comical' as to show how the experience of humour can be another dimension in building one's personality and strength of character. Humour often approaches the tragic and closeness of comedy and tragedy should be explored. Sympathy, empathy and weeping are the polar opposites of laughter, to be regarded as reactions to initially alarming events. In working on the aesthetic aspects of both laughter and tears, comedy and tragedy, Class 9 pupils experience in both main-lesson periods how phenomena in the world are held in the field of tension that unites these two extremes. This gives them opportunities to modify their own absolutist views and make them more realistic.

Essays and language

In addition to working with the content of literary works, the pupils of Class 9 also continue to study and cultivate their own use of language. Grammar is revised and firmed up, where possible in combination with foreign language studies. Spelling and punctuation are schooled, together with the different types of expression made possible by word usage and syntax. Subjective descriptive essays as well as objective reports and general essays are practised in equal amounts (compiling tables of contents, making précis of texts and conversations in class, reports, descriptions of pictures and experiments, re-telling something read aloud, descriptions of mood). Literary passages can be rewritten. Stylistic skills are developed in texts the pupils produce themselves.

Oral work includes conversations on a particular theme, dialogue, discourse taking into account the correctness of arguments and logical conclusions, and pupils' solo talks.

There are plenty of classical and humorous pieces that are suitable for recitation and fit in both with the content of the two main-lessons and with the inner situation of the pupils at this stage in their development.

Class 10

The pupils of Class 10 (age 16) begin to put aside the tumultuous and 'naïve' externalisations of Class 9. The difference between girls and boys becomes more apparent. They are extricating themselves from the group without yet being quite capable of standing alone. Class 9 pupils like to engage in quick-witted repartee. Class 10 pupils prefer to explain their views so that the reactions they get gives them a sense of their independence in which they find a degree of orientation. On the one hand, they are excessively concerned with their appearance while, on the other, they want to be accepted for what they are underneath this façade. On the whole Class 10 pupils emancipate themselves from their parents to a considerable degree. They experience independence, but also its price: loneliness. Language enters a crisis phase. The pupils are often *no longer* and at the same time *not yet* capable of expressing their inner experiences in a suitable way.

First main-lesson

The original curriculum foresaw working with Norse mythology through excerpts from *The Edda*, the *Volsunga Saga*, the *Iceland Saga*, the *Hildebrandslied* among other examples which can give the youngsters images that help them replace old blood ties with their own responsibility for themselves. The *Nibelungenlied* is treated in its entirety, with parts being read and others told by the teacher. In working with this the pupils discover, among other things, how a mythological picture-consciousness is transformed into literary pictures and then epic poetry. In addition they learn about the transition from being restricted within the Germanic tribe to a more Christian, ethical consciousness. In English, texts such as *Beowulf*, *The Seafarer*, *Tristan and Isolde* may be read. Medieval legends such as *Sir Gawain and the Green Knight*, *Piers the Ploughman* and tales from Chaucer are taken. The over-riding theme, beyond the actual content of these texts, is the transition from myth to literature. Some teachers study ancient mythologies such as the *Epic of Gilgamesh*, the *Old Testamen*t, the *Iliad* or *Odyssey* or Ovid's *Metamorphoses*. It is also possible to look at modern literature which has taken mythological themes or forms.

Second main-lesson

One of the two Class 10 mother tongue main-lessons can offer Nibelungen motifs through other, including modern, works of literature.

The art of poetry main-lesson, which is a part of aesthetic studies, completes (see Study of Art/ Aesthetics section) the Class 10 main-lesson programme.

By writing their own lyrical or other poems and working more independently with different forms of poetry the pupils are helped to make the transition from expressing themselves to encountering themselves, since the lyrical form makes it easier to describe one's own inner moods.

Essays and language

In working with dialectical themes the pupils can practise discussing and representing opposing points of view. This can be done in writing as well as orally. Writing literary descriptions of characters in novels is also something dialectical, but bound to an existing text.

Class 11

The pupils of Class 11 have reached an age where they are interested in understanding more subtle psychological processes than the predominantly black and white, polarised perspective of Classes 9 and 10. Their social awareness increases as they stop merely condemning what is going on in the world and instead begin to think they might be able to contribute to changing things. Their own experiences are now increasingly included in the basis on which they make judgements. On the whole the irritations of post-puberty come to an end and they reach a new stage in finding themselves. They begin to take an interest in their own biography and are now more concerned with the path to be followed in developing their individuality than they are with the goal at the end of it. If Class 10 was more concerned with origins and causes, in Class 11 the students begin to experience boundaries and start to ask whether there is something higher from which they can take their orientation, some kind of 'lodestar', some meaning. During this phase the pupils search for their own task within the overall reality of society.

English lessons aim to meet this need for a more exact and differentiated perception of the different levels of language and seek to help the students grasp these in a more individual way. The lessons focus on a more intensive confrontation with the human being's inner world and the process by which he or she finds ego-awareness. The pupils become aware of their responsibility towards other individuals.

First main-lesson

Wolfram von Eschenbach's *Parzival* provides the focus for one of the two main-lessons. This most important work of medieval literature deals with the evolution of consciousness and is thus highly suitable for Class 11. There are several important aspects: the encounter with the medieval courtly world, the limitations (and possibilities) of a society that is guided by external principles; the Gawain sub-plot which reveals a whole cosmos of human abysses and tasks in connection with the relationship between 'you and me'; the *Parzival* story itself which concentrates on inwardness and the individual's path through the stages of failure, guilt, atonement and grace. The *Parzival* story has a suitable form for an educational context because it combines history with the general and the individual, and the developmental process is more easily seen than in a modern novel. The medieval world picture was strictly formed and inward-looking. In the story the search for self ends in an idealised way with Parzival's integration into the world. In addition, the story contains many archetypes of psychological development encountered by Western humanity.

This courtly work offers many opportunities for essays, exercises on language and structure, historical studies and questions of literary form.

Second main-lesson

The second (or alternative) main-lesson could focus on *Parzival* motifs in the literature of the 19th and/ or twentieth century. There are many archetypal themes that keep reappearing in literature where they are given new treatment and lead to different answers (the process of becoming an individual, the search for God, being hurt and inflicting pain, 'you and me', the quality of love, guilt and atonement, responsibility for the consequences of one's actions, tolerance). It is up to the teacher to decide whether to focus more on literary history or whether to make a more systematic study of themes in selected modern works.

It is quite common for English teachers to focus on the Romantic Period of English literature (often with reference to other European literature, e.g. the German 'Sturm und Drang' period) against the background of social, artistic, political and philosophical trends. This includes the role of Imagination in artistic perception and creativity as well as the role of the Romantic Hero. This usually involves study of the lives and works of Blake, Wordsworth, Coleridge, Byron, Shelley, Keats and Clare.

Essays and language

These build on the foundations already laid: description, dialectic essays, analysis of poetic and other texts, style exercises, etc.

Class 12

The pupils are about eighteen years old in Class 12. Having passed through the stages of readiness for school followed by biological maturity, they now become socially mature. When they were little they let the adults lead them step-by-step into their 'inherited' world and integrate them into the values of their parents' social milieu. Later they rebelled against this, but now they are consciously seeking a society and a world that is worthy of the human being which they want to have a share in building. This step can be experienced either as a major step forward and great opportunity or as a profound existential crisis. What does it mean to live in today's world? Am I ready for it? To what do I want to direct my energies? Many questions arise concerning their hopes and fears about profession, partnership, lifestyle and aims in life.

Behind these there is another, more profound, perhaps hidden questioning: What are the limits of human knowledge? What is the foundation of moral action? What is evil? What is the meaning of human life?

English lessons must take account of the impulses that arise out of all this. Modern problems are reflected on through the mirror of world literature. An overview of literature is given.

First main-lesson

One of the two main-lessons in the original German curriculum (not necessarily the first) is devoted to Goethe's drama for humanity *Faust.* More than almost any other work of German literature it characterises the modern human being's search for knowledge. All kinds of themes open up as the text is studied. Discussions arise in class about the question of scientific research and its moral and ethical limitations, about evil, about freedom and responsibility, about love, egoism, guilt, transcendency. Other works can be taken (and usually are in English speaking countries).

Major novels include: I. Allende, *The House of Spirits*, K. Atkinson, *Scenes Behind the Museum*, S. Bellow, *The Rainman*, A. Camus, *The Outsider*, J. Conrad, *Lord Jim*, L. de Berniers, *Captain Corelli's Mandolin*, C. Dickens, *Hard Times*, F. M. Dostoievski, *Crime and Punishment*, R. Ford, *Wildlife*, E. Hemingway, *The Old Man and the Sea*, H. Hesse, *Magister Ludi/Glass Bead Game*, A. Huxley, *Brave New World*, Joyce, *The Dubliners*, F. Kafka, *The Trial*, N. Kazantzakis, *Christ Recrucified*, H. Melville, *Moby Dick*, A. Solzhenitsyn, *Cancer Ward*, L. Tolstoy, *Resurrection, Anna Karenina*, L. van der Post, *The Seed and the Sower*, T. Wilder, *The Bridge of San Louis Rey, The Eighth Day*.

Significant drama includes: J. Anhouilh, *Antigone*, S. Beckett, *Waiting for Godot*, A. Chekhov, *The Cherry Orchard*, Ch. Fry, *The Sleep of Prisoners*, J. Giraudoux, *Intermezzo*, H. Ibsen, *Brand, Peer Gynt*, A. Miller, *The Crucible*, J. B. Priestley, *An Inspector Calls*, T. Stoppard, *Rosenkranz and Guildernstern are Dead.*

Second main-lesson

If one main-lesson is devoted entirely to a single work, the other can serve to give a survey either over English or else even world literature. Several great works can be presented individually or by comparing them with one another. It would seem sensible to concentrate mainly on modern works, but let us not forget older works that might provide something of 'what human beings need for life' (R. Steiner). Literature (drama, epic, lyric) consists of creations by individual human beings, or even humanity as a whole, representing steps in human consciousness. Through literature these steps can be perceived by the readers and listeners. People's aesthetic judgement has changed over the centuries, so pupils would be well advised to keep an open mind as to modern literary endeavours. Rather than give the pupils a finalised view of poetry or literature, one should strengthen their sensitivity to different literary qualities. By allowing them to reflect and take their own measure of great works they will have been given an appropriate foundation for doing this.

Essays and language

The pupils can be helped to improve their understanding of the written language by a number of exercises in text analysis through which they can learn to recognise historical characteristics and types of work. They can comment on and discuss these verbally and in essays written to set questions. The thoughts, language and imagination they put forward are suited to the subject in hand. If necessary, any exercises practised in Classes 9 to 11 can be continued.

The Class 12 play

The high point in Class 12 is the public performance of a self-chosen, carefully discussed and artistically-produced play. The pupils take part in all the practical aspects of the production: making posters, costumes and scenery, preparing the music, and doing the stage directing and production themselves, quite apart from acting in it. It is impossible to overemphasise the importance of acting for each pupil's own biography as well as for the social community of the class. The drama gives the pupils an experience of the power of speech/language. Through wrestling with questions of rhetoric they gain a sense of how people can be influenced. This helps them be more aware of being manipulated, and it also gives them worthwhile yardsticks against which to measure and assess artistic productions of all kinds.

14

Eurythmy

When the original Waldorf School was founded, Steiner included eurythmy among the core subjects from the beginning. As an entirely new subject and one which is exclusively taught in Steiner-Waldorf schools, eurythmy has a unique position within the curriculum. Applied appropriately at different ages and in different phases of development, it is an important aid to human development. Eurythmy is an art of movement that engages the whole human being, integrating bodily movement with movements that arise within soul, thus creating a harmonious relationship between the soul-spiritual element and the body.

In contrast with gymnastics, which has different aims with regard to taking hold of the body and making it fit, lithe, harmonious and free, the important thing about eurythmy is that it is essentially an artistic process. Gymnastics has to do with the whole human being coming into a relationship with the physical laws which govern space, those of levity and gravity and the balance the human being achieves between these two polarities. Eurythmy also works with the polarities of levity and gravity, not physically but essentially through the inner experience of the soul, with what can be called *ensouled* movement and is therefore more akin to dance than gymnastics.

What makes eurythmy an art is essentially twofold; the fact that on the one hand, the soul has to play a part in how the movements are carried out, and on the other hand the fact that the movements are based on objective laws as experienced through the soul. The aesthetic aspect arises through the artistic judgement that is exercised in interpreting the nature of the content chosen to be performed in eurythmy, usually poetry or music. The artist chooses from the range of musical, stylistic, linguistic elements and moods and choreographs and performs an interpretation. To say that the soul plays a part means that the feeling life is stimulated and out of this inner movement, outer movement arises. As an art, eurythmy also strives to be true to the objective qualities inherent in speech or music that it gives expression to. Though eurythmy is a performing art, it also has important educational and therapeutic aspects because practising its elements cultivates an integration and harmonisation of the movement organisation with the affective aesthetic realm of the soul. Eurythmy is also increasingly making an important contribution to adult education and can even be found in the work place, where enlightened employers recognise its valuable contribution to social processes and personal development.

Eurythmy is a key element in initial teacher training within the Waldorf schools movement and continues as a regular part of on-going teacher development.

What is shaped emerges from movement and movement comes to rest in what is shaped. The human body is shaped by and through movement and it serves to reveal the ego or 'I' as a speaking being. In speaking and listening the movement organisation is actively stimulated, both as producer and receiver of the sound impulses. In speech, movement is focused and condensed to the point where it becomes acoustic energy that becomes audibly manifest in spoken sounds. Informing the shape, structure and content of what is spoken is the soul with its thoughts, feelings and intentions. In eurythmy, the inner movement that gives rise to speech is transformed and externalised in the form of outer movement. The body becomes an instrument to make this movement visible.

When human beings hear the spoken word, their movement organisation is activated and they begin to move in their soul; when they themselves speak their inner being becomes active in movement. Steiner was able to perceive these inner movement intentions that arise in the speaking and listening human being. Out of this he drew a language of gestures made by the whole human being, a 'visible speech'. It springs from a seed within the human being, and it shapes and educates the body as a means of expression, an instrument of expression. In the young child and probably in earlier times of human evolution, speech, song and human movements were once an all-embracing unity. Both during the course of individual development and through human evolution, these elements separate out. It is the task of eurythmy to reintegrate these elements into a new higher synthesis.

Eurythmy is the articulation in movement and gesture (incorporating other elements such as colour through costume and lighting) of the stream of movement, raised to conscious form through the soul. It is a language of movement with its own alphabet comprising archetypal gestures representing the spoken sounds, both vowels and consonants, as well as the tones of the musical scales and the intervals. It possesses its own lexis, comprising complex gestures expressing concepts such as soul moods, colours or the distinctive qualities of thinking, feeling or willing. Furthermore eurythmy has a formal syntax in the form of the elements of its choreography, movements in space which both integrate the elements of individual tones or sounds, the lexical elements into coherent phrases, sentences or melodies. These syntactical elements can also be used to express the equivalent of grammatical forms such as question, statement, command or determining qualities such as major or minor keys in music.

Each vowel gesture expresses the sound and colouring of a specific quality of soul (astonishment, marveling, asserting oneself, fear, joy etc.). Each consonant movement shows a specific force that differentiates and shapes. Human beings, especially children, when they are open to their experiences, enter into the varying movements of enlivening formative forces. In the swishing wind, for example, they may experience the sound represented by the letter S, in the movement of waves in water W, or in the growth and unfolding movements of plants L. Every sound of speech expresses itself in a characteristic archetypal form and specific movement.

The rhythmical movement of speech is another element that shows in the metre of a verse (e.g. hexameter), the rise and fall, the repetition of sounds (rhyme). The rhythm of speech movements lives in the dynamic of the breath. Breathing is contracting and expanding, damming up and releasing.

The human physical form musical laws and relationships within the proportions of the skeleton. Being able to hear the formative elements in music, Steiner taught how the notes and intervals could be expressed in gestures, thus making music manifest as 'visible singing' through bodily gestures, and especially through the arms, filled with the soul element. The inner feeling, for example, produced on hearing the interval of the fourth can be translated into a gesture formed by the hands and arms. This is not merely a subjective response but is intrinsic to the physical organism. The artistic element arises in the inner experience that accompanies the process and in the application of the gesture to a specific moment in a piece of music. Naturally eurythmy does not translate every element in a poem or piece of music but selects what expresses the chosen interpretation, just as a painter chooses a spectrum of colours from the entire palette to express certain qualities or moods of her subject.

Eurythmy is taught in groups, though as a therapy it is usually taught in one to one situations. It requires its own specialised spaces, ideally incorporating a sprung wooden floor. The architecture of the space must provide enough room for group movement yet offer a containing environment, free of external distractions (such as large picture windows) Such rooms require a colour scheme which does not distract but creates a quiet concentrated mood. Eurythmy lessons are usually accompanied by a pianist, though in the younger classes, other instruments are often used as well. The children require appropriate footwear, usually a form of gymnastic shoe which gives a firm grip yet is flexible enough to allow good sensitivity of the floor by the foot. As a performance art, eurythmy makes use of silk gowns which both allow a freedom of movement and which reveal the subtleties of movement, especially in the loose veil which covers the arms. Since the emphasis for the viewer is to be the whole movement itself, facial expression and the physicality of the body itself play a subsidiary role. In school the children only wear costume for performance and eurythmy lessons are usually conducted in normal clothing with eurythmy shoes.

Educational aims

The aims of eurythmy within the curriculum could be said to be entirely pedagogical. Knowledge of eurythmy is neither required by society in any formal sense, nor has anyone ever had to do an examination in the subject! Nevertheless the aims of eurythmy lie at the heart of the Waldorf curriculum. Steiner-Waldorf education without eurythmy would not justify the name.

As a new art form, however, and one that is at present only taught in Waldorf schools it is often little understood by the wider school community. An important part of the work of eurythmy teachers is working to increase this understanding through lay courses in the school communities and through talks and demonstrations. Its value is being increasingly acknowledged, not least given the general dramatic increase of pressures on the developing human being. The contribution of eurythmy to harmonising developmental processes, of integrating the spheres of thinking, feeling and willing and of cultivating an aesthetic sense cannot and should not be underestimated.

Given the vital contribution that eurythmy can make to child development, considerable effort is made by those responsible for its development to train more people, more effectively to teach eurythmy. There are still too few teachers qualified and able to work with this art form in schools. As such its further development has a high priority within the community of Steiner-Waldorf schools worldwide.

* Eurythmy aims to harmonise the child's soul-spiritual nature with the bodily organisation by making the body a more flexible and responsive instrument to the soul's intentions.
* Practising the elements of eurythmical movement helps the children become more graceful in their movements, more coordinated, more alert and more at ease with themselves. Eurthymy also reveals blockages and hindrances within the movement organisation. What the children reveal in their movements can, to the practised eye of the teacher, contribute to an overall picture of their potential and what must be overcome to release it.
* Through learning the gestural vocabulary of sounds and musical tones in eurythmy, the children form an inner connection to the qualities inherent in the elements of language and music, a process which both engages the whole human being whilst supporting the development of linguistic and musical literacy.
* The artistic work done through the choreography of poetry, prose text, narrative and instrumental music deepen the children's aesthetic appreciation of literature and music experientially, a method which complements other approaches within the curriculum.
* Working with geometrical forms and their transitions in three dimensional space help the children have a more comprehensive experience of the principles of geometrical form and cultivate an inner sense of orientation.
* When working in groups the children have to concentrate on their own movement while developing the social capacity to sense the movements of the group as a whole. When both these are successful, they enjoy their participation in this mutual flow of movement. Being able to move in a harmonious and coordinated way together with others requires not only peripheral perception but also a willingness to allow the others to have their own space. The mutuality of social processes is a quality which eurythmy cultivates at many levels.
* Experiencing eurythmy performances by other pupils or adult professional groups can work at a non-intellectual level that only an integrated artistic medium can engage. Eurythmy is not read but experienced in a holistic way, given openness on the part of the viewer. Children of all ages can enter into this realm of experience through good eurythmy performances, which reach beyond the stage and meet an uninhibited response in the audience through a rich tapestry of sense experiences. They can receive vivid living pictures which the soul can digest. Like all good art, eurythmy provides subtle yet powerful nourishment for the soul life.

Since eurythmy is only taught by teachers who have undergone a four or five year basic training in eurythmy, followed by a specific training in pedagogical eurythmy, it is not necessary in what follows to describe these in detail. To explain everything comprehensively to the non-eurythmist would require an entire book! The indications given here should make sense to trained eurythmists, who know, for example, what is meant by *walking a harmonious eight frontally.* For the general reader, the introduction has attempted to briefly explain what the educational task of eurythmy is.

The curriculum that follows is merely a summary of possible activities. Using fairytale images, the eurythmy can involve many sound gestures in various moods. Elemental beings, elves, gnomes and so on are figures that can be introduced through narrative. The texts can include nursery rhymes and verses. Pentatonic music on the lyre or flute can accompany the eurythmy. Contraction and expansion movements in and around the circle provide the main form gesture.

Copper rod exercises can be used from Class 1 onwards to enhance and amplify the child's inner experience of his or her bodily and spatial movement and orientation. These exercises are designed with the therapeutic aim of enabling the child to gain inner confidence through centring the child in his or her equilibrium. In some cases, such as exercises involving dropping or throwing and catch, there is an awakening effect which strengthens the child's courage. There are many social aspects in group exercises.

It is very much up to the individual teacher's judgement when and how to introduce these exercises.

Kindergarten

Fairy-tale mood provides the background for the lessons. The transition to Class 1 is marked by the introduction of geometrical form and structure based on the straight line and curve.

Class 1

Spatial forms and arm movements are developed out of and in accordance with the children's imaginative experience. The circle of children is experienced as the 'sun', or as the 'castle garden'; the straight line is the 'golden bridge' or the 'magic ladder', and so on. The archetypal form of the circle is the starting point for eurythmy lessons and all movements start from the circle and return to it. The content of the lesson is woven into a narrative whole, the different elements flowing one into the other. In an ideal situation, the lessons flows as one integrated movement, articulated by a strong clear overall picture.

* Walking straight and curved lines, spirals, lemni-scates or figure of eight patterns (without the children crossing between each other)
* Arm gestures for vowels and consonants are embedded in narrative and thus imitated unconsciously; this strengthens the natural movements and ability to imitate
* Short melodies in the pentatonic mode, the interval movement for the fifth, accompany the stories
* Various rhythms of walking, running, hopping, jumping, stamping and so on
* Fine motor skills are schooled by means of dexterity exercises, as is the distinction between right and left, forward and back

Class 2

The wholeness symbolised by the circle form now becomes polarised, through a dialogue of opposites. Following the main-lesson pattern, short animal stories now provide one point of departure, with different types of stepping being practised and perfected. More difficult tasks can be undertaken, e.g. the children walking forms round each other. The mood of the fifth remains the foundation in music eurythmy. This accompanies the lessons rather than being depicted in all its elements.

* Continuation of material begun in Class 1
* Circle and straight line continue; two circles now come into being. The forms are practised starting and returning to the same point, or starting, going round and returning to the same point
* Exercises in opposite pairs, e.g. educational exercises such as 'I and you', 'We', or mirror forms (children opposite each other)
* The same in music. Short dances in two circles with opposite pairs
* Dexterity exercises continue
* The seasonal round is accompanied with poems

Class 3

Forms and gestures of eurythmy are now shaped to accompany the psychological development of the children who experience a stronger differentiation between themselves and their surroundings in their ninth year. The children learn to become more independent in the space around them. However, to prevent the children separating too much, a prime exercise is contracion and expansion, which cushions the fall. More complex forms, including the spiral, triangles and squares are moved. Rhythms become more distinct both in spoken and musical work. There is a greater distinction between the elements of language, movement and exercises. Towards the end of the year (or in Class 4) the major and minor thirds come more to the fore in preparation for the first excursion into musical work. The sounds of speech are now recognised as such and separated off from overall word pictures. Thus the children can now learn the individual vowel and consonant forms. These processes will continue in Class 4, or can even be put off until then.

The subject of crafts and craftspeople links with the main-lesson themes:

* Rhythmical stepping movement to poems and music
* These can also feature geometrical shapes such as triangle and square in a playful way
* Different movements to specific motifs, e.g. the four elements, earth, water, air and fire
* Recognising question and answer in music and speech (question and answer spiral)
* The children are now expected to recognise some of the speech gestures
* Vowels are practised
* Continuation of dexterity and concentration exercises
* Experiencing the major and minor third (though this may be deferred until Class 4)

Class 4

Once the children have crossed the threshold to the middle of childhood we need to develop and practise new psychological forces of imagination and morality with them. Side by side with their mother-tongue lessons, their homogeneous experience of language now gains elements of differentiation as grammatical components make their appearance, in eurythmy too. In this way the children take in grammar not only through their understanding but also through feelings and will. Movement in a centrally oriented circle is now often exchanged for movement facing forwards, which gives a different sense of space. As independence develops, this is accompanied by all kinds of dexterity and concentration exercises and interval exercises (major, minor, thirds). In eurythmy, action precedes understanding, so any comprehension of active and passive in grammar lessons and of major and minor in music lessons will only be brought in during Class 5. Music eurythmy proper can now begin as the children experience 'the human being as an instrument'.

* Grammatical elements of language are depicted in spatial forms (nouns, verbs, active/passive)
* Mirror forms continued, rod exercises requiring quickness and dexterity
* Concentration exercises
* Alliteration in poetic diction is explored through movement and rhythm
* Major and minor thirds
* Learning to hear, move and recognise the beat and movement of the pitch
* Listening exercises with intervals
* The first gestures for specific notes, the C-major scale

By the end of this year the children should be centred in the six directions in space (right-left through major-minor, up-down hrough the pitch and forwards and backwards through the rhythm).

Class 5

Work with grammatical forms continues. Special emphasis is now on shaping the gesture of a sound or word. The beauty, rhythm and form of language can be practised, experienced and understood. The geometry of the human form is consciously discovered and experienced in the five-pointed star, which has also been walked in previous classes. The children walk this form to experience it spatially. As a link with history lessons, texts from ancient cultures are used. The mood of the ancient culture epoch is taken up and explored through its characteristic form of movement and gesture. Poetry from foreign language lessons can also be done in eurythmy for the first time. Two-part melodies are practised in music eurythmy. Concentration and dexterity exercises (e.g. rapid orientation in space through varied form elements) are enlivening and stimulating.

* More complex forms (various lemniscates, star forms), culminating in Dionysian forms, e.g. I, you, he/she/it forms
* Further grammatical forms
* Forms practised with frontal orientation
* Texts from ancient cultures. The character of the different cultural epochs explored through music, gesture and movement
* Foreign languages in speech eurythmy
* Continuation of concentration and dexterity exercises
* Various major scales
* Two-part melodies and rounds
* Stepping all rhythms – especially the Greek rhythms
* Specific pedagogical exercises given by Steiner, e.g. Peace and Energy Dance or Dance of the Planets

Class 6

Parallel with geometry lessons, various geometrical form metamorphoses and shifts are practised spatially (triangle, square). These exercises support the children's growing capacity for orientation and abstraction. At this age the unity of movement that has been taken for granted hitherto gradually becomes unbalanced. Rhythm and symmetry exercises and musical interval exercises can be a help in recreating co-ordination. The use of exercises using a copper rod, help the children to form a coherent inner image of their own spatial dimensions, which helps not only in co-ordination but in integrating their movement organisation at a time when rapid physical change and growth may lead to a loss of their sense of their physical boundaries.The dramatic element now enters speech eurythmy, and this can be used to enrich and deepen the children's life of soul. The octave is expressed as a general movement impulse in walking, jumping and speech gestures, as well as music. All the exercises must involve the co-ordination of sequences of movement and attention to accuracy. The Roman theme of strucure and law, which characterises the Class 6 curriculum, is reflected in eurythmy by a strong emphasis in all grammar forms.

From Class 6 onwards the social aspects of eurythmy need to be consciously cultivated.

* Elements of grammatical form, rod exercises
* Metamorphosis of geometrical forms. practised with frontal orientation
* Practising the musical scales in eurythmy gesture
* Interval gestures, especially the octave, with the corresponding spatial forms, in stepping, jumping, etc.
* The children are encouraged to find their own transitions from one gesture to the next.
* Listening exercises, e.g. identifying major and minor; intervals
* The complete grammar forms
* Difficult concentration exercises, e.g. involving sequences of stepping and clapping

Class 7

As in their English language lessons, the children can now also experience in eurythmy the more subtle shades of linguistic expression e.g. conditional clauses and various exercises in soul moods such as sadness, joy, seriousness, and above all happiness. More complicated form transformations in geometry give an experience of structure from outside. Exercises for upright posture become more conscious; these continue in various forms up to Class 12.

* Elements of grammatical form are expanded through dramatic gestures
* Foot position, head position, yes and no; in preparation for the soul gestures in Class 8
* Complicated versions of shifts in pentagon, hexagon, heptagon, octagon
* Concentration, foot and rod exercises
* Major and minor scales
* Interval forms
* Humorous pieces
* Phrasing of music/poetry
* Beat/rhythms
* Pedagogical exercises, e.g. look into yourself, look into the world

Class 8

All the modes of expressing spatial and soul elements are combined in longer dramatic poems. The fundamental laws of eurythmy movements are taken to a point from which it will be possible to continue building in a new way in the Upper School. Ballads and humorous pieces with their strongly contrasting soul moods and polarities correspond with the pupil's inner situation at this time. Here the soul gestures are needed to characterise the 'plot' of the ballad. Also, the children are well into the throes of puberty, with new experiences for the soul. They are becoming independent from their parents, having their own feelings and are often chaotic. The soul gestures show the reality of these movements and moods of soul. We all feel laughter, knowledge, but also despair or greed! In music eurythmy they can work on forms for larger groups; this cultivates social awareness. The tension in the interchange between major and minor is compatible with this phase in their lives.

* Soul gestures performed with the arms
* Ballads, humorous pieces, music using the interval forms
* Dionysian forms of thinking, feeling and willing
* Intensive work on major and minor
* Geometrical transformations, rod exercises
* Concentration exercises in many variations
* Pedagogical exercises e.g. The outer has succeeded…

Classes 9 to 12

There should be an obvious change in method at the beginning of the Upper School. The exercises practised and increasingly brought to awareness hitherto are now taken up and shaped anew through knowledge. Texts and musical pieces are freely choreographed or worked on by applying the laws that apply to the movements. The aim is twofold. On the one hand movement is to be schooled and expression-through-movement practised; on the other hand the young people are to learn to carry out and experience eurythmy as an 'expressionistic' art. Both viewpoints are intimately related.

In the educational exercises there is a transition from concentration exercises to more dynamic movement. Moving in space must be transformed from strictly geometrical forms to ones that are more free and artistic. Rather than copying what the teacher does, the pupils will increasingly be expected to apply their own inner motivation and ability to create forms. They should learn to make use of the different elements in an alert and independent manner. For Class 9 the approach must be for the students to observe: what do we have to express ourselves, and what do we experience from our environment. This includes the relationship of our physical body to the space around us. Contrast is the key to Class 9. As in Bothmer Gymnastics, we can build up a consciousness for the laws of space, weight and levity, light and darkness, contraction and expansion, joy and sadness and so on. The lessons themselves should be structured through the use of strong contrasts, e.g. use of major and minor keys, harmony and dissonance.

Class 9

* Dynamic of speech, music, movement in space; getting to know polarities
* Various poems and poets
* Perceiving and consciously utilising the structure and geometry of one's own body
* Independent execution and formation of gestures
* New element: shaping harmonies
* Minor/major dissonants

* The pupils are led to make make their own forms and share in making communal forms (choreography)
* Re-working basic elements
* Intensive work on threefold walking, making it flow and carry over
* Free rhythms, light/dark, loud/soft, etc.
* In tone eurythmy the students work simultaneously with the different voices in music
* Chords
* Strong melodic movements

* Beat, rhythm
* The morning verse can be taken in eurythmy
* Recapitulation of all the pedagogical exercises done in the Lower School but with greater consciousness

Class 10

* Understanding and including the contrasts of human being and world, individual form and circle
* Increasing external and internal agility
* Make the link with main-lesson subjects: poetry, history (ancient cultures)
* Learning to express soul experiences through gestures
* Dynamic is complemented by the psychological activities of 'thinking, feeling, will' and their corresponding expressions
* From dance to festive movement
* Musical dynamic; continuation and differentiation of what was learnt in Class 9

* Exercises in polarities
* Threefold walking
* Dramatic gestures
* Selecting and consciously practising basic forms for new themes
* Forms for pronouns, for epic, lyric and dramatic poetry. Verse forms, rhyme forms.
* Work on longer musical works
* Classical forms (e.g. rondo)
* Group forms to be worked on together
* Rod exercises can be done with a more aesthetic element

Class 11

Independence in shaping movements: individual form/environment.

* Moving freely and shaping the 'invisible' space behind, which can only be filled by applying one's consciousness
* Stylistic work
* Musical expression of bathos/pathos in eurythmy
* Linking up with main-lesson themes: in art history, especially 'Apollonian/Dionysian'; and in connection with art lessons: gestures and forms of colour moods
* Polarities
* Astronomy: planetary movements
* Solo work
* More difficult musical interpretation

* Planetary movements; poems in various styles
* Colour movements
* Silent forms
* The language of gesture
* Practise the qualities of notes and intervals building on the basic elements learnt
* Foot and head positions in relation to grammar and the soul moods
* Pedagogical exercise – I think speech

Class 12

Overview of all expression possibilities offered by eurythmy.

* The pupils themselves work out group forms, lighting, costumes (the complete work of art)
* Control over one's own body as an instrument of the soul
* Differentiating between movement, attitude and gesture

* Exercises in all styles
* Examples of work with modern poetry and music
* Eurythmy as an expression of the relationship between human being and world
* Understanding eurythmy as a modern art
* Eurythmy as a synthesis of impressionism and expressionism
* The Zodiac and Planetary movement
* The Twelve Moods by Rudolf Steiner

15

Foreign Languages

The aim of foreign language teaching in Steiner-Waldorf schools is to encourage a positive attitude towards people of other cultures and languages, as well as fostering human understanding generally through establishing the ability to empathise with another person's perspective and way of seeing the world. Learning foreign languages offers the individual other perspectives on his or her own language, culture, attitudes and mentality, thus helping the pupil see the world in a more differentiated way.

The aims therefore of learning foreign languages are composite. On the one hand, the practical, utilitarian goal of being able to understand another language through listening and reading and being able to express oneself with a good degree of fluency in speaking and writing. On the other hand, to introduce the students to the character, customs and traditions, literature, culture, geography, history typical of the peoples who speak the given language. The third, pedagogical aim of foreign language teaching is to assist the overall development of the child through the subject specific qualities, as well as giving the individual insight into different ways of viewing the world, thus broadening the pupil's own perspective.

Learning foreign languages orally strengthens the pupil's ability to listen to another person, to follow and grasp the other person's spoken and unspoken intentions, since it enhances sensitivity to language at all levels and not merely the semantic level. This encourages greater powers of understanding, forming balanced judgements and empathy, all qualities needed in complex social situations. Being competent in at least two other languages supports the ability of flexible, mobile thinking, since the different languages allow access to different realms of experience and this in turn stimulates greater interest in the world and other people.

Language is threefold in its basic nature. It facilitates self-expression, communication and provides a framework for dialogue, speaking and listening. Secondly, language is a means of structuring and representing concepts and thoughts. This enables the child to map his or her experiences. The universal principles of syntactical relationships enable the translation of meaning from one individual to another but also from one language to another. Every language can be translated into every other. Thirdly, language is revelatory by nature. In contrast to materialistic conceptions of language, Steiner-Waldorf takes the view that language, in its phonic, lexical and syntactical elements gives expression to something of the essence of what it describes. This is why language is such a powerful formative force. Gaining insight into the syntactical and grammatical structures common to all languages provides a good basis for the subsequent study of language and linguistics.

Teaching methods

Initial contact with the foreign language in school is a broad experiential and contextual one, which becomes increasingly more conscious through analysis. There is an intrinsic progression from oral to literate language and the oral element remains paramount. In building literacy on orality, there is a strong emphasis on the gesture and situation. Language holds a middle position between movement which is internalised to become speech and speech which is further internalised in thinking.

Given that a large percentage of communicated meaning in normal conversation is non-semantic, there is a strong emphasis on gesture, pantomime, body language and the entire non-verbal realm of orality remains important throughout the curriculum.[1]

Working intensively with language harmonises and extends the child's affective responses to the world. Not only do the pupils become more articulate; they have more to say. Thus the process of foreign learning languages can serve to meet the developmental needs of the child as well as enabling them to develop abilities which serve their own individuation process whilst developing social competence.

In working with the nature of language itself, and assuming that the teaching method respects the inner principles of language and language acquisition, the child engages his or her own being with the being of language itself.

During the first three years of instruction the child is immersed in the orality of the language within the context of the lessons, most, if not all of which are conducted entirely in the foreign language. The children are introduced to a range of activities, verbal exchanges (greetings, question and answers to everyday situations), verses, poems, counting rhymes, skipping chants, songs and games designed to engage them and carry them in the stream of the language without the need for translation or explanation.

Once a repertoire has been built up within the first three to four lessons, new material is continuously introduced whilst existing material is regularly repeated and extended through variation. As well as oral work, the children enact situations in a lively way.

It is not necessary for the children to have an intellectual grasp of all they hear and repeat. During this time they are able to develop a sensitivity to the basic intonation patterns of the foreign language in a way that will be much more difficult after the age of ten or eleven, when the plasticity of the speech apparatus and its neural counterparts are that much more formed and therefore less malleable. This is an important factor in Steiner-Waldorf language teaching methodology.

Teaching is entirely through the spoken word, in commands (do this, do that), question and answer exchanges, singing and reciting by heart (i.e. without visible text), and this is often accompanied by gesture, pantomime and the use of pictures. Whole exchanges of dialogue can be learned by heart and an extensive range of vocabulary and grammatical structures are acquired *in situ*, as it were, rather than in an abstract or schematic way. In fact during the first three years the children are systematically introduced to and exercise unconsciously all the major elements of grammar as well as building up a wide vocabulary of common words. Just as the movement curriculum supports the child enter into the stream of movement from the periphery, so too in language lessons the children are helped to engage in the stream of language, which forms their language organs (perceptual and speech producing organs), builds up active situational vocabulary in memory, forms habitual structures of expressions, idioms, intonations. In short the child is helped to step into the stream of language. At a later stage this stream, as in the movement curriculum is reflected back in awakened consciousness and ability.

By the end of Class 3 the children's vocabulary should include: parts of the body, articles of clothing, phrases describing the activities associated with daily domestic and school life, the objects visible in the classroom and home, the colours, the times of the day, the days of the week, months, seasons, typical weather conditions, common forms of transport, familiar professions and what they do, common phenomena in nature – plants, animals etc., being able to ask and answer simple questions using the vocabulary listed above. They will also have regularly used the main forms of the verbs, tenses, be familiar with personal pronouns, directional prepositions, some adjectives and adverbs and the common question words.

Assessment at this level is a matter of the teacher noting the apparent potential of the individuals in the class in terms of memory, pronunciation and courage to speak, and discussing these with the class teacher and parents.

From Classes 4 or 5 a more conscious learning of language coincides with the new developmental stage the children are now entering. They continue to practise what they have learned but begin also writing and reading, as well as being made aware of the structure and spelling of the language. Drawing on what the children have learned by heart and ear in the first three school years, the children start by writing what they already know and understand. Once the phonetic values and letters have been established the children can move onto unfamiliar texts.

The methods of book writing and use of materials follow the patterns established by the class teacher. In fact close collaboration is essential for all stages of foreign language learning, in terms of classroom management skills and habits, but especially in the teaching of grammar. The foreign language teacher must build on grammatical concepts established in the mother tongue by the class teacher. Topics being discussed in main-lesson, such as farming or arithmetic can reappear in the foreign language lessons, once the basic skills have been established in the main-lesson.

In terms of teaching economy, it can make sense wherever possible to delegate specific topics from the main-lesson to one or other subject lesson. Relevant aspects of geography and history, for example, can be taken by the foreign language teacher. However the main area of collaboration lies in the class teacher creating work habits and behaviour standards with the class that are resilient enough to encompass the foreign language lessons. Given the high risk factors, especially at self conscious ages, for pupils in expressing themselves in a foreign language, not to mention the sheer amount of things that have, ultimately to be painstakingly learned, the task of foreign language teaching depends on good co-operation.

The words of any language carry with them something of the outlook of the people who speak that language. Thus there is always an untranslatable content differentiating words in one language from those used in other languages for the same thing or concept. For this reason direct translation is avoided as far as possible. Therefore gesture, pictures, movement, direct situational experience or word-games are relied on to facilitate comprehension. Great imagination is required on the part of the teacher to awaken appropriate inner pictures in the child's mind that associate sounds, words and content. However, the effort is amply rewarded by a much stronger affective response by the pupil, which by and large leads to long term memory, rather than short term or 'list-orientated' vocabulary. Words on their own are relatively useless. They must be bedded into useful grammatical structures, i.e. whole sentences that can be varied.

The topics chosen by the teacher and the pace at which they are covered depends on the teacher's assessment of the capacities of a given class, but are likely to include simple conversations about school and home, family, the weather etc. There will also be question and answer sessions involving a knowledge of numbers, the time, the season, the times of the day, the content of the reading material, or recent events of interest to the class. Activities will usually include the recitation of poetry and speech exercises, singing, discussion of grammar points such as singular or plural, verb forms (which may be recited and learned by rote), the conjugation of verbs in various tenses, aspects of history, geography or culture.

Throughout the Middle School, the children continue their oral work, which always remains at the heart of the teaching. This often takes the form of acting out short plays or scenes. Reading material is introduced once the children are familiar with the letters and can read familiar sentences, usually in Class 5 and form a focus for vocabulary work. The children also build up their own reference book with systematic lists of vocabulary, often grouped by theme, grammar rules and tables showing declensions. This is preferred to the use of a set grammar book as it gives the teacher greater flexibility in the sequence of themes introduced and the act of formulating a rule they themselves have worked out is an important aid to memory. One can also limit the amount of grammar to what it is strictly necessary to know. Grammar is very much reduced to a 'need to know' basis in the Middle School.

The children often have a separate book to record all the poems, verses, songs and exercises they have learned (invaluable if there is an unexpected change of teacher). They also have exercise books in which written work is practised either in class or as homework. No text books are used to teach from, though dictionaries are introduced at the end of Classes 6 or 7, when they children are familiar with their use.

Block teaching

It is essential to have 3 weekly lessons in each language throughout the school, if high standards of language ability are expected. In the Upper School this may increase to 4.

Block teaching has been introduced in some schools (usually not before Class 5). This means that a class has a block of three to four weeks during which all language lessons in the weekly timetable (should be six) are given over to one language. The idea is to build on continuity, then allow one language to lie fallow for a period. The advantages and disadvantages are disputed by adherents and proponents, with no clear outcome. What is clear is that the benefit depends on the quality of the teaching. A good teacher can get a long way with some 18–24 consecutive lessons, but probably would also do so with the normal arrangements.

The practical disadvantages of longer absences of teacher or pupil because of illness can cause havoc with continuity, as can changes of teachers. New teachers may be challenged to master a Middle School class if they have to teach them every day. Blocks suit project work but not regularity of learning.

Pre-conditions for good languge learning

Language learning benefits from group sizes in which each pupil can feel actively involved and challenged at his or her own level. It also benefits from imaginative and artistic teaching. Teachers of foreign languages in Steiner-Waldorf schools, not only require to be fluent in the language, love to speak it and read its poetry and literature but also show a deep interest in the cultures that speak the language. On top of this they must be conversant with the anthroposophical understanding of the nature of language, the nature of child development and be well skilled in speaking, gesture, drama and mime. Without this background, the method here suggested will be very difficult to achieve. This is said out of a deep sense of responsibility to the children but also to many inexperienced teachers who are asked to teach in ways they neither understand nor have been trained for.

Summary of the main focus throughout the classes

Classes 1 to 3: building a basis of the language, establishing a love of language, basic vocabulary, all grammatical structures unconsciously practised, communication.

Classes 4 to 6: raising everything learned to consciousness, writing down what has been orally learned in Classes 1 to 3, extending what has been established.

Classes 7 to 9: learning new, self-directed learning methods, joy reading literature, awaken an awareness for comparative language studies. Discovering the lands, history and cultures of people of other languages.

Classes 10 to 12: work with the spirit of the language and the folksoul of people of other languages.

German

Class 1

The children usually take everything in a mood of wonder and empathy. There is a strong tendency for the whole class to repeat everything chorally as one, though this should not prevent individuals from speaking alone. By the end of the year each child should have mastered everything that has been learned as a class. There must be considerable repetition and all that is learned is done so thoroughly.

* Narrative songs (e.g. Dornröschen/Hänschen klein)
* Verses and songs involving actions (e.g. Zeigt her eure Füsse)
* Finger games
* Acting upon simple commands (steh auf, komm mal her)
* Counting (cardinal numbers)
* Naming parts of the body, daily activities (eating, washing, dressing), colours
* Emphasis on the appropriate use of prepositions in context

* Phrases for use in simple conversations (e.g. Wie heisst du? – Ich heisse..., Wo wohnst du? – Ich wohne in)
* Games repeating individual structures or items of vocabulary (e.g. Hast du...? / Ist es...?)
* Listening to stories and learning them

By the end of Class 1, the children's active vocabulary should include:

* The main colours
* The main items in the classroom
* Parts of the body
* Days of the week and seasons
* Numbers up to 20

They should also be able to respond to simple commands and basic questions.

Class 2

A strong element of dualism is necessary during this year, in ja/nein, in question and answer, in ich/du. The children have a stronger need to communicate than in Class 1. They respond best to authentic situations, such as having native speaking guests, making real recipes etc. The teaching should have a strong rhythmical element in both the lesson structure and the nature of the activities, with strong contrasts between quietly becoming conscious (sounds, exact pronunciation etc.) and lively involvement. There should be a dynamic balance between being loud and quiet, speaking and listening. There also needs to many variations around common themes (e.g. an ever increasing range of possible answers to a give question, wie kommst du zur Schule?)

* Activities from Class 1 to be continued and enlarged upon (e.g. poems/folk songs/items in the classroom/commands etc.)
* Recitation of cardinal and ordinal numbers
* Months of the year and when children's birthdays fall;
* Vocabulary of nature (mountain, river, tree, flower, moon etc.)
* Articles of clothing (e.g. Hampelmann-Lied)
* Daily routine activities (e.g. Ich ziehe mich an/ wasche mich)
* Listening to simple stories, acting out of stories etc.
* Talking about themselves, e.g. birthday, age, family (e.g. Ich habe einen Bruder etc.)
* The forms of 'sein' and 'haben' in sentence forms (e.g. 'Ich bin der Konig, Du bist die Königin, er ist der Prinz', etc.)

By the end of Class 2, most children should:

* Know the months
* Know a range of natural features (mountain, sun, moon, tree, etc.)
* Know cardinal numbers up to 100, ordinal numbers up to 10
* Respond to simple questions about themselves, e.g. Wie alt bist du? Wann hast du Geburtstag? Wo wohnst du? Hast du einen Bruder / eine Schwester?
* Wie heisst dein Bruder/deine Schwester/deine Mutter/dein Vater?
* Apply simple structures (e.g. Ist es...?/Hast du...?/ Ich möchte...)
* Follow a simple story
* Point out/name different items in their environment
* Know a number of songs, verses and rhymes by heart

Class 3

Wit, in both senses of the word, is the keynote for this year. The children have a much stronger feeling for language, for nuances both of pronunciation and meaning. They require longer, more varied texts to learn. They enjoy acting out humorous scenes and short plays which involve individuals learning and carry roles alone. This year also sees intensive preparation for the coming year and the introduction of literacy. Texts are learned that are later written, key elements of grammar are rehearsed orally (use of articles, verb endings and personal pronouns, singular-plural forms, even the kinds of words, once these have been learned in English grammar). Speech exercises, tongue-twisters, riddles and beautiful poems are the daily diet in recitation.

* Conversational work to be continued
* Topics include; numbers, colours, places (town, village, city, country), forms of transport, clothes, time (clock), more complex commands, items of food, sayings and simple stories
* Acting out and learning individual parts of a dramatised story
* Picture 'dictations'
* Verb forms and tenses in sentence structures (e.g. Der Bauer mäht das Korn, die Maurer bauen ein Haus, du backst uns Brot)
* Verses practising grammatical forms (e.g. tenses)
* Learn use of the main prepositions
* Learn use of question words
* Learn personal pronouns in context

More consciousness should be brought to the use of the language. Children should:

* Be familiar with basic items of food, clothing, furniture
* Be familiar with forms of transport, places and directions
* Be familiar with times of the day (morning, evening etc.) clock times (hours, quarter hours, minutes)
* Be aware of the different genders
* Take a more active part orally (e.g. supply the next step of a story which the teacher is re-telling)
* Apply structures practised more freely
* Recognise the most common question words, wer, wie, was, wann, wo
* Use the main spatial prepositions in context: in dem Raum, auf dem Tisch, etc.
* Recognise the main personal pronouns (ich, du, er...)
* Recognise possessive adjectives (mein, dein...)

Class 4

At around the age of ten, children gain a new level of self-consciousness. They need to individualise much that had been collectively learned. Writing is introduced as a conscious and more individual noting down of what has been accumulated in the collective memory. Furthermore, at this age they require a strong sense or order in their surroundings and in their work. A systematic structure to lessons, good planning (especially close co-operation between class teacher, eurythmy teacher and language teachers is essential) and individual attention is necessary at this age, not least because the introduction of literacy highlights weaknesses that some pupils have that have not been so apparent before.

Using material learned by heart in the first three classes, writing in the foreign language is introduced. The children learn to recognise vocabulary they already know. Before printed reading material is introduced, they read what they themselves have written. Care is taken in the introduction of the letters to distinguish between the German sound represented by the letter, its German name and its English name. It is better to take time to clarify all these things at this stage than have to continuously correct in the years to come. Both writing and reading require much practice. While imitation and repetition continue to play an important role, the children should begin to recognise characteristic spelling forms, inflections (word endings, plural forms etc.).

Vocabulary lists can consist of word families (key words relevant to a particular theme such as parts of the body, the classroom, seasons, colours, simple commands and question forms). These lists need only be in the foreign language and they can be illustrated where appropriate. It is not necessary at this stage for the pupils to write word for word translations. Wherever possible, nouns should be learned in sentences with appropriate verb forms and simple adjectives. After writing whole sentences, it may be useful to underline nouns and verbs with a distinctive colour. The writing of such vocabulary is the end of a long process of oral learning.

One effective way of practising vocabulary is to summarise simple stories using familiar words. The children may copy down two or three sentences giving the basic outline of the story. The text should include as much repetition as possible.

Other than copying such material from the blackboard, written exercises can include simple dictations (two sentences can be learned by heart and written down). The children should initially have access to the original text when writing a dictation, only when vocabulary has been thoroughly learned, is it appropriate to require 'blind' dictations.

In Class 4 elementary sentence structure is learned, nouns and simple verb forms are practised. Example sentences are drawn from the familiar range of classroom dialogue. Singing recitation, simple dialogue and word games continue to be a basic part of the lessons. Great care must be taken that the children really understand the grammatical forms being referred to. They should formulate the essential (i.e. pragmatic rules as opposed to those usually found in grammar books) rules themselves. Discussions about German grammar should be conducted in English.

Oral work should continue in a lively way with speech exercises, verses, poems and songs, as well as question and answer sessions, increasingly involving the children among each other in groups. Everything that the children now speak should be understood. To facilitate this a kind of consecutive translating can be practised , which means generally formulating the content. The children can be asked to 'translate' what other children have said in this manner. This does not mean literal word for word translations, but putting the gist of what has been said into one's own words.

In Class 4, the children are usually introduced to exercise book work based closely on the forms used for main-lesson work. These handwritten books form the equivalent of a text book. Initially one main-lesson book should suffice for simple writing exercises. Later it is useful to have a book for poems and songs, a book for vocabulary and grammar. The children should be encouraged to see written work as the equivalent of etudes in music, an essential craft leading to an art.

Situational games, little plays, guessing games and so on still form an important part of the lesson.

* The children write down and read verses, poems or songs learned in the previous years

* The alphabet is practised as well as spelling and short dictations
* The first introduction of grammar includes: present tense forms of common verbs with personal pronouns (other tenses can be read in context of texts), parts of speech, nouns with article, plural forms and common adjectives, prepositions in, an, aus, auf, über, unter, vor, hinter, zwischen, simple sentence structures (subject and object), use of singular and plural nouns with singular and plural verb endings (Das Kind singt ein Lied; Die Kinder singen schöne Lieder)
* Question words are continued
* Texts are written describing animals, the weather, household items, etc.
* The children continue to learn and recite seasonal and nature poems

By the end of the year the children should:

* Know the German alphabet
* Be able to spell out their name and some common words
* Read practised words and sentences accurately
* Be able to give simple descriptions
* Recognise nouns, verbs and adjectives
* Know the verb forms in the present tense
* Know the gender of some common nouns
* Know the plural forms of some common nouns
* Be able to construct simple sentences of their own

Class 5

At this age (age eleven) the children should have a strongly rhythmical memory. They can and should learn much at this age. It is also an age in which the beauty of language can be cultivated. Their enjoyment of the language is essential and to build on this the children's own creative imagination should be called into play whenever possible, even in thinking up suitable homework tasks. Lessons should never be tedious and to avoid this they should have a brisk and varied pace. Children enjoy reciting quite long poems and can sing complex rounds. Building on the simple structures learned in Class 4, the children strengthen their grasp of grammar. Vocabulary should now be consciously learned and practised. A first reader can be introduced. The first endeavours at creative writing can be attempted, including poems on given themes, such as nature moods or animals.

The oral work includes question and answer dialogue, speech exercises and many varied poems, all recited by heart (and learned by repetition). Apart from its intrinsic value, the reciting of poetry is a good way of cultivating clear pronunciation and sentence melody, as well as reinforcing idiomatic vocabulary. The content of such poems (seasonal, narrative, etc.) need not be explained in detail; an imaginative though simplified introduction can suffice.

With increasing diversity of vocabulary, the children should be encouraged to use the words they know in imaginative ways, for example by writing short stories. To awaken an interest in the words themselves, the children should hear and read vivid and characteristic descriptions of people, places and situations.

Vocabulary arising out of the reader is introduced before the new part of the text. Other topical themes will also have to be introduced as the need arises. Simple comprehension questions to the reading text or to other topics should be practised first orally with the whole class, then individuals are called upon. Only then should the questions be put in written form. Such questions and their variations can form the content for homework exercises, dictations etc.

Once new grammatical structures have been introduced (in English), practised and understood, a simple statement of the essential rules should be written (ideally in the pupils' own formulations) (in English) in a book specially kept for the purpose. These rules are best kept separate from whatever other exercise books are used. A self-made grammar book can be started in Class 5 and used through to Class 8. From now on, grammar should be raised to greater consciousness by using a comparative method, which compares German to English.

A love of reading should be encouraged.

Plays, as ever, are the best way of engaging a class's interest.

* Songs/poetry, plays, stories
* Practice reading using a class reader
* Answering simple questions on a story both in speaking and writing,
* Practise orally strong verbs
* Grammar: work with verb tenses, cases (accusative/dative), prepositions, basic adverbs and adverbials of time, manner, place, sentence structure (e.g. with modal verbs/subordinate clauses)
* Systematic build up of reader and theme related vocabulary, vocabulary tests, regular dictation

By the end of the year the children should:

* Be able to respond to simple questions to a text
* Be able to retell small portions of a story freely
* Be able to use and identify present, past and future tense of the verbs learned
* Be aware of the different sentence structure in English and German
* Know the position of the adverbs

Class 6

Class 6 marks the threshold to puberty. The young person's intellectual faculties need to be awakened to the conceptual structures of language and to a systematic overview of what they have learned and have yet to learn. They need to be able discuss how much they need to learn, how much can be learned in a month, in a term and this has to be regularly reviewed as they also need tangible evidence of progress. What have we learned? And what did we not manage to learn and what were the reasons? Where this does not occur effectively, the children respond with bad behaviour, express doubts about their ability to learn – or the teacher's ability to teach! They need to learn how to learn vocabulary in a more conscious way.

At this age the pupils can usefully learn the conjugation of verbs, declension of nouns, adjectives, the use of terms such as nominative, dative etc. In other words, order and structure and visible planning are important in Class 6!

Dramatic, heroic poetry and much humour are the essential ingredients in speech work. Short, dramatic scenes can be acted out. In oral work one can weave in as many idiomatic phrases and everyday conversational vocabulary as possible.

The geography and characteristic episodes, historical and mythical personalities form a main theme in Classes 6, 7 and 8.

Once a reasonable basis of grammar and vocabulary has been achieved, the pupils can be encouraged to express themselves more freely in German. Letters, simple descriptions, diaries, summaries of stories can form the material for written exercises.

At this age the teacher must reckon with considerable differences of ability within one class. Exercises should be differentiated to suit the range of learning needs. This does not necessitate dividing up a class. Obviously children benefit from relatively small group sizes of around 15. Classes can be divided into equal groups or according to the ability to work in a group. Dividing them at this age into language ability groups is counter-productive at this stage. However, children entering the school at this stage with no previous knowledge of the language should be taught separately until it is realistic for them to join the class.

* Songs/poetry (of a dramatic nature)
* Improvising or learning short dialogues of a dramatic or humorous nature
* Reading of stories, a balance between a class reader and allowing individual reading to take place is necessary – class reading at this age will have to be short. (Reading always benefits from the challenge of a specific task given to the class, something to discover in the text, even to observe how often a particular word appears)
* Questions/answers both of a conversational nature and on stories
* Grammar: comparison of adjectives, uses and forms of the genitive and dative; attributive adjectives of weak and strong declension, use and forms of passive/active voice, word order in main clauses and compound sentences, rules for gender of nouns
* Keeping a grammar book up-to-date for reference
* Maintaining a vocabulary list with genders and plurals; revision of grammar covered so far
* Geography: the geography of Germany, Switzerland or Austria can be done in Class 6 (e.g. in the form of an imaginary journey), combining descriptions of the main geographical features of the various regions (e.g. Alps, Vor-alps, Schwarzwald, Bavaria, Rhine Valley, North German Plane, Thuringia, North Sea and Baltic coast etc.) their economies and cities, something of the local traditions, dialect, folklore, culture, recipes, etc.

By the end of the year, children should:

* Be able to speak more freely about themselves and their environment
* Be able to speak more freely on what they have read in class
* Recognise and give examples (e.g. from a text) for the areas of grammar covered so far
* Understand the grammatical terminology involved
* Have a good imaginative picture of several regions of a German speaking country

Classes 7 and 8

The method for Classes 7 and 8 follow closely on that described for Class 6. Lively, varied lessons (i.e. never stay too long on one activity, especially grammar), with plenty to learn, regular tests and dictations, group work, involvement of the students in the lesson planning and structuring. Book work should be maintained at a high standard. Where this breaks down, it may be necessary to work more closely with the class teacher and parents to gain extra time to re-write shoddy books. Everything the pupils do must make sense to them. There is a strong emphasis on cultural, geographical, historical and topical themes. These may form the subject of reading literature and in Class 8 individual work projects (e.g. biographies, etc.). Idiomatic and colloquial language is also important and regular space should be given in the lessons for practising conversation. Class exchanges and penfriends should be encouraged.

Essentially the grammar themes listed for

Classes 6 to 8 overlap and may be taken in almost any order that practically suggests itself, with the more complex phenomena such as the conjunctive, reflexive verbs, separable and inseparable verbs, etc. left until Class 8.

The pupils should be introduced to two-language dictionaries and should begin to do simple summaries in translation of short, prepared passages.

* Biographies (related to main-lesson programme: scientists, explorers, etc.)
* Historical and cultural topics, modern life etc.
* Extracts from literary works
* Continuation of the geographical theme begun in Class 6 looking at those regions not yet covered
* Vocabulary work, idioms, colloquial speech, polite and impolite forms, slang, words with various specific meanings, e.g. da, denn, doch, irgend, ja, noch, schon, wie, translation of certain English words with multiple uses (about, after, any, ask, be, before, call, catch, change, enjoy, even, feel, finish, get, go, just, know, late, leave, lie, like, look, lose, marry, now, number, only, order, put, remember, so, take, that, then, time, very, work)
* Grammar: direct and indirect speech, revisions of all cases, the use of and translation of the gerund, prepositions (in das < > in dem) and the cases they take, simple subordinate sentence structure, comparison of adjectives and adverbs continued, pronouns; possessive pronouns, reflexive pronouns, reciprocal pronouns – *wir lieben uns, wir schreiben einander, sie reden miteinander* etc.; welche: *was für ein, wer, was*; demonstrative pronouns – *der, die, das – ich bin mir dessen bewusst, derselbe, derjenige, selbst, selber, eine, keine, jemand, niemand, jeder, alle, etwas, nichts*; the remaining tenses of the verbs; the subjunctive mood, the subjunctive mood in conditional sentences, verbs governing the dative, accusative and dative, the genitive, translation of English verbal ing-forms. The use of punctuation and especially the comma.

By the end of the Class 8, the pupils should:

* Understand the use of the cases
* Know all the tenses
* Know which case accompanies which preposition
* Be able to compose short pieces of writing of their own with reasonable accuracy
* Have acquired a firm grasp of sentence structure
* Be able to express themselves clearly in simple sentences in a range of everyday situations (age, where they live, shopping, social exchange, asking their way, etc.)

Classes 9 to 12

Rudolf Steiner gave no specific recommendations for teaching methods for foreign languages in the Upper School, except that the teachers should regularly change their methods around in order to avoid routines setting in, which are deadly for the lessons. The main points of view may be summarised as follows:

* Pupils and teachers should share an interest in the themes that are studied, which implies collaboration in their selection
* Enthusiasm is the main factor in language teaching, as a counter to scepticism
* Presence of mind and openness to the world need to be practised, in order to be alert to the latent questions that live in the souls of the students

Class 9

A new phase of teaching begins in Class 9, which could be described as a dialectical phase, in which the question is asked, what can language do? Two primary factors influence what can be done in this class. Firstly, due to a significant change in how the individual relates to his or her memories – a symptom of puberty – young people not only become self-conscious in their speaking but often claim to have forgotten or never learned large areas of vocabulary and grammar. The second factor, also age-related is an unwillingness to concentrate for long.

However, an alert intellect is what they usually bring with them and this suggests the solution. Class 9 age students need to systematically re-learn all the main elements of grammar, and re-build their active vocabularies. It is usually the case that they have not in fact forgotten everything, but the need to understand it anew makes it seem like it. Here grammar books can for the first time be really helpful in offering, abstract summaries, tables of declensions and lists that appeal to the more intellectual aspect of their thinking. Many students positively welcome the opportunity to write out the main rules and lists once more as an aid to their memory. Basically everything needs to be gone over again and this may take into Class 10, though the aims is to get through it quickly, as their interest and motivation will be hard to maintain. There is much opportunity for using the more able pupils to present aspects of grammar that they have grasped, to the rest of the class.

On the other hand their attention span prefers short, powerful texts, short scenes of a dramatic or humorous nature, dialogues. This is a good time to perform a German play with a class or group, with as much involvement of the students as possible in choosing, rehearing and producing the play. If a whole play is too much, short scenes can be taken. Texts for reading can also include newspaper extracts. Whatever is chosen, the students must find it stimulating, relevant and something they can form an opinion about.

Conversation should be cultivated as a key element in all lessons. If there is a very wide ability range in the class and this inhibits speaking, this should be openly discussed with the class and socially creative solutions be collectively found that result in groups of students speaking German to each other. Every opportunity should be taken to encourage foreign visits, exchanges, contact with young German speakers and so on. Likewise topical current affairs issues should be discussed. Humour remains all important in Class 9, along with the feeling, we are learning how to learn!

Class 10

The over-riding theme for this class is the language itself, its origin, its elements and how it works as it does. This includes the history and development of the language, etymology, comparison with other European languages, and especially the relationship to English. Extracts from literature of several periods can be taken as examples of their period. The same can be done with poetry. In both cases, that of studying the literature and history of the language, the students should be encouraged to form a characterisation of the qualities of the German language itself. Some linguistic theory may be taken to add a theoretical dimension to the discussions.

Examples of literature from which extracts may be taken include: *Altes Testament* (übersetzung von J. Zenk); Luther's *Bibel, Neues Testament, Das Nibelungenlied*; Schiller, *Der Verbrecher aus verlorener Ehre*; Goethe's *Die Leiden des jungen Werthers* or *Die Wahlverwandtschaften*; Nietzsche's *Die Geburt der Tragödie*; Kleist's D*as Erdbeben in Chili, Zwieg, Ungeduld des Herzens*, etc.

In discussions the students are often drawn out of themselves when debating the rights and wrongs of a matter they themselves feel strongly about. Topics can be chosen in consultation with them and vocabulary prepared. Homework should consist of preparation for a set-piece debate. The rules of debate must allow for moments in which each side can gather their arguments (and vocabulary) once more or take stylistic advice from the teacher as impartial adviser. Topics can be prepared as projects by individuals and presented to the class.

Class 10 can prepare a full German play involving as many of the group as wish to take part.

Class 11

Here the beauty of the language and its greatest proponents must stand in the foreground. The works of great poets of various periods should be studied and recited individually and in chorus. The students' ability to form aesthetic judgements should be exercised to the full with the analysis of classic and modern literary texts. These are often best approached through themes rather than merely through the content alone.

The power and subtlety of spoken language should be a main focus of practice and study, especially in its three primary elements of grammatically – speaking correctly, rhetoric – beautiful speaking and dialectic – to speak persuasively powerfully. Individual students can choose a theme or an individual poet and work on several pieces, coming to a presentation and performance. Class 11 can also sees the performance of a major piece of drama in German.

Topical texts and themes are taken for discussion.

Class 12

There can be an overview of the transition to modern literature using extracts or by taking one major work. The choice is vast and depends upon the knowledge of the teacher and the interests of the students, but should at least consider the following possibilities: Böll, *Die verlorene Ehre der Katherine Blum*; Borchert, *Die Hundelblume*; Feuchtwanger, *Jud Süss*; Frisch, *Stiller*; Fontane, *Effi Briest*, Grass, *Die Blechtrommel*; Handke, *Die Lehre der Sainte Victoire*; Hesse, *Das Glassperlenspiel*; Jean Paul, *Der Titan*; Kafka, *Erzählungen*; Lenz, *Verlassene Zimmer*; Rilke, *Die Aufzeichnungen des Malte Laurids Brigge*; Strauss, *Die Widmung*; Walser, *Ein fliehendes Pferd*; Wolf, *Christa*; Kindheitsmuster.

The three inner aspects of language as a unity, freedom in creativity, equality in communication forms and fraternity in meeting the being of the other. Comparative linguistic studies can be helpful, as well as studies of speech act theory. Recommended study material are Heinz Zimmermann's two books, *Grammatik* and *Sprechen, Zuhören in Erkenntnis – und Entscheidungsprozessen*.

In both Classes 11 and 12 there is an emphasis on the spirit of the German language and the Germanic folksoul. This should be approach through the language and literature in particular.

French

The aims and teaching methods are the same as those stated for foreign languages above. In Classes 1 to 4, the same basic method and content are used as those described for German. In Classes 3 to 4, the French alphabet, writing and reading are introduced, as in German. In Class 4 the first play with individual parts can be performed.

Class 1

* Narrative songs, e.g. Il était un petit homme, J'aime la galette, Pirouette cacahuète
* Verses and songs involving actions, e.g. Savez-vous planter les choux, Pomme de rainette, toc-hoc-hoc, Monseur Pouce es-tu là?, Sur le pont d'Avignon
* Finger games (Voici ma main…)
* Commands (Lève-toi, Ouvre la porte, Viens ici…)
* Phrases in conversation (Comment t'appelles-tu? – Je m'appelle…; Quel âge as-tu? J'ai … ans; Où habites-tu?
* Games with questions: Qu'est-ce que c'est? – C'est…; Qui a …? J'ai…; Est-ce que c'est toi?
* Situational vocabulary:
    * Activities: simple miming of daily activities, counting, guessing games
    * Colours, parts of the body, family members, animals, nature, days of the week, seasons

Class 2

* Simple stories with strong repetition; counting; guessing games; picture dictations
* Poems which make good plays (e.g. *L'histoire de la galette*, *Le chat et les souris*)
* Questions: Où habites-tu?; Comment s'appelle ta maman, ton papa, etc.; Est-ce que tu as des frères et soeurs?; Comment s'appelle ton frère, ta soeur?
* Simple structures of negatives: Est-ce que c'est ça? Non, c'est n'est pas ça; Est-ce que c'est toi? Non, ce n'est pas moi
* Songs: *Promenons-nous dans les bois*; *Jean petit qui danse*; *Derrière chez mois*
* Learning and acting out fables

Class 3

Conversation can include the time and weather, and the date.

* Quel temps fait-il? Il fait beau… etc.; Quel jour sommes-nous aujourd'hui?
* Acting out plays about the market using songs and stall-holder cries
* Verb forms: être and avoir in sentences – je suis un garçon, une fille…; j'ai un chat; il a un poisson rouge, etc.
* Notice words with 'le' or 'la'
* Use and recognition of question words and expressions: où, quand, quel, qui, combien; est-ce que / que'est-ce que
* Prepositions in sentences: il est devant la table; nous sommes à côté de…
* Personal pronouns: je, tu…
* Possessive adjectives: mon, ma, mes; ton, tu, tes, etc.

Class 4

Writing and reading are introduced using material the children already know by heart. Simple punctuation is introduced. Nouns and articles, adjectives, adverbs and whole verb structures are identified.

* Recitation of verses and poems
* Songs
* Conversation topics, as in Classes 1, 2 and 3, with more emphasis on description of animals, the weather and local surroundings
* Vocabulary for everyday situations is practised
* Writing down verses and short familiar texts
* Practise of recognition and articulation of phonetic elements distinct to French
* Verb forms in present tense learned by heart, written down
* Short dictations of learned text, verb forms
* Initial spelling exercises
* Use of the articles, practise gender and plural of familiar nouns
* Simple oral and later verbal descriptions e.g. of animals, the weather
* Word games, e.g. le loto, magie noire

Class 5

Stories, conversations and dialogues in keeping with the pupils' immediate surroundings.

* Stories, school, home, family, body, clothes, meals, course of day and year, telling the time, date, directions in space
* Introduction to France
* Songs, verses, easy poems
* First letters to penfriends

Suggested readers include D. Fink *La Claire Fontaine, Vols. I & II* (Pädagogische Forschungsstelle) and A. Denjean *La Tarasque à Tarasacon* (Pädagogische Forschungsstell).

Depending on the stage the class has reached, grammar now involves practising the following and subsequently explaining the rules in English (mother tongue), after which they are written down:

* Definite and indefinite article
* Agreement between subject and verb
* The apostrophe
* Present and future of: aller, venir, faire, prendre, mettre, avoir/être
* Verbs ending in er and ir (e.g. finir)
* Questions with 'Est-ce que'; interrogatives: qui, que, quand, comment, ou, pourquoi
* Negative: 'ne ... pas'
* Adjectives describing nouns and agreement with the nouns, i.e. including the feminine form of adjectives ending in e
* Prepositions, but in a context
* Pronouns in the nominative
* Modal verbs: vouloir, pouvoir, devoir (present tense in Class 5; future in Class 6
* Comparisons of adjectives: plus – le plus; moins – le moins

Class 6

Reading of descriptions or dialogues in subjects such as:

* Living in town and country, holidays, household
* Shopping, seasons and festivals, weather, illnesses, sport and games
* Poems, songs, anecdotes, stories and fairy tales (e.g. *Les contes de Perrault* or *Contes basques*
* *Poésies, textes et chansons pour les langues moyennes des écoles Waldorf*, Pädagogische Forschungsstelle, Stuttgart 1986)
* Geography of France: cotrasting regions, culture, customs and food and wine
* Suggested readers: D. Fink La Claire Fontaine, Vols. I & II; A. Denjean A travers la France par le légendaire de ses provinces. Also: reading an easy book.

Grammar

* Past: passé composé, passé simple, imparfait
* Irregular verbs: savoir, voir, dormir, etc. and repetition of verbs learnt in Classes 4 and 5
* Negative 'ne ... rien', 'ne ... personne'
* Nouns and adjectives with plural ending x instead of s
* Regular comparison of adjectives
* Demonstrative and passive pronouns
* 'Tout', 'tous', 'toutes'
* Relative clause with qui and que
* Clauses introduced with: parceque, puisque, comme (causal); quand, pendant que (temporal), avant que, après que; pour que, bien que

Class 7

Suggested subjects for reading and speaking:

* Leisure pursuits, stories from French history and legend. The history of Paris up to the present
* The people and countryside of France, poems and songs
* Dramatic scenes
* Possibly a longer, exciting story, e.g. Daudet Lettres de mon moulin, Tartarin de Tarascon; Lamorisse Crin Blanc, or Le voyage en ballon, or Le ballon rouge; Denjean Jacquelin
* In grammar the following are practised:
* Pronouns le, la, les, en, lui, leur, y/en
* The partitive: pas de, beaucoup de, etc.
* Pluperfect
* Irregular comparison of adjectives
* More irregular verbs
* Indirect speech in the present tense

Class 8

Lively descriptions of life in France:

* Professional life, history, travel stories
* Dramatic scenes, poems, songs
* A longer story or one-act play, or scenes from a longer play; Molière's comedies; Malot *Sans Famille*; Daudet *Le petit chose*; Dumas, selections from *Les trois mousquetaires*, or *Fabliaux du moyen-age*; Hugo *Fantine*, or *Gavroche*; Verne *Le tour du monde en 80 jours*

Grammar

* 'Subjonctif'
* Irregular 'subjonctif': pouvoir, faire, aller, vouloir etc.
* Indirect speech in the past tense
* Agreement of the participle with 'avoir' and 'être'
* Use of the 'conditionnel'
* Subordinate clauses: pour que, quoique, sans que
* Reflexive verbs, including imperative and negative
* Impersonal phrases and passive constructions
* The passive mode

Classes 9 to 12

In Classes 9 to 12 the pupils consolidate what they have learnt in comprehension, speaking, reading and writing and begin to apply it in all realms of daily life and in connection with media, literature and other complex themes such as youth culture, professions, etc. Since one of the important aspects of learning foreign languages is to gain a feeling for the speakers of that language, the lessons will also include the more receptive, artistic aspect that works more on the feeling life, and is just as important as active practice which makes a stronger call on the will. The pupils need to increase the accessibility of the language and their fluency in it. Vocabulary and phrases are expanded to comprise the pupils' wider horizon, and exercises in pronunciation and spelling continue as before. Grammar is deepened and widened during Classes 9 to 12. Special attention is paid to the tenses in subordinate clauses, agreement of the tenses and the proper use of prepositions.

Class 9

Conversation and reading themes are now expanded to include descriptions from the lives of great individuals (inventors and discoverers, social reformers).

* Stories or dramatic scenes
* Poems and songs
* Retelling, speech exercises, making up stories to pictures
* Conversation in everyday situations

Literature and reading

Biographies, e.g.

* Henri Dunant (founder of the Red Cross)
* Napoléon, Robespierre, Jeanne d'Arc
* Albert Schweitzer
* Joffo: *Le sac de billes*

Romans policiers, e.g.

* Simenon: L'Affaire Saint-Fiacre, or Le témoignage de l'enfant de choeur

Discoverers, e.g.

* Champollion, Marie Curie

Novellas, e.g.:

* Malot: *Sans famille* (also in Class 8)
* Hugo: *Gavroche*, or *Cosette*

Recitation

Ballads and poems, e.g.:

* Hugo: *La retraite de Russie, Ceux qui vivent, Paris, O soldats de l'An Deux, Le mendiant, Entrevue au crépuscule*
* Verlaine: *Chanson d'automne, Il pleure*
* After Claudel: *Jeanne au bucher*
* Baudelaire: *L'Albatros*, etc.

France and its history

* Bretagne, Provence, Paris, Alsace
* The French Revolution, e.g. theatrical depiction by Mnouchkine or summaries of original texts
* The Jews in France (1940)

Practising the language

Comprehension:

* Oral and written retelling of what the pupils have read (letters, short dialogues)
* Recounting a sequence of events
* How to use a dictionary
* Work with intonation and vocabulary continues

Grammar:

* Practising the 'conditionnel', the 'gérondif', reflexive verbs
* Exercises on 'passé simple', 'passée composé', 'imparfait'
* des 'participe passé'
* Exercises on 'partitif'
* Forms like 'pour que' or 'pour'

* Infinitive clauses
* Relative clauses: 'qui', 'que', and also 'lequel' etc.
* Pronouns, also with 'passé composé' in the negative.
* Negative in several clauses: ne - ni - ni; ne - pas - ni
* Temporal expressions
* The derived adverb and how to use it
* Difference in meaning between adjective and derived adverb

Exercises and written work:
* Comprehension – oral and written
* Oral retelling of material read, written précis
* Answering questions on the content of a text
* Free essays on themes from the reading material

Class 10

Beginning of a systematic overview of French literature: popular songs, newspapers and magazines. Students can prepare short talks on such topics.

Literature and reading

Novellas, short stories, e.g.:
* Rochefort: *Les petits enfants du siècle*
* Daudet: *Les compères battus, La farce du Cuvier, Les lettres de mon moulin*
* St Exupéry: *Le petit prince, Gargantua*
* Corneille: *Le Cid*
* Hugo: *Jean Valjean*
* Mérimee: *Carmen*
* Branche: *Mort et élévation*
* Biographies of authors and poets: Ronsard, Daudet, Baudelaire, St Exupéry, Prévert in the form of talks

Recitation:
* Ronsard: *Mignonne allons voir*
* Baudelaire: *L'étranger, Initiation au voyage*
* St Exupéry: extracts from *Le petit prince*
* Prévert: *Jour de fête, Déjeuner du matin*
* Eluard: *La bonne justice*

France and its history

* France in the Middle Ages
* Origins of the French language
* Le Canada, la Tunisie, le Maroc

Exercises

* Retelling from varying perspectives
* Formulating agreement and disagreement
* Short talks
* Comprehension exercises
* Letters

Grammar

* Indirect speech in the past
* Agreement of tenses
* Consolidating 'subjonctif' and 'conditionnel'
* All subordinate clauses
* How French relates to Latin and English
* Emphasis on parts of a sentence, e.g.: ce n'est pas moi qui

Exercises and written work

* Verbal and written exercises on vocabulary and the content of texts in the form of essays, reports and retellings.
* Talks on a biography or a country

Class 11

* Texts from the seventeeth to the twenty-first century
* Exercises on style
* Selected scenes or a whole play are performed
* Selected passages from newspapers and journals
* Encouragement to go on pupil exchanges or visit France

Literature and reading

Selections from:

* Molière L'Avare, *Le médecin malgré lui, Le bourgeois gentilhomme*
* Maeterlinck: *Les aveugles*
* Camus: *L'étranger, Le malentendu, L'hôte, Les justes*
* Voltaire and Rousseau
* Bosco: *L'enfant et la rivière*
* Taine: *Voyage en Italie, Les origines de la France contemporaine*
* Balzac: Un épisode sous la terreur, etc.

Recitation

* Vian: *Chant pour la vie*
* Rimbaud: *Le dormeur du val*
* Selections from Molière
* Hugo: *Sur une barricade*, etc.

France and its history

* The Enlightenment
* Napoléon III and the Commune
* Minorities in France: the Bretons, the Basques, Occitanean culture; l'Algérie

Practising the language

Essays and short talks on topical subjects such as:

* 'Islam in France', or 'Life in the Banlieue'
* Conversations in class with pupils taking different parts
* Attempts to write poetry
* Work on stylistic nuances

Comprehension exercises

* Comparing the vernacular with literary language

Grammar (including revision)

* Other ways of expressing the conditional
* The adjective and its comparison
* Use of the free pronoun 'soi'
* Uses and forms of pronouns
* Revision of the 'passif'
* Forms and use of 'futur antérieur'

Exercises and written work

The pupils should be quite independent in writing their own essays, reports, retellings, letters.

Class 12

People of the twentieth century

* Contemporary literature
* France's important contributions to world literature and history
* Passages from newspapers and journals

Literature and reading

Texts from literature describing social conditions (Balzac, Zola or similar), and texts by authors writing about the meaning of life, e.g.:

* Sartre: *Les mouches, La putain respectueuse*
* Beckett: *En attendant Godot*
* Ionesco: *Les chaises, La cantatrice chauve, La leçon, Le Rhinocéros, Le pièton de l'air*
* Camus: *La peste*
* Mauriac, Gide, Lusseyran: *Et la lumière fut, La pollution du Moi*

Recitation

* Apollinaire: *Le pont Mirabeau*
* Aragon: *Rien n'est jamais acquis*
* Sartre: Extracts from *Les mouches*
* Queneau: *Il pleut*
* Eluard: *Un compte à régler*, etc.
* Yves: *Bonnefoy*

France and its history

Topical and cultural questions in the French-speaking world:

* Political institutions
* Minorities
* Corsica
* Nouvelle Calédonie
* La 'francophonie'
* Education, media, people and their environment
* Youth, tomorrow's world, advertising
* City life, art, religion, drugs, sport

Practising the language

Pupils' interpretations of subjects, people, scenes.

* Debating
* Translating from the viewpoint of comparative linguistics
* Noticing the 'genius' of the language
* Comprehension exercises
* Differences between verbal and written language
* Intonation and vocabulary

Exercises and written work

* Free essays and discussion
* Reports, letters

16

Gardening and Sustainable Living

Most children will not become farmers, many will not become gardeners, or even have gardens, but every morsel of food they put in their mouths has some relationship to farming. Every beverage they drink, the air they breathe, the water in our rivers has a direct and moral relationship to the farm and garden.[1]

The foundations of this subject are laid in the early years when young children explore their immediate environment and learn to use some simple tools to dig, plant bulbs, etc. The tradition of having a 'season garden', or small display of natural items along with an indication of a seasonal festival, also adds to this.

Gardening gives young people a real understanding of nature because they gain experience through practical activity. Working and observing over several years, and reporting regularly on what has been learnt, they build up a feel for the way nature works and our human dependence upon it. Through their communal work in the school garden they gain a foundation for grounded judgement and responsibility. Gardening lessons as such begin in early puberty and can become a real educational help. Younger pupils, however, also interact with nature in a variety of ways and this should not be neglected. With puberty, a growing awareness of increasing independence manifests initially in considerable psychological irritability and lack of equanimity. The steadying rhythms of work on the land can be a great help at this age. The teacher becomes an expert who can show them the processes and complexities of nature. Strong links exist and can be brought to the attention of young people with lessons in geography and environmental studies.

Every school has different options for gardening, depending on local circumstances. The size, variety and arrangement of the school garden should be governed entirely by educational criteria.

Space permitting, the following facilities are ideal:

* Garden house with space for theoretical and practical work, especially in wet weather or in winter
* Tool shed: there must be several of each tool well maintained, properly stored and of suitable size
* Greenhouse with pricking out and potting facilities, and also cold-frames for early planting
* Tree nursery, herb garden, tree and bush fruit, flower beds, lawns

* Beds for annual vegetables, herbs and flowers for cutting
* Composting area

The gardening programme can culminate with a period of practical work in agriculture in Class 9 or 10, or with a forestry period in Class 10.

Getting to know and appreciate gardening skills and knowledge

Learning these skills can help the youngsters gain respect for the skills of others. They also learn to have confidence in their own skills and become better able to assess their own possibilities.

Earthly maturity (puberty): working with the earth is helpful

Gardening provides a degree of stability during this time of physical and psychological change. Meaningful work strengthens the limbs. Psychological qualities such as reverence, gratitude, endurance and wonder are awakened. The schooling of the senses and of causal thinking has positive consequences for the development of more subtle experiential capacities and also of the capacity to think clearly.

Laying the foundation for a practical sense of responsibility

This is best achieved by getting youngsters to care for domestic animals, but it is also experienced when they care for a plot of land for several years, improving the soil and learning how to make and use compost, or when they grow young plants and care for garden beds including harvesting their produce.

Harmony and peace are found through working in nature

The work can lead to a 'healthy tiredness' (especially in Classes 8 and 9). The beauty of the garden and the orderly interplay between natural things (plants, soil, animals, weather, sun, etc.), and also experiencing the regularity of the seasons, can lead to harmonising soul experiences in the long term.

There is a specific educational problem that can lead to widespread feelings of helplessness, especially amongst the young: the creeping destruction of nature. The threat hanging over everything often appears insurmountable, and at an age when they are strongly oriented towards their own future, young people often find their will paralysed by a fundamental feeling of resignation. This can be overcome through proper, caring work in the school garden, on a farm or during a practical period of forestry. The youngsters have a direct experience of how the situation in the garden, the farm or the forest makes direct demands on them and how their own personal efforts lead to the creation of 'new life'. Through this it becomes a matter of course for them to want to help and share responsibility. A practical period working in agriculture is especially important in this connection for Class 9 or 10.

The suggested tasks for the different age groups are not a rigid list: the size of the school garden, its situation, soil, climate and other local factors influence how we can do gardening with the pupils, and suggestions about which new tasks to introduce at the different stages may be helpful. In keeping with real life, where necessary the older pupils should take on tasks they have already done when younger. This goes for all the routine gardening jobs such as weeding, which all pupils should be taught how to do.

Where possible the pupils can also learn about forestry and woodland work. One need not be in the country to do this: city parks offer a wide range of trees and hedgerow plants.

All suggested tasks are cumulative – that is, each year adds to the range of tasks, rather than replacing tasks from the year before.

Before Class 6

Depending upon the resources of the school, activities might include:

* Planting autumn bulbs, planting or training willow wands, etc
* Making and/or positioning bird feeders
* Taking part in a 'nuisance patrol', e.g. checking rabbit fencing, making scarecrows, or other devices to deter bird damage
* Harvesting, seed collecting, egg collecting, etc
* Assisting with the construction or turning of compost heaps
* Cultivating herbs, cutting and drying
* Sowing green manure crops, raking leaves for leaf mould, work on the comfrey patch, etc
* The role of worms, bees and birds, protecting hedgehogs and other common garden creatures (e.g. making bumble-bee nest boxes etc)
* Other occasional work of a suitable type craft work using natural materials
* Activities related to the broader curriculum, e.g. activities relevant to festivals, farming and related activities as a lesson theme in Class 3, project related to 'building', etc

Where tools are used, the correct use should be taught and children can be introduced to the idea of risk assessment and ensuring that practical tasks are conducted in a safe manner.

Class 6

Getting to know and carrying out basic practical activities such as:

Gardening

* Sieving soil and compost
* Preparing beds
* Cultivating and harvesting
* Hoeing, initially with the short hoe
* Mowing grass with the sickle
* Making bunches of flowers or herbs
* Weeding reasonably sized patches

Woodland work

* Seed collection and sowing
* Special composts
* Grading of seedlings

Simple 'ecology', the role of insects and other garden and woodland creatures, including "pests" and their relationship to plants and one another

Class 7

Gardening

* Growing crops that need more complicated care, pricking out seedlings, potting
* Making and spreading compost
* Mixing seeding and potting compost

* Knowledge of soil cultivation and digging
* Finding out the geological history of the ground underneath the garden
* Making new beds. Using garden line and drilling rake
* Harvesting and cleaning vegetables ready for market
* Marketing of garden produce and keeping accounts
* Harvesting herbs and herb teas and preparing them correctly
* Making advent wreaths
* Making straw or reed mats

Woodland work

* Tree planting
* Weeding and maintenance of seedlings and saplings
* Thinning out trees by felling
* Cutting firewood
* Greenwood work, hurdles, tool handles

The principle of rotation and soil, garden and other soil diseases and their effect on food production. Practical introduction to the place of selective breeding, hybrids, etc

Class 8

Gardening

* General gardening jobs that require skill, endurance and physical effort
* Mowing grass with the scythe. Haymaking
* Repairing tools and buildings
* Manufacturing foods from produce (pickles, chutney, herb salt, jams; using wax if bees are kept)
* The study of cultivated plants and the soils they need. Simple crop rotation sequences and their advantages/disadvantages

Woodland work

* Establishing, maintaining and harvesting willow beds
* Coppicing hazel
* Charcoal burning
* Greenwood turning – poles for stools, chairs, ladders

Class 9

Class 9 usually has a longer gardening main-lesson. The pupils get to know about landscape gardening, building paths, steps and fences, ponds, water recycling projects.

* Propagation techniques are studied in theory and practice
* Caring for soft-fruit bushes, fruit trees and decorative shrubs, pruning

Class 10

The pupils learn the mysteries of grafting (as suggested by Steiner). This subject can be dealt with in great depth, which can leave little time for anything else. It depends how much time is available.

Classes 11 and 12

In the Upper School, environmental studies and ecology overlap with gardening in a far more explicit way, including examining some contemporary questions related to soil depletion, water conservation and drainage, GM crops, etc.

Depending on the school's resources there is much scope from practical environmental and landscaping projects, especially involving the timber cycle, with the preparation of timber for carpentry and joinery. Managing nature reserves, biotopes and ponds can even be done on a small scale. Here scientific observation plays an important role. All this can lead to individual project work of a practical, scientific or artistic nature.

17

Geography

Earth Sciences, Environmental Studies, Human Geography and Economics

> *The child shows a motivation and striving to go out over the environment, to form a unique world image as a part of achieving a singular identity. This is part of humankind's yearning and capacity for individualisation. Every child must integrate a world image with a corporal awareness, in order to know where she is and who she is.*[1]

Classes 1 to 4

Geography, in all its various aspects, forms a key integrating subject within the whole curriculum. Defined at its broadest it encompasses many aspects of the world around us. Learning about the world around us is a complex subject covering many fields that relate to many other subjects. Essentially though, the methodology of geography teaching in Steiner-Waldorf schools has fundamental themes:

* Physical or natural geography
* Social geography
* Inner or developmental geography

The first systematically describes the phenomena of the earth, its surface, interior and atmosphere. The second considers the human influence on the environment, its economic consequences and the relationship between the particular character of a geographical region and the social and cultural development of the people who live there. The third refers to how individuals' awareness of their environment is reflected in how they see the world and experience themselves within it and follows how this process evolves through the child's development. The methodology of the Waldorf curriculum seeks to integrate these three approaches.

The core of this method is to proceed from the whole to the inter-related parts and to start in the known world and proceed to the unknown before returning to the known. It is a voyage of discovery.

> *The regions of the earth are not to be studied as mere divisions of the earth's surface, but rather that the areas of the earth's surface are to be studied for their particular character which is a product of their phenomena. It is their inter-relationship with each other which fills the areas with their content… Geography in Steiner-Waldorf education entails the use of a comparative method.*[2]

Furthermore, as Alexander von Humboldt pointed out, geography must contain something aesthetic, which proceeds from a premonition of the inter-relation of the sensual with the intellectual towards a feeling of universality.

> *Descriptions of nature can be sharply limited and scientifically exact without thereby losing the living breath of the power of imagination.*[3]

This aspect is fundamental to geographical education.

The basis for geography teaching is the concept of the earth as morphological and physical totality, or the earth as an organism. This implies a consciousness both of the inter-relationships of the parts within the whole and also of the whole as a developing being. This highlights the importance of climatic geography in which we can readily see the parts as aspects of a whole earth climatic system (ocean currents are another related example). Exploring the characteristic phenomena of the different climatic zones can be done either generically, as types regardless of location (tundra or equatorial zones) or by specific reference to actual regions. Both methods belong within the Waldorf curriculum.

The relationship to true regional diversity is also important. It is important for the pupils to be able to visualise both the similarities with what they know and the differences in distance and scale of unfamiliar parts of the earth. Steiner stressed this:

> *In dealing with space we densify the spirit and soul of the child, we drive it down to the ground. By teaching geography in such a way that the child sees what we are telling him we bring about this consolidation in him. But there must be the true seeing in space. The child must, for example, be conscious that the Niagara Falls are not the river Elbe! We must help him to realise that a vast space stretches between the two.*[4]

Geography is a subject that can lead the children 'down to earth' and thus prepare them for earthly maturity. Before they go to school and even during their first two years at school, children have a rather dreamy awareness of the world as a totality. Learning about the environment leads them to more wakeful and differentiated perceptions. Up to the age of seven or eight this unity exists of its own accord; thereafter it needs cultivating by means of ever more contact with the world. This includes vivid and colourful descriptions of the archetypal professions, crafts and the locality. Such descriptions are complemented by practical activities such as farming, processing cereals, house-building, gardening. How this is done will vary in ways that depend on the nature of the locality. The production and processing of natural materials is the basis of human economy and this relationship to nature is an important aspect of geography.

If we want to help the children enter into a partnership with nature we must enable them to go beyond mere intellectual knowledge of the kind gained by learning of nature indirectly, such as through electronic media, and penetrate to real feelings for the natural world, feelings that will always lead to activity and a responsible relationship between human beings and nature.

For Classes 1 to 3 the general aim of learning about the environment might be formulated as: getting to know and feeling connected with one's surroundings and with the work human beings do. In Class 4 differentiation begins to be more pronounced. Local knowledge of the immediate area widens spatially (to include geography, simple astronomy, and the study of human beings, animals and plants) and temporally (history). From Class 4 onwards the differentiated subjects are named accordingly, but they ought to remain integrated within an overall experience of the world around us.

Environmental studies would thus be part of history lessons, for example, how the consequences of the Greco-Latin culture, of the Middle Ages and of recent history, as well as the aftermath of the Industrial Revolution's inventions, still influence our life and environment today. Similarly, environmental studies in geography lessons would show how climate and soil are related to the transport and trade, the economy and way of life of different societies. Environmental studies also relate to English lessons in the form of business essays and to arithmetic lessons in the form of commercial arithmetic. Steiner even considered that religion lessons would also be a part of environmental education, as his suggestions that the steam engine or something astronomical might be included in them.

The general educational aim for the children's ninth to twelfth year is thus to meet the children's need to experience reality, i.e. the overall meaning of the realities of nature and the world, so that they can develop their love for the world. This is a cross-curricular aim.

Environmental studies also play an essential part in the sciences of nature (physics and chemistry). Steiner considered it important for the youngsters in Classes 7 and 8 to have physics lessons about life, lessons that give them an understanding of their relationship with their surroundings:

> *We are living in a world made by human beings, shaped in accordance with human thoughts, a world that we use while knowing nothing at all about it. That we do not understand something made by human beings, something that is, to all intents and purposes, human thought, is a fact that is of great significance in connection with people's mood of soul and spirit ... The worst thing of all is to share in the experience of this world made by human beings without taking trouble over it.*[5]

This leads, from the pupils' twelfth year onwards, to the formulation of the general educational aims with regard to the way in which 'the world and the life around us' influences all lessons: the children should attain elementary concepts, knowledge and skills with regard to the more important functions of life. This is not only to give them confidence but also to give them the longing to know all about what is going on around them.

In summary one can say that up to the age of twelve, the task of the geography curriculum is to bring the child down to earth; to awaken them to the world around them. From this point on the curriculum moves through cultural geography in Classes 7 and 8 to relating to the world as a whole living organism in the Upper School.

In some schools, Class 8 pupils carry out year-long projects in connection with which environmental studies offers them opportunities to deepen their knowledge of life subjects, thus satisfying their curiosity, or developing it further.

We should point here to environmental studies within the curriculum in the Upper School, as practised in the various practical projects, and also the subject 'technology and life' which Steiner introduced as early on as 1921. Some Steiner-Waldorf schools have made this integrated environmental approach as the basis for developing quite new forms of the Upper School.

Class 1

Small children take their surroundings, i.e. other people, animals, plants, stones, stars, sun and moon, as well as the seasons of the year, for granted. If we can constantly renew this unity of the different realms, we shall strengthen the children's confidence, gratitude and self-assurance. In the basic mood of children during their first seven-year period, these feelings can be expressed as: 'the world is good!'

During their first year at school, children should learn to see differentiation in the overall totality of nature while at the same time becoming increasingly more awake to the way everything belongs together. They are encouraged to reflect on things through stories, through looking at nature, following the seasonal changes and through descriptions of experiences that emphasise what is special about what they see; what is huge or tiny, what is delicate or immensely powerful in nature. Such stories and observations will only get through to the children if they are told 'with soul', i.e. if they are filled with humanity through personification. This lets them sense that there is nothing in the world that is meaningless or without significance. These experiences are particularly important as a preparation for the real situation in which we find ourselves today because they not only lay foundations, but also set the pattern for the future.

* The kingdoms of nature, the elements, the seasons of the year and the stars should be described as though they themselves were speaking. By this we do not mean unreal stories or inventions but imaginative tales that speak of the essence of things. They can be in the form of parables or nature legends.

Class 2

In Class 1 the children have learnt to see their surroundings through 'new' eyes and have begun to hear what these surroundings are telling them. Now, in Class 2, they experience how human beings are linked to the kingdoms of nature. The feelings that result from this, an active identification with nature – what could be called 'love for the world' – are very important. These feelings evolve until the children become 'mature for the earth' in Class 8, when they can be experienced as responsibility.

* Fables, such as those of Aesop tell of the relationship between human beings and their surroundings in anthropomorphic form.
* Saints' stories, notably those of Celtic saints, express a similar quality. The figure of St. Francis of Assisi, with his reverence and humility towards all created things, can serve as a yardstick by which to measure the lessons. Such stories lay a foundation for morality.

During the first two years of school, environmental studies belong as an integral part of every lesson. Let the children talk about what is going on in nature, what they meet with on their way to school, what they discovered on an outing, and so on. Things they bring to school with them (bird nests, leaves, conkers, fruit, stones, animal horns, snails, etc.) can provide the starting point for talking about the world around us. This does not mean that there need not be specific main-lesson blocks for some of these subjects, but simply that in Classes 1 and 2 there is no need to make separate subjects out of nature studies. The 'outdoor classroom' should be regularly visited and experienced in all weathers and seasons.

Class 3

Children reaching the age of nine undergo a decisive alteration in their relationship with the world: the world that was a part of them becomes the world that surrounds them. The children need to understand and literally grasp, as far as they can at this age, the links they sense they have with the world. In the coming years this can develop into an understanding of nature, animals, human beings, work and technology. Complex work processes that take a long time to complete can be understood by the children, for example, through a house-building main-lesson, or a farming main-lesson that shows them the whole sequence from ploughing and sowing to the end result, bread. Their intelligence is schooled by means of concrete reality. It is important that at the moment when they meet and sense what they are working with, their links with it are not broken and turned aside into mere rational and factual abstractions, but that their own activity leads them to the wide-ranging implications.

* The human being and the earth: the farmer and the work on the farm, ploughing (the horse, harness, shoeing, the plough), harrowing, sowing (various kinds of cereal), different soils (drainage of wet ploughland), harvesting, threshing, milling, baking, dairy farming. Once traditional methods have been introduced, children should see what tractors, combine harvesters, etc. do
* The miner and other traditional occupations to do with working the earth (turf cutter, stone mason, dyke digger)
* Making use of the elements in house-building: brick making (drying, baking), preparing mortar, bricklaying, carpentry, roofing
* 'Archetypal' callings such as shepherd, hunter, fisherman, woodcutter, charcoal burner, baker, tailor, shoemaker, potter, carpenter, tanner, saddler, spinner, weaver, or blacksmith
* As much as possible, children should have direct, hands-on experience of these trades

The emphasis among these various possible themes will vary depending on the geographical location of the school.

Class 4

Steiner's imperative, 'all lessons must give knowledge about life', should be taken into account. Local geography is an important aspect of environmental studies. Previously the lessons have turned on general aspects (links with nature, knowledge of work processes), but now they focus the children's attention in both space and time. A new, more concrete source of knowledge opens up, encompassing both time and space.

The immediate surroundings of the school, the locality, the town or city are shown to the children in their geographical/spatial and historical/temporal development, right up to the present situation. Through these studies, their more generalised relationship with the world can be transformed into a sense of belonging, both socially and spatially.

* Observing the sun as a way of recognising the four compass directions
* The rising and setting motions of a few characteristic constellations round the North Star, and the movements of the moon
* Drawing of bird's eye view of the school (or the child's home) and the town or village it is in
* Descending from a high viewpoint (hill, tower) into the surrounding landscape changes one's view of what can be seen

* Different children's routes to school are described and drawn
* Making clay or papier mâché models of the immediate surroundings and shapes of the landscape
* Drawing first simple maps
* Historical events and legends illustrating the development of the locality are told
* The different ways the local soils are tilled, local industry, workplaces and infrastructure are examined. Vivid descriptions of typical local industries and professions
* A visit to the local railway station, docks or airport can give the children a sense of how their home town is linked to other places, why people travel to their hometown, what commodities are imported and exported.

Classes 5 to 12

As with all subjects, the task of geography lessons is to accompany and support the children in their physical, psychological and spiritual development. In addition to this, Steiner also wanted geography to occupy a central position because it can be linked up with so many other subjects (biology, physics, chemistry, astronomy, mathematics, history, etc.) and thus provide a general sense of unity. He also stressed the moral component of geography lessons by saying that learning about people living side by side would help the children to love their fellow human beings.[6]

Geography must give the children an interest in the world and courage for life. They must learn to understand the earth as a natural space with specific life rhythms in which human beings are enveloped but which they can also change through economic and cultural activity. The foundation for responsibility and an awareness of ecology must be laid early.

The curriculum alters its emphasis in keeping with the stage of development the children have reached. Building on the local geography of Class 4, the children in Classes 5 and 6 are first led closer to the earth through looking at local ways of farming and industry in which human beings are in partnership with nature in different regions and their inter-dependencies. This helps them in their development. In Classes 7 and 8 they then get to know the character and culture of other peoples, particularly in other parts of the globe. Geography lessons thus have a sense of movement and counter-movement. During the middle period of childhood the children find their home on the earth in physical space, i.e. there is movement towards the earth. Then, as puberty approaches, when they attain earthly maturity, there is a movement towards the psychological and cultural differentiation of the earth.

Class 5

Teaching geography to children in the middle part of childhood means giving them many facts linked to experience. The pupils are to learn something about the world, but in such a way that feelings are linked to that knowledge. Original causes remain in the background. A selection of regions and landscapes of their own country are described. The important thing is to expand the study of economics and infrastructure begun in Class 4 to wider regions.

The children can go on 'journeys of discovery' along rivers, travelling beyond their immediate surroundings. They can 'travel to the coast' or into hilly regions.

* Contrast life by the sea, in the hills, in the lowlands
* Mining and other industries
* Continuation of map drawing, use of wall maps, atlases
* The economic and geographic links between the home and neighbouring countries, stressing mutual interdependence
* The regional and physical geography of their country or larger region. In the UK this would usually be the whole of the British Isles

Class 6

In Class 6 there are two aspects to geography. On the one hand, the home country is related to the continent it belongs to. On the other hand, there will be a short but systematic overview of all the continents. These are contrasted with one another as to their main topography and morphology (outline, river systems, mountains, skies, climate, vegetation, etc.). Astronomy belongs here in the way it relates to the earth and the seasons. Geology and botany also come into the geography main-lesson. Industry and commerce are extended to include a few striking examples where global links are significant. The teacher will make careful choices, bearing in mind what he or she intends to bring into the discussions of other parts of the world in Classes 7 and 8.

The main-lesson

If the school is European, the main-lesson will be on Europe. In their earlier geography lessons the pupils will already have been shown contrasting landscapes and lifestyles. Now Europe as a whole can be seen from the aspect of polarity, e.g. by looking at the different influences of water, air, light/warmth and of the rocks and soils in different regions on landscape and economy. This may mean a comparison between a lowland country such as the Netherlands with an Alpine country such as Switzerland, or between regions with a traditional economy connected to the sea, such as Norway, with a landlocked country such as the Czech Republic.

Overview of the earth as a whole

* Shape and distribution of the continents and oceans. Ocean currents. Relationship of the tides to the moon
* Dependence of the vegetation belt on the position of the sun and climatic conditions. Seasons in relation to the earth's orbit
* The rocky foundations, old and young parts of the earth
* Young folded mountains (e.g. the Alps, the Himalayas, the Andes), the rift valleys, e.g. the Red Sea Jordan valley, Rhone Valley, etc.
* The great rivers and their individual characteristics, e.g. the Rhine, the Danube, the Dnieper
* Tropical rainforest, savanna, the outback of Australia, salt deserts as ecosystems
* The globe should be looked at as a whole from different perspectives, i.e. not only with Europe at the centre
* Breaking new ground, forest clearance and the creation of dustbowls, with striking examples of soil erosion
* Mineral deposits and trade relations
* Opening of transport routes (e.g. Trans Siberian Railway, the Suez and Panama Canals)

Obviously one cannot cover all these topics but a balance is sought that exemplifies as much of the whole as possible.

Class 7

In Classes 7 and 8 the transition is made from agriculture to industry and commerce to the cultural situation in different parts of the globe. This is one of the shifts of emphasis that Steiner recommended.[7] This necessitates the teacher selecting the material for both the classes. The cultural aspect, in turn, leads to history playing a part in geography lessons: in Class 7 particularly the Age of Discovery, including the transition from the Ptolemaic to the Copernican view of the world. This shows the children that today's view of earth and universe is one that has evolved and that it is not a system set in stone for all time.

So that the different characters and cultures of other parts of the world do not remain in the realm of ideas, Steiner suggested letting the children paint or do other artistic or practical work in the style of those cultures. Other main-lessons, too, can be enriched by biographies of discoverers and descriptions of other parts of the world.

In connection with the theme of discovery, the astronomy of the visible sky should be studied. Obsrvations should be made and charts showing the main constellations shown.

* Since the Age of Discovery is the subject of history lessons in Class 7, it could be argued that America would be the obvious choice for geography, or Europe if the school is in America, i.e. where did the colonists come from? Africa, too, with its polarity between the black African and the Islamic cultures can be taken as a whole. In the following, therefore, we shall assume the sequence: Class 7 Old World, Class 8 New World. Class 7 might even have two geography main-lessons.
* As well as the historical perspective connected with European Colonialism, the link between agriculture, raw materials (cotton, rice, wheat, coffee, tea, etc.) and manufacturing industry should be stressed. This in turn should be placed in a context of global climate zones, e.g. SE Asian rice, rubber, hardwoods, North American Prairie wheat, Caribbean bananas, South American beef, Australian wool and mining, etc.
* Building on the astronomy in Class 6, the visible night sky should be described and observations made of the constellations. The appearance and paths of the planets can be described and the cycles of the moon observed.

Africa

The main geographical regions of Africa can be characterised from a climatic, topographical, plant zone perspective:

* North Africa, West Africa and the Equatorial Regions, the Sahara and Sahel, Eastern Africa and Southern Africa
* Different ways of life in black Africa and Islamic Africa in the different vegetation zones (e.g. Pygmies and rain forest peoples, shepherd nomads, Samburu, Masai, farmers and plantations, oasis populations, miners)
* The continuation of various religions and traditional African societies
* The Colonial and post-Colonial influences of France, Britain, Holland, Germany. Confrontation with Western world views. Examples of developing nations and their economic relationship to the developed world. The problems of famine and civil war in the Horn of Africa, the tensions between tribalism and modern commercial interests in West Africa, multi-cultural societies in Southern Africa, etc.

Asia

* Main geographical regions, Himalayas/Hindu Kush, Indian subcontinent, Tibet/Mongolia plateau, North and South China, SE Asia, Thailand, Philippines, Indonesia, Japan, Korea
* Macro-landscapes in their cultural and geographical polarity (e.g. the influence of Buddhism, Hinduism, Islam and Christianity); SE Asia as a subcontinent of islands, the huge populations of Eastern Asia, the Pacific Rim as a rapidly developing region and the modern significance of the Asian tiger economies
* How the role of Asian peoples is changing in the modern world. The future of China and the Pacific Rim countries, in relation to the global economy
* Issues connected with rainforest exploitation

Class 8

As they increasingly enter into the world, Class 8 pupils want to come to grips with world problems. Conversely, their own problems also take on 'world' dimensions. So especially in geography lessons, the interplay between 'me and the world' should be catered for. By concerning themselves with the cultural and soul life of other peoples, as well as their cultures and values, the pupils experience that psychological characteristics of peoples can differ greatly. This can help the youngsters find a foothold in their search for their own inner soul life.

Another approach to geography lessons in Class 8 is to ask oneself where metamorphoses, polarities and intensifications take place in geographical phenomena.

If America is the subject of lessons in Class 7, North and South America can be compared. This helps develop the pupils' powers of imagination. It helps prevent fixed ideas from creeping in, but leads rather to knowledge that can come alive and grow. The pupils should learn to understand how the different mentalities of Hispanic and Anglo Americans came about in a historical process.

A further theme in Class 8 is the moods and changing patterns of the weather.

* Introduction to typical landscapes of North and South America, e.g. by means of an imaginary journey, use of place names to show cultural influences
* Structure of the double continent and its diverse animal and plant life
* Arrival of the Native Americans and their adaptation to different geographical areas
* The Spanish-Portuguese and the Anglo-French occupations and their consequences (mineral wealth, technology, destruction of nature)
* Encounters between individuals in America. Different psychological make-up of the various social and ethnic groups. Development tasks and possibilities. The demographic issues in the USA
* Cloud formations observed and painted. Meteorological readings taken and charted: rainfall, humidity, air pressure, wind speed; including the use of instruments e.g. barometer, wind vane, etc. High and low pressure, weather fronts. Cultural aspects of climate in Northern countries and the length of day; Mediterranean lifestyle and climate; desert peoples; arctic peoples; tropical environments

If America has been studied in Class 7, a geographical and economic comparison between Africa and Europe, or Europe and Asia can be undertaken.

Classes 9 to 12

In the Upper School, geography and all the other subjects continue in their task of accompanying and supporting the pupils in their physical, psychological and spiritual development. At this age this is helped by looking at the earth as something whole, beginning with the physical consistency of the rocks and the life processes in the earth (vegetation zones as organs of the earth, rhythmical processes inside the earth and in its mantle of water and air). Then comes the transformation of the earth by human activity (human geography). The earth should be understood as an organism, which means that this concept must be clarified and that a Goetheanistic or contextual approach taking the phenomena as the starting point must be developed. It is good to avoid giving merely abstract, value-free knowledge or overstressing physical and mathematical chains of cause and effect. Rather than conditions, it is processes that need to be described, leading on to the cultural situation of the population in different regions.

Geography in the Upper School must develop into eco-geography. Examples must show the ecological effect of human activity on the different life conditions in the world (rainy and dry seasons, steppes, rainforest, monsoon and Gulf Stream climates), and the highly adapted lifestyles and industrial practices of the various societies. The consequences of disregarding ecological and socio-cultural structures by colonial and neo-Colonial exploitation must also be described. Towards the end of the Upper School, geography can become 'study of the earth's evolution'. By learning from the skills of indigenous populations we can sow the seeds for a 'partnership with nature'. Discussions of a social order that is in keeping with human dignity can open up perspectives for the future.

Class 9

In Class 9 the pupils become 'mature for the earth', to use Steiner's phrase, and their bodies are more weighed down by gravity. In biology, for example, this phase is accompanied by studying the most 'earthly' part of the human body, the skeleton and the sense organs. The corresponding element in geography is the 'earth's skeleton', the world of minerals and their formations (the rocky mantle of the earth). The crucial factor here is the vividness with which teleological forces can be described. The macro-cycles of continental movements, mountain building, vulcanism, faulting and earthquakes need to be experienced as dynamic processes and not reduced to abstract and therefore incomprehensible diagrams or graphics. The students have to be able feel the three dimensional forces, of rift valley formation for example, as something they can grasp with their whole bodies, not merely with their intellects. This calls for a lively, participatory kind of teaching, one which cultivates a living and plastic imagination of nature's forces. Although picture material will be essential, the students first have to create their own inner pictures of the processes involved.

* Shape and distribution of continents and oceans
* Morphology and formation of folded mountains
* The 'mountain cross' of the earth, the great rift valleys, volcanoes, mid-ocean ridges and ocean trenches. From continental drift to plate tectonics
* Mineralogy, rhythmical processes in rock formation
* An overview of the earth's history
* Geological layers showing former ice ages and the effects of glaciation
* A survey of the other main forms of erosion

Class 10

The view Class 9 pupils have of the world is fairly homogeneous. In Class 10 this begins to fragment into perhaps quite contrary aspects. The youngsters can lose some of their confidence and begin to doubt things. At the same time they begin to discover their own internal soul space and are thus able to approach worldly phenomena with a greater degree of subtlety. For example this is the time when the most vital organs are discussed in biology; the processes of these organs can be traced as having an effect even in the psychological realm. In the geography main-lesson the earth itself is seen as a living organism with vital processes going on inside the depths of the earth, in its rocky crust, in its watery and airy mantle and even in outer space. In each case the most rhythmical processes are the ones to be studied.

* The mantles of the earth: from the lithosphere to the stratosphere
* The inner structure of the earth
* Movements of the tectonic plates
* Characteristics of water and how it flows: rivers and ocean currents as living organs of the earth: interchange between deep and surface currents.
* The links between ocean currents and climate, e.g. the Gulf Stream, trade winds, el Niño, etc.
* The layers of the atmosphere: meteorology (with practical exercises): the planetary winds: the earth's magnetic field
* Interplay between climate and vegetation: the ecosystems of the earth as organs of an organism
* Movements and rhythms of the earth

Class 11

Pupils in Class 11 take a clear step towards finding themselves. They gain confidence in their own inner powers of thinking, feeling and willing. They can begin to understand subtle correlations in the web of cause and effect, the kind of thinking necessary to grasp complex phenomena such as ecosystems. This makes it possible to lead the pupils beyond what they have been able to imagine so far. In biology, for example, the pupils are asked to look at the world of the cell, and of unicellular animals, i.e. the world of the unimaginably small. In geography there can be an astronomy main-lesson, to enable the pupils to enter the world of the unimaginably vast. On the other hand cartography does justice to the pupils' new capacity for abstract thought through the task of depicting the round globe on a two-dimensional flat surface. (Steiner suggested cartography for pupils of this age as a continuation of the surveying main-lesson.)

The specifically geographical theme for this class is eco-geography. It examines the interplay between outer space, the relief structure of the face of the earth, climate, vegetation and the human being. Following on from the geography main-lesson of Class 10 (the mantles of the earth), this new main-lesson would need to include more economic and social geography. These should not concentrate solely on negative developments such as pollution and ecological destruction, but must also show the beginnings of a study of how the earth evolves. Examples of the positive influence on ecosystems through increased bio-diversity in some traditional forms of land cultivation can be discussed with a view to the feasibility of replicating similar effects through modern land management programmes. The whole concept of what constitutes health in an ecosystem should be discussed so that it becomes clear that nature left to her own devices is not the only answer, that people can live on the land in sustainable ways. Technology lessons throughout the year can lend further depth to these subjects.

* The earth's landscape zones as ecosystems and the significance of bio-diversity
* History as a process of economic steps
* Mineral wealth and its exploitation: world trade
* Poverty in developing countries created by exploitative practices
* Aspects of a just economic/social system
* Examples and assessment of ecological industry today
* Tasks for the future
* Aspects of modern astronomy and cosmology (can also be done in Class 12)

Class 12

The young people's horizon widens in Class 12. They get a closer focus of their own life tasks, and they also regard the problems of the world with a greater sense of responsibility. The step towards maturity they are taking now requires a change in the style of teaching them. They want an overview; they look for links with other subjects; they discuss questions of lifestyle in a highly technical world. By the end of their time at school the young people ought to have reached the realisation that a new partnership between human beings and the earth is needed, and that every single individual must work towards this.

* Seeing the earth from the point of view of its natural as well as its cultural structures
* Early forms of humanity and the emergence of Homo sapiens sapiens: the significance of human evolution for the biosphere: language, technology, culture, religion and history as factors determining the creation of different peoples and nations
* Geographical and cultural origins of society
* Population changes and what the earth can support: starvation and affluence
* The task of overcoming racism and nationalism. The importance of education
* Steiner's ideas about a threefold social order as one possibility. Successful projects and initiatives. Examples of responsible behaviour towards the earth with regard to nature and the socio-cultural structure

18

History

Classes 5 to 8[1]

Initially the children find their home in the landscape and history of their immediate surroundings. For the first three years at school, the children relate to historical events in a non-chronological and mythical sense. The narrative content of many lessons gives them archetypal pictures of human relationships and life paths, challenges and quests whilst familiarising them with social relationships of older cultures, with kings, queens, knights, peasants, holy men and women. Such myths and legends also provide them with an implicit understanding of narrative, the primary mode of history itself.

The children's awareness of the past emerges out of the context of the present in an anecdotal, experiential way. They discover that things have occurred in the past, that what happens now has consequences for the future. They are aware through many layers of experience that time passes, that many things take time to occur. Anticipation of and preparation for the future are intrinsic to the celebration of the festivals of the year. They learn about the cycle of the seasons and of the major cycles of life and death in nature. In Class 3 they learn about traditional forms of economic relationships when they learn about farming, fishing and forestry, about house-building and the traditional trades of blacksmith, wheelwright, carpenter, stone mason and so on. In the legends of the Old Testament they learn, among other things, about one people's struggle for national identity in an archaic society and encounter the political structures of ancient civilisations such as Pharaoh's Egypt or Babylon. They do so not analytically but biographically and mythically, in other words in the medium of orality, that is, as tales told.

In Class 4, the historical pictures they glean from the study of their local environment give them a first sense of historical time. Discovering their locality also means hearing tales and legends about earlier peoples who lived and worked here. It involves visiting their buildings, temples or churches, finding their traces on the land, hearing their language in the place names, perhaps seeing their bones and artifacts in the museum. Local geography also reveals the economic roots of the local environment, be they ancient or recent and industrial. For the children this is all past, all ancient history.

Until they are able to grasp the abstract concept of linear time, the children are hardly able to awaken to the literacy of historical progression.

Learning about measurement in Class 3 and the verb tenses in Class 4 certainly help this process. So too does the spatial awareness of geography itself. Just as some, perhaps all, earlier cultures identified their land with the biography of their people, so too children develop a consciousness of events in time through an understanding of place. In particular the relationship of human activity to nature reveals our story. It tells us why communities settled here, what they did, how they lived, and this tells us something about *who* they were and that is where history begins. This in turn reveals something of who we are too, and that is the point of history.

This aspect of geography, which includes human, economic and social geography, is a recurring theme throughout the curriculum, one that merges with the study of history itself. The relevance of history to us today has more to do with people and their relationship to the natural world around them, how they have transformed it and in so doing transformed the nature of human societies in their wake. The stories of kings and battles and treaties and religions and empires only become meaningful in the context of place and what people have made of themselves in that place, and later how they have related to other places.

In Class 5 proper history lessons begin. Gradually the children look outwards from their familiar surroundings, both in time and space. This four-year period, between Classes 5 and 8, begins with mythological images of earlier times in human evolution; from the high civilisations of ancient times, via classical antiquity and the Middle Ages to the reality of our present civilisation and its political and social situation. This path gives the pupils a sense that to be human means to evolve, and that the concept of the human race embraces the whole variety of all the peoples who have played their part in the processes of history. Over these four years it is most important that the emphasis should be on cultural and economic history. The way people actually lived and worked the earth is the important thing, leading finally to how so many inventions have transformed the earth and the life of human beings on it. The journey leads from myths to the steam engine and thence to the discovery of nuclear energy and the consequences of harnessing it.

In Classes 5 and 6 history is told in the form of stories up to and including the end of the Middle Ages. Biographical accounts are the main feature, but not necessarily only of 'great men'. In Classes 7 and 8 the pupils' interest is directed towards those aspects of modern history up to the present that can be depicted through descriptions of conditions, motivations, causes, effects and consequences: discoveries and inventions of the Industrial Revolution and its consequences. In other words the transition is made from depicting history in images and stories to a more causal and rational mode of depiction that is in keeping with the changes the pupils undergo as they develop. Nevertheless, the vividness, mobility and drama of the depictions must not disappear.

What history and why?

The history curriculum here outlined describes topics that *can and are* taken in the various classes as teaching content. Obviously it is impossible to cover all the themes described in the time normally allocated for history teaching. What criteria should we use to make the choice? Paul Law, formerly history teacher at Michael Hall School in England formulated an answer as follows:

> *To teach history economically one should try at every point to present examples or 'pictures' that are symptomatic of the forces shaping historical development. Such symptoms are not selected because they are typical or obviously important, but because through grasping them in an imaginative way the pupil will be able to reach an insight into the forces at work below the surface.*[2]

This advice is most relevant for the Upper School but also applies from Class 6 upwards. Economical in this sense means on the one hand, effective use of time and resources but on the other alludes to the integration with other subjects. Clearly history involves geography, literature, science, art, technology, mathematics, foreign languages and so on. Wherever possible the teaching benefits when relevant aspects from all these subjects cross-reference and interpenetrate each other.

The other key methodological starting point is to begin discussions of history in the present. That means not only taking current issues and seeking their explanations, their origins, their backgrounds in historical processes, it also means starting from where the students are in terms of their interests and general development. Essentially history serves the primary purpose of helping us understand the world we live in. The past is really only of interest to school pupils inasmuch as it reveals the present, both in terms of providing insights into what is happening in the world around us, but also as a reflection of developmental processes in the children themselves. This aspect highlights the leitmotiv of the evolution of consciousness within the history curriculum. Essentially we are studying the past to discover the evolution of human consciousness at different times in different cultures in different places and comparing that with our own.

Furthermore, the future too belongs to the study of history. The unrealised potential within each human being is the resource that needs tapping. Ideals are an expression of this potential since ideals provide the motivation for change and progress. History as a subject has an important role in both showing how ideals have motivated in the past but also in activating young people to a sense of their own historical potential. It is not a question of sowing ideological seeds – indeed this past century has demonstrated drastically what can happen when whole generations are indoctrinated with the ideals of the 'ruling' generation, or at least those in power. History can be a dangerous instrument, even in most subtle ways, of creating mindsets that limit freedom of thought and action. History's contribution to the cultivation of the basis for human freedom lies not in directing the rising generation to think this or that thought, but to support the creation of the faculties of thinking, judgement, moral initiative and social awareness within them. By definition we cannot know what the next generation will make out of the world we have created in the past. But we should give them the tools to ensure that they can do what seems necessary out of who they are and who they will become. History has to be a process of emancipation, otherwise it loads a millstone around their necks.

Class 5

The study of history proper begins in Class 5. Now the children are beginning to be interested in larger contexts and, as Steiner put it, to take on board historical 'concepts'.

Initially they are introduced to the ancient cultures of India, Persia, Mesopotamia and ancient Egypt. Though it is rarely taught, there is no reason why the ancient cultures of China, Meso- and South America cannot be added to this list. Following a background of Greek mythology comes Greek history from Homer's time up to its encounter with oriental culture at the time of Alexander's campaigns.

It is important that the methods used should give the children a vivid concept of space and time in a living and pictorial way through experiencing how very different and how far away these former times were and how those cultures related to their landscapes and climate. They should also be given many interesting examples of how our culture today is founded on the achievements of past ages. This can enable a feeling to arise in the children that the different flowers of human civilisation unfold in the many peoples of the earth, that every culture has its own essence and yet at the same time contributes to the history of humanity and to our own civilisation. In this way the horizon of the youngsters is stretched far beyond their own geographical boundaries, and the foundation is laid for an understanding of how culture belongs to humanity as a whole.

At this age the children still need to be told things in a mainly pictorial manner. So the emphasis is not on an entirely scientific, fact-oriented, chronological presentation. By presenting history in the form of vivid pictorial narrative, the teacher lets the children share and feel the deeds and sufferings of historical figures. The context should speak for itself without unnecessary interpretation. In this way history lessons have their effect on morality and conscience. This does not mean that a moralising tone should creep into the lessons, but it does have a bearing on the teacher's responsibility in deciding what material to present and how to put it before the children.

The pupils recite and sing texts and verses from the various cultural epochs. In connection with ancient Greek history they might also be introduced to the Greek language and script.

- Mythological content from the ancient Indian Vedas, Upanishads and the Bhagavadgita; how the caste system arose. The childhood of Krishna; Krishna and Arjuna. Though belonging to a very different historical time, the life of Buddha can be taught to show the evolution of the Hindu religion
- The ancient Iranian culture: development of sedentary communities; beginnings of farming and animal husbandry; the life of Zarathustra; texts from the Avesta and the Bundahesh.
- The city cultures of Mesopotamia; the Epic of Gilgamesh; cuneiform script
- Motifs from the mythology of ancient Egypt; examples of the great achievements of Egyptian culture such as the pyramids, royal graves, irrigation systems, hieroglyphs; establishment of a state system; how the geography of the Nile Valley influenced the Egyptian feeling for life and death
- Ancient Greece: The Iliad, or Odyssey; the rise of the Greek polis (Sparta, Athens); figures and events from the time of the Persian Wars; the age of Pericles; Alexander and the spread of Greek culture
- Legends from the Pre-Columbian cultures of Central and South America; life of the Mayas, Toltecs and Aztecs
- Legends from Ancient China

Class 6

By the age of twelve, children are ready to experience causality in history. The period to be taken covers about 2000 years, the history of the Romans and the Middle Ages up to approx. 1400 AD, so there needs to be clear criteria for the choice of topics.

During this period, history makes the transition from the origins of civilisation to the dimension of human events. The leading historical personalities now emerge as representative of social groupings. Now that the pupils are beginning to understand cause and effect, it is important for them to encounter the duality that comes to expression between personalities, groups, institutions, power bases such as patricians and plebeians, Rome and Carthage, Romans and barbarians, Arabs and Franks, Emperor and Pope, monks and knights. The history of the Romans and the Middle Ages can be viewed from this perspective. By means of examples the pupils experience the beginning of a dialectical principle which they will come to understand fully when they go through history for the second time in the Upper School. The foundation for this has to be laid in Class 6. History focuses increasingly on human confrontation, even in religion.

The Latin language is one of the special aspects of Roman culture that the pupils should now encounter. In Class 5 they were introduced to Greek, and now, in Class 6, the same can happen for Latin. A central theme is to identify the way Greco-Latin history affects us right up to the present time so that the pupils can see the many ways in which modern society still reflects the qualities of 'Roman-ness' in, for example the idea of the citizen – the *res-publica*, in civil justice, in civil engineering – roads, aqueducts, sewage systems, heating, federal administration, etc. This principle of identifying factors still at work in our times, albeit in transformed ways, also applies to the effects the Crusades had on cultural development during the Middle Ages, e.g. through the influence of Arabic culture in the development of science, trade, banking and so on. The rise of Islam and its factions can be paralleled with modern historical and cultural developments, including the rise of Islamic fundamentalism.

- Enable the children to form concrete concepts of linear time, through spatial representations, through sequences of generations, through vernacular history using the testimony of older people, the sense of distance in time must be almost physically experienced
- Roman history
- The dual aspect of Rome's founding; Romulus and Remus (Rhea Silvia-Mars), the seven mythical kings, patricians and plebeians
- The rise of the Roman Empire and its constitution, traditional Roman values
- The confrontation between Rome and Carthage (Hannibal and Scipio)
- The organisation of the Roman army
- Caesar and the beginning of a new system of imperial power
- Roman achievements in civil engineering, road building, aqueducts and viaducts, heating and sanitation systems, typical Roman villa, baths, etc. Technical limitations, e.g. the lack of the harness and stirrup, poor shipbuilding and navigation skills, inability to feed large urban populations
- Visits to and study of Roman sites in the locality.
- The spread of Christianity in the Roman Empire (Paul, Early Christian church, catacombs, persecution, Constantine, Diocletian etc.)
- Decline of Rome: the Huns and Goths, migration of the peoples

* The Middle Ages
* Mohammed and the spread of Islam
* The Franks, Charlemagne and the re-establishment of the Roman Empire
* The Norman Conquest
* Monastic culture, contrast two of the Cistercian, Benedictine, Dominican and Franciscan Orders
* The rivalry between Pope and Emperor
* The Crusades. Richard the Lion Heart
* Chivalry and orders of knighthood
* The meeting of East and West (Frederick II). New vocabulary in European languages from Islam and the East, e.g. cotton, alcohol, coffee, algebra, etc.
* Beginning of city culture, guilds and cathedral building
* The Battle of Agincourt as symptomatic of the end of Feudalism
* Technological innovation in the Middle Ages, e.g. water wheels, tidal mills and windmills, magnetic compasses, shipbuilding, use of steel for armour and weapons, gunpowder and clocks

Class 7

At this age, children need to build bridges to the world based on their own personal powers of judgement. Their relationship to a teacher as an authority declines. Therefore the type of teaching must change to enable them to accept the material of the history lessons through their own understanding. The pupils should begin to learn that historical events belong to a broader context and that the consequences of these events can be equally wide-ranging. The way cultural and technological developments influence historical events and how both express a changing consciousness is a central theme. The most important task is to awaken the pupils' interest in the world, and the main part in this is played by recounting history in the way it relates to individuals, events and experiences.

The period from the end of the Middle Ages to beginning of modern history is now at the centre of history lessons. In his lectures on the curriculum Steiner described the task for the seventh class as follows:

In the seventh class the object is to make it so that the child really can understand what kind of life modern man evolved with the advent of the fifteenth century, and then to describe the circumstances in Europe and outside of Europe, up to about the beginning of the seventeenth century. This period of time is of the utmost importance, and it must be treated with great care. It is even more important than what follows.[3]

By telling the pupils about the discoveries and inventions, about art, and about new forms of trade and of religious life we show the pupils what is new, what has never existed before. It is also important to show them the new way in which people of the Renaissance related to the world through their senses. They should learn how practical, mechanical, technical matters took an increasing hold of people's awareness, while their relationship to miracles and wonders, to holy things, waned. Since the pupils in Class 7 are going through a similar shift of relationship, history does not take place outside themselves, in a museum, but is always topical and contemporary. Bringing in this topical aspect is also one of the aims of history lessons.

* The history of European explorations of other continents and their consequences for the indigenous populations (including an initial understanding of the problematical aspects of

colonialism, e.g. the testimony of Bartolomé de las Casas concerning the plight of the Indians of South America), Henry the Navigator and the Portolan mapmaking, Columbus, the Spanish Conquest, Magellan, the English Colonies in North America. Cultural and economic aspects of the New World and new commodity imports to Europe. The origins of the slave trade. Sir Walter Raleigh, Francis Drake

* The invention of printing (as an example of modern inventions: the consequences up to the present – example of cause and effect); other inventions such as commercial arithmetic and international banking
* The Renaissance, rise of Florence. Humanism in its reflection of classical values
* Examples of how modern science began (Galileo, Kepler, Copernicus, etc.)
* Joan of Arc and the historical consequences of her actions
* Jan Hus, Martin Luther as examples of a new inner religious independence, and at the same time of attitudes weighed down by tradition
* The rise of new kinds of trade and commerce (e.g. the Fugger family, the Medicis, the Hansa league)
* The English Reformation and Elizabethan Age, Henry VIII, Elizabeth I, the Spanish Armada, Sir Walter Raleigh, James I, Shakespeare's life
* The Thirty Years' War
* The plague
* Land enclosures and the wool industry

Class 8

In Class 8 we should endeavour to bring history right up to the present day. Most of what nowadays passes for history lessons need be mentioned only as an aside. It is much more important for children to hear how the steam engine and the mechanical loom have transformed the world, than about such curiosities as the Ems Telegram (which contributed to the outbreak of the Franco-German War).[4]

The interplay between causality and purposeful human actions can be observed throughout the Industrial Revolution, and it would be good to clarify the difference between the two. This is an historical paradigm of the first importance.[5]

These two indications, from Steiner and Christof Lindenberg respectively, offer criteria for teaching history in Class 8.

Examples of causality are to be found in the social consequences of the great inventions. Both the positive developments (medicine, chemistry, transport and social mobility, trade unions, etc.) and the negative (poverty of the workers, child labour, slavery and serfdom, intensive exploitation of mineral resources, colonialism and conflict between imperial powers, etc.) aspects should be treated. The emphasis in Class 8 is on the experience of the individual in a rapidly changing world. The ideologies that motivated them are usually left until Class 9. History can be taught through brief but colourful accounts of personalities whose lives portray the symptomatic signature of the times.

History is taken up to the present time with special emphasis on the way human life has been changed by the Industrial Revolution and new technology. As throughout the curriculum, history is taught symptomatically and thematically rather than through adherence to strict chronology and the quantity of fact. Key moments, symbolic images, typical biographies or eyewitness accounts, extracts from literature, journals, the press and media are all used as sources to exemplify the issues being presented.

Examples of important history themes include:

* Accounts from the Pilgrim Fathers or pioneers in the New World and the founding of the US, its political concept and the Constitution; the Slave Trade and the Civil War, the resistance and fate of the Native American peoples, the biographies of Red Cloud, Geronimo, the consequences of the Battles of Little Big Horn and Wounded Knee
* Accounts of life in the British Empire, from the nineteenth and twentieth centuries, e.g. the Boer War, the life of Mahatma Gandhi, Florence Nightingale, Dr. Livingstone, Marcus Garvey, etc.
* Social consequences of factory work, child labour, slave plantations, transportation
* Mass emigration, Irish Famine, the immigrant in America
* The invention of the steam engine, James Watt, George Stevenson, development of railways, canals, Arkwright's spinning machine, Eli Whitney's cotton gin
* Newer technologies; telegraph, telephone, gramophone, light bulb and their social consequences. Biographies of Edison, Madame Curie, Liebig, Fleming
* First World War, life in the trenches

The following biographies can provide a background for an outline sketch of historical events:

* Lenin and Russian Revolution
* Wilfred Owen (the poet)
* Hitler and rise of Nazism
* Mao Zedong and the Cultural Revolution
* Martin Luther King
* Nelson Mandela

These should be balanced with biographies of other participants, victims, and the use of literature e.g. Anne Frank, Jacques Lusseyran (*And There Was Light*, the autobiography of a blind hero of the French Resistance), Laurens van de Post (*The Seed and the Sower*, account of life in a Japanese prison camp), John Hersey, (*Hiroshima*, account of six survivors), Benjamin Wilkomenski, Primo Levi (concentration camp survivors).

* The Berlin Wall and the Cold War, Korean and Vietnam Wars. Revolutionary movements in South and Central America, The Fall of the Wall, collapse of Soviet empire
* First World-Third World issues, North-South problem (using concrete examples, e.g. the coffee trade, oil exploration and rise of pan-Arabism, famine cycle in Horn of Africa)
* Environmental issues, rainforest, nuclear testing, environmental pollution
* Freedom and independence movements, regional conflicts: The Civil Rights Movement and Martin Luther King, Nelson Mandela, Fidel Castro, Vietnam, Israel-Palestine, Northern Ireland

Classes 9 to 12

In Classes 5 to 8, history lessons have depicted the progress of humanity from a mythical, prehistorical cultural stage up to the development of a material civilisation and its religious, social, political and ecological consequences. This has brought the pupils more and more practically into the present time. This progress is now repeated and deepened at a new level, in keeping with the developing capacities of the young people. The transition in consciousness from Class 8 to Class 9 with respect to history has been likened to the transition from the Middle Ages to Modern times.[6] The analogy is not to be taken literally but does characterise the shift in perspective.

The content and method of the lessons take account of the pupils' growing capacity to understand ideals as the moving forces in history and their developing capacity to take in overall insights. Rather than giving them finished images, it is now more a matter of appealing to their own capacities to form judgements. The teacher becomes the helper in bringing to birth knowledge that arises out of the young people's own forces of personality. History lessons should help them tread the path from *passing* judgements to *forming* judgements, which is the equivalent of building up a new relationship between their own individuality and the world.

In Class 9 modern history up to the present is reviewed once again. Class 10 brings a revision of the period from prehistory, through the Neolithic period and the origins of agriculture and the early urban civilisations up to Alexander the Great. And in Class 11 the Greco-Roman period up to the Middle Ages are looked at anew. This represents a second run through, at a new level, of the epochs of history. The final perspective comes in Class 12. Here the previous focus on the different periods of history is widened out to provide an overview of human history, universal history, as a whole. The students learn to understand themselves as active participants in the evolution of humanity; they learn to understand the historical position they themselves occupy in history. They come to see themselves as inheritors of the past, yet at the same time they should have the feeling that their destiny bears the seeds for future evolution and that through their own destiny they are also linked with the future destiny of humanity as a whole.

On entry into the Upper School the students expect to learn new tools for learning about history. They have a need to experiment and this means learning the various methodologies of historical research. This means above all emphasising the questioning role of the historian. Material can be presented anew, not simply as factual information but as a source that needs interpretation. Particularly important in understanding contemporary history is the awareness of the absence of a moral dimension, of materialism and its consequent loss of higher meaning. This realisation needs to be counter-balanced by the perspective that each individual is called upon to act out moral intuition based on insight, rather than on any external authorities.

The corollary to the element of questioning and experimentation is the adolescent's need for security and certainty. For this reason the teaching should avoid being too abstract and intellectual. The teaching material should be as concrete and factual as possible, it should in a sense 'speak for itself'. The methodology used, however, should cultivate a critical and questioning attitude. The basic criterion is whether one can move from facts to thoughts. One method, which combines both of these processes, is to extract the facts from original sources, or for the teacher to present the facts in imaginative ways (e.g. in a fictional interview with one of the chief protagonists). The information gathered can then be interpreted by presenting it from a variety of perspectives, from the viewpoint of opponents, from the view of worker or factory owner, from the 'terrorist' or 'freedom fighter', etc. 'Stories' can be presented in the style of different kinds of newspaper or reportage. This exercise can lead to discussion of the role of the media in relation to world events and to the formation of what constitutes history. At any rate, history must avoid the impression of being an unfolding tapestry that records objectively what happened. Like the Bayeux Tapestry itself, it records a particular perspective, that most common view in history, namely that of the victors and the literate classes, and must of necessity be interpreted to reveal its full historical value. The recent trend of history 'from the bottom up', that reveals the everyday lives, concerns and consciousness of the people, as opposed to the great and good, offers many rich veins to mine for the symptomatological approach.

Class 9

The task of this class is to study recent history up to the present, that is the period covered in the previous class, but this time the emphasis is on the ideas that motivated and drove historical development. Steiner's suggestion was to take a key motive for each century from the fifteenth up to the present:

* For the fifteenth/sixteenth centuries, the theme of humanity's expanding horizons and the significance of this
* For the seventeenth century, the dissolution of old social structures and their replacement by new political ones
* For the eighteenth century, the ideas of the Enlightenment in Europe and America
* For the nineteenth century, the 'flowing together of the history of the various peoples'.[7]

To this we must add the twentieth century. The motifs for this past century must involve the antagonism of Communism, Fascism and Capitalism, the emergence of a global economy and the tensions between First and Third Worlds, including the emergence of the Pacific Rim economies as well as the incomplete consequences following the end of the Cold War. The twentieth century cannot be so easily encapsulated.

The purpose of studying these dynamic historical processes is to understand the present world as it can be perceived by a fifteen year old. Furthermore history for this age only has meaning if it identifies ideas which lead towards the future. An analysis of modern history can lead to a picture of social dysfunction, disintegration and pathology, of injustice, of suppressed and violated civil and human rights, of inexorable, of unmanageable historical forces. This would, however, only be part of the picture. If history lessons are to engage the student's interest and inner activity, then they must offer not only a key to interpretation, they must offer the possibility of redemption. History also has to reveal in its inner progressive nature that human beings always have the potential for creating social health as well as social sickness.

Within the key themes that this period of history reveals, each has a shadow and a light side, even if historical events appear to over-emphasise the dark side. Technology is a classic example. Ideology and propaganda can always be countered by the possibility of freedom of thought; state control by individual initiative; fear by courage; injustice by justice; power by the balance of checks and balances; pessimism by optimism; utopianism by applied insight. History provides enough examples of all these balancing forces. Only when the students discover that each one-sided force in history can be countered by another and that the individual possesses ultimately the only source of social renewal, can the present be understood in terms of the future. History in Class 9 must be future orientated!

The aim of awakening interest and motivation in the students is not achieved by overt moralising but by developing historical judgement based on the recognition of the appropriate guiding principles for each aspect of the social organism.

Specifically this means the recognition that the functional principle for the spiritual, intellectual and religious realm is freedom, without which this realm cannot function, to the detriment of social health. It means the recognition that public life, politics, the legal and justice system, social contracts and so on cannot function healthily unless the equal rights of each individual are respected and protected and that fairness and transparency are the prerequisites of this. Finally it must be recognised that economic life depends on the principle of mutuality and co-operation between people, organisations, industries and nations, as well as commitment to a non-exploitative attitude to the natural world. The students can well grasp that these functional social principles, if applied to the wrong realm, can lead to social instability and dysfunction. Freedom applied to the economic realm leads to gross injustice and the survival of the strongest. Mutuality in politics leads to corruption. Equality in intellectual life leads to stultifying conformity.

It is important to balance the domestic history of one's home country with wider perspectives of world history. The home country serves best as a specific example of global processes.

* Starting with current affairs (that morning's news headlines for example), the major themes of contemporary history can be introduced. The best advice is to start where the pupils are, what they know and understand and then trace the roots back into history. Many of these can quickly be traced back to the end of the Renaissance, if not earlier, e.g. the idea of nation states and its development, the dissolution of tradition societies, industrialisation and the post-industrial world of the developed nations, the formation of empires and the consequences of their disintegration
* Motifs for the twentieth century might be: the collapse of empires, post-Colonialism, totalitarianism, Fascism, Communism and its collapse, Pax Americana and the Cold War, the move away from the Eurocentric view of the world, the rise of the Pacific region, the arrival on the scene of developing countries, in short, the globalisation of our picture of the world
* The emergence of a worldwide consciousness is beginning to form not only in culture, commerce, technology and politics but also with regard to ecological factors. The historical events of this century mirror both the negative and the positive aspects of these processes. It is important for the pupils to get to know not only unhealthy tendencies and catastrophes but also the positive forces at work in ideas about social forms and a healing partnership with nature. The twentieth century is now the main focus of history lessons
* Emancipation of the individual at the beginning of modern times; humanism and the Renaissance as expressions of individual development, invention and discovery
* British history as an example
* The English Civil War, the Rise of Dissent and Non Conformists, Quakers, Levellers, Diggers, etc.
* The 1688 Restoration, Constitutional Monarchy, the rise of Parliament
* The Enlightenment and the effects of the Enlightenment on politics (Locke, Montaigne, Rousseau)
* The background of the Irish Question
* The American Declaration of Independence and the founding of the USA, the structure of the American Constitution (figures like Benjamin Franklin, Tom Paine, Thomas Jefferson); the American Civil War, mass immigration to North

America, the Monroe Doctrine, US foreign policy from the First World War to the present

* The ideas of the French Revolution (liberty, equality, fraternity); the course of the Revolution leading up to Napoleon, including leading figures before and during the Revolution, e.g. Rousseau, La Fayette, Danton, Robespierre
* The idea of human rights and the fight for their realisation up to the present day
* Development of the modern state, absolutism, parliamentarianism, US Constitution – checks and balances on power
* The rise of national states in the nineteenth century in the dynamic tension between opposing interests (e.g. history of unification and independence of Italy, Argentina or Germany): nationalism and liberalism as forces that build societies and states
* The development of industrialisation and the associated social question: the spread of European interests across the globe (worldwide transport and communication systems, world economy, imperialism)
* The rise and realisation of socialist ideas; Marx and Engels; the rise of trade unions; Communism in the twentieth century; the Russian Revolution, origins and outcome, Stalin; the collapse of the Soviet Empire
* The First World War, its consequences in and outside Europe
* Steiner's idea of a threefold ordering of society
* The Second World War, its political background, summary of main campaigns, its end and consequences
* The United Nations, European Union, NATO, ideals and problems
* The problems of post-imperial age: rise of national, ethnic, religious conflicts in many regions

Class 10

A primary concern of Class 10 age students (sixteen year olds) is the question of causality and origins. How things came to be as they now are, is a fundamental question that young people ask of the world. The possible answers to this question require us to go into deep history, into earlier, radically different modes of consciousness. It is necessary to see in a broad sweep, the transition from hunter-gatherer lifestyles to highly structured urban civilisation and to reflect on the changing human consciousness that accompanied such transitions. Rather than a simplistic view of the march of technical and political progress, the students should learn to see different kinds of socio-economic organisation as the reflection of different kinds of mentality and consciousness. Furthermore such change also reflects a fundamental shift in human relationships to the natural world.

The evolution of human consciousness that this major period of pre- and early history expresses, qualitatively reflects the changing consciousness of each individual in the course of his or her biography. Thus the exploration of the origins of human society is also a process of self-discovery. In terms of consciousness this period spans the shift from a participatory consciousness in which the external world is experienced as being, as 'Thou', to an observer consciousness in which the external world has become inanimate, has become an object of study and thinking has become internalised.

This is the time for a second look at the cultural history of humanity from prehistoric times, through the Neolithic revolution to the high civilisations, ending with the decline of the Greek city states and the spread of Greek culture by Alexander the Great. The archaeological techniques involved in gaining knowledge about remote periods in history offer examples both of deductive and inductive thinking as well as discovery through doing (making stone tools from flint for example). It is important for the pupils to use their own thought processes, so that they have a genuine experience of the matters they have come to understand. A central theme for this main-lesson period is the inter-relationship between human societies and the environments they live in. Ideas and technologies, religions and social structures have their roots in the deepest human experience of the environment, of the earth, the sky, the cycles of the seasons, of the rise and fall of the life-giving river, of night and death and the heavenly constellations. This is hard for modern consciousness to grasp since we are so detached from these realities. The Class 10 student, in his or her inner development, is very much in tune with the forces of the earth, yet needs to awaken to the realm of ideas that articulate these relationships. This period of history reveals the emergence of nature forces as creative numinous realities in the imagination of human beings in particular times and places. These natural formative forces, transformed through human consciousness were harnessed to incredible feats of city and temple building, to vast irrigation systems and to complex religious activity. At the end of the period, these forces have become increasingly individualised and internalised. This transformation is mirrored in the souls of the sixteen to seventeen-year-old students.

* The Human Revolution of the Upper Palaeolithic: Ice Age societies, culture and art, new technologies and the expansion of humans into all continents and new environments, Australasia, the Pacific Islands, North and South America, Siberia, North West Europe
* Ice Age art can be seen as a flowering of the highest cultural level, in a very specific context. In Ice Age art we can see not the beginnings of culture but an already advanced stage of development, in which the idea of ritual, religion, and the sacred place were well established. The images can be seen as equivalent to vivid mental images – the ability to produce them marking a significant stage in evolving human faculties. They can also be seen to contain the fundamental elements of conceptual or symbolic language
* The end of the Ice Age, rise in sea levels and corresponding loss of land in many parts of the world: Mesolithic societies, diversification of cultural and economic life, with a loss of artistic quality in a return to very primitive forms in art. The significance of the invention of the bow, which belongs in the period
* Neolithic Age: origins of agriculture in the Golden Crescent, Catal Huyuk, Mesopotamia, Nile Ganges, Yellow River, Yangtze, MeKong river valleys, Central and South America
* From settlement to city: centralisation of authority, writing, bureaucracy, trade, state religion
* A comparison between the Egyptian culture and the European Megalithic culture

It is important when dealing with these issues to avoid the classical concept of progress. Firstly many of the developments that we traditionally associate with civilisation were established long before, e.g. animal husbandry, temple and ritual structures, production of ceramics, metallurgy and probably writing. Secondly the transition to settled communities based on farming lead initially to a decline of living standards and life expectancy, an increase in disease and greater human conflict. The so-called advantages of civilisation were a long time coming. It is more appropriate to see these steps as wrestling from a change in consciousness, than as the result of material progress

* Ancient Hindu culture and the radical changes it underwent as exemplified by the Bhagavad-Gita and later Buddhism. The origins of the caste system
* The ancient Persian culture and the mythical figure of Zarathustra
* Chaldean culture and the Epic of Gilgamesh
* The ancient Hebrew civilisation and its development of a script culture
* A survey of the Old, Middle and New Kingdoms of ancient Egypt, showing the key elements of its religious and socio-economic structures, their consistency and stability interspersed with chaotic and dramatic change
* Bronze Age societies. Hallstadt and Celtic cultures in Europe, the Toltec and Maya cultures in Central and South America, Ancient Crete
* The origins of Chinese culture and its Neolithic revolution, the Zhou Dynasty in China, Lao Tzu, Confucius. The nature of traditional Chinese society
* Rise of ancient Greek city state. Examples of world views from the main schools of philosophy.

Class 11

In Class 11 the students usually make significant steps in their inner development and maturity. This very inwardness and capacity for reflection, the potential for love, devotion and service that awakens at this age finds a significant reflection in the esoteric streams flowing through the Middle Ages, notably those historical forces associated with the Celtic Christian Church of Iona and Lindesfarne, of learned scholasticism, the aesthetic and devotional qualities cultivated by the Minnesånger or Troubadour tradition, of Sufi mysticism, of Franciscan poverty and selflessness, of chivalry and knightly virtues, of Knights Templar and St Martin of Tours, of master cathedral builders and so on. However, the Medieval period also gives expression to the forces of the will, migration of peoples at the end of the Roman Empire, to Viking raiders, to the rise of Islam and the East-West conflicts that arose, to forces of power struggle between church and state, Emperor and Pope.

Several strands run through the historical period covered in this class, which spans the transition of Antiquity to the Middle Ages. Many of the themes flow artistically together in Wolfram von Eschenbach's *Parzifal*, which is studied in literature, and in Medieval art, studied in the Art History lessons. The history lesson can culminate in these subsequent studies.

The history lessons in this class show the way the world of the Middle Ages came about as the heritage of a Greco-Roman, a Germanic and a Judeo-Christian stream of evolution. Furthermore the medieval world with its tensions between state and church, and between Western and Eastern culture, provided the preparation for modern individualism in the culture of the city.

Since there is such a wealth of material to draw on, the history teacher will have to decide on some points of emphasis.

* An overview of main themes of Greek Philosophy
* Spread of Christianity, e.g. the life and travels of Paul
* Rise and spread of Islam, its contribution to Western culture
* The migration of the peoples following the fall of the Roman Empire, e.g. Angles, Saxons, Jutes, Vikings
* Development of countries, local politics, feudalism

* The significance of the monasteries and their influence on economic and cultural life
* Secular and ecclesiastical power, Emperor and Pope
* West and East; the Crusades
* The town with its special relationship to trade and crafts, development of the towns, the plague, social problems
* Gothic cathedral building
* The Medieval world picture (Augustine, Thomas Aquinas, Meister Eckhart, Nicolas of Cusa). Also the views of the common people e.g. as described in works such as *Montcullou* by E. Le Roy Ladurie, or *The Cheese and the Worm* by Carlo Ginzburg
* The transformation of the Medieval world view, e.g. development of maps from Mappa Mundi to Toscanelli's world map

Class 12

There are three main motifs for Class 12. Firstly there is the requirement that the pupils gain an overview of world history. Secondly by taking specific individual cultures or peoples as examples, the pupils should be shown 'the biography of a culture' (which can be one that reaches its culmination, or that breaks off, is incomplete, or gets stuck at a particular stage). Thirdly they must come to understand that, as history has proceeded, individual human beings have tended to become independent earlier and earlier and that their further development has become less and less a matter of external norms or social conventions, in other words that individuals are becoming progressively more free.

The first motif gives the pupils an experience of being a member of humanity and shows them the reality of the idea of evolution. The second motif gives them a sense of belonging within their own destiny. The third motif points to their own path towards the future.

* Overview of the main epochs of world history from pre-history to modern times
* An understanding of contemporary history, of developments that have taken place since 1945, and of daily history, and a capacity to form judgements about these
* Showing the inner laws of great cycles of evolution (e.g. Jaspers' Time Axis Model)
* Various forms of government, economic recovery, making and implementing laws, administration, social and political problems
* Human rights, citizens' rights, development of political awareness, being ready for democracy
* Creating an awareness that every individual is history and creates world history through his or her deeds
* Collaboration amongst different nations
* International law
* Present developments, changes, situations and tasks of different nations
* Present changes in Europe: peace politics
* Present economic orders and possible ways of structuring social organisms, state or economic situations
* Topical events: united Europe; EU; development of a pluralistic, democratic order of society
* History of different nations from the point of view of their developmental dynamic (e.g. Greece, China, Japan, USA, Russia)
* Philosophy of history and changing trends in what each period understands history to be

19

Life Sciences

The whole structure of the Steiner-Waldorf curriculum is profoundly ecological.

The teaching method itself, going from the whole to the parts, confirms this and encourages children to keep the widest perspective on their studies at any age. As examples: in the kindergarten an active awareness of the seasons, in the Middle School a sense of the wisdom revealed by the intricate relationships of plants and animals, in the Upper School an appreciation that analytical thinking and holistic thinking each make their different contribution to our understanding of living processes.

The themes taken up in different classes within the life sciences relate organically to the curriculum throughout the school, subconsciously nourishing a sense of unity within the whole.

As with other aspects of the Steiner-Waldorf curriculum such as writing and reading, what is recognisably learning in the conventional sense does not appear until much later than is usually the case. Nevertheless, as with writing and reading, the skills only seem delayed to the superficial eye and closer attention will show that seed preparations are being made in the soil of earlier consciousness for the faculties to germinate and grow rapidly in later years. It is hard to avoid such growth metaphors to explain the richness and depth of the curriculum and the teaching process.

It is remarkable that, many years before public awareness of environmental issues arose, the Steiner-Waldorf curriculum had laid the basis for the cultivation of an ecological consciousness in children.

Kindergarten

As elaborated in the section on Early Years, Steiner-Waldorf education perceives the very young child as having a qualitatively different consciousness from that of the adult or even the older child. There is not the same separation or distance between self and the world. The consciousness is much more within the environment and within what attracts attention, with sense impressions deeply absorbed and played out through the limbs as activity and imitation.

Any study of the life sciences needs to have its foundation in such intense experiences but modern life does not provide much time for young children to be actively present in a natural and living environment.

A Steiner-Waldorf kindergarten lays the basis for this in number of ways:

* The celebrations of the festivals make the rhythms of the earth, moon and sun an integral part of the child's awareness of the world
* The time spent in creative play (working with wood, wool, water and sand, for example) brings a wealth of sensory experiences which cultivate keen observation in later years
* Their teacher's care for the beauty and orderliness of the Kindergarten environment, inside and outside, will encourage those same qualities in the children. It will also go deeper, nurturing a respectful and precise attitude to their investigations of nature when they are older
* Stories, fairy tales, verses and artistic activities develop the imaginative faculties, without which the foundations of scientific method are barren and the holistic quality of thinking necessary to comprehend the complexity of the living world is stunted

Classes 1, 2 and 3

The underlying mood of these classes carry all the themes relevant to the life sciences. The stories that are chosen during these stages of development reflect the changing relationship of the young child to the living world.

In Classes 1 and 2, the stories carry themes of transformation – the frog changing into the prince, the death of the snake and the appearance of the princess. They allow the children to understand the language of the animals and to be aware of other beings – gnomes, fairies – that guard secrets or protect life. Such imaginative elements are not fanciful, but lay foundations for a healthy feeling relationship towards the complexities and intricacies of animal/plant relationships and the hidden qualities of the biosphere studied in the Upper School through the faculty of clear thinking.

In Class 3, creation stories give an holistic image of the origins of the earth, plants, animals and human beings. Other stories relate how particular people, holy people or saints, cultivated a special relationship with the animal world (e.g. St. Francis). In the farming main-lesson, the children learn how the farmer works with the forces of nature. As well as ploughing, sowing and harvesting there are hedges and fences to maintain, lambs to protect, land to drain and crops to weed.

All of this forms the prelude to a more conscious study of the living world in the following years, as well as unconsciously confirming that an ecology which respects and cares for the Earth has its ethical basis in the moral development of human beings.

Classes 4 to 8

There is a distinct threshold in the inner development of the nine year old and in Class 4 this establishes itself with the children experiencing more distance to the people and the world around them. The imaginative faculties are still deeply drawn by a story, but the content now needs a sharper definition. Observations and descriptions of the living world which combine accurate detail with a sense of the character of the plant or animal and the environment in which they live, form a bridge to Classes 6, 7 and 8.

The characterisation of a cow in Class 4, for example, can allow the particular quality of the animal to emerge from the details of its physical form, its movements, its diet and its whole way of life. The gaze, the movements, the chewing, the teeth, the chambered stomach, the digestive power which creates the richness of milk from its unlikely source, the birth and development of the calf – all these characteristics do more than define the cow as an 'herbivorous mammal'. They allow a feeling relationship to the cow, which is neither sentimental nor a fantasy, but a healthy union of the artistic, feeling faculty and exact observation. This can include those ways in which a creature's behaviour seems to reflect inner qualities such as greed, loyalty, pride, cunning and determination. At this stage of a child's development it is an appropriate step towards objectivity for the children to recognise that to be human is to be aware of these qualities and to keep them in balance.

Teaching Class 5 about the oak tree, for instance, with its unique characteristics and gestures, through lively description, painting, and poetry leads their own experiences towards an accuracy of observation which does not degrade the essential nature of the oak into a mere category. The children's experience of animals remains relatively holistic in quality and there is no need to introduce ideas such as that of 'species'. The aim is to characterise the animals studied qualitatively so that their life-patterns, relationship and adaption to their environment can be appreciated.

The Class 6 geology, the Class 7 health and nutrition themes and the Class 8 study of the human body increasingly draw on the children's own observations. The emphasis is on the phenomena as they can be experienced (through direct observation or the description of the teacher) rather than on the theories that may be current in contemporary science.

Gardening as an activity emerges from the general care for the classroom plants to the cultivation of a plot, where flowers and vegetables can be grown, compost can be made and responsibilities for the land awakened in a practical way. Weekly lessons can accompany all life science main-lessons through to Class 8.

Upper School

The threshold between puberty and adolescence gives birth to the faculties of thinking in a new way. While the early trials of adolescence have strong physical and emotional characteristics, it is the awakening thinking which guides young people towards some clarity on the great issues of identity and meaning which rise up before them increasingly: who am I?, what is life for?

The emphasis of the life sciences in Classes 9 and 10 is on the human body and the processes that provide the physical basis for consciousness, health and reproduction. The intention is to provide a basis for appreciation and wonder of the living form. The curriculum seeks to avoid presenting analogues of the body as a machine, or human motivation in merely determinist terms, in a way that tends to narrow or reduce the outlook of young people. They can, however, begin to compare and contrast current and historical models for life science, learning to recognise how theories evolve or are rejected through proposing hypotheses and testing them over time. Meanwhile, adolescents need to exercise their burgeoning thinking capacities on understanding the processes within the body, recognising its complexities and mysteries and to facing the issues that arise through the advance of medical science.

Alongside these studies, practical work with plant and animal should include field studies and bring a direct environmental and ecological emphasis to the life science curriculum.

By Classes 11 and 12, the adolescents' faculty of thinking has strengthened and matured to become more deeply engaged by ideas. The life science curriculum meets this with a study of botany and zoology in which current cell theory, genetics and Darwinism play a major part. This emphasis is echoed in a study of atomic theory, light wave/particle duality and astronomy in the chemistry and physics main-lessons. Young people's thinking is now mature enough to appreciate that there are alternative scientific viewpoints than the ones currently portrayed in the textbooks or through popular science and technology. Through an historical approach to scientific ideas and the consequences of technology, they can gain the perspective to recognise that a healthy science sees theories rise and then fall as new phenomena are explored.

The life sciences curriculum in a Steiner-Waldorf school can lead young people to a clear understanding of contemporary scientific theory, an awareness of the human and environmental issues, issues raised by technology, as well as leaving them with a lively, open-minded attitude to the future of both.

Class 4

The focus of this main-lesson is the unique quality of the human being, which is to a large extent free of the instinctive behaviour of the animal world and whose physical body lacks those special features which allow the animals to live so intricately in their environment. The self-consciousness of the human condition is in part gained through the harmonious balance of those physiological features which are found as specialisations within the animal world. For example, the human arm and hand reflect this – their freedom of use and movement arises from *un*specialised joints and digits. The apposition of thumb and forefinger and the ability of human arms to open wide arises from this.

The characterisation of particular animals, as already described above, brings this principle to bear on the organs of the body as well. It can become very clear, by observation alone, that the metabolic system is brought to a particular, one-sided emphasis in the cow or other ruminant. The senses are particularly acute in the ever-active mouse or other small rodent – a vole quivers with nervous sensitivity. The form of the head is emphasised in the sea-urchin, while its close relation, the star fish shows itself as more of a 'limb' creature. There is no intention here to impart such comparisons as a theory, but to use this approach to unite what appears to be an overwhelming diversity and to relate it to the human being in an artistic and meaningful way.

Above all, the children need to gain a feeling for what is truly human through having the body upright, the hands free, with the power of speech and self-awareness.

Rudolf Steiner gave many examples to illustrate how the threefold dynamic inherent in the physiology of the human body can be seen displayed in a one-sided way in the animal world. His writings deepen this approach to include the spiritual basis of the human being and these give a teacher the widest possible context out of which to teach as well as examples to use in the classroom.

- The polarity of the human head and limbs with the mediating form of the trunk
- A small selection of familiar and unfamiliar animals to use as the basis for the characterisations and relationships referred to above. Examples: the cow, mouse and lion (or animals from similar families) illustrate diverse tendencies as do the octopus, snail and sea urchin from quite a different world. It is far better to create a rich experience with a few well-chosen creatures than to attempt too many, with the danger of the lessons becoming just 'nature study', valuable as that may be

* Different animal limbs illustrate the theme described above concerning the human hand, etc.
* The human hand and arm as a picture of human freedom – not the physiology of joints and bones, but the gesture and practical reality of their movement. Similarly, the human foot, femur and spine in relation to uprightness, leading to the theme of uniqueness in the human being
* Examples of how the limitations of the human body are balanced by technological and cultural achievements. From the spade to the aeroplane, human invention achieves what the instinctive behaviour of the badger and the birds achieve, with their specialised limbs
* Animals which reflect fundamental soul qualities and inner faculties: the eagle's perspective from the heights; the bull's power of will; the balance of strength, lithe grace and fearlessness in the lion

These characterisations of the animal world continue through Classes 5, 6, 7 and 8, with choices of animal-related topics moving from characterisation to observational nature study as causal thinking begins to consolidate during this phase. The emphasis continues to be on qualities, contrasts and relationships of creatures both with the human being and with one another, and so avoids reducing the rich ecological picture to, e.g. simplistic 'eat/be eaten' strategies.

Class 5

This is the relative calm of puberty before the storm of adolescence.

Elegance and harmony are visible in the children's running and gymnastics. It is an appropriate time for the study of plants, whose growth and movement has a quiet beauty of form, gesture and colour. Feelings of respect, gratitude and interest need to permeate this main-lesson and deepen the children's sensitivity for the earth as a living organism.

Every plant needs to be observed in the context of its relationship to the landscape, the soil and the climate. A single plant in a pot or, worse, cut up and examined under a microscope, speaks of isolation and fragmentation and such studies belong to the Upper School. Children of this age need to appreciate the range of plant forms over the earth, the gestures of typical plant species, the relationship to insects and soil, and the development from seed to flower and fruit. While observation and naming of plants should play its part, any systematic identification of species cuts across the warm familiarity that local trees and flowers should engender at this age. While plant parts can be named, emphasis on the polarity and contrast of root and stem, leaf and flower, seed and fruit is more nourishing to the interests of Class 5 than the details in the usual textbook.

The study of plants requires quiet, accurate observation, a sense for movement in growth and the appreciation of transformations of form and metamorphosis of organs. Goethe's studies of the plant and recent research that has taken the same direction are a rich source of material for leading the children into such an holistic approach.

* Familiar local landscapes and the types of plants that grow there; it is important that children learn the common names of local plants and trees

* The contrasts of different regions over the earth: desert, forest, tundra; the progression from pole to equator and from the ascent of a mountain in the tropics
* Some of the major plant types (e.g. fungus, lichen, moss, ferns) considered more as gestures of form in relation to the flowering plant than in detailed comparisons and evolutionary considerations
* Observation of the germination and growth of seeds, again with more emphasis on form and gesture than on technical details
* The concepts of root, stem, leaf and flower discovered through their polarities in different plants
* Trees as communities of plants and animals and their relationship to the weather, the soil and the landscape; starting a tree nursery which could be maintained through the following classes to culminate in the planting out of the seedling in a suitable location, could be a long term project

What has begun here should continue into Classes 6, 7 and 8, linking naturally and practically with the gardening curriculum. Geography and geology also provide opportunities. As with the continuing animal main-lesson, the aspects of the plant world chosen and the method of teaching will meet a more causal mode of thinking as Class 8 approaches.

Zoology

Taking up the methodology of Class 4, several groups of animals can be studied in greater detail, showing how within one group polarities occur as specialisations. These can include:

Birds

* Birds of prey with their heightened sense of sight and sound, including eagles, buzzards, falcons and kestrels and owls
* Carrion birds such as vultures and crows
* Song birds
* Water birds; swans, geese, ducks; sea birds such as albatross, gulls, petrels, cormorants; waders such as oyster catchers, herons; penguins and diving birds
* Terrestrial birds; chickens, ostrich, emu

Carnivores

* Bears
* Big cats, compare the lion as generalist with the cheetahs as specialists, cats of tropical forests such as tigers, mountains – wild cat, panther
* Wolves and foxes

Herbivores

* Mountainous goats, steinbock
* Deer, compare antler with horn formation
* Giraffe and antelope with their specialised anatomies and grazing habits
* Hippos, pigs, rhinos

Study can be made of animals that have small litters and invest time in rearing their young, and those with larger litters and a shorter period of intensive nurture.

Class 6

The study of minerals is at the heart of this class as they meet the 'threshold of causality' and the children's thinking seeks for how one thing affects another as a 'cause'. The relationship between plant structure, environment and the seasonal life-cycles can be made explicit.

Geology provides the physical basis for soil types, mountain flora and fauna. Geography gives every opportunity of widening appreciation for climate, vegetation zones and the economic aspects of plant cultivation, while the beginning of woodwork brings them experience of the qualities of different woods.

From Class 6, a gardening curriculum needs to involve the children with the plant world in a direct and practical way. There need to be weekly or twice-weekly lessons which can continue right into the Upper School. The emphasis is on the care of the soil and the tending and harvesting of flowers and vegetables. The opportunities will vary according to the school's location and the resources available, but the primary need is to maintain and develop the children's connection with the plant world. The practical reality of the rotation of crops, composting, pest control and winter storage are met with over the years as well as long-term projects such as a tree nursery, where seeds germinated in the early years could be planted in the Upper School.

Zoology

Mammals

* Elephant – as highly intelligent social animal with specialised development of trunk (as hand) and ear – relationship to humans
* Dolphins and whales – as intelligent social animals of the ocean
* Seals – as specially adapted aquatic mammal (highly oxygenated blood formation)
* Kangaroo – as marsupial with highly developed foot form

Reptiles

* Snakes – dominant quality of the vertebral structure
* Tortoise – dominant quality of hardened skin plates

Fish

* Describe several typical fresh and saltwater fish
* Migration of salmon and eel
* Problem of over-fishing

Molluscs, brachiopods and bivalves and gastropods

* Mussels, common sea shells
* Snails
* Worms – earthworm in connection with gardening

Insects

* In connection with botany studies – life cycle of the butterfly
* In connection with gardening – beetles, woodlice, etc.
* A threefold approach to insects; metabolic types – beetles, nerve sense types – butterflies, rhythmic types – bees
* Life cycle of bees – including care for and cultivation of bees – honey, wax, etc.
* Ants and their colonies

Botany

Flowering Plants

* Monocotyledons – lilies with their bulbs and rhizomes
* Cruciferous plants
* Grasses, unbellifers, papilionaceous flowers, chichoriaceae and the compositae groups
* Labiate flowers and other composites as examples of a concentration in the inflorescence
* Crowsfoot and roses and their many variants

The progression of these flowering plants can be followed throughout the year. The seasonal 'waking' and 'sleeping' of the year can be discussed.

Class 7

At this age, the emphasis on the human being through Classes 4 and 5 becomes a conscious focus.

A main-lesson in health and nutrition provides what Rudolf Steiner described as the last opportunity to draw on a healthy instinct for what is 'good for you' both in food to eat and nourishment for the senses. The parental role and influence that has guided the younger children now needs consolidation before the more adolescent attitude takes a hold. There is also opportunity now for touching on areas of personal hygiene and sexuality before the adolescent stage of acute self-consciousness.

Nourishment through the senses, through the lungs and through food relates this main-lesson to the whole environment and to the developing responsibility of the young person for their own health.

Responsibility for oneself includes respect for the other. In a way appropriate to the particular class, conversation about the responsibilities involved in sexual relations and parenthood, and discussion around topics like contraception and love need to be cultivated during this time. This could begin simply through explaining the basis of menstruation or it could develop through a discussion about the media and teenage magazines.

If the class teacher has had conversations at parents' evenings through Classes 4, 5 and 6 so that there is an awareness, understanding and respect between parents of the different ways in which they all handle these topics in the home and the different levels of awareness that their individual children have, the classroom contribution can be a more fruitful one. Behind such issues lie the profound questions of freedom, instinct and the nature of the human being.

- The care of the senses: practical knowledge about eyesight (e.g. reading in good light), hearing (walkmans and discos), taste and smell (synthetic flavours and perfumes) touch (fabrics and allergies)
- The care of the lungs: basic knowledge of the heart and the circulation with enough detail to be practical (e.g. protection of the trachea by cilia; the intimate relationship of air and blood through the delicate membranes of the alveoli) but not with the goal of an anatomical study
- The care for diet: basic knowledge of the digestive system but, as above, emphasis on what is needed to appreciate factors for long term health (e.g. the need for roughage to stimulate the intestinal lining, the need for rhythms in eating, avoiding exercise and baths after a heavy meal): protein, carbohydrates, fats, minerals and vitamins but with the sense that the health of the whole body is more than the sum of these constituents in a numerical balance: other nutritional philosophies (e.g. vegetarian, macrobiotic, vegan); organic food; fast food: the issue of 'dieting': the role of regular exercise
- The need for sleep and a balanced day's activities
- Related illnesses (e.g. lung cancer, emphysema, obesity, anorexia, diabetes)
- Substance abuse: alcohol, nicotine and those that seem most relevant to the class and their experience (e.g. opiates, hallucinogens): the fundamental nature of addiction (whether to caffeine, chocolate and sugar or to bad habits like biting fingernails) and the steps to recognise it and change
- Healing plants (e.g. camomile, calendula); their uses in ointments, teas, etc.
- Personal health and hygiene: sweating, care of

teeth and breath, skin, scalp (and the media manipulation around these): washing the hands, touching food and their connection with health (e.g. bacteria, headlice, roundworm infection)

Class 8

This age sees such a transformation within the whole being of the child that one can refer to the end of childhood. Rudolf Steiner describes this life phase as 'earth maturity' (*Erdenreife*). As well as new spurts of bodily growth and maturity, far-reaching new psychological dimensions open up, with a loss of orientation in relation to home, school and friendships. The dissonance between bodily and psychological processes raises the unconscious existential questions that lead young people across a threshold into Class 9.

The educational task is to accompany this important maturational step and the focus is the outer physical body.

Bringing attention to the 'deadness' of the mineral skeleton in an artistic and practical way, grounds the young people into their new bodily experiences. The details of the skeleton need not be pedantically correct anatomically; it is more important to show how bones confront gravity and resist it with uprightness or transform it into movement (e.g. the unique arch of the foot and curve of the spine, the mechanics of locomotion) and how mathematics (e.g. Golden Ratio) and physics (e.g. the role of lever principles) have relevance. The gesture of individual bones (e.g. femur) can be related to the whole architecture of the skeleton if drawing and modelling keep the artistic element alive through observation.

- The structure of the eye and/or the ear is another way to make conscious how the outer becomes inner, transformed through their form and function.
- The form and function of the spinal column and its relation to uprightness
- The shape of the foot, its arch and its relation to uprightness
- The Golden Mean and its relation to the skeleton
- The polarities and contrasts of form in head, chest and limb bones
- The relationship of bones and muscles in major joints and the lever principles involved
- A study of the forms of particular bones, e.g. contrasting vertebrae, femur
- The form and function of the human eye and/or ear

Classes 9 to 12

The essential question in Upper School teaching is not how to spread the enormous range of content in the life sciences over the timetable, but rather: what best serves the developmental process of adolescence? What role can the life sciences play in helping the young person in their discovery of themselves and their understanding of the world? The pupils are not there for the subject, rather the subject is there for the pupils. Adolescence engages a deep range of hidden questions that young people become aware of and opportunities are needed throughout the curriculum for them to be articulated.

One area of immediate interest to the adolescent and one that holds the potential to address fundamental questions about life, death and the human condition is the study of what is conventionally known as human biology. However, biology implies the study of organisms, so this sets up an expectation that real knowledge about the human being comes through a study of the human physical body and its constituent parts and processes, cells and genes, all of which add up to make a person. Biology implies animals and plants, human biology being the particular study of a particular organism, a species of mammal whose nature can be explained as any animal can be – reproduction, survival etc. A higher animal, but animal nevertheless.

Classes 9 and 10

The title 'human science' already allows the possibility that such a study can include all human experience from self-awareness, creative genius and inner feelings, to bruises, sweating and digestion. This approach can engage Classes 9 and 10, and the question of whether humans evolved from animals can be left open for study in Classes 11 and 12.

Alongside the Classes 9 and 10 human science main-lessons (ten to twelve weeks over the two years in blocks of three or four weeks), other life science studies are taught.

Class 9 need to engage in practical fieldwork with observations and projects which have an emphasis on the care and renewal of the land – composting, planting trees, tending ponds and hedgerows, for example. These would then become the basis for classroom studies, which could retain their link to the whole context of the environment from which they arose.

In Class 10, the increased powers of thinking are well met through laboratory-based studies of a more conventional kind, where the control of different variables in the growth of plants or the relationship of water to soil, brings the forming of an hypothesis and the concept of experimental proof into focus. By postponing the usual early emphasis on hypothesis, measurement and proof until Class 10, intellectual clarity can be developed at the same time with losing a wide perspective on the living world.

Another feature of life science study in Classes 9 and 10 is the introduction of biographies through which scientists can appear as real human beings with whom young people can identify. The qualities that are needed in real scientific investigation, rather than cardboard textbook cameos, come to life: single-minded dedication, passion, meticulous observation, inspiration, creative and lateral thinking, co-operation with others, fortuitous meetings and conversations, as well as practical ability and clear thinking.

Class 11

In Class 11, young people's thinking powers have matured to form the basis for a power of judgement, which had been all too easily clouded by the passions and extremes of adolescence or swayed by peer group pressure.

With their thinking more in hand, they are ready for a focus on the ideas and ideals in contemporary science, such as cell theory and genetics (parallelled by the atomic theory in the earth science curriculum). By taking an historical approach, there is a context for the theories showing how they arose out of the previous ideas through particular personalities and key experiments.

The study of botany provides a good basis for this, with practical work on plant cells and use of the microscope and with practical genetics through the germination of seeds. Narrowing the view of life through the microscope needs to be balanced by a macroscopic perspective. The study of landscape and of the major vegetation zones of the earth can provide this, and help in translating from one realm to the other can be given by projective geometry. The history of science provides a context, too, in which analytical and classificatory thinking (e.g. Linnaeus) rose to prominence, spawning a growth in knowledge about plants and a technology that advanced from fertilisers to genetic engineering. At the same time it reduced our relationship with the biosphere to a mosaic of factors, but no real wholeness.

The problems of the environment are the direct result of a certain way of thinking about the living world, which can be contrasted with Goethe's in a study of his method and approach to plants which emphasises exact observation, while retaining the context of the plant in its environment and its relationship to the whole.

The study of botany also provides the basis for consideration of the theory of evolution in general and Darwin's in particular, a theme to be taken up more strongly in Class 12.

Class 12

A holistic life science curriculum needs to make the human being central to enquiry into the nature of life. This has been an implicit theme throughout the Steiner-Waldorf curriculum from the kindergarten, articulated in ways appropriate to the age of the children.

Now, in Class 12, the issue needs to be raised in the fullest possible way so that environmental and ecological aspects can find their context within fundamental questions about the nature of the human being and the evolution of the earth. Social, political, spiritual and moral questions lie at the heart of an environmental education and all the Class 12 curriculum themes are relevant.

The focus in life science for Class 12 is zoology. The immense range of animal life is examined through considering the architecture of the main phyla. Each phyla establishes a new aspect of independence (e.g. from the water in reptiles, from the temperature in mammals) and consciousness (e.g. amoeba, insect colonies, dolphins). The question of evolution and a detailed study of Darwinism lead inevitably to the issue of the responsibility of the human beings for the earth and for all life, now that they possess the commercial power to exploit it to extinction and the technological power to manipulate it at the genetic level.

Class 9

The rationale is elaborated with some examples out of the wide range of topics that could be chosen for a particular class.

Skin and sense organs

Adolescents are exploring inner and outer boundaries. They are also intensely occupied with their surface appearances and their senses. The skin and the sense organs have a natural interest for them.

* Structure of skin, eye, ear, organs of smell, taste, movement and balance: adolescents are exploring inner and outer boundaries. They are also intensely occupied with their surface appearances and their senses. The skin and the sense organs have a natural interest for them.
* Health and social issues: sweat, spots, cuts, bruises, fingerprints, skin colour (and racism), eye care, glasses, blindness, deafness (how do we relate to those we meet who are deaf and blind? How does society treat them?)

Rhythmic system – heart and lungs

Heart beat and breathing are very direct bodily experiences and carry health issues which are relevant to an adolescent (e.g. smoking, fitness).

The central heart and the peripheral circulation need equal emphasis, demonstrating the heart and capillaries as polarities. The circulation of blood can be contrasted with the lymphatic system. The heart as pump model suggests a mechanistic relationship that does not match what is now understood from cardiac psychology and systems medicine generally. There is a complex interplay between circulation of the blood, emotions, circadian rhythms and the hormonal and nervous systems, a characterisation of which can be given.

* Structure and function of the heart, veins, arteries and capillaries
* The embryology of the heart and circulation
* Structure and function of the pulmonary and systemic circulation
* Composition and function of blood
* Structure and function of respiratory organs
* Lung disease – smoking and industrial disease, air pollution

This could lead on to consider many ethical/ rights issues such as:

* The change of attitudes to the protection of workers over the last century
* Our personal involvement in buying products from other countries where safety and health standards are well below what we now expect
* Present laws about the age at which people can buy cigarettes
* 'Passive' smoking
* The predicament of young children whose parents smoke
* The rights of non-smokers in any house community
* Air pollution and the fact that air recognises no national boundaries.
* Blood transfusions, heart, lung and other transplants: the reality that foreign proteins are rejected by the immune system leads to the topic of blood groups, 'rhesus' babies, vaccination, AIDS and the whole nature of disease
* Illness and health: the limitations of the 'germ' theory, which omits the part played by the immune system and the degree to which this is strengthened by exposure to illness. Can some illnesses (e.g. childhood illnesses, common colds) actually be necessary? What should the role of medicine be – to 'knock out the invader' or to strengthen the immune system? Is health the same as the absence of illness?

Class 10

The rationale is elaborated with some examples out of the wide range of topics that could be chosen for a particular class.

The increased maturity of Class 10 goes hand-in-hand with a new stability in their thinking. They can follow more complex and abstract processes such as those in the digestive tract, where different food substances are subject to a sequence of breakdowns through the action of different enzymes. A study of the metabolic system is an appropriate challenge for them.

The anatomy and physiology of the skeletal and muscle systems have received some attention in Class 8 and it may be better to leave this topic to Class 10. Although the teaching approach is different, a Class 9 that has just entered the Upper

School may not be keen on material that seems to take them back to their previous year's work. This is not necessarily so, but leaving the skeleton until Class 10 also allows comparative studies with animals, which raise evolutionary considerations which can be handled in more depth at that age.

Metabolic system

* Food and nutrition – including cultural and philosophical values (e.g. macrobiotic/vegan)
* Organs and biochemistry of digestion – nourishment as an active process, not a passive filtering of lists of chemicals
* Liver, gall bladder, pancreas, spleen: diabetes, medically and socially
* Kidneys – no passive filtering but active, selective re-absorption

Skeletal system

* Anatomy and physiology of the skeleton and muscles – polarities of form and function; those features that allow uprightness and freedom of the arms
* Comparative study of human and mammal skulls
* Joints and levers
* Bone formation and growth – ageing and bone disease
* Personal health in posture (e.g. sitting and lifting)

Nervous and hormonal systems

This is another topic where it is hard for most adolescents to grasp more than a crude 'electric cable/computer' model until Class 10. Similarly, the endocrine system, where crude 'chemical switch' models can prevent any real appreciation of the subtle and powerful interactions of glands and organs.

* Structure of brain/central nervous system; cerebro-spinal fluid
* Nerve function – inadequacy of telephone/electric cable model; limitation of the motor/sensory model
* Latest research on brain function – inadequacy of the 'mapping' approach and the computer analogy
* The open questions: memory, thinking and consciousness
* The endocrine glands – sensitivity of the body to hormones; (e.g. growth, excretion); special influence of the pituitary; ovulation and menstruation

Embryology

Hormone influence leads naturally into a study of human embryology, a rich area for Class 10, and again one which demands the emotional and intellectual maturity that has been achieved by most pupils by the end of Class 10. The ability to follow the development of several features at the same time, to appreciate the transformations of shape and size, to relate to the responsibilities and the issues involved in sexual relationships and parenthood, demands that the young people have emerged from a general phase of sexual knowledge and interest. A number of young people in Class 10 will have entered a serious relationship and for those who have not, the prevailing mood of a Class 10 is usually one in which both sexes can feel comfortable in asking questions and stating their opinions, without fear of the crudities that are more prevalent in Class 9. While it is assumed that all young people of this age are fully conversant with 'the facts' it can also be surprising to find there are confusions and misunderstandings, too. If the mood of the main-lesson is one of genuine respect for the developing body of a unique individuality, deep questions can stir in the young person, along with the sense of wonder for the way in which conception, gestation and birth take place so smoothly.

Child development and the idea that we continue to grow inwardly our whole lives, with new crises and new opportunities, can help to balance the picture young people can have that 'growing up' is all about getting to be 18 or 21. The knowledge that their mother and father may be going through the physical and psychological passage of menopause and mid-life, could contribute to their finding a new relationship with their parents. It would also help to change their perception of old people, whose inner needs are not so easily perceived as their more obvious outer ones.

* Pregnancy and birth – physical and emotional changes for mother and father.
* Implantation and the development of the embryo from conception to term along with the surrounding membranes.
* Conception, abortion, embryo research, surrogacy and similar topics
* First three years of physical and emotional development; standing, speaking, memory
* Child development, personality, temperaments
* Adulthood – what is it?
* Old age

Class 11

Here are some examples out of the wide range of topics that could be chosen for any one particular class.

* History of the microscope: from the early Dutch lens makers (e.g. Lievenhoek) to the electron microscope. The scanning electron microscope reveals the richness of form, even at a magnification of 50,000. Experience in the preparation of slides allows pupils a more critical appreciation of the magnification, clarity and the colour of the images and diagrams seen in books etc.
* The plant cell: a detailed study of its main features
  * The importance of the cytoplasm in relation to the nucleus
  * Mitosis and meiosis
  * Sexual and asexual reproduction
  * Boundaries of plant/animal (e.g. Euglena, Chlamydomonas)
* Genetics
  * Mendel's experiments and their modern interpretation in breeding
  * Chromosomes, genes, DNA: the essential features of genetic engineering
* Classification: features of some of the major phyla: algae, fungi, lichens, ferns, mosses, grasses, conifers, flowering plants
* Ecology
  * The role of plants in photosynthesis, decomposition and nitrogenation within the carbon and nitrogen cycles and in the hydrosphere
  * Relationship to animals (e.g. seeds/herbivores/pollination)
* Plant and insect relationships: examples of unique inter-dependent relationships
* Plant and landscape
  * The precious nature of soil structure and its community of organisms.
  * Trees, grasses and soil erosion, on a small and large scale
  * Diversity in forests and animal habitats
  * Monoculture and overgrazing

* Earth as biosphere: a consideration of the whole Earth provides a balance to the microscope and genetic details.
* Goethe's botanical studies: an historical and practical introduction to a Goethean approach to plant and landscape observation. Current research along the same line.
* Agriculture and forestry: a consideration of the degree to which cultivation of the plant world has been distorted by other values (e.g. consumerism) and how the distribution of plant resources (e.g. food, timber) over the world is subject to commercial and political factors (e.g. the patenting of genes and terminator technology).

Class 12

Here are some examples out of the wide range of topics that could be chosen for any one particular class.

Some of the botany could be carried over from Class 11, but the main focus for Class 12 is zoology, with an introduction to the main phyla and their diversity.

The opportunity should also be taken to select detailed features which touch key issues in biological theory and raise fundamental questions about the relationship of human beings to the animal world.

Some examples below:

* *morifera* (sponges) – the sieving of a sponge through a nylon mesh and its ability to regenerate as a colony with form and function
* *coelenterata* (hydra) – the ability of the sea slug to ingest hydra without triggering the nematocysts, then to use those nematocysts within their own skins as a defensive mechanism
* *mollusca* – the unexpected complexity of the eye of the squid, which anticipates the mammalian eye well before the evolution of mammals
* *arthropods* – the complex structure of hives and colonies; metamorphosis and the reconstitution of living organisms
* Echinodermata – the embryonic development of the starfish shows that lateral symmetry (fundamental to the architecture of higher animals) develops first before radial symmetry overwhelms it
* Vertebrate development from the point of view of an increasing independence from the environment e.g. regulation of warmth and the internalisation of organs such as the lungs
* Evolution, including an historical appreciation of the development of a Darwinian interpretation of evolution, the fossil record (accounts of fakes and frauds such as the Ichthyosaurus fake in Museum of Wales, Piltdown Man, the Brontosaurus, Archaeoraptor Liaoningensis, might be examined alongside reliable samples, including Charles Walcott's discoveries in the 'Burgess Shale')
* Comparative embryological development and the polarity of precocial and altricial development
* Ethical questions of biological and medical intervention in human, animal and plant life
* Conservation and human responsibility for stewardship of the earth's biological resources – philosophical, economic, political, social aspects of environmental degradation. The task of education and the urgency of changing attitudes. The role of tourism and consumerism on world habitats
* The overall aim of the movement curriculum is to support the central process of integrating the child's soul-spiritual being with the

bodily organisation through the medium of movement.

* This aspect of the curriculum assists the development of the child's sense of movement, spatial awareness, sense of balance and inner equilibrium and sense of bodily well being through fine and gross motor control. The movement curriculum seeks to help the child to form and differentiate her overall awareness and control of her movement organisation and be able to marshal its energies in the places at the right time, thus enabling the child to direct those forces in a meaningful way.
* The curriculum aims to assist the child to transform the activity of the movement organisation, thus bringing inner mobility to thinking, feeling and willing, thus enabling a more complete expression of individual intention.
* The curriculum works to support the child's developmental path in age-appropriate ways.
* The nature of the movement organisation is such that an imagination of an action occurs before the actual movement is physically carried out. The relationship between the movement organisation and imagination is an intimate one. Thus the teaching method requires that the children be given meaningful and age-appropriate pictures as an impulse to movement or activity.
* In supporting the child's developing movement organisation, a basis is formed for social interactions, social skills through awareness of other people in relation to the self and thus to real social competence.
* The movement curriculum seeks to support and complement other aspects of the curriculum.

20

Movement

Games, Gymnastics, Sport

The movement curriculum takes up the central developmental process that every human being has to engage in, that of coming into, taking hold of and expressing themselves though the physical body. This process begins in the womb and continues intensively throughout childhood. From the earliest focusing of the eyes and turning of the head, through the child's learning to raise herself, manipulate the hands and grasp the world around her, through the long process of becoming upright and on and out into the world, the stream of movement is the medium through which the spirit of the individual enters the world. This stream of movement is essentially spiritual in nature. It is a force that literally mobilises the child and places her into a meaningful relationship to the world. Through movement the individual enters the world physically and so its primary instrument is the physical body.

Movement as a continuum

The movement curriculum works with and helps form the individual's path into her movement organisation and helps facilitate her finding a secure centre from which to reach out into the world. Since this entire process is a continuum and one that is individual, the curriculum should respect this process and not restrict it or artificially limit it to specific stages. The movement curriculum in this sense has to be an entirely open system that responds to the perceived changing needs of the children, rather than an enclosed one that predetermines what should happen when – a point which also applies to the whole curriculum. The indications given here are divided into age groups merely as points of reference and not seen in any sense as binding to specific classes.

Three factors inform but do not determine this process; insight into the archetypal nature of child development, insight into the nature of movement itself and the external circumstances, resources and possibilities.

Early Years

In pre-school settings the educational task is to support the establishing of behaviour patterns and sequences as habit (which includes everything from dressing, behaving in groups, listening to others, doing the washing up and tidying up after play). All these habits school the movement organisation in meaningful ways. Through practical activities and age-appropriate work in kindergarten, the children learn archetypal activities and the movements that belong to them, such as baking bread, laying the table, doing simple handicrafts, gardening, etc. The process of growing from the periphery into the bodily organisation from the fingertips and toes inwards, is strengthened by finger games, gesture accompanying song and speech, skipping, drawing, painting and so on. In all these activities the child learns through imitation both of the conscious intention of the adult and the activities themselves. Thus the imagination is stimulated from without, as it were. The imaginative content lies in the activity itself.

The key elements in the pre-school setting are providing a sense of security and continuity, a meaningful context for meeting, working and playing together. Balance and equilibrium are necessary not only for sound movement but for the perception of sound, for speaking and listening. Rhythm is the living balance of inner and outer and consists of repetition of the similar, rather than strict repeating of the same. Rhythm involves progression, it moves on. Manual dexterity and nimbleness of foot take years to establish but are the essential prerequisites for inner mobility. Many activities at home and in the kindergarten contribute to the development of all these qualities.

The transition to school: Classes 1 to 2

Children enter school when they are ready to begin formal learning. In movement education, the transition is marked by several changes of emphasis. In activities such as form drawing, the dynamic of movement is progressively internalised from outer movement in space to the ability to picture the movement inwardly until it can be translated through the hand and arm onto the paper as lines, the 'traces' of movement itself. The ability to 'read' such movement from the paper is an important preparation for the process of reading text. Form drawing and the letters and numerals themselves explore in two dimensions what has been experienced spatially in three. Literacy itself is the ability to translate the inner movement of thoughts and feelings into structured form (writing and sequences of numbers) as well the obverse; the ability to recreate in the soul the movement which has been 'frozen' in the letters.

The teaching approach

Imitation is translated movement. In the pre-school years this is largely an unreflected process. Once the child is able to begin to form independent mental images, imitation has to be transformed. Once the child begins formal schooling, imitation remains an important part of learning, not least in movement, but the process undergoes an important change. Rather than taking part in what the adult does (implicit learning), the child has to be stimulated to act out her own inner picture of the task. That means the teaching takes place through pictures. The teacher engages the child's imagination with a (usually) verbal picture and the impetus to act comes from the child's understanding and translation of the picture. In other words they are imitating the gesture or impulse of the picture which they have formed in their own souls, stimulated by the teacher's words. The children are invited, as it were, to climb into the picture and be part of it. The child can only really move once a picture has been given. Otherwise the movements become unfocused, self-gratifying or formless. The movements children make in response to rapid, dis-continuous, fragmented images, such as those given by television, accurately reflect these very qualities.

As well as working through pictures, movement education becomes increasingly task-orientated, which means more focused and placed within a more limited context. In a game involving rabbits and foxes, the task is for the rabbits to run away and the fox to catch them. The logic of the context is given; that's what rabbits and foxes do. Defining parameters through the rules of the game, equally focuses the task. The steam of movement can be channelled by simple and direct instructions, such as *run over to those trees, jump over the stream, climb on the rock.*

A further element in the first school years is to provide the children with opportunities within games to gradually leave the security of the group, be chased and separate themselves. Initially a high degree of security needs to be provided by available safe places. Progressively throughout the Lower School the safe places become fewer and further apart and the challenge correspondingly greater. Tension and excitement are very much part of this challenge to leave the safe place. Tension increases attention and focus and is an awakening experience. Games like Grandmother's Footsteps in countless variations are classic examples. The children are drawn out, away from the safe place and need to be very alert not to be caught. The possibility of scampering back to safety remains important. The rhythm of excitement and relaxation is an important element too. The rules of the games provide scaffolding within which the children can take the risks they are ready and willing to take. The teacher can extend or contract the scope of the scaffolding as needed.

Another element in movement education in the first two classes is rhythm. Rhythm has many dimensions in the whole life of a class of children but especially important are skipping games, clapping games, which also school hand co-ordination and sequencing, bean bag exercises involving passing, throwing and catching. Where songs, rhymes or chanting accompany such exercises, the movement is kept light and closely linked to the breathing. Music also provides a group experience in which the song carries the activity and is less focused on the individual. In such activities co-ordination, dexterousness, spatial orientation, rhythm, learning to follow instructions and increasing confidence are exercised.

Given that all these activities can be incorporated into the young child's holistic experience of learning through the main-lesson, foreign language and handwork lessons it is not necessary to have separate movement lessons in the timetable. However the movement teachers should work closely with their colleagues in advising and supporting movement education throughout the curriculum.

The essence of the teaching approach is direct observation in the classroom or gymnasium. Out of this arises the possibility to directly respond to the situation of the children by adapting the activities and the mood in which they occur to the children's actual needs. The key lies in the way the child is engaged in challenge and how far in front of him or her it is placed, i.e. how far the children have to reach beyond themselves. This goes for all teaching but especially for movement education.

In what follows the elements of the curriculum and key exercises are outlined. Details of the games and exercises referred to and their many variations are to be found in the recommended literature.[1] Unless otherwise stated the games named in the curriculum contents are described in Kim Brooking-Payne's book, *Games Children Play.* The Bothmer gymnastics exercises referred to by name only in the curriculum refer to specific exercises developed by Fritz von Bothmer, the original gymnastics teacher in the first Waldorf School. These are described and illustrated in Bothmer's book *Gymnastic Education*.

Class 3

Class 3 involves a progression to more formal movement education, often accompanied by the introduction of specific subject lessons dedicated to movement taught by specialist teachers, where previously movement was an integral part of main-lessons. Even where this step is taken earlier or later, the transition to more formal and longer periods of movement education is nevertheless important.

This transition involves a number of changes in the teaching approach, which lay the foundation for the methodology for the subsequent classes. These include:

* The gradual separation of movement from speaking, singing or listening. The children are encouraged to focus on the movement, that is not speak along with the teacher or other children whilst doing the activity.
* A change of context from the classroom to a games hall or gymnasium. This provides more space and new equipment. The children have to first feel at home in the new space and familiarise themselves with its specialist equipment, safety aspects, social rules of behaviour, appropriate clothing, hygiene. The gymnastic equipment is introduced to the children in an imaginative and play-orientated way, so that they become familiar with it before using it for formal exercises (parallel bars can be used as bridges; mats as islands, walls and pools of water; vaulting horses as horses, etc.)
* A key aspect of the above point is learning to be a coherent group within a large space, coming together in 'huddles' for discussion, presentation of new tasks, leaving the huddle to enter the space and returning to it once more. This rhythm of coming together, separating into the activity and returning to base once more is fundamental to the practicalities of the movement curriculum and is crucial to developing social competence.
* The moral dimensions of the movement education are established through the dynamic of playing games. The separation of the individual from the group, the formation of separate, sometimes rival groups, poses the question of how the whole group and the individuals within it meet again. Separating, interacting and joining again highlights the importance of relationships and their moral basis. This is facilitated by the rules of engagement, the rules of the games. In many respects the rules *are the game.* Many social and moral skills are called for such as honesty (was I tagged or not? did I step over the line or not?), commitment (supporting my team, trying my best to achieve the objective), tact (how hard can I tag my classmate? What means can I use to play the game but avoid hurting someone? When is the game over?), recognition of appropriate authority (accepting the judgement of other players or the referee/teacher), fairness, co-operation and so on.
* The progressive separation of the individual from the group and the cultivation of the ability to act alone or with others, is a primary aim of the curriculum and this passes through various stages. In Class 3 the emphasis is on the experience of 'we', that is a sense of the collective group going into the world to face group challenges.

* The tasks are given using verbal pictures that are strong in imagery. Such pictures (you are going to walk over this narrow bridge but be careful not to fall into the snapping jaws of the hungry sharks below!) enhance the challenge, provide simple rules, generate the warmth of excitement and provide an imaginative and highly effective approach to discipline. Such images involves the kind of willing suspension of disbelief on the part of the pupils that characterises play itself, whilst leaving the individual essentially free. At a later stage the children can themselves suggest images to embrace the game or tasks involved.
* The groups activities and the qualities of the tasks engage the children in their warmth organisation. This means activities in which strong sympathy is awakened and the teachers' approach to the children should be hearty, encouraging and generous.

Possible activities include:

* Bothmer's First Roundelay, *We come, we come…* which involves running in a circle, doing the activities and gestures described in the text, such as galloping, trotting, leaping, stepping rhythms and standing still
* Practising coming into a huddle for instruction and returning after the activity
* Tag games involving all against one adversary. Typical examples, *stuck in the mud, sharks and octopuses, dragon tag*
* 'Jungle' games, using images such as climbing through the jungle, climbing the castle walls, being on a ship in storm etc., the children clamber over a course of obstacles made by gym equipment, which represents outdoor challenges not usually available to children today and involving climbing, jumping off, leaping across, rolling, crawling through confined spaces, balancing etc.

Class 4

The emphasis shifts from 'we' to 'I', in the sense of 'here am I, there are you'. This also involves experiencing polarities such as dreaming and waking, weak and strong, safety and danger or creation and destruction. The rhythm of such polarities emphasises the breathing element of contraction and expansion. The principle of separation becomes stronger in games that involve one against the group. More tension is involved in games in which the children need to awaken from the picture that the teacher has bedded the game in and those still dreaming get caught or tagged.

At this age the children may begin to regularly challenge adult authority or feel themselves isolated from the group context. Here the social and moral aspects of learning and respecting the rules become very important. As the individual increasingly becomes aware of his or her own space, both in a literal and inner sense, the curriculum needs to respond by beginning to formally school the child's sense of the qualities of the dimensions of space, above and below, left and right, front and back and their integration through self-activity.

* Bothmer's Second Roundelay, the exercise, *I stand. I walk. I run…*, in which the experience of the archetypal elements of spatial awareness and the planes of movement are introduced and integrated in a playful rather than formal way. An iambic (short-long) is used to give the exercise a strong rhythm. The strong swinging movements emphasise a different element of rhythm. The child experiences their own self-

activity of placing themselves into their own space

* In gymnastics the children are introduced to more formal elements. The teacher demonstrates before the children. Pictures are still used to describe the elements of the exercises, such as forward and backward rolls
* Tag games involving chasing and catching, rapid changes of role – from chaser to chased, games that involve focusing on achieving a specific goal. Typical examples include, *fire and ice, scarecrows, hunters and hares*
* Games that involve some image of confrontation with negative forces, e.g. *river bandits, shark's jaws.*
* Games involving listening and attentiveness e.g. *MacPherson*
* Simple throwing and catching games in increasingly difficult situations (e.g. balanced on a bench).
* Activities which introduce build-up games to softball and its basic principles e.g. *clocks, trains and stations, Swedish rounders*
* Playground games can be re-introduced or taught if the children are unfamiliar with them, e.g. wall tennis, four-square, hop-scotch, marbles, reflex games such as knuckles, crocodile jaws, jacks, noughts and crosses, leap frog, etc
* More difficult jungle challenges

Class 5

This age very much marks the heart of childhood, the last year before the onset of physical puberty starts in earnest. The child lives strongly in the processes of the blood and the dynamic between the pulse and the measure of the breathing. The children like to roam around in an unruly way as much as they seek the measured discipline of rhythmic movement. They also want to be challenged. Both courage and caution, both risk and circumspection are valued at this age. The loss of childhood innocence is to be compensated for through powerful grasping of reality. Rhythm in movement is important at this age. There needs to be a balance between levity and gravity, between imagination and intellect, between individual and group challenges. Holding the centre in a rapid alternation of rhythms strengthens the child's self-activity. This is an important transition stage before team games are introduced. Without the ability to hold the middle, to stay in their own space, positional sense in team sports is much harder to achieve and one sees the phenomenon of both teams chasing here and there after the ball as a whole group.

The Ancient Greek Olympic ideal stands as a leitmotiv for Class 5. The original games were rituals in which the individual sought to give expression to the creative powers of the Gods. The ideals of truth, beauty and goodness must permeate the activities and the five classical exercises, running, jumping, throwing the discus and javelin and wrestling, mirror the archetypal inner movements which form a basis for moral education.

The exercises are now given with much more matter-of-fact picture images and the children no longer stand in the circle. They face their teachers in rows.

* Bothmer gymnastics: the *light beat* exercise, which involves a rhythmic interplay between lightness and weight.
* Gymnastics: trend to more individual exercises; leap-frog, straddle vault; vault over the buck using the spring board; forward/backward roll over symmetric bars; cartwheels; balancing,

swinging, jumping with increasing challenge (e.g. with eyes closed). The five classic Greek exercises are introduced.

* Games: at this age there is a transition between play and sport, the games being neither. Typical games include: cat and mouse house, ship shark shore.
* Swimming: many schools introduce regular swimming lessons at this age.

Class 6

The soul experience of the children at this age penetrates into the muscles, which hold a balance between fluid and solid. The human being seeks a new level of balance at this age when the physical processes of puberty cause rapid growth of the limbs, leading to clumsiness and greater individual diversity of physique among a class of children than at any other age. Uprightness is important and that requires an inner balance of forces. The play element now gives way, the principle of specific exercises and exactness, clarity of form, order and structure is striven for in the exercises. The element of objectivity comes to the fore, through measurement, keeping scores in games and acknowledging the teacher as referee/umpire. The pupils can stand in lines for exercises, ordered by height, tallest at the back.

* Bothmer gymnastics: *triangles*; the main element being the fall out of levity and the transition to an alert uprightness. Rod exercises strengthen the experience of uprightness in relation to stretching up, whilst standing firmly on the ground.
* Gymnastics: formal stations in the build up of the exercises, handstands, handstand to handspring, some work on the bars, rings, with increased need for health and safety awareness. Outdoor athletics including running and jumping disciplines.
* Games: the transition to team sports. This requires the preparation of the following skills: having winners and losers, outwitting opponents, sometimes physical contact, keeping scores. Dodge ball games are a good preparation, involving contact, direct encounter (having a ball thrown directly at you). Typical games include: wall ball, soft ball, prisoner, over-the-net ball games, invasion and territorial games, hitting field games.

Class 7

The pupils now have the strength and supple flexibility to move quickly from one activity to the next. This mobility is an expression of the fact that they already have good muscle development but are not yet fully engaged with the static properties of the bony skeleton. This is an age in which the children express their movement development through the ligaments and sinews.

They have the ability to separate themselves from the group and sufficient personal standing in the world to be ready for the challenge of competitive sport. They are capable of the individual standpoint, which not only enables them to take and maintain a position but the perspective to begin to oversee the game and its tactics. In order to really participate in team sports the pupil must be able to form a clear picture of where they are in relation to their surroundings, they must be aware of the dimensions and boundaries of the field. This requires good sensory integration. One of the reasons team sports are not introduced earlier in the curriculum is the danger of this exact conception of spatial relationships may inhibit the imagination. If the pupils at this age do not have a strongly established sense of imagination or inner picturing ability, they can be overwhelmed by the emotional forces which are awakening in them at this stage of puberty. When such forces are drawn in without the ability to channel them, it can cause considerable emotional distress. The imaginative and mental picturing element works to channel and order surges of emotionality.

* Bothmer gymnastics: swinging movements lead to an experience of centre and periphery. The individual finds his or her own rhythm and discovers the moment of impulse to movement. The exercise *The Rhythm* complements the exercise *Fall into Space*, which was specifically created to take hold of the spatial experience in puberty. Bothmer originally suggested that the exercise *Jump into the Middle Point*, should precede the *Fall into Space*. This is very much a matter of judgement for the teachers concerned.
* Gymnastics: the somersault, falling off a box onto mats, learning to enjoy weight through many swinging and pendulum exercises, such as hanging from the bars and using the swinging to experience the new centre of gravity (new because of the stretching growth that comes with puberty); vaults, such as handsprings, through vaults, straddle vaults over the length of the box, handstands. Wrestling in various forms can be practised, such as Indian wresting, Greek/Roman style wrestling (as described in Brooking-Payne).
* Games and sport: games are used as warm-ups to sport. Half the session is given over to training, to learning and practising new technique. The individual skills are separated out and given specific focus. The main sports include basketball, hockey, softball, tennis or cricket. In athletics running, including cross-country – often in connection with orienteering using maps and marked out courses, and jumping. The pupils should start playing in tournaments.

Class 8

At this age the pupils encounter the full weight of their physical bodies and their sense of movement penetrates to the skeletal structure. They feel both burdened by the new weight of their bodies as well as energised by new physical strength. They need much opportunity to explore and experience this new combination of weight and strength and so there should be more emphasis on gross motor movement than on too much fine technique. From a movement and physical point of view, this age really marks the end of childhood.

Many outdoor pursuits can be introduced at this age including rock climbing and abseiling, canoeing and kayaking, hiking, mountaineering, skiing and so on. In all these examples the activities provide their own challenges, depending on the local resources of the school. What now becomes important, apart from the self-reliance and survival aspects of the sports is the relationship to the environment. The students must learn that outdoor pursuits are most rewarding when they enhance our experience of nature. Sport must never contribute to environment degradation, nor should the attitude develop, which sees the mere overcoming of the natural environment as an objective.

At this age gender differences need to be especially respected. The manifest differences in physical strength and size need to be acknowledged in contact sport as well as the quite distinct energy resources of the two genders. There is a need for a balance of integrated and separate activities. The integrated activities have a very different but essential character. Both genders need some time on their own, the boys needs to be able to explore the limits of their strength and power, the girls need protection in the bodily intimacy of many gymnastics exercises involving being held or exposed positions.

* Bothmer gymnastics: the exercise *Jump into the Middle Point.*
* Gymnastics: continuation of Class 7, though the exercises have a different quality because of the pupils' development. Somersaults and handsprings and vaults are continued. The main difference in Class 8 is that the pupils are often more hesitant and need to more consciously gather up the dynamic of their forces before the run-up to a vault. In circuit training correct and age-appropriate techniques are learned. There is an emphasis on fitness and developing strength, e.g. through press-ups.
* Games and sport: the sports played in Class 7 are continued and volleyball is introduced. There is a measured graduation of competition, which is seen as an important pedagogical instrument. Competition is an element used and controlled by the teacher to cultivate teamwork, as a catalyst for stimulating engagement, for pushing individuals to new levels of achievement, for drawing the best out of individuals by calling on their potential. Computation remains healthy as long as it is within an ultimately secure, trusting environment in which emotional and literal safety nets are available as needed.

Class 9

At this age the students need to learn to take responsibility for the consequences of their own actions. The frontal plane of the will, meeting and 'con-fronting' the world, needs to be encountered and a breakthrough made. The individual must literally take the plunge and break into the future with a new and conscious step. This takes both courage and new levels of consciousness. A certain laziness, often the expression of emotional uncertainty, needs to be overcome. Students at this age need to leave childhood behind them and stand on their own feet.

In the Upper School it is necessary to make provision for more movement than the timetable actually permits by encouraging after school clubs in which the students simply have more time to develop their abilities but in which students with specific abilities can develop their full potential, which is not always possible in whole class situations because the socially inclusive element takes priority. Ultimately the provision of meaningful activities offers youngsters an alternative to many less useful activities they may otherwise be drawn into. Regular competitions and matches with other schools are also important.

* Bothmer gymnastics: the exercise *The Plunge* exemplifies what the Class 9 student needs to experience, involving a facing of the world, a plunge or leap, literally into the space before them, a fall into gravity, a breakthrough with a conscious stepping into the present/future with certainty. Other exercises at this age may include, *Rhythm of two interlacing circles (frontal walk).*
* Gymnastics: the new emphasis is a conscious overcoming of obstacles through courage and inner focus. Continue forward and backward

somersaults, more challenging vaults, e.g. through vaults, floor work, parallel bars, handsprings.

* Sport: the sports already introduced are progressed with an emphasis on timing and more focused application. Volleyball plays an increasing role in the Upper School. In athletics shot put, discuss and javelin can be practised. Other sports include archery and fencing.

Class 10

At this age the students need to develop a new awareness of their surroundings. The archetypal activity of throwing the discuss embodies many of the qualities the Class 10 students need to develop; the encounter with the object, engaging in dialogue with the world, going within into oneself but emerging and proceeding from the centre to the periphery without loss of inner balance, giving something to the world but following the consequences, retaining the connection. The key element is finding dialogue with the world. This entire activity is also about finding a goal and uniting oneself with it.

The curriculum from Class 10 onwards essentially builds on what has been established, practising and developing technique and competence.

* Bothmer Gymnastics: *The Discus* exercise, also *Walking with Circling Arms (horizontal walk)*: all these exercises have a strong relationship to the consciousness of the horizontal plane and holding the middle.
* Gymnastics: continuation of previous classes with an emphasis on finding a rhythm in the flow of movement and an experience of uprightness. An aesthetic element can be important at this age, and movements can be increasingly seen as an integrated sequence.
* Sport: continuation of the sports already introduced with an emphasis on social play.

Class 11

At the age of seventeen, young people need to set themselves aims and ideals to strive towards. This requires the ability to make judgements and choices. A certain decisiveness is called for to follow a chosen path between competing, and destabilising alternatives. The archetypal gesture of throwing the javelin expresses this well. Symmetry and balancing left and right are key elements to be exercised at this age. Many sports, such as cricket offer opportunity to develop skills requiring strong symmetry, in batting or bowling for example, both of which require a strong sided-ness to be maintained in overall balance. The same is true of many racket games such as tennis and badminton. Accuracy and precision can be consciously practised. Rapid reflexes, sharp perception for an opening, a sense for tactics, as well as overall control are needed as essential skills in most sports. At this age the students are now mature enough to take all these into consideration. The students also need to be able to take increasing responsibility for sports through thorough understanding of the rules, as well as the health and safety aspects. Being able to understand the essence of a particular game is now important.

* Bothmer gymnastics: the exercise *The Javelin*, also *Distorted Height (Eagle), Symmetry Walk*
* Sport: continuation of sports already introduced, with an emphasis on tactical skill

Class 12

At this age the young person should be able to attain a freedom within the planes of space and hence an integration of thinking, feeling and willing. They should now be able to form and experience an overview of the whole range of possibilities within spatial awareness and with it the ability to see the wood for the trees.

* Bothmer gymnastics: The human form is experienced in its threefold spatial qualities culminating in the exercise *The Cross.*
* Games and sport: the sports introduced so far should be practised to a high level of skill. It is particularly interesting to the students to be led through the movement curriculum of their entire school career from the Lower School onwards, playing the games and practising the full range of exercises once more, with opportunity to reflect on the development processes involved.

21

Music

Music speaks to human beings and they experience its language in their soul. As with language, music has a realm belonging to understanding and knowing which is grasped through music theory, a realm of feeling comprising everything to do with harmony, moods (major and minor), tension and relaxation, and a third realm, that of movement involving rhythm. All three realms are mirrored in the life experience of human beings.

> *Music lives in the moment, in becoming. It consists of transitions, of the space between, of the formed flow of time. Its arising and its disappearing belong to its nature. What remain are inner space impressions; expectations, fulfilment, memory, are its constituent forces. The picture nature of music is at the same time moved and moving picture. The picture nature is of a flowing quality. The plastic nature of music is similar: the plastic qualities are in flow, in constant change. Architectural space and music stand as polar opposites, though in a way they determine each other: movement become form and moved-moving 'form'. How can music understood in this way be grasped, experienced and cultivated?*[1]

From this point of view writing a curriculum for music teaching is indeed challenging. Given that the fundamental approach to Waldorf education is a pedagogical one, that is to say, one that is directed towards the development of the child through music, then the task could be described as one of matching the nature of music to the nature of the child. Method and content are inextricably woven together.

So both the nature of the child and the nature of music are the starting point for any music curriculum.

> *Active immersion in musical substance, experience through practice of its nature, progressive, step by step awakening to musical principles and finally proceeding to a basis for knowledge based on direct experience.*[2]

These are the main goals of music teaching in the Waldorf school.

Music is not a simply subject on the timetable: it is a 'state of mind', one threaded through teaching and learning explicitly and implicitly. This state of mind calls to be created in every lesson. It means diving into the stream of structured time we call music, uniting, in some degree, with the deep musicality which lies within the rhythms, tones and harmonics of our existence. Out of a sense for this a music curriculum can arise.

Aspects of child development

Up to the age of about nine, thinking, feeling and willing work with and in each other in a relatively simple manner. In music, the D-pentatonic mode with its 'mood of the fifth' conforms mostly closely with this situation. In this mood (i.e. in the *quality* of the fifth), the phenomena of melody, harmony and rhythm weave together. There are as yet no harmonic chords, just as there is no keynote or rhythm bound to a strict metrical beat. Just as a pentatonic melody is not bound to a keynote, so a freely swinging rhythm can find its orientation in the qualities of inhalation and exhalation of the breath.

By taking the mood of the fifth as the starting point, we help to create ears of potential that will be needed later on for the comprehension of the range of contemporary and traditional music, including world music, in which we may hear the different sensibilities of time and place expressed through tuning systems that are unlike those we may be used to, or sound-worlds that seem, at, first strange and alienating.

After their ninth year, children experience an 'interruption'. The earlier harmony of faculties deserts the child and there is a turning towards the reassurance of physical things. To help them find their orientation, we turn to the past, for to some extent the present can be understood out of the past. The same goes for music, so we now look for the traditional harmony of the third. The leading note that forces us to seek the keynote, and also a rhythm that is based on beat, now gain in importance. Having first worked out of what was already there in the children, the teacher now leads them to music that has already 'found itself':

> *Begin by working in conformity with the child's physiology. Then work in a way that compels the child to conform to the music.*[3]

What the teacher has to do in the music lessons is thus to prepare the transition from 'it sings in me' to 'I sing'.

Something objective enters into the music when the children play musical instruments. Since music mirrors the human soul it is an excellent medium for forming and educating.

It is becoming increasingly important to experience music not as something separate from life but as an archetypal human element. This means that music belongs not only to actual music lessons but also to all other subjects.

When children learn a musical instrument, they experience that skill comes from practice. The reward for this, however, is not the good report or praise from the teacher, but beauty itself. In creating beauty, the youngsters should feel themselves right at its centre. In music this can only be achieved through active, alert playing combined with immediate correction, and, in this, music differs from the other arts. Music lessons thus provide an elemental experience of being within the art.

> *In sculpture and painting we look at beauty and experience it; in music we ourselves become beauty.*[4]

Class 1

The transition from pre-school to school is characterised by the expectation that the children will join in. Imitation remains a strong factor in music teaching throughout, indeed correcting by demonstrating is the most effective method of teaching. Thus the teaching methods consist on the one hand of the teacher playing or singing and the children joining in, whilst on the other hand the teacher empathetically corrects 'mistakes' such as wrong notes, phrasing or rhythms.

Stories create the mood for listening to music and feeling it; the melodic element is in the foreground. Singing and movement often still go together. By alternating between getting the children to make music or sing, and then letting them listen, music can have an awakening, harmonising effect on the soul. Active listening is cultivated through singing and movement with moments of 'pure' listening. Group work is important for the cultivation of social feeling, while solo singing or playing has an awakening effect.

Simple instruments are introduced in Class 1, as described below. Some content suggestions follow.[5]

Singing, playing instruments

* Freely floating melodies in D-pentatonic mode (DEGAB); these are learnt by listening and playing by ear. Pitch can be indicated through hand movements
* In addition to singing, each child learns to play the child's harp, lyre, cantele or recorder-like pipes by ear. The children learn the simple melodies that have been sung first
* Tuned and untuned percussion can be used e.g. drum, tambourine, gong, cow-bell, chimes, xylophone cascades, etc.
* Ear-training through listening to music played by the teacher or by groups within the class
* Training of finger skills using the instruments and through finger games
* The child's harp, of lyre, for example, can be used for experiencing moods through improvising
* Simple rhythms are not yet tied to a beat, nor are they practised separately from the song through clapping, stamping, walking or jumping. Dancing augments the possibilities of movement, which is itself a musical quality

Instrumental

* Preparations are made for all the children to have individual lessons on an instrument (Class 3) as they move up through the school

Class 2

Continuation and intensification of work in Class 1, but with the exploration of the range of other pentatonic modes: more attention is paid to the rhythmic element through 'metre': rhythm is still not related to beat but is a component of the melody.

Singing, playing instruments

* New songs are introduced, including some for different times of day, and some that have a latent element of a keynote E/G modes. Singing melodies within the range of up to an octave. Repertoire; singing some traditional folksongs, such as those from Hebridean and non-European culture, which may be hexatonic or reaching beyond the conventional pentatonic scales

* To train the ear, songs are sung and also played on pipes or other instruments (alternation between activity and listening)
* Work with instrumental groups now becomes possible
* Free conversations in music showing different moods
* The primary experience of the notes as light or dark is taken further and becomes a spatial experience of high or low
* Rhythm and melody are gradually made more conscious (e.g. let the children show the pitch of notes with their hands while their eyes are closed, etc.)
* Rhythm exercises on one note

Class 3

The psychological development of the children now makes it possible to begin introducing musical notation. Given the predominantly pictorial mode of the children's thinking, the introduction of musical literacy needs to recognise this in how notation is introduced. The keynote becomes more prominent in songs. The choice of individual instruments should be determined during Class 3.

Singing, playing instruments

* Singing is still in unison. Pentatonic material gives way to medieval modes including the diatonic scale
* Singing the modal and diatonic scales, some with ostinato parts, sung drones, occasional quodlibets, etc
* The diatonic pipes are introduced and C major scale learned. Folk tunes provide good material for modal melodies
* Work with groups of instruments continues, and the instruments learnt individually are included in this
* Violin may be introduced
* Cultivation of listening, e.g. by letting the class listen to children play pieces learnt in their private lessons
* A wider range of percussion instruments can be introduced, calling for greater precision and sense of pulse
* The melody of tunes can be drawn using pictures showing pitch (rising and falling line), long notes and pauses

Study of music

* Musical notation is introduced: the stave, the treble clef. Imagery is used to introduce pitch notation; the place of Middle C. Notation applied to work with instruments and singing

Class 4

In connection with fractions learned in the main-lesson, the focus is on fixing the length of notes. The children write down what they have heard and then read this to make it audible (they should also sense the intervals). The children's feeling for music should from now on be 'earthed', i.e. it should find a secure base in the diatonic mode. The keynote now comes increasingly into its own. The children are more conscious of the world around them. By the end of Class 4, all the children should be able to sight-read simple melodies.

There should be one singing lesson a week, with another for Lower School choir.

Singing, playing instruments

* Folksongs, travelling songs, trade and work-songs, songs for times of day and seasons of year. This can also include art-composed music suitable to the age both in content and musically (e.g. Papageno's bird-catching song from Mozart's *Die Zauberflöte*, *John he was a piper's son* from the *Beggar's Opera*, Schubert's *Das Wandern* from *Die Schöne Müllerin*)
* The writing and reading notation, including sight reading with regular practise
* Rounds are introduced, including easier canons, descants and quodlibets
* The instruments learned in private lessons should be integrated into regular ensemble work. Recorders and bowed instruments accompany the singing and are very important for the cultivation of making music together. Identification of the notes of the scale and their pitch names. Reading notation from the board, progressing to sheet music. Two and three part music on the descant recorder (not singing). Strings and fingering of the violin are learned
* Conducting: the children should have opportunities to conduct the class in pieces that have simple tempi. The emphasis at this stage is on time-keeping and is done without score and confined to pieces that are known

Study of music

* Stories (short episodes) from the lives of composers
* First studies of intervals
* Fixing note lengths
* Simple types of beat, also elementary conducting (one child over against the group)

Class 5

Once proper polyphony of two to three voices has been practised, more harmonic settings can be tried. The children now have a new need for harmony, and this makes it possible to do a lot of very beautiful singing with them; this provides an inestimable foundation for all their later musical activities. The children must begin to practise adapting to the requirements of the music. They continue to learn valuable music by listening. More songs are added to the repertoire.

There should be a minimum of one music lesson, plus one lesson in the Lower School choir.

Singing

* Folk ballads are used to practise songs with harmonic accompaniments in alternating listening and singing
* Part-songs in manageable two and three-part songs sung without accompaniment
* Exercises including identification of specific intervals and singing lower intervals up to a perfect fifth. Scales: diatonic keys should be studied and practised
* More rapid sight-singing can be expected

Instrumental

* Building up a class orchestra (possibly an orchestra for the Middle School)
* Strings: introduction of viola and cello to those chosen by the teacher in consultation with the parents

Study of music

* Introduction to simple forms of songs
* Identifying the location of the key note from the key signature
* Simple keys and those they relate to are discussed and written, and simple modulations are improvised. Exercises based on the theory of music such as group improvisations on the three 'key' chords of tonic, dominant and sub-dominant
* The major scales
* The pupils should be systematically made conscious of musical terminology, e.g. stave, da capo, allegro, first time bar, C clef, octave, timpani, double sharp, slur, up-beat, concerto, etc.

Class 6

The lessons are increasingly guided towards aesthetic appreciation. First attempts at music drama (e.g. Mozart) can be introduced. The children should be singing in a formal choir. Through the acoustics main-lesson, the children become aware of the scientific aspects of music, e.g. vibrating Chladni plates, exploring the timbre of different materials.

Ideally there should be two choir lessons a week and one instrumental lesson. The main-lesson can incorporate recorder ensembles.

Singing

* Taking music over into movement through folk dances
* More folksongs in several voices and ballads
* Intensive choral work

Instrumental

* Introduction to the class of orchestral wind instruments
* Some children will move on to orchestral instruments such as brass and woodwind
* Instrumental groups or class orchestra, or possibly a Middle School orchestra

Study of music

* Continuation of music theory, intervals, arpeggios, the experience of the octave, major and minor scales, major and minor chords diminished, modal scale, cadence, dominant seventh, etc.
* Study of instruments (percussion, plucked, orchestral, wind)
* Working with parallel keys and reading key signatures
* Transposition of melodies
* Inventing melodies through improvisation and writing them down
* Understanding of music as an art begins at this age e.g. the children learn how different motifs belong to different epochs of music history. This does not have to be systematic

Class 7

The children should enjoy their music and see it as an end in itself. A beginning can now be made in helping them form judgements about music. They learn to distinguish the characters of different compositions, e.g. from Haydn to Beethoven, etc. The pupils should be exposed to a wider range of music by encouraging attendance at concerts. Rhythm becomes increasingly attached to beat.

Cultivation of voices is important at this age and especially care of the boys' voices as they begin to break.

There should be two lessons of choir and two lessons of instrumental music.

Singing

* Question-and-answer ballads (e.g. Carl Loewe, Robert Schumann)
* Duets, piano accompaniment (Monteverdi, Carissini, Purcell, Mendelssohn, Brahms)
* Simple Kunstlieder and arias, including pieces from opera, e.g. *The Magic Flute*
* World music can be approached through songs from different cultures and related to the geography lessons

Instrumental

* Instrument group or class orchestra, as well as Middle School orchestra
* Begin with the guitar (the whole class). Cadenzas, etc.
* Literature still mainly Baroque (overture, suites by Purcell, Telemann, pre-Classical (Bach and sons) and Classical (Mozart, Haydn)

Study of music

* Experiencing the intervals in chromatic scales (and relationship of fifth, connections with major and minor – transposing)
* Introduction to bass clef
* Rhythmical improvisations, musical pieces with spoken text
* Biographies of important composers

Class 8

Continue cultivating musical appreciation and judgement. Questions of musical style and character can now be discussed. Feelings of the search for truth, loneliness and growing individuation can be met by solo songs and ballads from the Romantic period. Experience of the octave is accented as a search for one's own spiritual quest and discovery of one's centre (e.g. the tritone problem). Continued care of boys' voices is needed as they break.

There should be two lessons of choir and two lessons of instrumental music.

Singing

* Songs in two to four voices, a capella and accompanied
* Among others: older polyphonic folksongs, songs about death, songs criticising contemporary life, songs with strong rhythms. Humorous pieces are also appropriate at this age
* Spirituals, ballads, Kunstlieder with piano accompaniment (e.g. by Mendelssohn and Brahms)
* Melodramatic ballads (Schubert: *Die Winterreise*)
* Contrasting major and minor

Instrumental

* Various, including work on the music for the class play
* Literature should include arrangements of Romantic orchestral works (Schubert overtures, Tschaikovsky *Swan Lake* or pieces from his collection *Album for the Young*

Study of music

* Theory of melody (genuine and non-genuine melodies); improvisation
* Rhythmical and melodic musical dictation; rhythmical improvisation; improvisation of cadenzas
* Continuation of biographical descriptions

Classes 9 to 12

Progress through the Upper School begins in Class 9. It may be seen as leading the pupils from 'egoism' to sociability as they become more mature individuals able to make their own decisions. At the same time this is a historical path from baroque (self-orientated/ single themes) via Classical (dualism/ dialectic) and Romantic (transitions, entry into spatial thinking, awakening of social awareness) to the twentieth century and the urgent questions of the present time, and anxious searches for clarity about what is important... Musically one might speak of a metamorphosis of the moods of fifth, third and octave: the 'emptiness' beginning with the fifth (Class 9), the third opening up towards the other person (Class 11), and the subjective, psychological mood turned towards knowledge in the octave (Class 12).[6]

Music is a valuable social component of education in the Upper School, providing a beneficial compensation, as the young people become more strongly individual. This is important in itself, but there is more to it. For the period in question, music is also a field of experience and activity that challenges individual young people to make their contribution to the whole in a fully conscious manner.

Youngsters in Class 9 display symptoms of egocentric, existential questioning and critical attitudes that do not yet have a proper focus. Seen together, such symptoms and attitudes have a certain 'Baroque' quality. This is not yet a subject that can be examined with them. It is an open motif around which proper themes can be developed later on, a motif that can bring new life to the forces of death now felt physically right down to the skeleton. It prevents the youngsters' own feelings from growing cold and rigid in the stereotypes of the rock and pop worlds to which pupils nowadays are especially susceptible. The desire to shackle the immaterial art of music to the skeleton must be transformed by music itself, so that it can once again become an art that is open to the spirit...

Class 9 bears the rather Baroque stamp of egocentricity and single-track mindedness, endless doodling, loneliness and yet being part of the crowd, solo/tutti. In Class 10 the young people can begin to listen to one another again, which is a prerequisite for objective discussion and a willingness to consider, or at least respect, opposite views. A breath of new air blows through the class community. The youngsters are no longer exclusively searching by means of criticising everything like a kind of out-breathing process. They are also finding answers, moments of containment in hearing each other's views, like a kind of in-breathing that allows them to come to themselves and remain within themselves...

In Class 10 the pupils have the opportunity to enter intensively into the form language of Classical music and follow its development from Haydn via Mozart to Beethoven's later works.

For the most part indicative (diatonic) forms have determined processes in the class. Having once encountered one another by means of an objective discussion, we can in Class 11 then approach the possible, the indeterminate, the vague, the irrational i.e. the subjunctive as a new reality between sense experience and knowledge. A new mood provided by the interval of the third as the sixth is now a sign of turning towards the other: 'Participating in the inner life of the other'.

... We must also take a new look at the 'programme music' of the Romantic period. It is not merely a matter of repeating a non-musical content by means of music. It is music awakening in images, a process that can bring in imaginative associations, even though these are initially external and materialistic. We follow the path from materialistic images (Smetana Vltava) to the imaginatively inspired works of the great impressionists (Debussy La mer). This path is also a way of practising what Steiner described as the feeling for the octave. Pupils sense that their subjective feelings (stuck in tonality) begin to let go and loosen, so that they can be led to a light of consciousness of which they have an inkling ...

In the composition and improvisation exercises we try to use the more important style elements of the Romantic period. By means of non-harmonic modulations new and unsuspected spaces are opened up that call tonality and orientation towards a keynote into question. The way is then open for an art that can take responsibility for itself. The score no longer offers any security. Art becomes a space for the essential, enabling it to appear – untouched – in a space that is etheric and spiritual. The prerequisite for this is that the wish for art to become artistic knowledge should enable us to extricate ourselves from subjective, dreaming imprisonment within. T. S. Eliot coined the phrase for this: 'Precise emotion'.[7]

Pupils in Class 12 experience that their feeling for the world and for themselves has changed. They no longer feel so much obligation towards the dreamy, warm life of the group. Instead they take on responsibility more and more for themselves and their life's motifs. This is not so much an 'awakening' as a 'resurrection'. Young people look for this not only in themselves but also in contemporary art. They hope for the genuinely new, the future-oriented, the unknown, the unheard-of – in music also. So in Class 12 music lessons, one can begin to find a way towards atonal music. Harmony theory provides no safety net here; the only thing that counts is:

... to be open and ready to search out the musical phenomena and the inner logic of their unfolding, to sense the truth they contain, and to practise and school a new kind of 'thinking' in connection with them. As an example of this one need only look more closely at the last of Schönberg's Six Little Pieces for Piano, Op. 19...

When we examine the development undergone by music during the twentieth century from that point onwards, we discover that as music has grown more materialistic on the one hand and less materialistic on the other, there has nevertheless not occurred again a transparency, and transcendence (an openness for the spirit to flow in) carried by such a high degree of awareness as was experienced at the beginning of the century...

Seen from this angle, music is indeed an essential ingredient in education, essential because outwardly music, the least material of the arts, is without purpose; it speaks directly to the inmost core in every human being.[8]

Class 9

The pupils learn to understand and perform simple vocal and instrumental works in appropriate styles. Basic structures of some works are studied, and a beginning is made in looking at some of the streams in music history. Many schools form an Upper School choir combining all classes and an orchestra involving those capable of contributing. Large choral works are studied and performed, often together with staff and parents.

Study of music

* General studies: the line system and notation of music, scales, circle of the fifth, intervals, chords and inversions are continued both in instrumental and choral work and in improvisation and composition exercises
* Works are described, characterised, compared and assessed
* Look for links with history and the other arts, e.g. the connections between music and society
* Experiencing phenomena of contemporary music

Music theory

* Rounds, fugues, suites, cantatas, oratorios, introduction to counterpoint style
* Differences between homophone/polyphone, temperate mood
* Study of the different instruments, e.g. the organ and other keyboard instruments

Biographies

* E.g. comparing Mozart/Beethoven, Bach/Handel

Concert and opera visits

* Classical works, with preparation and subsequent assessment

Singing, choir

* Voice work
* Extending the repertoire (choir): folksongs, Lieder, examples of light music, political songs, etc., a capella, with accompaniment, unison and in several parts
* Singing songs in the foreign languages the pupils are studying

Upper School choir

* All the classes in the Upper School form this choir to work on pieces that can be performed in public

Instrumental music

* In the school orchestra or chamber music groups pupils work on pieces for performance to the rest of the school or in public

* Improvisation, e.g. with the school's collection of percussion instruments

Class 10

Work is done on the formal structures of sonatas, fugues, etc. The pupils learn about the significance of the sonata in Classical music, especially in the way this relates to the human being. The students can take a more active role in performing music in concerts, dealing with publicity, programme notes, front of house activities and taking music into the local community.

Study of music

* Forms of instrumental and vocal music: motifs, themes, sonata, symphony, concerto, opera
* Basic harmony studies
* Studies in composition, the students can be encouraged to compose their own pieces in harmony and counterpoint

Biographies

* The pupils work up biographies of well-known composers or interpreters including good jazz and pop musicians[9]

Concert and opera visits

* Classical works, with preparation and subsequent assessment

Singing, choir

* Voice work
* Expanding the repertoire of songs
* Folksongs, Lieder, opera arias, songs from musicals, chansons, a capella or accompanied
* Singing songs in the foreign languages the pupils are studying

Upper School choir

* All the classes in the Upper School form this choir to work on pieces that can be performed in public
* Classical choruses in four voices

Instrumental music

* In the school orchestra or chamber music groups pupils work on pieces for performance to the rest of the school or in public
* Improvisation

Class 11

The pupils learn to perform Lieder in an appropriate way. They also learn to recognise Romantic forms by ear or by reading the score.

They develop an awareness of the new view attained by musicians in the nineteenth century and discover how the 'universal language' of Classical music relates to the origins of national folk music and jazz.[9]

Study of music

* Music main-lesson (See also Art Studies in Class 11)
* Apollonian/Dionysian: expressions and forms of a musical work of art
* Development periods in the history of music from early days up to the twentieth century
* A look at the harmony of Pythagoras

* Using chromatic scales
* Significant works from important epochs with emphasis on the Romantic period
* Describing, comparing, categorising various works
* Programme music

Music theory

* The form of the main sonata movement

Biographies

* Reports by the pupils on great Romantic composers: Schumann, Chopin, Brahms, Wagner, Verdi, etc.

Concert and opera visits

* Classical and Romantic works, with preparation and subsequent assessment

Singing, choir

* Voice work
* Solo singing
* Expanding the repertoire of songs: folksongs, Lieder, Romantic choir works, chamber ensembles (also solos) a capella or accompanied
* Singing songs in the languages the pupils are studying
* Four-part choral works (including Romantic ones)

Upper School choir

* All the classes in the Upper School form this choir to work on pieces that can be performed in public (seasonal and festive themes)

Instrumental music

* In the school orchestra or chamber music groups pupils work on pieces for performance to the rest of the school or in public
* Improvisation

Class 12

The pupils should be able to recognise and describe characteristic phenomena of twentieth-century music. Interest in the directions composition is taking in our time includes interest in the current situation in which human beings find themselves. The pupils should study examples of how musicians today, also with electronic and digital means at their disposal, can be responsible for music's continuing development. An understanding of the main streams of music history should help the pupils develop an awareness of today's relevant questions.

Study of music

* An overview of music history: music in the past, present and anticipated future trends, viewed both from the past and from the twentieth century
* Theory of harmonies
* Development of music after World War Two
* Important works of the twentieth century (e.g. Stravinsky, Hindemith, the New Viennese School, Serialism, Minimalism etc.) are described, characterised, compared and put into context
* Music and technology (electronic, synthetic and computer-supported music)

Biographies

* Pupils' studies on twentieth century composers, or
* Pupils' projects on music and the human being

Concert and opera visits

* Classical and modern works, with preparation and subsequent assessment

Singing, choir

* Voice work
* Expansion of song repertoire
* Choral works, folksongs, Lieder of the twentieth century, and solo singing, a capella or with accompaniment

Upper School choir

* All the classes in the Upper School form this choir to work on pieces that can be performed in public. Difficult works are tackled

Instrumental music

* In the school orchestra or chamber music groups pupils work on pieces for performance to the rest of the school or in public
* Improvisation
* Solo work of gifted pupils
* School-leaving concert

22

Philosophy

Class 12

There are many opportunities to explore philosophical questions in the context of other subjects such as history, art, science, literature, religion and even to an extent in foreign language lessons. The philosophy main-lesson in Class 12 provides an opportunity to explore basic philosophical issues and methods. A starting point is to establish that people have been motivated by ideals throughout history and that these ideals often express changing worldviews. This forms a basis for all real knowledge. Highly complex and important concepts are accessible to everyone when they are presented in an appropriate way.

Philosophical questions arise as a matter of course in many subjects in the Upper School. Philosophy serves as a link to other lessons taught by the literature or the history teacher.

Young people of eighteen or nineteen are particularly open to philosophical questions. They want to survey what they have learnt from a 'higher vantage point'. Finding oneself now gains a larger dimension; personal perspectives widen to include humanity as a whole. Philosophy in Class 12 is much more than dry academic learning; it is rather, the 'love of wisdom', as the name implies.

Differing philosophies can suggest a variety of answers to basic human questions. The students learn to reproduce, classify and evaluate different philosophical trains of thought by means of text analysis, open discussion and essays for homework. These tasks are intended to provide a context for initial answers to the pupils' own, usually unconscious, questions. As Kant might have said, 'rather than learning about philosophy we should learn to philosophise.'

The following suggestions are guidelines only. It is obviously not possible to cover all or even most of these topics in one three week main-lesson.

Introduction

* Origins of philosophical questions
* The special position of philosophy in relation to the humanities and sciences
* Taking up philosophical questions arising in other subjects such as English, history, art studies, religion, etc.

The knowing human being

* Fundamental questions in philosophy, theories of Knowledge and endeavours to answer

them, e.g. by critical rationalism, positivism, scepticism, etc.

* Theories of truth

The acting human being

* The initial question of human freedom
* Absolute and relative values
* Considerations of freedom as dealt with by various philosophers (Socrates, Plato, Kant, Nietzsche, Jaspers, Steiner)
* The responsibility of the scientist

A choice of themes

Philosophy of history

* The history of human consciousness as shown in the philosophical questions raised
* Lessing's *Education of Mankind*

Philosophy of language

* Comparison of older and newer theories of language (e.g. Humboldt, Whorf, Chomsky, Pinker)
* The nature of language as taken from the pupils' own experience (with a side glance at modern lyric poetry)

Philosophical anthropology

* The nature of the human being in various cultures and religions
* Gender issues
* The problem of death
* The tragedy of human limitations

Aesthetics

* Matter and form in art
* Schiller's *Letters on the Aesthetic Education of Mankind*, selected passages

Philosophy of the state

* Comparison of various views of state, law, power in the history of philosophy (Plato, Aristotle, Macchiavelli, Rousseau)
* Consideration of Utopias (e.g. Plato, Thomas More, Karl Marx, etc.)

23

Physics

The main aim of science teaching is to grasp the core of science that is relevant to the human being as well as presenting it in an imaginative way to appeal to the emotions. This means developing a faculty of observation for the real gestures of nature. Indeed science lessons begin at the age when the child gains an ability to see the world causally and they must serve to cultivate this thinking faculty. Indeed this can occur in such a way that a qualitative thinking is developed that continually considers the changing connection between the human being and the world.

Through the limiting of science to size, number and weight (as Galileo did), that is, to the purely quantitative, the question of the *being* of natural phenomena has been lost. During the rise of the modern age, man began to ask how he could control nature, and finally to see this control as what is essential. This trend has been connected with the development of causal and theoretical model views, because it is only possible to have absolute mastery over natural processes when you can explain them causally. If this is not initially possible, phenomena are reduced conceptually to explainable processes.

The danger is that these concepts of imposed quantitative and particle-like models of nature are taken up by pupils as objective reality. From this experience for example a curriculum formulated in 1977 already has this warning:

> *It is essential to use models which are not too perfect when beginning teaching. There must be elementary phenomena which cannot be explained by the models used. Only by this means do the pupils altogether gain the insight into the principle of the insufficiency of models.*[1]

What is more valuable from a pedagogical point of view are however the following principles:

* 1. In place of models which cannot be experienced, should be thought processes which have their basis in real perception.
* 2. Initially an emotional connection to the phenomena must be awakened in the child. This must then be raised from the subjective level in order that the intrinsic qualities can be grasped in cognitive activity.
* 3. Thereby science teaching in the Waldorf school takes its departure from the sense qualities. Indeed it can in this respect even be described as an extremely sense-orientated method. This plays an important role and has

a hygienic-pedagogical aspect. The lively joy in cognition is healing for the student aged between twelve and fourteen years, and can even possibly lighten the tendency towards all-too-strong self-pre-occupation.

The phenomenological world view, the creative forming of thought connections with natural events requires, however, even more. It should not only be done out of an honest pedagogical endeavour towards a human-centred acquisition of knowledge. Rather it involves a epistemological discussion of the basic ideas of the empirical method of science.

The active participation of the individual person in the world characterises Rudolf Steiner's theory of knowledge. In his basic books on this subject *A Theory of Knowledge* and *The Philosophy of Freedom*[2], Rudolf Steiner described the connection between sense impression and thinking.

> *Our whole being functions in such a way, that it flows in reality towards the elements of each thing observed from two sides; from the side of perception and from that of thinking.*[3]

Science teaching in the Waldorf school seeks to do justice to this basic rule.

Classes 6 to 8

The whole of physics teaching does not start from theories or models, but from the experienced and observed phenomenon. Wherever opportunities offer themselves, contrasts should be demonstrated for comparison. Even though the single disciplines of this subject are defined, one should try not to go through them in isolation but to cultivate the aspects common to other subjects where they appear in an interdisciplinary way. It is therefore self evident, that connections to art and technology should be presented, when they offer themselves and are appropriate to the age being taught.

The Middle School attempts to provide a rich experience of physical phenomena upon which the Upper School can conceptually build.

Class 6

The experience of phenomena in simple, very clear experiments leads the pupil into the realm of physics. For this purpose, acoustics can be placed at the beginning. Various entries offer themselves; to name but two:

* a) Introduction to basic acoustic phenomena (vibration, pitch, volume, tone colour)
* b) Beginning with familiar musical instruments, pupils can recognise vibration as the physical equivalent of tone
    * The connection of the sounding body to volume, pitch and tone colour is presented
    * Intervals on the monochord
    * Sound transmission
    * Resonance

The pupils anyway get to know the physical-physiological qualities of the larynx (compare with biology in Class 8).

From experiences in painting they go on to:

* Colour studies
* Simple optics (i.e. studies without theory).
* The point of departure is the contrast: light – darkness
* The observation of illuminated coloured surfaces gives rise to after images in the eye, these lead to the concept of complementary colours (Goethe's 'summoned' colours)

* Colourful and coloured shadows are demonstrated and the conditions under which they arise are shown
* The phenomena of colour derived in an opaque medium when illuminated from behind and from the side
* The goal in colour studies is the observation of coloured fringes on dark/light borders as seen through a prism
* Fringes appear on dark/light borders
* Apart from colours, shadows are an area of study.
* Magnetism is presented starting with naturally occurring magnetite
* The question 'how is something magnetised?' is answered, and which materials have (ferro)-magnetic properties

Ordinary magnets are presented and the compass (without casing) demonstrated. This leads to discussions on:

* The concept of north and south pole
* The concept of magnetic attraction and repulsion
* The magnetic field of the earth

Electricity is dealt with as regards the phenomena of attraction and repulsion in electrostatics, using charges obtained by friction.

Heat studies considers:

* The contrast of warmth and cold
* Sources of heat and cold are demonstrated and discussed together with the possibility of creating cooling (still without any technical details).
* Combustion and friction are looked at more closely as heat sources.

Class 7

Mechanics is central to the teaching after which the further contents of acoustics, optics, thermodynamics, magnetism and electricity are discussed. In mechanics, levers are studied. Here it is clear that the concept is dominant. The content is in key words:

* Levers in several variations: effort arm and load arm
* Digital balance (which is decimal and sensitive)
* Inclined plane
* Winch
* Pulleys, block and tackle
* Wedge, screw, linkages, gears

Combinations of these 'basic machines' should be discussed and the aim is to arrive at the understanding of the means by which a weight-driven clock works.

* The development of formulas for the lever and inclined plane
* As summary, the Golden Rule of mechanics (i.e. that gain in force is paid for by greater distance travelled formally known as 'velocity ratio')

Acoustics

* Chladni plates (can also be done in Class 6)
* Rotating plate with holes and air jet
* Gramophone
* Sound directing. Echoes (can also be done in Class 8)

Optics

Observation of:

* Shadows and images (combined with drawing)
* Light images on planes and curved mirrors practised

* The pin-hole camera (compared with the human eye) (can also be done in Class 8)
* Camera obscura

Warmth

* Conduction
* Thermometers

Magnetism

* Declination and inclination of the earth's field
* The basic phenomena of magnetism
* The subject of electrodynamics comprises approximately:
  * Sources of current (cells, dynamo)
  * Electrical appliances in relationship to flow of current
  * Magnetic effects, electromagnets.
  * Technical applications: electric ovens, boilers, irons, fuses
  * Indications of the dangers of electric current, also in lightening must be given

Class 8

The areas of hydrostatics, hydrodynamics, aerostatics and aerodynamics with a strong practical bias stand primarily in the foreground for this age. In detail:

* The Archimedes principal (for water and air)
* Hydrostatic buoyancy (depth pressure)
* Connected containers (hydraulic scales)
* Cartesian diver
* Specific weight of solid, liquids and gaseous bodies
* Stability (e.g. of ships)
* Static pressure (in water compared to air)
* Principal of pumps (especially leading to the hydraulic ram)
* Laminar and turbulent flow
* Vortices and resistance (in water and air in connection to the resisting forms which they pass)

In the area of meteorology (this is often taught in connection with the geography main lesson, some of which comes also in Class 10, see geography curriculum) the following can be done:

* Air moisture content and cloud formation (dew point)
* Cloud types (Cumulus, Cirrus, Stratus, Nimbus and their combinations)
* High and low pressure areas (with fronts developing over time)
* Cyclone alleys
* Weather maps, weather forecasts
* Wind force according to the Beaufort scale, special winds such as the Mistral, Föehn, trade winds, monsoon and typhoon. Climatic phenomena such as maritime and continental climate, tropical and sub-tropical and polar climate

In acoustics one investigates for instance:

* Speed of sound (also in other media than air)
* Sound directing: reflection (echo) and absorption (can also be done in Classes 7 and 9)
* Kundt's tube
* Acoustics in building, acoustics in various musical instruments

In thermodynamics the content could be for example:

* Change of state of liquids, solids and gasses, evaporation
* Anomaly point of water and its significance for nature (can also be done in Class 9)

* Warm and cold water pipe systems, convection, radiation
* Conduction and insulation mediums in various materials (can also be done in Class 7)

Processes and laws of electricity

* Warming effect, chemical effect of electric currents
* Conduction properties of various materials, also earthing
* The magnetic effect of a current and its applications:
  * Electro-motor, dynamo (possibly generator, in any case this should be dealt with in more depth higher up the school), measurement (Ohm's law).

Classes 9 to 12

In Classes 6 to 8 science lessons were given by a generally trained class teacher who taught many subjects. In particular, the relationship of the subject matter to the human being was presented in its physiological, economic, and ecological aspects. The starting point generally for teaching was experiments. Investigations were kept simple, so that the children could recall most of them at home. Where possible the children were encouraged to observe physical phenomena. Experiments and demonstrations of phenomena were arranged, and the pupils went on to deliver independent, written descriptions.

In science lessons in the Upper School, the impressions based on experience of the Middle school are then ordered further by thinking and finally grasped as laws. The pupils should thereby be protected from valuing half understood theories above their own experience and judgement while building up their picture of the world. From this it should be clear that theoretical content, which today as a rule is considered the basis of subjects – and for this reason is often placed at the beginning of a teaching programme – is only taught in the Upper School in Waldorf schools. Therefore the model of the atom is only dealt with in the Classes 11 and 12. Where theories enter into the teaching, they should at least be elaborated as thought spheres about phenomena, as for instance the atomic theory which comes from the quantitative laws of chemistry, the emission of light etc. Otherwise the world appears, as it surrounds mankind, as meaningless compared to an elaborate model of it and the ability to judge retreats when confronted with the given content.

The aims for physics teaching in the Upper School are:

Knowledge and understanding

* Fundamental physical phenomena and the attempts to describe their processes
* Physical dimensions and concepts defined – with consideration of aspects relevant to man – as well as the main laws of measurement and defining equations; estimates of the order of magnitudes of physical results
* Understanding of certain phenomena of daily life by means of physical processes
* Understanding of the physical basis of technical apparatus
* A knowledge of the main lines of historical development in physics and the biographies of significant scientists
* A knowledge of the idea of physical models and their capacity to predict

Abilities and skills

* To observe precisely and formulate observations
* To carry out simple experiments and interpret their results
* To construct independent concepts from observations
* To construct independent experiments so as to make observations
* To recognise uncertainties and evaluate their influence
* To present measurements graphically and evaluate them
* To understand physical processes with the help of known laws
* To recognise the possibilities and limitations of physics in describing reality
* To be able to judge the real component in models
* To produce independent reports of what is taught
* To look at things in their entirety, holistic observation, and present their connection to human life

Insights, evaluations and attitudes

* Readiness to communicate and co-operate in observation, investigation and experimenting
* Recognition of the difference between quantitative and qualitative investigation and their results
* Insight into the meaning of dynamic and feedback processes (change-causing-relationships) and their challenge to human thinking
* Arrival at an awareness of environmental and energy issues on the basis of their own insight
* Insight that the physical method of thinking must be constantly modified
* Insight that science and within it physics represents and important part of human culture
* The ability to judge information and presentations of the mass media thoroughly
* The ordering of different scientific investigative methods and their significance for the interpretation of results
* The evaluation of the wisdom of nature – also as an example for human endeavour

Class 9

The pupils are guided in experiencing so that they can understand the processes of the surrounding world, especially those of technology. For this reason questioning thinking and judgement is practised especially in practical things from the realm of technology. The manufacture of materials should feature particularly in experiment description. A mathematical formulation of the rule is usually only given for certain examples, e.g. for exercises to do with the area in hand, where a meaningful calculation is possible, and where the pupil can gain a feeling for quantities. Understanding for physics and its methods should be deepened and a glimpse of the physical content of everyday objects and technology be given.

* Transformer
* Introduction to Potential difference, current, resistance
* Morse transmitter (telegraph)
* Bells, relays
* Washing machine

Heat and engines

This is mostly built up on the suggestions of Rudolf Steiner, leading to the understanding of the steam engine, but a more contemporary development is advisable.

* The investigation of air pressure by Otto von Guericke
* Historical development of the steam engine and its importance in the historical development of Europe
* The function of the boiler
* Comparison of the heating value of various fuels (in ideal combustion situations)
* As regards basic laws thereby you can arrive at:
  * 1st and 2nd law of thermodynamics
* The development in new areas of technology could for example take the following themes:
  * Absolute zero; the Kelvin scale
  * The steam turbine
  * Fridges and the contrasting function of the heat pump
  * Internal combustion engines – 4-stroke, 2-stroke, diesel, perhaps the Stirling motor
  * Radiation
  * Rocket propulsion

Electricity and acoustics

Here one begins with the suggestion of Rudolf Steiner's, to present everything that will make a telephone comprehensible.

* Introduction or recapitulation of the concepts of potential difference, current, and resistance (see Class 8)
* Ohm's law with examples involving calculation
* Introduction of the concept of electrical work, electrical output and their units
* Calculation of electricity costs
* Function of the telephone: acoustically and electronically
* Dialling technology
* Business significance of various communications technologies
* Fax machine, photocopier

For the Acoustic Doppler effect one can use Rudolf Steiner's suggestion:

* The treatment of relative motion of binary stars with the help of the Doppler effect (can also be done in the geography main-lesson)

Further possible themes:

* Principle of the electric motor
* Comparison of the efficiency of various machines
* Biographies of important physicists or alternatively independent presentations by pupils on Watt, Guericke, Papin, Morse, etc.
* Optional energy requirement and inquiry into the means of energy saving
* Comparison of the readily available energy sources
* Solar energy and its possible significance in the future (could otherwise be done in Class 10 or 11, see technology curriculum)
* Hydrogen as possible energy carrier

Class 10

The pupils experience their relationship to their surroundings increasingly consciously and thus stand in a tension between high ideals and uncertainty of appropriateness. In many subjects one can address the question of origins. Through transparent and fundamental concepts in mechanics one can attempt in various ways to give conscious clarity and security. For this the mathematicisation of physics is handled in an experiential way. The pupils can experience satisfaction in the dominance of statements won through mathematics using observation and measurement (for instance in the parabolic trajectory of a thrown object).

Discovering the principles, proportions and conditions with equations of quantities is practised.

The pupils receive a living, conscious vision of the great spiritual scientific turning point of the late Renaissance and the birth of physics by grappling with decisive historical questions as found in the biographies of significant personalities (Galileo, Bruno, Kepler, Tycho Brahe). They thus grasp how the human being as observer is caught in the facts of the physical world, its laws, from the outside, and in the lawfulness of logic, in thinking, from the inside. By their own development in consciousness as well as the recognition of their own mistakes the students learn the conditions of research and see the 'great spirits' of earlier times in the correct light. They also learn the value of learning from failure for all research and development. So the pupil experiences, how security of understanding comes about, and learns, to connect himself to the earth and its laws in a new way.

Classical mechanics

Kinematics (uniform movement)

* Measurement of speed
* The concept of average speed
* How to represent speed using vectors
* Parallelogram of velocity
* The concept of acceleration
* Development of the laws of motion for constant acceleration using an inclined plane v=at, s=½ att
* Free fall, acceleration due to gravity, units of force
* Vertical and horizontal motion perhaps diagonal motion
* Principle of independence (of perpendicular motion)

Statics

* Hook's law; application to balances
* Measurement of forces, force equations
* Representation of forces by vectors
* Elastic and plastic deformation, pressure, stress
* Centre of gravity of a body
* Force and reaction of a body on a slope

Dynamics

* Concept of mass, force
* Newton's laws of motion
* Go into the historical development of these concepts and the biography of Newton
* Law of conservation of energy
* Recapitulation of the golden rule of mechanics
* Mechanical work
* The concept of energy
* The law of conservation of energy
* Friction and static friction and cohesion
* Rotary motion
* The rotation of the earth
* Centrifugal and centripetal force

Optional, Coriolis effect

(see geography in Class 10)

* Law of moments and balancing using moments
* Impulse and momentum, elasticity
* Newton's law of gravitation
* Kepler's laws
* Optional: Kepler's *Harmonices Mundi* (or in astronomy main-lesson)
* Pendulums
* Rhythms in the solar system
* Wave motion in mechanics
* Mechanical oscillation and waves

* Superposition of waves (constructive and destructive interference, if not in Class 11)

Astronomy

An astronomy main-lesson could be considered (although otherwise covered in physics; Rudolf Steiner did not expressly require a main lesson) with the themes:

* The protective covering of the earth
* The solar system heliocentrically
* The nine planets, asteroids and comets
* The sun and its rhythms
* Solar effects on the earth – life-history of a star
* Kepler's 'Harmony of Worlds'
* Sun and moon and their rhythms in relationship to the earth

Optional

* The golden section as rhythmical principle of form in the solar system
* Telescopes, microscopes, cameras, (human eye) (and Class 11)

Class 11

Following Rudolf Steiner's indications, which were to handle the modern discoveries of physics (at that time alpha, beta and gamma rays), electrical theory, electromagnetic theory, and the basic phenomena of radioactivity as well as the conceptual development in physics in the nineteenth and twentieth centuries should be worked through. Electrical and magnetic fields in particular are investigated. With this the students' intelligence, which has been schooled in observation and measurement, is turned to areas requiring mathematical thought. The principle of taking experiments as the point of departure, should, however, remain as in earlier classes.

Electricity

* The history of electricity
* Optional: electrostatics (revision)
* Concept of the electrical field
* Capacitors
* Van de Graaf generators (as examples for electrostatics)
* Current induced magnetic fields
* Faraday's motor principle
* Revision work on the concept of potential difference, charge, current, resistance but on a more general level
* Connection between potential difference, current, resistance, force
* Warming effect of a current
* Conduction rules in various materials
* Induction: Inductive resistance, Lenzes rule, Lorenz force,
* Eddy current breaking effect
* Superconductivity
* Energy as calculation standard (extension of the energy laws from Class 10)
* Induction due to reciprocally acting currents; polarity of the electric and magnetic field
* Change in time of current and potential difference of a charging and discharging capacitor
* Capacitor rules, units, calculation of capacity, dielectrics
* Oscillatory discharge
* Current (quantitative)
* Potential difference and current diagrams for damped electrical oscillations
* Phase in electrical oscillations

* Undamped electrical oscillations, synthesiser
* Length of vibration and frequency; Thomson's wave formulae

Signal generator, boundaries of audibility

* Transmitters and receivers; to which belong resonance, triodes, electron tubes (cathode ray tube), emission spectra (continuous, hot wire spectra); development of the concept of the electron as well as Millikan's investigations, transistors
* Transmission dipole, dipole laws, electromagnetic vibration fields, electromagnetic wavelengths
* The history of transmission
* Radio broadcasting, applied radio building possibly

Atomic physics

* High tension spark inductors; gas emission (emission tubes)
* Cathode rays, x-rays (details of subatomic particle of moving positive and negative charge carriers – ions, electrons) and their counterparts in alpha, beta and gamma rays, oscilloscope
* Radioactivity, natural occurrences of radioactivity, radioactive fallout; fission, nuclear reactors, man made radioactive isotopes, means of detection; (Geiger-Müller-tubes, cloud chambers)
* History of the technological development of the atom bomb (dangers, protection from radiation)
* Atomic fusion
* Optional: semiconductors, diodes, transistors (see Chapter 27, Technology).

Class 12

By now the maturity is reached which permits the young person awareness of how he or she acquires concepts. Now theoretical scientific questions can properly be addressed; for example the significance of the physical model of inductive and deductive thinking etc. Thereby one attempts to develop not blind belief in science but rather a personal capacity for judgement. This can be a decisive aid to the development of the personality. This can be done in optics – if not already done in Class 11 – or in the development of the atomic model. Besides conveying important basic knowledge a survey of the phenomena and ideas which characterise modern scientific knowledge should be given.

The various ways in which light meets matter can determine the approach to teaching.

The domain of optics can be used to show:

* Phenomena starting from their surroundings
* Analytical thinking in the domain of a complete manner of observation
* A symptomatic approach
* A discussion of points of view – development of judgement
* Building bridges between optics, man and art
* Cross curricular teaching is especially worthwhile here

Optics

(see list in Class 8)

* Aspects of geometrical optics
* Concept of shadow, umbral, penumbral
* Brightness
* The concept of contrast and its significance for vision
* Comparison: eyes – photo cells; qualities, quantities, objectivity also in the domain of qualitative investigation
* After images and coloured shadows (successive contrast, simultaneous contrast) and their physiological basis
* The human eye and equivalent technical apparatus (e.g. lenses, aperture in a camera); short- and long-sightedness, spectacles
* The Weber-Fechner law (properties of optical stimulation and perception, geometric and arithmetical consequences)
* Sense perception and consciousness, sensory deception
* Goethe's theory of colour (prismatic colours); colour qualities
* The polarity between the green and red spectrum, its counterpart in plant and the human being

* Optional: Chlorophyll, haemoglobin: chemical structure

* The basic phenomena of chromatography according to Goethe; the Goethean method in science. Polarity of light and darkness according to Goethe and its significance for the creation of colours through darkening (Rayleigh scattering)
* Additive and subtractive colour mixing (use of technology) – difference in brightness
* Spectral and physical colours
* Plane mirrors
* Convex and concave mirrors
* Mirror laws: mirror plane (technical application)
* Microscope – electron microscope (resolution capacity)
* Refraction, total internal reflection (laws) (critical angle), Newton's basic experiment with prisms
* Diffraction (point light, laser; laser light – sunlight)
* Wavelength of light, spectroscope, spectrometer
* Polarisation – double refraction (technical application in tension/compression optics), asymmetrical structure of space – concept of isotropy
* Atmospheric colour occurrences in nature and their causes through diffraction, interference, refraction, polarisation
* The rainbow and its cause; perhaps indications about the golden section applied to the rainbow
* Photo-electric effect (technical application)
* Electron volt, Plancke's quantum effect
* Wave-particle duality and its significance for the consciousness of physics in the twentieth century (the development of models in science); regarding the methodology in dealing with borders of physics; making hypotheses
* The three models of light: wave, particle, ray, their significance and evidence for them
* Theory of relativity, quantum theory
* Biographies of significant researchers of the twentieth century (e.g. Einstein, Planck, Hahn, Schroedinger, Bohr, Heisenberg)

The pupils learn here by example to know about modern consciousness questions and the problem of science and ethics

* Mathematicisation of physics and fallibility law
* Formula structures, energy equivalence of mass; light and matter
* Optional:
  * Line spectra in emission and absorption, spectral analysis, meaning of spectral lines
  * The measurement of potential difference by means of a photoelectric cell and the sequence of wavelengths
  * Millikan's experiments (if not in Class 11 in connection with the electron), Rutherford's ray experiment, wave-particle dualism in matter.

In optics the following are taken up:

* Colour generation using prisms
* Lenses, focal points
* Virtual and real images
* The means of collection sunlight using a magnifying lens or concave mirror

24

Practical Projects and Work Experience

Agriculture practical: Class 9

It is increasingly becoming necessary to give young people, while still at school, the opportunity to undertake practical tasks and prove themselves in the world of real work. Especially after puberty, both boys and girls need experiences of concrete conditions in modern working situations.

For Class 9 pupils an intensive immersion in the life of a farm is in keeping with their age, when questions about life in general are beginning to awaken in them: What is the relationship between human being and earth, plants and animals? What problems result from technology and modern social conditions? Existential questions are rephrased as the youngsters become increasingly aware of them. Linked with their elemental urge to use the strength of their limbs, youngsters of this age want to test their will and fulfil tasks that require energy, care, courage and presence of mind. They also have a healthy natural urge to go out and experience nature, an urge that all too frequently remains unsatisfied in industrial regions. Such activities must appeal to their interest in understanding, their energy and their idealism.

Through concrete work on a farm the pupils should concern themselves intensively with the production of agricultural raw materials, and with the care of the earth and the landscape. Singly or in groups they work on a farm where, usually for the first time, they gain insight into the work and livelihood of one of the archetypal occupations. It is helpful if the farmers can be persuaded to explain the economic realities of produce prices, the capital costs of new equipment such as tractors, EU Subsidies, etc.

Suggested tasks

Getting to know all activities from planting, weeding, fertilising, to harvesting and storing. Initial experiences of animal husbandry, including milk processing. Getting to know the farm in its full extent as an organism, including the prevalent social conditions. Working with people and machines. Suitable farms are those using organic, biodynamic or ecological methods while also being favourably disposed towards young people. In 'contrast', a conventional farm might also be considered.

A diary is kept describing the farm, its geographical, commercial and social situation, and also its daily routine. This is to help the pupils work consciously on their experiences. It is also helpful to have a general discussion in the class, following such a practical, in which the students can exchange views and describe what they have learned.

Alternative

As an alternative to farming, Class 9 students can undertake practical projects involving building work or ecological work (clearing ponds, hedging, stone walling, path laying, protecting natural habitats, etc.). The emphasis should be on practical skills, manual work, socially relevant and useful tasks, teamwork and accountability.

Surveying: Class 10

This subject, a part of 'technology and real life', has the following aims:

* The pupils should learn that mathematics is not only about understanding links between things but can also be used for making accurate calculations which can be confidently checked. The mathematics content involves logarithms, sine and cosine and the procedures these involve
* Pupils who find it difficult to understand complicated situations can gain a new access to mathematics through this practical aspect that places more emphasis on confidence and reliability
* Sixteen year olds who are not only interested in understanding how things relate but also want to have concrete experiences can gain an objective independence through this subject, which taxes intelligence as well as physical will
* The pupils learn how to make accurate maps

All the main steps from surveying the land to plotting the map are covered in practice. The pupils gain an idea of how an ordinary object in daily use is made and they learn the importance of surveying as a basis on which buildings can be planned. The pupils learn that they have to subject themselves to the requirements set by the aim of the work, the measuring method used and the measuring apparatus. Care, patience and critical self-appraisal are called for. The youngsters discover all sorts of possible mistakes and gain a practical idea of what it means to work with accuracy.

* Most measuring is done in groups
* Agreement has to be reached as to who is going to do what
* Space and time both play a part in the measuring process, and individual pupils have to be aware of the whole process so as not to miss the point when their own contribution has to be made
* Drawing the map requires care and accuracy
* The ability to make a mental picture and to think abstractly is strengthened
* The concept of accuracy is widened as it becomes clear that both measurement and drawing have to be accurate
* Mistakes, their causes and ways of correcting them can be discussed and made plain

The surveying period varies both in planning and emphasis, depending on the location and possibilities of the school. Duration is one to two weeks. If only one week is available, preparations are made in a number of preliminary lessons, and the map is not drawn on site, but later in additional lessons during the course of the school year.

Various related topics can be touched on, such as: national grid surveying, cartography and projection, geography and astronomy.

Forestry: Class 10

This period can also be taken in Class 9 or Class 11, with a different emphasis. Qualitatively, the forestry period comes between the surveying period and the social period. Surveying involves techniques of understanding geomorphology through measurement while social work involves devotion to the needs of one's fellow human beings; forestry leads over from the one to the other.

Field ecology and forestry techniques help research the ecosystem of a woodland so that it can be properly understood and the necessary forestry measures carried out. The following framework curriculum for forestry will need adapting to local possibilities.

The youngsters need to extend their knowledge to include the way of life and needs of plants and animals, in order to expand their understanding of the forest as an ecosystem. In addition, practical work within the forest gives them a close experience of what the forest needs.

Practical work

Together with forestry personnel responsible for the woods in question, a programme of forestry tasks is worked out, possibly with input from the pupils as well. Some suggestions:

- Reforestation (e.g. after storm damage)
- New planting
- The timber cycle
- Revitalising ponds, streams, dry meadows or other selected micro-biotopes
- Setting up forestry installations (feeding places, lookout towers, fencing, etc.)

Supplementary environmental studies

- Climatic measurements
- Microclimate: comparative measurements at various exposed sites (middle or edge of forest, meadow) of air and soil temperatures (daily round), atmospheric humidity, use of the hygrometer and evaporation (evaporimeter), soil humidity, wind direction and speed, precipitation
- Accompanying observation of the macroclimate
- Practical application of surveying knowledge: setting up climatic measurement sites and botanical and zoological test areas
- Botanical investigations
- Zoological investigations: birdsong, bird nests, etc. small mammals, game (tracks, droppings etc.)
- Soil studies: digging soil profiles

Ecological themes are discussed in the group and recorded in workbooks (ecosystems, biotopes, food chain, food pyramid, etc.).

Let the pupils work in small groups. Each day begins with a consultation about the day's work and ends with an exchange of day reports. Each group keeps an accurate record of work done and observations made. All these reports are combined in a final report. If the forestry period takes place at the same time each year, observation of annual changes should be aimed for. Previous reports serve each new class as a basis for their work.

Experience of the workplace: Class 10

This is a good age for students individually to choose a workplace and do a three-week work experience placement. The range of workplaces can be broad. It is important that the students' visits are well-prepared and that their temporary employers have a suitable programme for them. At the end of the three-week block the students should have two to three days in which to share their experiences with each other. Their reflections on work, different professions, human relationships in the workplace etc. can be most rewarding for the others. A daily work log should be kept. It is very useful if the students receive at least one visit from the teacher responsible during their working hours.

First Aid: Class 9 or 10

Knowledge of human anatomy and physiology gained in biology lessons is applied from the viewpoint of saving life or health in accident situations. The theoretical basis for efficient first aid methods is established. Accident prevention is also emphasised. Practice is as important as theory. Resuscitation is practised on a dummy. Bandaging techniques and lifting are practised on each other. The pupils discover through theory and practice that giving first aid is an important service to one's fellow human beings.

Theoretical and practical knowledge of first aid in accordance with the training guidelines of the Red Cross, St John's Ambulance or other organisations.

- Need for and obligation to give help
- Tasks of the first aider
- Chain of help
- Danger zone: assessment, making secure, giving aid
- Lifesaving measures when victim is unconscious, has stopped breathing, has no circulation, is bleeding heavily or is in shock
- Wounds and how to treat them. Bandaging
- Animal bites, acid burns, burns, frostbite, hypothermia, bruising
- Joint damage, fractures, chest wounds, abdominal wounds
- Poisoning

Industrial Work Experience: Class 10 or 11

By studying and working with the newest technologies and their effects on the earth and human beings, the pupils learn to be aware of the age in which they are living, and for which they will share responsibility. The industry period gives them an insight into work carried out by large groups of people on a scale that could never be achieved by single individuals. On the other hand they also learn how, through co-ordination, individuals contribute to these large-scale achievements without which modern society would hardly be able to function. They see the social problems that arise with regard to the individual's self-realisation. All this, and the attempts that are made to solve these problems are experienced by the pupils in one setting. In discussions following on the industry period the pupils come to realise how an individual's own cultural and spiritual endeavours are his own private affair (liberty), how legal regulations have to apply to everyone (equality), and how economic measures and the physical and psychological worries of one's fellow human beings have a brotherly basis (fraternity). This is the principle of a threefoldness in human life that is experienced again and again throughout the pupils' time at school. It should lead to an understanding of society and a motivation to work at shaping it.

It may be that large industries are not available or accessible to the students. Placements can be in a variety of small businesses, preferably in manufacturing. Experience in the service industries (shops, restaurants, clubs) should follow. Many students already know this area from part-time work.

Many schools, notably in Switzerland, have developed Upper School programmes involving regular training and placements in the work place (e.g. two days a week) from Classes 10 to 12. This involves some reduction of the school timetable and long working hours. The motivation through this interface with the world of work has proved very rewarding. Other schools, particularly in Germany, have long offered apprenticeships within the school, in practical subjects such as childcare, nutrition, woodwork, metalwork or textiles. These programmes are integrated within the school timetable.

In countries such as Britain, the demands of the public examinations take upwards of half the timetable, thus limiting the scope for practical work experience. The need for these experiences is becoming increasingly urgent.

During the industry period the pupils are under the special guidance of the works staff member who is responsible for them and of the specialist teacher at their school. Timewise the pupils participate in the routine of the establishment to which they are temporarily attached. They can earn from experience about:

* Industrial production
* The social situation of employees
* Strain caused by onesided work (or dust, noise, temperature etc.)
* Insight into wider implications
* Management questions
* Help in finding one's own way

Social Practical: Class 11 or 12

Sensitivity to others, responsibility and presence of mind in action are practised in a social setting and unaccustomed situations have to be dealt with.

The attitude at work requires the ability, or the effort, to disregard one's own interests, to enter entirely new social situations, and to devote oneself to others by noticing what they need and helping them.

Practical work in a social setting helps the pupils unfold a new kind of awareness. They participate in shaping human social life and experience the importance of each individual for the life and development of others.

The pupils' work timetable and tasks are the responsibility of the institution's staff member who is their monitor.

Preparation and supervision are carried out by a teacher or other adult connected with the school. During the social period the pupils meet for an internal weekend to share their experiences in discussion groups and to prepare for when they leave the institutions where they are temporarily working.

* Experience gained by working with groups marginalised by society
* Getting to know the biographies of people who have special needs or are socially deprived

* Experiencing the daily routine in social institutions
* Working with people who have special needs or are disabled
* Taking responsibility for others
* Not panicking; taking appropriate action
* Getting to know the professional problems of caring and teaching personnel
* Experiencing different types of social responsibility and integration

Possible activities include:

* Sharing and playing a part in the daily life of the institution
* Taking on simple caring tasks such as washing, bandaging, feeding, dressing, going for walks, playing
* Finding out the history of the institution
* Finding out the structure of the institution and its connections with other establishments

Possible institutions include hospitals, care homes, old-people's homes, establishments for people with special needs such as schools, workshops, homes, kindergartens, children's homes, etc.

Theatre Practical: Class 12

With the guidance of a professional or drama teacher, Class 12 work on a full-length play (opera, musical or cabaret) for public performance. In many schools plays have also been performed in Classes 9, 10 and 11, perhaps including a foreign language play. The difference is that, at the latest by Class 12, the pupils should be producing the play themselves with professional guidance.

One view is that the pupils should organise the whole project themselves as far as possible, taking responsibility not only for their parts in the play but getting into groups to prepare all the different aspects. The aim is to reach a standard, at latest by the first night, at which they would be capable of going on tour as an independent ensemble without any director. The different teams, possibly with the occasional assistance of specialist teachers, prepare every aspect of the project (lighting, scenery, decorations, props, costumes, masks, music, sound, advertising, graphics, posters, photos, programme design, production, calendar planning, back-up, box office, prompting, scene changing etc.). The full educational effect of a project like this is reached through the whole complex range of tasks to be carried out before, during and after the performance, on the stage and behind the scenes. The aim is to produce a complete work of art involving not only a successful performance but also all the preparation and accompanying work. The pupils' powers of perception and will are put to the test in the social arena where the purpose is not to bring gifted individuals to the fore but to let all the participants – with all their strengths and weaknesses – take part in creating a 'social work of art'. Usually Class 12 plays are produced with a teacher or specialist director. Nevertheless, the students should be as involved creatively at all levels as much as possible. It is not particularly pedagogical if the students are merely players, instruments of the director's artistic will and self-image. We stress this point, as there is often the danger that due to shortness of time, the director simply drives the thing to completion and afterwards the pupils are exhausted.

This Class 12 play may be regarded as the climax and culmination of the English lessons. The pupils have to develop not only a theoretical understanding of the text but have to interpret it through gesture, facial expression and speech.

Many of the exercises carried out in English lessons during preceding years can be drawn on in achieving this:

* The speech exercises have schooled clarity and power of articulation
* Daily recitation (and also, in eurythmy lessons, making the gestures for the sounds of speech) has schooled the pupils' feeling for speech sounds as soul gestures
* The games lessons have cultivated a sense for spatial awareness and fluency and power of movement

During rehearsals they continue to work at experiencing qualities of speech:

* The way a sentence spans tension and relaxation
* The exclamation, the rhetorical question etc., as dramatic high points
* The dramatic pause, and much else

The pupils have to transform these qualities of speech into individualised movements, gestures and facial expressions in a way that contributes to the achievement of the overall concept of the performance. They must avoid both overplaying and unprofessional clichés. The aim is that the pupils should make their own interpretation and that they should put their all into creating the play and also enjoy doing so. This should arise through the way their fellow pupils see them (as themselves and as the character they are playing) combined with the way the play is directed (as an overall work of art) and the individual role (through working on the role itself and with the way it fits in with the play as a whole).

Art trip: Class 12

Not only in botany but also in art it is correct to say: 'You only see what you already know about'. Art is such a wide field, constantly changing, that more than anywhere else a capacity to form judgements is needed. It is not only a question of cultivating the narrow range of sympathy and antipathy. In fact the temporary and preliminary nature of these two extremes needs to be overcome before a process of perception and discovery can really begin.

What the pupils have learnt in the Upper School has lead them up to the ability to apply their aesthetic sense in forming judgements. This is now experienced and exercised 'in situ'. Obviously many of the items found in museums and art galleries during the trip are not in their original setting, but there is a difference between seeing and perhaps sketching a Rembrandt in London's National Gallery or the Rijksmuseum in Amsterdam. An important line to follow is to see how an artistic stream has continued to the present time, been renewed or broken off in its country or city of origin.

More important than visits to museums or concerts are architectural studies and visits to the studios of living artists. Some of the questions the pupils can ask themselves are:

* What can I discover about a building through its proportions, its historical period, its national, ethnic or geographical connections?
* What is the social, biographical or national background out of which a particular contemporary artist is working?

In this sense the art trip not only strengthens the community of the class (as do all class trips) but it also has a social function with regard to society at large through finding appropriate ways of understanding how the art of a nation, of a particular historical period, or an individual artist or group of artists comes about. Once more, and perhaps for the last time, the young people can feel themselves to be pupils, protected and supported in the group. But at the same time they are now free and individual personalities facing the challenge of making their own stand and finding their own opinions.

The Class 12 project (whole year)

The following applies in schools where Class 12 pupils undertake a year-long project.

The pupils can choose a theme from a single subject or one that draws on several. They bring what they have learnt, including new material, together in a report that can also be presented in public. It can be their final task in school, consisting of a written, an oral and an artistic or practical part and it should combine intellectual, artistic and practical work.

The theme is chosen in consultation with a mentor in collaboration with the Upper School meeting. The pupils carry out their own research, observations, interviews, experiments, conversations and so on. This forms the basis on which further reading and researches into other sources of information can be built. The pupils should summarise various points of emphasis, recognise causes and effects and provide tentative answers for questions raised by the work. The form given to the written part of the project should approach that of scientific papers (quotations, sources, etc.). The method should involve the pupil's own experience and formulation of his or her independent assessment of the material and facts arising from study of the subject. A general educational aim is that the pupils should experience their own capacity to work, learning how to plan, organise and sustain a project of some magnitude over a lengthy period of time.

By experiencing their own individual interests and capabilities at the end of their years at school, the young people begin to mature in their own self-confidence and self-knowledge. Their personality gains firmer contours and they can begin to look forward towards the path they are going to take through life.

When they present their project in public, they gain objective insights about how they have handled their subject matter from the way the teachers and audience react and the questions they ask.

The project should be evaluated by the students themselves, by their specialist mentors and perhaps by a panel of other teachers or appropriate individuals from outside of school. This written evaluation as well as documentation of the project itself should be accredited by the school and form part of the student's portfolio, leaving report or record of achievement.

25

Social Skills

The Cultivation of Social Competence Throughout the Curriculum

Social skills and social competence are not subjects that appear on any school timetable. However, their cultivation is a central aim of Steiner-Waldorf education. Developing social understanding based on sensitivity for other people is a faculty that essentially involves educating the will. For this to happen children must experience an environment in which social competence is apparent in the relationships around them. Social competence is also dependent on the inner commitment of each adult within the school community to moral development.

Social awareness needs to inform the school organisation in implicit and explicit ways. This does not mean necessarily ensuring a working atmosphere of total harmony, which would be entirely unrealistic. It does, however, mean that everyone works to create conditions in which social awareness comes to the fore and that conflicts and misunderstandings when they occur are dealt with in an open and constructive way.

The primary organisational structures of a Steiner-Waldorf school, the central element of collegial self-management, the conscious working with the functional principles of the threefold social order, should all provide a fertile environment for children to observe social skills at work.

The curriculum, however, also provides many opportunities in inter-disciplinary ways, of cultivating social awareness in age-appropriate ways.[1]

> *Social competence is never merely a matter of knowledge.*[2]

Competence is based on sound judgement, which requires a living thinking founded on an experience of reality. Grasping the dynamic of social processes requires mobile thinking, which itself is based on pictorial concepts capable of growth, adaptation and development through on-going new experience and reflection. Social interaction also requires the ability to hear and understand the other person as well as being able to express our own views. Much of our social, political and commercial life depends on mutual understanding and agreements, often between a number of different partners. The ideas involved are also often highly complex. Developing a living thinking is the key to creating real social competence.

In an age in which electronic means of communication are expanding exponentially, the inability to communicate clearly or empathise with others appears to be increasing. Children need to have developed real communication skills before they are exposed to electronic communications media.

Another key social ability is that of self-directed initiative and the capacity to work at something. Children's innate drive to be active needs to be focused into play, transformed from creative play into the capacity to work which enables the individual to recognise need in the world and be able to respond to it.

The theme of social skills weaves throughout the curriculum and the teaching method. In what follows, guidelines are given as to how social skills can be fostered. The individual teacher will find many other points of reference. Our intention of including this theme within the curriculum is to highlight its central position and to stimulate thought on the matter.

Classes 1 to 3

In painting and drawing the children learn to recognise that shape arises out of colour and that there are subtle boundaries between the colours. The colours are explored in their individual characteristics and their various encounters are experienced, described and reflected upon. This process is a vital basis for understanding that social processes are not sharply defined or arbitrary in their relationships. The most important fields of discovery concern the overlaps in which something new arises.

Through the experience of movement and form drawing, children experience different points of perspective, sometimes facing the world from 'inside', sometimes being on the 'outside' looking in. Meeting at the crossing point and negotiating rights of way are also important social experiences.

In learning to read and write, the children experience that the intrinsic relationship between symbol, sound and meaning is not arbitrary, that form and content belong together, another important social skill.

Number work is particularly social in its emphasis on going from the whole to the parts. Experiencing division as a sharing helps establish the principle of fair sharing of value added. This enables the individual later to think of wages not as reward for work done but rather as an agreed division of what has been mutually earned.

> *On the other hand one must understand that all those who have shared in producing and marketing a product must be able to live from the final selling price, i.e. that each 'profit margin' represents a portion of the final price. Even the large questions concerning the share of the GDP taken by the state, by the cultural sector or by the social security system are in the end a matter of reaching agreement about fair shares.*[3]

Other moral and social aspects of arithmetic involve number stories (see the chapter on maths teaching).[4]

Learning to sing and play the flute together is a wonderful schooling of listening skills and responding to others. This is equally true of foreign language lessons in which the child learns to understand what the other person means on the basis of non-semantic perception (tone of voice, gesture, body language) as well as through the language itself. This requires the cultivation of a specific kind of empathy and rhythmic exchange between speaker and listener.

The manual dexterity learned in handwork forms a basis for later conceptual grasping of complex ideas. Handwork also reinforces a strong sense of mutual dependency between people (the farmer who shares the wool and the person who buys a woollen garment) and between the human being and the kingdoms of nature. This primary experience is the basis not only for ecological thinking but also for a sound grasp of economic principles.

Classes 4 to 7

As described in the chapters on crafts and nature study, there are important social dimensions to the blocks involving farming, work skills and house building, especially regarding the basic principles of economics, namely mutuality, the meeting of needs and the transformation of raw materials into useful commodities. The important elements to stress to children at this age include:

* The experience that all economic activities are mutually inter-dependent. The farmer depends on the tractor factory; the factory on the production of steel and other raw materials; these often have an international source; all workers and their families need food, clothing and housing; commodities need transport; all these processes require banking, insurance, lawyers, advertising, health and safety regulation; above all these activities need research and development, which means human thought.
* The experience that all economic activity is based on the transformation of natural resources of raw materials and energy and that this has consequences for the natural world.
* The experience that the economic process is reflected in financial relationships of various kinds.

The children need to experience these primary principles in real and tangible situations and not merely as theory. The emphasis at this age needs to be on positive examples, rather than on the many negative examples of exploitation, injustice, corruption and incompetence.

Wherever possible experience needs to be direct and modern. Whilst introducing the archetypal professions of shepherd, woodcutter, fisherman, the children also need to see their modern equivalents. The study of the locality should include the links a city or region has to other regions and other parts of the world. This may mean a visit to a local airport to see what freight and what passengers arrive from which destinations or it may mean looking at the products on display on a supermarket aisle and exploring their countries of origin.

Arithmetic is applied to practical life and examples are chosen which strengthen moral and social awareness, rather than abstractions or hypothetical situations. In English, not only are communication skills practised but the study of grammar makes relationships more conscious. Who did what to whom, how, where and why? The relevance of direct and reported speech for social responsibility cannot be underestimated. Faithfully reporting another person's words and opinions is a real skill. Writing business letters was something Steiner felt strongly about as an antidote to sentimental, self-indulgent thinking.

> *If you stuff the children mainly with sentimental idealism between the ages of thirteen and fifteen, they will later develop an aversion to idealism and become materialistic people… If you want to gather children around you in order, in your religious fervour, to tell them about the glories of the divine powers in the world, then… what you say will go in one*

ear and out of the other and never reach their feelings. If, having written a business letter with a group of children in the morning, you have the same group again in the afternoon carrying in their subconscious what has been brought about by the morning's business letter, then you are fortunate if it is now a matter of teaching them some religious concepts, for you yourself will have roused in them the mood that is now calling for its antithesis.[5]

The concept of business letters includes a wide range of formal letters, enquiries, orders, booking requests, letters of complaint and so on. These combine objectivity, clarity, precise terminology and awareness of rights and obligations. In the arithmetic of Class 6, the introduction of compound interest and algebraic formulas forms a similar basis for later understanding of economic relationships.

In history lessons which begin in Class 5, the children learn about the forms of early societies and their close relationship to their specific environment, Catal Hayuk in the Fertile Crescent, Ur in Mesopotamia, Egypt and the Nile, etc. With the history of ancient Greece comes the polis, the city-state with its colonies and hinterland. Roman history introduces the concepts of citizenship, civil justice and the 'voice of the people'. The transition from theocracy to republic, and from there to Empire provides important historical models of social and political processes.

The discussions in Class 6 about the Medieval period focus on the three realms of; the church and especially the monastic orders, courtly and knightly chivalry, the urban guilds, all of which offered models for social relationships. The encounter between the Christian West and Islam in both its positive and negative aspects is an important study in inter-cultural relations. Class 7 and the Age of Discovery provides many opportunities to explore culture clashes as well as grasping the seeds of modern economic processes. Steiner stressed that the economic changes in Europe following the Reformation were the most important factors in modern historical development,[6] and involved the transference of land ownership from the Church into secular hands.

Topics such as the invention of printing, the development of banking and early capitalism, the rise of public theatre, the new technologies of warfare and so on have important sociological implications.

Class 8 and Class 9 address the Age of Revolutions and central themes are the rise of national identity, the increasing demand for individual rights and freedoms, the dehumanising effects of industrialisation and urbanisation. Mass education and the media are also important themes, as are the economic relationships that arose out of colonialism and the post-colonial world. The social, rights and economic aspects of modern history form an important part of the history curriculum.

Geography has a central position within the curriculum. The main emphasis throughout the geography curriculum is on human geography. Up to Class 6, one could describe geography as essentially concentric, that is, it relates from the home locality progressively to ever broadening horizons. Physical geography, including topography, geology, climate, vegetation and so on influence the developing child in profound ways. In this period geography is about experiencing the soul-spiritual forces of the earth and assisting the children to gain a firm footing on the earth.

From the age of 12 onwards geography becomes global.

It is an outgoing, out-reaching subject that fosters a fraternity towards the different regions of the earth.[7]

The social significance of geography teaching within the curriculum was stressed by Steiner as follows:

Teaching the child in this way, we place him into space and he will be interested in the world, in the whole wide world. And we shall see the results of this in many directions. A child with whom we study geography in this way will have a more loving relationship to his fellow men than one who has no idea of what proximity in space means; for he will live to feel that he lives alongside other human beings, and he will come to regard and respect them.

Such things play no little part in the moral training of the children, and the lack of attention to geography is partly responsible for the terrible decline of the brotherly love that should prevail amongst men.[8]

The introduction of gardening in Class 6 and its development through to Class 10 involves not only an appreciation of the relationship between effort, work and produce but also hands-on experience of the value of ecological methods of agriculture. Nature study and the sciences likewise cultivate an ecological awareness but human biology, particularly topics such as nutrition and health, provides an important balance to the influence of advertising and consumerism.

Social studies: Classes 8 to 12

In most of the suggestions given above, the emphasis has been on developing social awareness more indirectly, through the subject itself. From Classes 7 and 8 upwards, social issues can be discussed directly. In his meetings with teachers, Steiner made the following suggestion with regard to teaching social science, 'in Classes 7 and 8 you could give them what is discussed in *Towards Social Renewal*'.[9] It is unlikely that Steiner meant literally reading the book but rather that the phenomena of the threefold social order could be discussed.

For Steiner, it was crucial that all teaching from the age of thirteen onwards should be related to practical life and that this should be inter-disciplinary, to counter the tendency to specialisation that characterises so much of modern life.

Steiner also suggested that the study of life skills and skills related to practical life, should be taught, such as shorthand and typing (its modern equivalent would be using a computer) and double entry bookkeeping, managing personal finances and similar topics. He further recommended that people directly involved in economic life should be called on to draw up such teaching programmes.[10]

With adolescence, school needs to be ever more connected to practical life in the modern world. This is probably even more necessary today than it was in 1919, given each child's access to global media.

Space does not permit a full description of the possibilities for cultivating social skills and awareness in the Upper School. The following list of brief references will have to stand as stimulation to extensive research. The following ideas need to be woven into the curriculum as motifs, linking and integrating the many subjects.

Class 8

* Study of other societies with an emphasis on pre-industrial cultures as a contrast to effects of industrialisation

Classes 8 and 9

* Modern history from the perspective of contemporary issues

Class 9

* Physics, the motor car and diesel engine, their social and cultural impact
* Ecology main-lesson
* Work experience, forestry or agriculture practical

Life skills: Classes 9 to 12

This subject can be taught within the arts and crafts blocks as it benefits from smaller groups. They can also be integrated into the main-lesson programme. The topics form into groups:

* Rights and responsibilities – the legal system, the role of the police, solicitors, lawyers, courts
* Substance abuse – laws relating to drugs including the penalties; types of drugs and their effects including alcohol and tobacco; aspects of addiction
* Money skills – how to keep a bank account, cheques, credit cards, currency exchange, budgeting, stocks and shares
* Health and nutrition – basic facts of healthy living and lifestyles; principles of good nutrition, practical experience planning quality, low-cost quality meals, cooking and catering
* Personal and social skills – personal relationships, responsibility and sexuality, homosexuality and heterosexuality and gender issues, marriage and long term relationships, parenting skills, HIV/AIDS, conflict avoidance and resolution, group skills
* Citizenship – the political system and its structures, voting, political parties, the role of government, issues of individual responsibility
* The world of work – the changing pattern of work in a post-industrial society, applying for a job, employment rights and obligations, careers, the students should experience different work places and have the opportunities to meet a wide range of people who explain their profession e.g. nurses, engineers, architects, designers, journalists, caterers, police, etc.

Language lessons: Classes 8 to 12

Foreign languages should include detailed study of the land, climate, economy, history, traditions, political systems, justice systems, current affairs of the countries where the language is spoken. An emphasis should be given to languages as bridges to other cultures.

Social responsibility: Classes 8 to 12

Students should increasingly take on social responsibility within the school community such as; playground supervision, play support for younger children, manning road crossings, assisting at school events, conferences (and not merely as fundraising activities for Upper School classes), helping with local community with ecological projects, helping elderly, disabled, etc. people, generating support for refugees, developing world projects, etc.

Class 10

* History – the close link between geography and culture in the origins of early civilisations, the emergence of tribal structures and political forms.

Classes 9 to 12

* Anthropology – discussion of the nature of the human being, the significance of uprightness and the relationship to the animal kingdom. The question of human evolution and origins of language, art, technology, social forms, religion, relationship to death, relationship to the environment. The nature of perception and cognition and how we know about the world. Steiner suggested that studying the relationship between the physical organs and their connection to soul experience is necessary to understanding how the social organism functions.[11] This is also the best way to approach the questions posed by contemporary evolutionary psychology or sociology.
* The relationship between polarities of all kinds and their reconciliation through the Goethean approach is a process which can be explored in all the arts, but equally in the sciences and humanities. Likewise the threefold approach of recognising the distinctive qualities of thinking, feeling and willing and their correlation to the nerve-sense, metabolic-limb and rhythmic-circulation systems of the organism, is an essential part of understanding threefold social processes.

Work and technology: Classes 9 to 12

* All aspects of craft and technology should be related on the one hand to their geographic origins and natural resources, on the other to their economic aspects. Steiner was very concerned to awaken genuine interest and understanding for economic questions.
* Related to this is the importance of real work experience in the workplace with meaningful tasks.

Class trips

Group artistic activities, performances, class trips and excursions are all fields of rich social experience, especially if these aspects are reflected upon.

Class 11 or 12

* Economics main-lesson. Characterisation of the distinction between cultural sphere, rights – justice – political – social sphere and the economic sphere, through concrete examples. Introduction to basic principles of economics, production and distribution of goods and services to meet human needs. The concepts of price, income, value. The idea of work. The origin and function of money; how value arises, different kinds of money. Social relationships within the economy. Examples of real economic processes, e.g. the true price of a cup of tea, tracing the packet of tea in the supermarket back to the grower.

Whilst some of these topics may have been covered during the class teacher period, it is important to deepen them in the Upper School by focusing directly on them for short concentrated periods. The lessons should consist of accurate information and discussion with students being required to do research and seek out direct experience. Bringing professionals in is always useful, though the support of the teacher is often necessary.

One criticism often heard from former Waldorf pupils is that they felt that their education was inspiring but too remote from real life. This would be a criticism that Steiner would take very seriously, given his maxim *all* teaching should relate to and be a preparation for real life. What was once possible effectively through implicit teaching, now needs a more overt approach, so that the students can experience the relevance of the topics. This makes great demand on teachers, not only to be very well informed but to be able to focus the discussion on the higher, moral principles whilst enabling the students to form their own judgements. Preaching does not work.

The above suggestions make it clear that the social sciences permeate the whole curriculum in an interdisciplinary way. It places the human being and human society at the heart of the teaching. But it is more than just a question of teaching content.

As we have seen the school's self-management structures and collegial working practises are influential in setting the tone. When pupils experience the support teachers give each other, how they complement each other's strengths, how they deal with problems, how they strive to research and deepen their understanding and above all, how they enjoy their work, they could have no better social education. When pupils realise that teachers set themselves aims and objectives, review and evaluate their work, consult on changes, they receive a practical demonstration of good working habits.

In the classroom, the teachers' respectful attitude to each child, their courage for the truth, their authority and generosity, all profoundly influence the child's developing social attitudes. When the self-activity of the pupil is encouraged, when pupils are shown how to work, how to tackle challenges and above all, how to learn from mistakes in a positive way, that self-activity is fostered. As the pupils get older, the process of engaging self-activity must become more and more conscious. At the end of their school time, each pupil should be able to say: 'They taught me how to work and learn and how to work together with others.'

26

Study of Art and Aesthetics*

Classes 9 to 12

The aim of this subject is to awaken the students' interest in and understanding of art. Working with art also helps to develop and deepen certain psychological skills, including a heightening of the powers of perception and the ability to form judgements. There are three main aspects that involve all four classes in the Upper School:

1. Making sense perceptions subtler and schooling a more intensive and more conscious way of seeing and hearing through the study of the visual arts. This involves activating a full range of sensory experience including the activation and transformation of the lower senses (sense of balance, sense of life, sense of movement) into the senses of word and concept as a basis for the cultivation of a living thinking.
2. Developing the ability to judge the aesthetic qualities of all the arts, both spatial and temporal. Schooling the capacity to perceive subtle qualitative differences. Developing a vocabulary of concepts and a terminology to discuss artistic qualities such as form, volume, tone, colour, movement etc.
3. Gaining knowledge of art and art history and their development in relation to the evolution of human consciousness.

The study of art appears as a distinct new subject at the beginning of the Upper School as an answer to the physical and psychological changes the young people are undergoing and the questions and needs that arise as a result of these. Just as the scientific subjects gain new emphasis now, so the study of art provides a kind of balance. In contrast to a world in which immutable natural laws reign, art provides a view of a realm in which human freedom can open up.

At the ages of fourteen and fifteen, the students also begin to feel the heaviness of their bodies and therefore also come into closer contact with the forces of gravity. The images art gives them, can provide a contrasting experience of lightness, even levity. Their soul life also takes on a new character as puberty progresses. They become more inward, more personal, more enclosed. A world of wishes, urges and passions pours in on them. This initially chaotic and unruly world of desires is confronted through art by an orderly world of regular forms and harmonies.

*For painting and drawing, please see Chapter 10, Art Studies.

But it is not only this new world of urges that is besetting them, for they now confront the world and themselves with high ideals, noble aims and other demands. Great works of art can provide some initial response to their desire for perfection. At least through pictures they can satisfy their longing for the ideal, and the thought may awaken that perhaps the appearance of the picture may be revealing a spiritual reality.

The themes from the world of art taken in these four classes arise out of the inner requirements and needs of the youngsters, but choice of subject matter and emphasis is entirely up to the teachers. They are free to use whatever realms of art they are familiar with or find particularly rewarding. How the teaching is done and making it suitable for the age of the youngsters are what is important; what is chosen is secondary.

Class 9

The visual arts ('the arts in space') of painting and sculpture are the main focus here. Studying great works of art is intended to awaken enjoyment and enthusiasm for the beauty and greatness in art. The feelings become more subtle and refined, observation more alert as the young people learn to see. Initially questions of composition and form are only hinted at. Developing an aesthetic sense is schooled first by getting to know and experiencing great works of art.

Another aspect lies in considering what is characteristic for the three great historical periods chosen: What did the ancient Egyptians find 'beautiful'? How did the Greeks experience beauty? What was the ideal and concept of beauty during the Renaissance? By seeing how art evolved, something can be understood about how humanity has evolved. The stages of Egypt-Greece-Renaissance can be seen as revealing steps in the evolution of Western consciousness.

Ancient Egypt

A description of the special geographical conditions of the country (Nile Valley, desert) can provide a basis for an understanding of Egyptian culture. It is above all a culture of death, (though filled with a sense of the vitality of life) and Egyptian art is closely bound up with this. The statues (standing, sitting, kneeling, squatting figures) show the human being as belonging to the realm of permanence. The reliefs and paintings make only the essential visible. Architecture (mastaba, pyramid, temple) need only be shown peripherally, as the great framework in which the sculptures and paintings have their place. It is important to establish that the sacred script of hieroglyphics forms a conceptual basis and canon to architecture, painting and sculpture. Such art also has to be 'read' and marks a significant cultural stage towards a script culture and the emergence of literacy.

Ancient Greece

Once again a description of the landscape and how it is experienced provides a good beginning (the multiplicity of islands, valleys and bays isolated from one another by mountains and sea, the temple in the landscape, being close to nature in worshipping the gods). Greek sculpture is studied by showing its development through various stylistic states: archaic, classical (stern style, 'soft' style), Hellenistic. It is a matter of showing this development as a process (in contrast to the timelessness in Egypt): the budding, concentrated potential of archaic times, then unfolding, flowering, ripening in classical times, with both the over-elaboration and withering and dying in later times. For Greece, too, architecture is left as a unifying background rather than a separate subject.

Renaissance

As an introduction, early Christian art can be shown (the catacombs, the Ravenna mosaics). Some sense of typical medieval art forms such as gold background panels, wooden carving, cathedral sculptures, manuscript illustration, should be given as a preparation for the innovations of the late medieval period. The Middle Ages, with its attitude of turning away from the world, is not particularly interesting for Class 9 pupils, so needs to be briefly characterised rather than dwelt on. Then comes the transition from late medieval art to the early Renaissance. Giotto, Ghiberti, Brunelleschi, Masaccio, Donatello, Uccello and Piero della Francesco can be shown as representatives of a new interest in the world (discovery of linear perspective, etc.). The life and work of Leonardo, Michelangelo and Raphael provide the climax of the main-lesson.

The examples used should be limited to key studies so that the pupils are not flooded with a wealth of images that can lead to an inflation of expectation and superficiality. It is better to take one picture per lesson for an intensive study, perhaps showing a few related works as a follow up in the next lesson. Given the volume of images young people have to digest these days, sitting in a darkened room looking at slides can become a very passive activity. Teachers must find creative ways of overcoming this if art studies are to engage the self activity of the students and not merely entertain them with culture, however highbrow.

Class 10

The art of poetry and language

This main-lesson looks at the power of the spoken word, its use in art and its abuse when used to convey ideology. The study of the art of poetry explores the means by which poetry and language can become an art form. Time is now experienced as a dimension that plays a part in artistic formation. The polarity of 'spatial arts' and 'temporal arts' is looked at for the first time. Seeing and hearing are now experienced as two qualitatively fundamentally different, though intimately linked, modes of experience. Now form and style come to the fore. The young people are to learn that feelings can be given shape and form through poetry.

This main-lesson may begin by examining the origins of language and its essential nature as a means of communication, as symbolic representation and as revelation of qualities in the world. The relationship between movement and language on the one hand, and language and thought on the other is explored phenomenologically. The differences and transitions between orality and literacy are an important theme.

The main theme however is the study of the craft of poetry, its various meters and rhyme schemes. Examples of poetic forms such as epic, ode, sonnet, ballad, lyric and so on are all studied using examples from literature as well as the pupils' own creations. One way of doing this is to take a basic text, such as a fable and reproduce its content in a variety of different poetic styles as varied as Japanese haiku style or limerick. The full range of moods created by these different styles will fascinate and entertain the pupils. This is a task that equally appeals to students who are gifted in literacy skills as to those who are not since poetry is essentially an oral skill and poetry is a medium that does not depend on correct spelling or even extensive vocabulary. It is important that each style is objectively evaluated as to the mood it creates and expresses, whether heroic or comic, deeply inward or superficial.

The possibilities of assonance, alliteration, onomatopoeia and their effects on poetic style can likewise be explored. So too can the effect of words of different etymological origin, such as the difference between words from Anglo-Saxon, Latin/French, classical Greek, Arabic origin, to name the main examples. This can lead to a study of modern expressionist poetry where the meaning of the words is often subsumed by the tonal quality of the sounds. Related to these topics is the study of slang, jargon, cliché and the power of words in advertising, political usage and the media generally.

This a main-lesson that should stimulate the students to intense levels of creativity in the realm of language.

Painting and graphics main-lesson

This main-lesson looks at the techniques and expressive power of a wide range of graphic arts as well as painting. Here too, form, technique, composition and style come to the fore. In keeping with the students' wish for knowledge, the emphasis moves from getting to know to recognising, from seeing (or hearing) to understanding.

If there is enough space in the main-lesson timetable, there can be a second main-lesson on painting. One of the main motifs could be the contrast between northern and southern Renaissance and Baroque art. Emphasis is on the great masters of northern art in the sixteenth and seventuries centuries: Dürer, Grünewald, Holbein, Rembrandt. Another important theme is a study of the new reproductive techniques used by many of these artists in graphics (woodcut, copper-plate, etching) which can be linked to practical exercises in these disciplines. Only through practising the techniques, even in simplified form does the medium and its conceptual aspects become clear. The basic principles of reversing the images, of removing what later remains and vice versa, of building up images through the superimposition of different plates or different stages in the printing challenge the student's thinking as well as their artistic sensibilities. Copying the work of masters in pencil drawing can reveal the structure of the images. Studying a sequence of plates of one motif in altered states by Rembrandt (self-portrait etchings for example) can reveal the range of moods and forms of expression open to the artist.

The social and cultural significance of the ability to reproduce works of art and the relationship of art to books should be studied, leading to questions of modern means of reproduction and their significance for the role of art in society.

Class 11

As the young people withdraw into themselves at this age, music is a new subject that will suit them (Hegel called it 'the art of pure inwardness'). It is given either as a separate main-lesson or in combination with painting or literature. In the latter case, more general views gain more weight and the pupils are shown wider horizons. Similarities and polarities in art are examined. The way painting and sculpture contrast with speech and music can, for example, be taken as a motif.

Music

If a separate main-lesson (usually given by the music teacher) is devoted to music, examples are given of how music has historically developed, and the students learn to analyse form and style through listening. They are shown how music is unique among the arts in the way it is 'form taking place in time'.

An overview of the history of music can be given from ancient cultures to the present day, including Greek modes, music in Medieval churches from plain chant to polyphony, troubadours and minstrels, the birth of opera, the Baroque – Bach and Handel, the development of tonality – Haydn, Mozart, musical patronage, the Romantic revolution and the birth of the artist as individual creator – Beethoven; Romanticism in music – the development of symphony, concerto, grand opera etc.; the lives of great composers in the nineteenth century; the breakdown of tonality in the twentieth century, atonality, twelve-tone systems; examples of twentieth century composition.

Nietzsche's concept of Apollonian and Dionysian as contrasting qualities can be applied to music. (Some examples of these polarities include: pentatonic/chromatic, sound/melody, Handel/ Bach, Debussy/Wagner).

Looking at artistic phenomena from the perspective of the Apollonian/Dionysian polarity can also be helpful for the other arts, for example in a comparison between Impressionism and Expressionism in painting or in poetry.

Painting

This main-lesson begins with the Romantics: Caspar, David Friedrich, Constable, Turner, Blake, moves on to neo-classicism and then leads to modern painting. Impressionism and Expressionism are the first point of emphasis. Then the path leads on via the great innovators (Cézanne, Gaugin, Munch, van Gogh, Monet) to the school of the 'Blauer Reiter', the classics among modern painters. Consideration of these artists and their paintings should always include wider cultural context. Just as the contrasting pair 'Impressionism/ Expressionism' links up with the polarity of Apollonian/Dionysian that is to be found in music, so can one's view also take in other, more general aesthetic polarities such as: classical/ romantic, sculpture/music, music/painting, eyes/ ears, space/time, etc.

If music and painting are treated in a combined main-lesson, then the close relationship between music and painting discovered by artists in the 19th and 20th Centuries can be a fruitful avenue of approach (Gauguin, Debussy, Scriabin, Klee, Kandinsky and others).

Class 12

In keeping with the requirement for this year to treat lesson material from a universal point of view, the framework here should be an overview of the totality of the arts. However, architecture is the main theme for Class 12. Only now that they have reached this age can the young people really understand architecture. Their bodies, or rather the static element of the skeleton has developed to a stage where they can 'feel' their way into and 'understand' inwardly the static and constructive laws of architecture.

Architecture is looked upon as the universal art that includes and integrates all the other arts within its realm. This can lead on to the idea of a total or all-encompassing work of art. In connection with this, one can attempt to satisfy the desire for knowledge in Class 12 pupils by bringing in a separate chapter on the philosophy of art (aesthetics).

Architecture is considered in the special position it holds amongst the arts. Its development will be looked at from three points of view: artistic shape and form, technical construction and social function. The great steps in the evolution of these will be shown using examples. There are various lines along which these considerations can be carried out, e.g. the appearance and development of inner spaces; space and building; the qualities of space (e.g. longitudinal or centrally oriented spaces), the character of a space as an expression of a religious attitude, and so on. The evolution of architecture should mirror the cultural and historical stages in the evolution of human consciousness. Obviously the study of architecture should lead right up to the present time.

One can also go more deeply into the meaning and essence of art. Schiller's *Letters on the Aesthetic Education of the Human Being* can provide a suitable point of orientation. This can lead on to thoughts about art in our century, e.g. Paul Klee, Joseph Beuys or John Berger and to the aesthetic problems of modern art.

A longer art trip can be very enriching in Class 12. In order to avoid being merely tourist consumers of art, it is good to get the young people to do something themselves, e.g. draw the buildings they see, or better still, take part in some small social project. Such a trip should be the culmination of four years of study of art. Italy is naturally a popular choice in Europe but there are many other possibilities.

27

Technology

including Information and Computer Technology

Pupils in Steiner-Waldorf schools experience technology as a subject in its own right. From finger-knitting and other crafts in the early years, through to electronics and computer logic construction in the upper school, students are evolving their technological skills, creatively and in the real world. Knitting is interesting and significant in that it is the earliest form of programmed technology – a knit/pearl sequence is binary code instruction.

Steiner-Waldorf education aims to help pupils to become ethical and confident users of a range of technologies, whilst also recognising the historical, societal and biographical aspects of technology, e.g. mechanical programming of weaving during the Industrial revolution, etc.

Waldorf education aims to enable children and young people to be fully engaged in and to take ownership of the technology that surrounds them and of which they make use. In order to achieve this, pupils are helped to understand technology in its innermost nature, and they become able to direct that technology, taking full account of human agency in this process. What follows is thus a inter-disciplinary account of the curriculum pertaining to technology and ICT, and teaching is likely to take place through integration during the course of a year of many different subject themes.

Kindergarten to Class 6

In order to negotiate the ethical, cultural and social issues involved in the use of technology, children need to be helped to develop a healthy self image and feeling for the needs of others through real relationships. This is a task for the curriculum as a whole. The following aspects in particular support this:

* Activities that enable children to engage in a rich story life through imaginative lessons and whole body learning
* Activities that support the development of emotional well being and resilience
* Activities that allow children to explore and value, through story and play, their relationship to time and place
* Activities that encourage children to think and act cooperatively, empathetically and sustainably

Understanding and using technology

* Children explore how technology extends their ability to do things, e.g. making knitting needles extends what is possible with finger knitting, scissors cut paper more accurately than folding and tearing

* Children explore the relationship between tools and material, e.g. trying to cut felt with paper scissors
* Children learn to choose appropriate technology for a task, making tools they need to achieve a task, e.g. the difference between a mallet and a hammer, wooden peg, nail and screw, etc .
* Children reflect on how well a technology they have selected and used achieved its purpose
* Children learn to use specialist equipment for specific purposes and compare results with informal or ad hoc devices, e.g. 'kitchen-sink' science, hose-pipe rainbows compared to a prism, etc.
* Children learn to work safely with sharp tools and manage real-life risks with appropriate strategies

Activities could include:

* Outdoor and indoor play involving co-operation, balance, climbing, hoops, balls, etc.
* Using garden tools, including trowels, spades, wheelbarrows
* Card weaving, felting, finger-knitting, sewing, peg loom and use of a variety of media, etc.
* Making simple equipment, e.g. knitting needles, peg looms, reed or quill pens, etc.
* Story of items used in school, e.g. crayons, pencils, musical instruments
* Variety of creative work and forms of expression. The technology of communication from writing, reading, images, diagrams, graphs and tables
* Clear observation, records and exposition – analysis of results: did I find out what I wanted to know, what evidence do I have for my conclusion?
* Designing presentations, experiments and demonstrations

Classes 7 to 9

By this age, the sense of 'personal space' has become strong enough for pupils to begin to recognise and learn to respect the space of others, including their 'creative space'. Drama, eurythmy and presentations to others also help to develop a feeling for an audience and ability to see a situation from more than one viewpoint. Young people at this age also begin to explore more consciously the themes and values suggested previously and, in addition:

* Learn to understand the basis which continues through to modernism, i.e. Renaissance/ Reformation individualism and the (so-called western) Enlightenment, the development, especially in the UK, of materialism (Francis Bacon, Puritanism and the Civil War, agrarian & industrial revolution) and banking systems form Italian city states to German finance houses etc) alongside mechanisation and the growth of industrial centres; World War 1 as the first truly industrial war (this theme to developed more fully in the upper school)
* The development of personal creativity (from the studio system to single individual artists, baroque composers copying and borrowing from one another to the 'unique individual voice' of musicians from the Classical Period onwards)
* Representation through commissioning of portraits
* Legal questions including 'intellectual property rights' and plagiarism/piracy. The unique experience of a concert or other performance; the differences between this and its recording (e.g. what is being paid for when someone pays for downloading, or streaming music and the idea of 'getting music free')

* Creating plans: intention and implementation – what is a template? Mind mapping
* Tools and machines related to the human being and as extended capacities (e.g. limb joints and levers, why a garden fork usually has four prongs etc); gun powder; Jethro Tull and the seed drill; mechanical weaving and spinning; steam pumps, etc.
* Malthus, Adam Smith and the concept of natural selection (the story of Baron Gaspard de Prony and the division of labour; Herman Hollerith and the punched-card; Henry Ford, etc.)
* Activity and friendship circles – co-operation, compromise, community – the nature of 'social networking'; appropriate protection and cyber-bullying
* Creating posters, 'cartoons' designed to persuade (e.g. those of the Civil War period); editing (including the use and limitations of spelling and grammar checks , typesetting, publishing, etc.)
* Utilising online or computer-based reference sources (e.g. how authoritative is Wikipedia?), translation and similar applications
* Presentation of data; spreadsheets and all types of chart
* Computing: from fingers and stones to numbers; the abacus; Napier's 'bones' (make and use); Blaise Pascal's 1642 calculator (cogs and levers); Lord Byron, Lady Lovelace and William Babbage (the analytical engine/ difference engine); the slide rule, etc.
* Circuits and the on/off switch; solid geometry, nets, scale and algebra; binary logic (e.g computer science unplugged: www.csunplugged.org)
* Introduction to QWERTY (and its history) and touch-typing

There is an inevitable overlap between the above and Classes 9 to 12.

Classes 9 to 12

As should be clear from the foregoing, technology is not a process that can be separated from the human beings who bring it about; nor is it merely about producing artefacts. There are several dimensions and these should to be taken into account through the curriculum. They are both an extension and intensification of what has been covered previously:

* The natural dimension involving scientific, engineering and ecological perspectives
* The human dimension involving anthropological, physiological, psychological and aesthetic perspectives
* The social dimension involving economics, sociology, politics, cultural history, legal and ethical aspects

Division of labour has become a sine qua non for modern developed societies and technology has thus become the concern of specialists and engineers. However increasing environmental problems have led to a greater awareness of the human and social implications and to the realisation that a multi-dimensional, integrated concept of technology is needed. The isolation of the different specialisms makes it essential to attempt a reintegration of technology as a whole. The evolution of technology comes about through the human being's innate capacity for development.

Technology lessons build on the whole lower school involvement with materials, crafts, social, historical and economic studies. Key subjects include learning about farming and house building in Class 3, and the geography curriculum from Class 4 on which explores human economic relationships to the local environment and its natural resources and the links between regions around the world. History lessons show the significance of technological discoveries for social, economic and cultural developments in a wide range of fields (navigation, energy production and use, weapons, means of communication, farming, raw materials, trade, etc.). Craft and handwork lessons throughout the school also form a practical and experiential basis for understanding technology.

The Class 9 physics main-lesson is oriented towards primary technology and will have provided, among other things, a history of technology by means of a few examples (e.g. combustion engines, telephone, turbines, etc.). Technology as such has some quite specific pedagogical tasks to fulfil, namely to school accurate observation, practical thought processes and social awareness. The chemistry curriculum too provides an understanding of substances, materials and their production and application to technology, especially petrochemical and fossil fuels.

Work experience provides opportunities to see industrial and agricultural processes at work. A topic for study in technology lessons might be to investigate a nearby factory, including discovering the firm's commercial profile and depicting the production process including preliminary phases (purchase of parts and material) and subsequent tasks (advertising, marketing, selling). In their social and industrial work-experience projects the pupils will gain direct experiences of the social aspects of work and its results. Lessons can also take the form of excursions to power stations, recycling plants, water reservoirs, mines, etc. Such visits are best preceded by and followed up with detailed discussion. The use of modern media such as film and video is especially suitable in the high-tech realm. Many industries provide excellent information on their technology.

Classes 9 and 10

These lessons are intended to provide life experience rather than exact knowledge.

> *It is important during this age to introduce to the students the world outside, so that they come to grips with and understand life as such ... Our curriculum should be such that it allows the children to become practical in life; it should connect them with the world ... It is, therefore, necessary to give ... lessons in mechanics – not only in theory, as in physics, but practical mechanics, leading to the making of machines.*[1]

An overview of what the pupils have learnt in handwork and craft lessons (woodwork, etc.) combined with theoretical concepts from physics and mathematics will help students develop in a holistic way. Technologies throughout human history should also be discussed.

In information technology there are four prime aspects which we have touched on previously, and which now need to be secured throughout the Upper School:

* Basic computer literacy: word processing, typing and the use of software to produce, edit, store and retrieve text; using databases, spreadsheets, graphics, desktop publishing, etc. The use of the computer as an instrument in support of other tasks (including what is the

internet and happens when an email is sent?)
* An understanding of the basic principles of information systems in relation to the history of information storage (e.g. going back to the origins of writing and looking at its cultural significance); understanding how hardware and software relate; how software programs are designed and how file systems work; safe working practices and legal aspects such as copyright; firewalls, internet security (bugs, spam and hacking)
* The social, cultural and personal influence of computers, including both the time-saving, liberating aspects as well as the possible negative, obsessional and anti-social aspects. Economic questions such costing and how 'hi-tech' companies are financed (perhaps including why an expensive mobile phone handset might be given away 'free')
* What's inside the box? – the 'race to the smallest', fundamentals of programme writing (e.g. using Raspberry-pi or other devices)

Content suggestions include:

* Spinning wool, flax and cotton
* Weaving using various types of loom
* The textile industry
* Production of man-made textiles
* Soap production
* Water wheels and water pumps
* Turbines: high, medium and low-pressure turbines
* The screw and its many applications
* Henry Morse and the telegraph
* Icons and markers
* Online learning programme, such as INGOTS
* Evaluation criteria for information sources

Classes 11 and 12

Technology now deals with two very important realms: power/energy on the one hand (e.g. the electricity industry) and substance/material on the other (e.g. paper manufacture). Technology in earlier classes started with traditional technologies; in Class 11 and 12 everyday technology needs to be explored and the principles of how they work explored. So far as possible, this should include cutting edge technologies of all kinds, some of which will be introduced by the students themselves.

* End of course project could include a major multi-media element utilising skills and capabilities learned so far
* Power stations and the energy industry (water, wind, calorific and nuclear)
* From steam to internal combustion the jet engine and rockets
* Automobile mechanics and basic maintenance
* A study of the qualities of flowing water
* Paper manufacture
* Bookbinding and use of cardboard (see handwork in Class 11)
* Algorithms, artificial intelligence and John Searle's 'Chinese Room'
* George Boole and Boolean logic
* Alan Turing and the enigma machine
* John von Neuman and 'Neuman architecture'
* Tim Berners-Lee and the world wide web
* Reproductive media, particularly digital printing; image and reality (Photoshop, image manipulation and its influence on body image)
* Using graphics and animations, 'mixing' sounds and combining visual, sound and other media effects for a specific purpose
* Deconstructing the computer, component manufacture and implications (e.g. value and supply of raw materials); recycling parts

* Radio signals and television
* Fossil fuels, what is 'sustainable' energy?
* Chemical technology and artificial fibres including natural fibres and artificial fibres made from natural materials: (celluloid, resins, etc.)
* Semi-synthetic products (classical resins)
* Fully synthetic materials (polymers, plastics), e.g. from natural rubber to synthetic rubber
* Environmental and recycling problems: quality controls (soil, water, air)
* Illustration of cascades and fractals, path curves and chaos theory
* Technology companies such as Microsoft, Apple, Google, Facebook
* Mobile devices, microwaves

References

Foreword

1. Translated into English and modified for the English-speaking world by Eileen Hutchins and Tilda von Eiff. This may be a belated moment to name and thank Tilda von Eiff, whose name never appeared in the SSF editions. As, at time of going to press, she is still hale and hearty, the editors take this opportunity to thank her for her contribution.
2. *Steiner Waldorf Education in the UK, aims methods and curriculum*, ed. M. Rawson, SSF, 1997.

1. Introduction to the Tasks and Content of the Steiner-Waldorf Curriculum

1. See e.g. Newman, H.H. Freman, F.N and Holzinger, K.J. classic study of *Twins*, University of Chicago, 1937; Plomin, R and Daniels, D, *Why are children in the same family so different from one another?* OUP for the International Epidemiological Association 2011; Maslow, A. *Towards a Psychology of Being*, New York, 1999; Jensen, P. *Ignite the Third Factor*, Thomas Allen, 2008
2. Steiner, R., *Occult Science*, p250, RSP 1969.
3. Steiner, R, *Human Values in Education*, August 21st 1924, Arnheim
4. See Alexander, R, (ed), *Children, their World, their Education: Final report and recommendations of the Cambridge Primary Review*, CUP and Routledge 2010
5. Ibid, What is Primary Education for, Chapter 12
6. Pring, R and Hayward, G, papers for the independent Nuffield Review of 14–19 Education www.nuffield14-19review.org.uk
7. This is an explicit requirement for schools in England and Wales, see for example: https://www.gov.uk/government/uploads/system/uploads/attachment_data/file/283014/Independent_school_registration.pdf
8. Steiner, R, *A Social Basis for Education*, 11th May–1st June 1919, Stuttgart
9. A survey in Germany put the question: "What should national educational policy prioritise: the encouragement of high achievement by a minority or equal opportunities for all?"; 82% chose equality for all. (Spiegel 22-12-97, p34). Similar research for the UK is not known, but we would hope for a similar result.
10. See Steiner, R., *Intuitive Thinking as a Spiritual Path: A Philosophy of Freedom*, 1995, and *Theosophy: An Introduction to the Spiritual Processes in Human Life and in the Cosmos*, 1994, both published by Anthroposophic Press, for an introduction to anthroposophy. For an introduction to his educational ideas see *The Education of the Child* and *The Child's Changing Consciousness and Early Lectures on Education*, 1996 and *Waldorf Education*, 1996, both AP.
11. Steiner, R., *Anthroposophical Leading Thoughts*, p11, RSP 1985.
12. Steiner, R., *Theosophy*, p25, AP 1994.
13. See Georgy S. Levit: *Biogeochemistry, Biosphere, Noosphere: The Growth of the Theoretical System of Vladimir Ivanovich Vernadsky* (1863-1945).
14. Steiner, R., *Theosophy*, p49, AP 1994.
15. Ibid, p44.
16. Ibid, p45.
17. Steiner, R., *Rudolf Steiner in the Waldorf School, Lectures and Addresses to Children, Parents and Teachers*, p79, AP 1996.

2. The Stages of Development in Relation to the Curriculum

1. See Avison, K.A., *A Handbook for Waldorf Class Teachers*, section on School Readiness, SSF.
2. See Engel, S., *The Stories Children Tell*, 1995 and Whitehead, M., *Language and Literacy in the Early Years*, 1997.
3. See Wells, G., *The Meaning Makers*, 1987.
4. Steiner, R., *A Social Basis*, SSF 1994.

3. The Steiner-Waldorf Approach

1. Steiner, R., *Practical Advice to Teachers*, p163.
2. For examples of record keeping see Avison, K.A., *A Handbook for Class Teachers*, SSF.
3. Steiner, R., *The Younger Generation*, p148, AP 1967.

4. Evaluation and Assessment

1. Drummond, M.J., quoted in Mepham and Rawson: see below.
2. See Dweck, C.S. Self Theories, *Their Role in Motivation, Personality and Development*, Philadelphia 1999 and (same author) *Mindset,* Random House, 2006. Black, P. William, D. *Inside the Black Box,* Nelson, 1999 and (same authors et al) B. *Assessment for Learning: Putting it into Practice,* OUP, 2003.
3. Hughes, G. Et al, *Implementing Ipsative Assessment,* Institute of Education, 2011.
4. See for example: http://www.cbi.org.uk/business-issues/education-and-skills/in-focus/employability/ Employability covers a broad range of non-academic or softer skills and abilities which are of value in the workplace. It includes the ability to work in a team; a willingness to demonstrate initiative and original thought; self-discipline in starting and completing tasks to deadline.
5. See, e.g: Kolitko-Rivera, M. *Rediscovering the later version of Maslow's hierarchy of needs: Self-transcendence and opportunities for theory, research, and unification* http://www.academia.edu/3089048/Rediscovering_the_later_version_of_Maslows_hierarchy_of_needs_Self-transcendence_and_opportunities_for_theory_research_and_unification
6. See *Pupil Assessment and Record Keeping in Steiner Waldorf Schools*: an information pack compiled by Trevor Mepham and Martyn Rawson, SSF 1998.
7. Bloom, B. S.; Engelhart, M. D.; Furst, E. J.; Hill, W. H.; *Taxonomy of educational objectives: The classification of educational goals.* Handbook I: Cognitive domain. New York, 1956.
8. See, Erwin, L. Sanderson, H; *One Page Profiles with children and young people, http://www.helensandersonassociates.co.uk/media/38450/oppinschlguide.pdf*

5. Leadership and Management

1. Husserl, E. The Crisis of European Sciences and Transcendental Phenomenology: An Introduction to Phenomenological Philosophy, Cambridge 2012 (original German edition 1936, first English translation 1954).
2. See Steiner, R., *Towards Social Renewal*, RSP 1977. See also 'Working together in a Waldorf School', a special number of the journal *Paideia*, SSF 1999, which contains a series of articles on the subject in relation to school organisation.
3. Steiner, R., *The Threefold Social Order and Educational Freedom in the Renewal of the Social Organism*, RSP 1985.
4. Ibid.
5. Steiner, R., *The Foundations of Human Experience*, p30.
6. Ibid, p30.
7. See, for example, Gronn, P. *Distributed Properties: A New Architecture for Leadership* in Educational management and Administration, Vol 28, No 3, 2000; MacBeath, J. Dempster, N. *Connecting Leadership and Learning: Principles and Practice,* Routledge 2009; www.ascl.org/publications/educational-leadership *When Teachers Run the School.*
8. With acknowledgement to Jonathan Wolf-Phillips of New Leadership Ltd. See www.new-leadership.com
9. August 17, 1923, Ilkley.
10. See Gladstone, F., *Republican Academies*, SSF 1997, for a compilation of Steiner's comments on self-management and pedagogical study in Waldorf schools. See also Manfred Leist, *Parent Participation in the Life of a Waldorf School*, AWSNA.
11. See Steiner, R., *The Foundations of Human Experience*, pp45 to 48. See also the author's article, "What is the Spirit of the School Trying to Tell Us", in *Paideia* No. 16, April 1998.
12. See Steiner, R., *The Renewal of the Social Organism*, published in *Paideia* No. 16. *Freie Schule und Dreigliederung*, 1919.

6. Early Years Care and Education

1. Smilansky, S., *Sociodramatic Play: Its relevance to behaviour and achievement in school, in children's play and learning.* Klugman and Smilansky, ed. New York Teachers' Press, 1990.

7. Horizontal Curriculum

1. Steiner, R., *The Renewal of Education,* April 24, 1920.
2. Steiner, R., *The Foundations of Human Experience*, Lecture 1, AP 1996.
3. Steiner, R., *Soul Economy and Waldorf Education*, Lecture of 1/1/1923, AP 1986.
4. Steiner, R., ibid, Lecture of January 3,1922.
5. Steiner terms puberty *Erdenreife* which literally means 'ripe for the earth' or 'earth maturity'. This expression conveys the sense of a readiness to experience the full forces of earthly existence.
6. Steiner, R., *Soul Economy and Waldorf Education*, Lecture of January 1922, AP 1986.
7. Steiner, R., Müller-Wiedemann, H., *Mitte der Kindheit*, Stuttgart, 1989, p119.
8. Steiner, R., *A Modern Art of Education*, Lecture of August 15, 1923, RSP 1981.
9. Steiner, R., *A Modern Art of Education*, Lecture of August 15, 1923, RSP 1981.
10. Steiner, R., *Practical Advice to Teachers*, RSP 1976.
11. Piaget, J., *Theories and Methods of Modern Education*, Frankfurt, 1974, p3.
12. The original German curriculum incorporates Steiner's suggestion that the period of German Classical Literature and in particular the biographies of Goethe and Schiller were appropriate for Class 9. Here the emphasis is on the friendship between these two outstanding personalities, a friendship that went beyond mere sympathy but had profounder sources. The key element was the mutual spiritual recognition which each found inspiring. There is no obvious parallel in English literature. The motif of a friendship which both inspires and yet leaves free is so crucial to this age, that other opportunities must be found within the curriculum to awaken this ideal.
13. Steiner, R., *Conferences with the Teachers of the Waldorf School in Stuttgart*, meeting of 17/6/1921, SSF 1986-1989.

Part II

8. Introduction

1. See the bibliography for the full references to these basic works.
2. Steiner, R., *A Modern Art of Education*, op. cit., August 1923, at an exhibition of work by the pupils.
3. Steiner, R., *Practical Advice to Teachers*, op. cit., lecture of September 5, 1919.
4. From notes written down by Rudolf Steiner and quoted by J. Tautz in Lehrerbewusstsein im 20. Jahrhundert, Dornach 1995, p.116.

9. Arithmetic and Mathematics

1. Baravalle, H. von, *Methodische Gesichtspunkte für den Aufbau des Rechenunterrichts and Waldorfschul plan*, (Mathematics Teaching and the Waldorf School Plan) Stuttgart, 1984.
2. Schuberth, E., 'Wie Können Wir durch den Mathematik-unterricht erzieherisch wirken?', in *Erziehungskunst* Book 4, 1976.
3. Ibid.
4. Ulin, B., *Finding the Path: Themes and Methods for the Teaching of Mathematics in a Waldorf School*, AWSNA, 1991.
5. Steiner, R., *Soul Economy and Waldorf Education*, op. cit., lecture of December 31, 1921.
6. Ulin, B., *Finding the Path*, op. cit.
7. Steiner, R., *Discussions with Teachers* op. cit., discussion of August 25, 1919.
8. Steiner, R., *The Kingdom of Childhood* op. cit., lecture of August 16, 1924.
9. Steiner, R., *Three Lectures on the Curriculum* op. cit., second lecture of September 6, 1919.
10. Some of these attainment targets differ, usually by a year from those in R. Jarman's recent book *Teaching Mathematics in Rudolf Steiner Schools for Classes I – VIII*, Hawthorn Press. The Curriculum Research Group see Jarman's summary as more appropriate for possible teaching content, whereas the checklists given here are intended to be a minimum attainment for most children within the normal ability range.
11. Schuberth, E., *Der Mathematikunterricht*. op. cit., p 159.
12. Brater, M., Munz, C., *Die Pädagogische Bedeutung der Buchführung*, op. cit., p199.
13. Steiner, R., *Conferences with Teachers*, op. cit., Vol 4, meeting of March 30, 1923.

10. Art Studies

1. From notes of a lecture given at a conference on art and education at the Waldorf School, March 1923. This translation is taken from, Jüneman, M. and Weitmann, F., *Drawing and Painting in Rudolf Steiner Schools*, Hawthorn Press, 1994.
2. An introduction to this theory can be found in the book by Jüneman and Weitman quoted above. This book gives a most comprehensive account of the practice and theory of painting and drawing in Steiner Waldorf education.
3. Steiner, R., *Conferences with the Teachers*, op. cit., meeting of November 15, 1920.
4. Steiner, R., *The Child's Changing Consciousness*, op. cit., lecture of April 19, 1924.
5. Jüneman and Weitmann, op. cit., p46.
6. Steiner, R., *Conferences with the Teachers*, op. cit., meeting of February 5, 1924.
7. Translated from *Methodische Grundlagen zur Anthrosopie* (GA 30, Dornach 1989, Introduction).
8. Jüneman and Weitmann, op. cit.
9. Kranich, E-M., *Formenzeichnung*, Stuttgart 1985, p30.
10. Kandinsky, V., *Der Blaue Reiter*, Munich, 1979.
11. It is very difficult to describe form drawings in words and considerations of (a different kind of) space prevent the reproduction of drawn examples. The reader is advised to refer to the illustrated booklet, *Formdrawing*, by Arne Breidvik, SSF Resource Books, reprint 1999.
12. Bühler, E., *Formenzeichnung. Die entwicklung des Formensinns in der Erziehung*, Stuttgart 1985, p158.

12. Crafts

1. Steiner, R., Basel Course 1920.
2. Eggleston, John (ed.) *Learning Through Doing: A national enquiry into the value of creative practical education in Britain*, 1999, p5.
3. See report by Rawson, M., *Learning to Work, Working to Learn*, SWSF, 1997.
4. Quoted in Mitchell, D., and Livingston, P., *Will-developed Intelligence*, AWSNA, 1999, p9.
5. Steiner, R., *Education of Adolescence*, lecture of June 15, 1921, p.71
6. Steiner, R., *Education of Adolescence*, lecture of June 14, 1921, p. 53

13. English Language and Literature

1. Skillen, N., "The Uses of Orality", in *Steiner Education* Vol. 32, No. 2, SSF, 1998.
2. Steiner, R., *The Renewal of Education*, lecture of 20th April 1920, SSF, 1981.
3. More detailed advice on the cultivation of oral skills and the introduction of writing and reading can be found in Avison, K., *A Handbook for Class Teachers*, SSF, 1995, and Rawson and Masters, *Towards Creative Teaching*, SSF, 1997.
4. Steiner, R., *The Renewal of Education*, op. cit. Lecture of May 4, 1920.
5. Steiner, R., *Three Lectures on the Curriculum*. Lecture of September 6, 1919, SSF, 1991.
6. Kainz, F., *The Psychology of Language*, Vol. 4. Stuttgart 1967, p52.
7. See Steiner, R., *The Renewal of Education*, op. cit. Lecture of May 5, 1920.
8. See Steiner, R., *The Kingdom of Childhood*, lecture August 15, 1924, RSP, 1982, also *The Renewal of Education*, op. cit. Lecture of August 28, 1920.
9. Steiner, R., *The Child's Changing Consciousness and Waldorf Education*. Lecture of April 18, 1923, AP, 1996.
10. The statements come from the lecture cited above, p94, AP, 1996.
11. Steiner, R., *Three Lectures on the Curriculum*. Lecture of September 6, 1919. SSF, 1991.
12. Ibid.
13. Steiner, R., *Waldorf Education for Adolescents*. Lecture of June 15, 1921. SSF, 1993.
14. Ibid.
15. Steiner, R., *The Child's Changing Consciousness*, op. cit. Lectures of April 17 and 18, 1923.
16. Rather than clutter the text with references to available reference material, a comprehensive bibliography for each subject is given at the end of the book.
17. Steiner, R., *The Renewal of Education*, op. cit. Lecture of May 4, 1920.
18. One of the best examples of this approach is described by Michael Rose in "Towards a Living Grammar" in *Paideia*, No. 17, September 1998, SSF. A series of articles in *Paideia*, No. 14, may also be of interest.
19. Steiner, R., *Practical Advice to Teachers*, op. cit. Lecture of August 25, 1919.
20. Ibid.
21. Steiner, R., *Waldorf Education for Adolescents*, op. cit. Lecture of June 15, 1921.
22. Steiner, R., *Practical Advice to Teachers*, op. cit. Lecture of August 26, 1919.

23. See Bibliography for anthologies of suitable poetry.
24. Steiner, R., *Practical Advice to Teachers*, op. cit. Lecture of August 25, 1919.
25. Steiner, R., *Conferences*, op. cit. June 19, 1924.
26. Steiner, R., *Three Lectures on the Curriculum*, op. cit.
27. Steiner, R., *Conferences*, op. cit., June 12, 1920.
28. Steiner, R., *Three Lectures on the Curriculum*, op. cit. Lecture of September 6, 1919.
29. Steiner, R., *Practical Advice to Teachers*, op. cit. Lecture of August 6, 1919.
30. Steiner, R., *Three Lectures on the Curriculum*, op. cit. Lecture of September 6, 1919.
31. Steiner, R., *Three Lectures on the Curriculum*, op. cit. Lecture September 6, 1919.
32. Ibid.
33. See Rawson and Masters, *Towards Creative Teaching*, op. cit., pp117-124, for examples of what is described here.
34. Steiner, R., *Conferences*, op. cit., April 28, 1922.
35. Ibid., 25th May 1923.
36. Steiner, R., Excerpts from *Two Education Lectures* from the German GA 302, typescript Z 418 in Rudolf Steiner House Library, London, lecture of June 22, 1922.

15. Foreign Languages

1. See Kiersch, J., Language Teaching in Steiner Waldorf Schools, FB 2014, chapter 3, and the Appendix by Norman Skillen, for an explanation of the importance of movement in language teaching.

16. Gardening

1. Peters, H. *Gardening in Schools*, SSF.

17. Geography

1. Brierley D.L., *In the Sea of Life Enisled: An introduction to the teaching of geography in Waldorf Education*, Antropos Akademi, Oslo, 1998.
2. Ibid, p13.
3. Ibid, p16.
4. Steiner, R., *Waldorf Education for Adolescence*, op. cit., lecture of June 14, 1921.
5. Steiner, R., *Practical Advice to Teachers*, op. cit., lecture of September 3, 1919.
6. See Steiner, R., *Waldorf Education for Adolescence*, op. cit., lecture of June 14, 1921.
7. Steiner, R., *Practical Advice to Teachers*, op. cit., lecture of September 2, 1919.

18. History

1. The outline of history given here is based on practice in British Steiner-Waldorf schools. However, more space has been given to the general principles than to the content, which will naturally vary in other countries.
2. Law, P., *Notes on Teaching History in the Upper School*, SSF, 1979.
3. Steiner, R., *Three Lectures on the Curriculum*, op. cit., lecture of September 6, 1919.
4. Steiner, R., *Practical Advice to Teachers*, op. cit, first lecture.
5. Lindenberg, Ch., *Teaching History*, AWSNA, 1989.
6. Law, P., *Notes on History Teaching in the Upper School*, SSF, 1979.
7. This is quoted in Lindenberg, Ch., *Teaching History*, 1989, p121.

20. Movement

1. See the following three reference books:
Brooking-Payne, K. 1996, *Games Children Play; How games and sport help children develop*. Hawthorn Press;
von Bothmer, F., *Gymnastic Education*, translated by Olive Whicher, available from Michael Hall School movement department or RSP;
van Haren, W., and Kischnik, R., *Child's Play* volumes 1 and 2, Hawthorn Press.

21. Music

1. Ronner, S., Was Bedeutet Lehrplan für die Musik?, *Lehrerrund brief*, No. 67, November 1999.
2. Ibid., p4.
3. Steiner, R., *Three Lectures on the Curriculum*, op. cit., third lecture of September 6, 1919.
4. Steiner, R., *Practical Advice to Teachers* op. cit., lecture of August, 23 1919.
5. A detailed compilation of the indications on music teaching by Rudolf Steiner can be found in Dr B. Masters, *Steiner Education and Music*, 1999. This curriculum draws on Brien Masters' music curriculum, except where indicated.
6. Riehm, P. M., 1989, in Beilharz, G. (ed) *Erziehen und Heilen durch Musik*. Trans. J. C.
7. Ibid., p83.
8. Ibid., p90.
9. Steiner made no mention of jazz in his curriculum indications, though he must have been aware of its existence. Some music teachers may feel it unworthy of consideration. Dr Brien Masters certainly dissociates himself from this

curriculum indication. The editor, however, feels it certainly should be included as it is a theme regularly taught in the Upper School and can be justified as such.

23. Physics

1. *Materialen zum Unterricht (Material for Teaching)*: Hersisches Institut für Bildungsplanung, Frankfurt, 1977.
2. Steiner, R., *A Theory of Knowledge Implicit in Goethe's World Conception*, AP, 1968; *Intuitive Thinking as a Spiritual Path: A Philosophy of Freedom*, AP, 1995.
3. Ibid., Chapter 5, p67.

25. Social Skills

1. We are indebted to Dr. Christoph Strawe for first drawing up a coherent study of all the social elements embedded within the existing Waldorf Curriculum. See Strawe, C., "Developing Social Skills, Social Understanding and Social Sensitivity in Steiner Waldorf Schools", in *Paideia* No. 16, SSF, April 1998.
2. Ibid. p32.
3. Ibid. p37.
4. See also Harrer, D., *Maths Lessons for Elementary Grades*, AWSNA, 1985, and Jarman, R., *Teaching Mathematics in Rudolf Steiner Schools for Classes I – VIII*, Hawthorn Books 1998.
5. Steiner, R., *Practical Advice to Teachers*, lecture 3, RSP, 1979.
6. Steiner, R., Lecture of October 12, 1919. German title *Soziales Verständnis aus geisteswissenschaftlicher Erkenntnis.*
7. Brierley, D. L., *In the Sea of Life Enisled. An introduction to the teaching of Geography in Waldorf education,* 1999, p119.
8. Steiner, R., *Waldorf Education for Adolescence.* SSF Publications, 1993, p38.
9. Steiner, R., *Conferences with the Teachers of the Waldorf School in Stuttgart.* Vol. 1, conference of March 8, 1920, p71.
10. Steiner, R., *Conferences with teachers...*, op. cit. Vol, 1, conference of September 25, 1919, p47.
11. Steiner, R., *Von Seelenrätseln* (GA 21) partly translated in *The Case for Anthropsophy.* Tr. Barfield, O., RSP, 1977.

Technology

1. Steiner, R., *Education for Adolescence*, lecture of June 16, 1921, pp. 83ff

Bibliography

The purpose of this bibliography is to provide a comprehensive overview of the primary and secondary literature related to the Steiner-Waldorf approach and curriculum. Obviously the range of literature that teachers can refer to in their research and preparation is vast. What has been included here are titles specifically relating to the Steiner-Waldorf approach in the English language, which, as far as we know, are in print.

Abbreviations

As used in the references and bibliography:

AP	Anthroposophic Press, New York
AWSNA	Association of Waldorf Schools of North America, New York
FB	Floris Books, Edinburgh
GA	Gesamptausgabe, German volume of Steiner's complete works. Given where no translation is known
RSP	Rudolf Steiner Press, London
SSF	Steiner Schools Fellowship Publications
WECAN	Waldorf Early Childhood Association of North America, New York
n.d.	No date known

1. Basic works on Anthroposophy by Rudolf Steiner

Intuitive Thinking as a Spiritual Path: A Philosophy of Freedom, AP, 1995 (GA4).

Theosophy: An Introduction to the Spiritual Processes in Human Life and in the Cosmos, AP, 1994 (GA9).

Towards Social Renewal, RSP, 1977 (GA23).

2. Educational works by Rudolf Steiner

The Foundations of Human Experience previously *Study of Man,* AP, 1996. 14 Lectures, Stuttgart, 1919. *Allgemeine Menschenkunde als Grundlage der Pädagogik. Pedagogischer Grundkurs* (GA293).

Practical Advice to Teachers, RSP, 1976. 14 Lectures, Stuttgart, 1919. *Erziehungskunst Methodisch-Didaktisches* (GA294).

Discussions with Teachers, AP, 1996. 15 Discussions, Stuttgart, 1919. *Erziehungskunst Methodisch-Didaktisches* (GA295).

Education as a Social Problem, AP, 1969. 6 Lectures, Dornach, 1919. *Die Erziehungsfrage als soziale Frage* (GA296).

The Spirit of the Waldorf School, AP, 1995. 6 Lectures, Stuttgart and Basel, 1919. *Die Waldorf Schule und ihr Geist* (GA297).

Rudolf Steiner in the Waldorf School – Lectures and Conversations, AP, 1996. Stuttgart 1919-1924. *Rudolf Steiner in der Waldorfschule, Vorträge und Ansprachen* (GA298).

The Genius of Language, AP, 1995. 6 Lectures, Stuttgart, 1919. *Geisteswissenschaftliche Sprach-betrachtungen* (GA299).

The Younger Generation, Educational and Spiritual Impulses for Life in the Twentieth Century, AP, 1984.

Conferences with Teachers, SSF, 1986, 1987, 1988, 1989. 3

Volumes 1919-1924. *Konferenzen mit den Lehrern der Freien Waldorfschule* (GA300).

The Renewal of Education, SSF, 1981. 14 Lectures, Basel, 1920. *Die Erneuerung der Pädagogisch-didaktischen Kunst durch Geisteswissenschaft* (GA301).

Education for Adolescents, previously *The Supplementary Course – Upper School and Waldorf Education for Adolescence,* AP, 1996. 8 Lectures, Stuttgart, 1921. *Menschenerkenntnis und Unterrichtsgestaltung* (GA302).

Balance in Teaching (first four lectures), Mercury Press, 1982 and *Deeper Insights into Education* (last three lectures), AP, 1988. 9 Lectures, Stuttgart, 1920, 1922, 1923. *Erziehung und Unterricht aus Menschenerkenntnis* (GA302a).

Soul Economy and Waldorf Education, AP, 1986. 16 Lectures, Dornach, 1921-22. *Die Gesunde Entwickelung des Menschenwesens* (GA303).

Waldorf Education and Anthroposophy I , AP, 1996. 9 Public lectures, various cities, 1921-22. *Erziehungs- und Unterrichtsmethoden auf anthroposophischer Grundlage* (GA304).

Waldorf Education and Anthroposopy II, AP, 1996. 9 Public lectures, various cities, 1923-24. *Anthroposophische Menschenkunde und Pädagogik* (GA304a).

The Spiritual Ground of Education, Garber Publications, 12 Lectures, 1 Special Lecture, Oxford 1922. *Die geistig-seelischen Grundkräfte der Erziehungskunst* (GA305).

The Child's Changing Consciousness and Waldorf Education, AP, 1996. 8 Lectures, Dornach 1923. *Die pädagogische Praxis vom Geischtspunkte geisteswissenschaftlicher Menschenerkenntnis* (GA306).

A Modern Art of Education, RSP, 1981 and *Education and Modern Spiritual Life*, Garber Publications, 1989. 14 Lectures, Ilkley, 1923. *Gegenwärtiges Geistesleben und Erziehung* (GA307).

The Essentials of Education, AP, 1997. 5 Lectures, Stuttgart, 1924. *Die Methodik des Lehrens und die Lebensbedingungen des Erziehens* (GA308).

The Roots of Education, AP, 1996. 5 Lectures, Bern, 1924. *Anthroposophische Pädagogik und ihre Voraussetzungen* (GA309).

Human Values in Education, RSP, 1971. 10 Public lectures, Arnheim, 1924. *Der pädagogische Wert der Menschenerkenntnis und der Kulturwert der Pädagogik* (GA310).

The Kingdom of Childhood, AP, 1995. 7 Lectures, Torquay, 1924. *Die Kunst des Erziehens aus dem Erfassen der Menschenwesenheit* (GA311).

3. General introduction to Steiner-Waldorf education

Barnes, H., Howard, A., Davy, D. and Leichter, H.J., *An Introduction to Waldorf Education*, Mercury Press.

Blunt, R., *Waldorf Education, Theory and Practice*, Novalis Press.

Carlgren, F., *Education Towards Freedom. Rudolf Steiner Education A Survey of the Work of Waldorf Schools throughout the World*, FB.

Childs, G., *Steiner Education in Theory and Practice*, FB.

Clouder, C. and Rawson, M., *Waldorf Education*, FB.

Edmunds, F., *Rudolf Steiner Education, The Waldorf School*, RSP.

Mattke, H. J. and Zick, S., *Waldorf Education World-Wide*, Rudolf Steiner College Bookstore, Rudolf Steiner Library & AWSNA.

Margulies, P., *Learning to Learn. Interviews with Graduates of Waldorf Schools*, Rudolf Steiner College Bookstore.

Nobel, A., *Educating Through Art*, FB.

Petrash, J., *Understanding Waldorf Education*, FB/Gryphon Books USA.

Waldorf Waldorf Waldorf, Published by Freunde der Erziehungskunst Rudolf Steiners/SSF. Exhibition Catalogue on occasion of the 44th Session and the International Conference on Education of UNESCO in Geneva.

Wilkinson, R., *Commonsense Schooling*, Robinswood Press.

Wilkinson, R., *The Spiritual Basis of Steiner Education*, Sophia Books.

4. The Waldorf curriculum

Rawson, M. (edited by), *Steiner-Waldorf Education in the UK: aims, methods and curriculum*, SSF.

Rawson, M. and Masters, B. (edited by), *Towards Creative Teaching*, FB.

Rawson, M. (edited by), *An Upper School Curriculum for the UK*, SSF.

Stockmeyer, M., *Rudolf Steiner's Curriculum for Waldorf Schools*, SSF.

5. Aspects of Steiner-Waldorf education: education studies, teaching skills, being a teacher

Aeppli, W., *Rudolf Steiner Education and the Developing Child*, AP.

Avison, K., *A Handbook for Waldorf Class Teachers*, SSF.

Barnes, H., *Religion in the Rudolf Steiner School,* Rudolf Steiner Library.

Chilton Pearce, J., *Evolution's End: Claiming the Potential of our Intelligence*, Rudolf Steiner Library.

Edmunds, F., *Renewing Education*, Hawthorn Press.

Ege, K., *An Evident Need of Our Times: Goals of Education at the Close of the Century*, Adonis Press.

Fentress Gardner, J., *Education in Search of the Spirit,* AP.

Finser, T. M., *Research: - Reflections and Suggestions for Teachers for Creating a Community of Research in Waldorf Schools*, AWSNA.

Finser, T. M., *School as a Journey, the 8-Year Odyssey of a Waldorf Teacher and His Class*, AP.

Furness, C. J., *The Creative Training of the Will in Education*, Rudolf Steiner Library.

Gabert, E., *Educating the Adolescent, Discipline or Freedom*, AP.

Harwood, A. C., *The Recovery of Man in Childhood*, AP.

Husemann, Dr. A. J., *Knowledge of the Human Being through Art, A Method of Anthroposophical Study*, Mercury Press.

Lissau, M., *The Temperaments and the Arts, Their Relation and Function in Waldorf Pedagogy*, Rudolf Steiner Library.

Maher, S. and Bleach, Y., *Putting the Heart Back into Teaching. A Manual for Junior Primary Teachers*, Rudolf Steiner College Bookstore.

McAllen, A. E., *Sleep, An Unobserved Element in Education*, Hawthorn Press.

Mitchell, D. (edited by), *Developmental Insights: Discussions Between Doctors and Teachers*, AWSNA.

Molt, E. and Murphy, C., *Emil Molt and the Beginnings of the Waldorf School Movement; Sketches from an Autobiography*, Floris Books.

Moffat, P. S., *Forward Toward What? For Ourselves and Our Children*, Rudolf Steiner Library.

Müller, H., *Reports Verses in Rudolf Steiner's Art of Education,* FB.

Piening, E. and Lyons. N., *Educating as an Art*, Rudolf Steiner Library.

Querido, R., *Creativity in Education*, Rudolf Steiner Library.

Rist, G. and Schneider, P., *Integrating Vocational and General Education: A Rudolf Steiner School (Case Study of the Hibernia School)*, Rudolf Steiner Library.

Schwartz, E., *Adolescence: The Search for the Self Weaving the Social Fabric of the Class,* Rudolf Steiner Library.

Schwartz, E., *Gratitude, Love, and Duty: Their Unfolding in Waldorf Education*, Rudolf Steiner Library.

Schwartz, E., *Millennial Child*, AP.

Schwartz, E., *Seeing, Hearing, Learning. The Interplay of Eye and Ear in Waldorf Education*, Rudolf Steiner Library.

Schwartz, E., *The Waldorf Teacher's Survival Guide,* Rudolf Steiner College Press.

Sloan, D., *Education and Values*, Rudolf Steiner Library.

Smit, J., *The Child, the Teachers, and the Community,* AWSNA.

Smit, J., *How to Transform Thinking, Feeling and Willing,* Hawthorn Press.

Smit, J., *Lighting Fires. Deepening Education Through Meditation*, Hawthorn Press.

Smit, J., *The Steps Toward Knowledge Which the Seeker for the Spirit Must Take*, AWSNA.

Soesman, A., *Our Twelve Senses*, Hawthorn Press.

Spock, M., *Teaching as a Lively Art*, AP.

Steiner, R., *A Talk to Young People*, Mercury Press.

Tautz, J., *The Founding of the First Waldorf School*, AWSNA.

Tautz, J., *The Meditative Life of the Teacher*, AWSNA.

Taylor Gatto, J., *Dumbing Us Down, The Hidden Curriculum of Compulsory Schooling*, AP.

Weihs, T., *The Curriculum as Healer*, Rudolf Steiner Library.

Wilkinson, R., *Commonsense Schooling*, Robinswood Press.

Wilkinson, R., *Spirit, Basis of Steiner Education*, RSP.

Zimmerman, H., *Speaking, Learning, Understanding the Art of Creating Conscious Conversation,* Lindisfarne Press.

6. Child development

Aeppli, W., *The Care and Development of the Human Senses*, FB.

Aeppli, W., *Rudolf Steiner Education and the Developing Child*, AP.

Anschütz, M., *Children and Their Temperaments*, FB.

Ayres, A. J., PhD., *Sensory Integration and the Child*, Rudolf Steiner College Bookstore.

Baldwin, R., Kahn, T., Masheder, M., Oldfield, L., Glöckler, M. and Meighan, R., *Natural Childhood The Practical and Holistic Guide for Parents of the Developing Child*, Gaia Books.

Baldwin, R., *You Are Your Child's First Teacher*, Celestial Arts.

Childs, G., *Understand Your Temperament! A Guide to the four Temperaments*, RSP.

Childs, G., *Your Reincarnating Child*, RSP.

Elkind, D., *The Hurried Child: Growing Up Too Fast Too Soon*, Perseus Books.

Frommer, E. A., *Voyage through Childhood into the Adult World*, Hawthorn Press.
Gardner, *Youth Longs to Know*, RSP.
Harwood, A. C., *The Way of a Child*, AP.
Holzapfel, W., MD, *Children's Destinies*, Mercury Press.
Kellog, R., *Analyzing Children's Art*, Rudolf Steiner College Bookstore.
Klocek, D., *Drawing from the Book of Nature*, Rudolf Steiner College Bookstore.
Klugman, E. and Smilansky, S., *Children's Play and Learning: Perspectives and Policy Implications*, Rudolf Steiner Library.
Koepke, H., *Encountering the Self, Transformation and Destiny in the Ninth Year*, AP.
Koepke, H., *On the Threshold of Adolescence, The Struggle for Independence in the Twelfth Year*, AP.
König, K., *Brothers and Sisters, The Order of Birth in the Family*, FB.
König, K., *Eternal Childhood*, Camphill Books.
Large, M., *Who's Bringing Them Up? Television and Child Development: How to Break the T.V. Habit*, Hawthorn Press.
Lievegoed, B., *Phases of Childhood*, FB.
Luxford, M., *Adolescence and its Significance for Those with Special Needs*, Camphill Books.
Meijs, Jeanne, *You and Your Teenager, Understanding the Journey*, FB.
Riera, M., PhD, *Uncommon Sense for Parents with Teenagers*, Rudolf Steiner College Bookstore.
Salter, J., *The Incarnating Child*, Hawthorn Press.
Schmidt, G., *Nutrition and Education*, Rudolf Steiner College Bookstore.
Schwartz, E., *Rhythms and Turning Points in the Life of the Child*, Rudolf Steiner College Bookstore.
Staley, B., *Between Form and Freedom, A Practical Guide to the Teenage Years*, Hawthorn Press.
Strauss, M., *Understanding Children's Drawings*, RSP.
Wilkinson, R., *The Temperaments in Education*, Rudolf Steiner College Bookstore.

7. Early Years

Britz-Crecelius, H., *Children at Play Using Waldorf Principles to Foster Childhood Development*, Rudolf Steiner College Bookstore.
Copple, R., *To Grow and Become*, AWSNA.
Eliot, J., *Let's Talk, Let's Play*, AWSNA.
Glas, N., MD, *Conception, Birth and Early Childhood*, AP.
Grunelius, E. M., *Early Childhood Education and the Waldorf School Plan*, Rudolf Steiner College Bookstore.
Heckman, H., *Nokken, A Garden for Children*, AWSNA.
Jaffke, F., *Work and Play in Early Childhood*, FB.
König, K., *The First Three Years of the Child*, FB.
Mathieson, A. (edited by), *the World of Childhood*, Antropos Forlag, Oslo.
Müller, B., *Painting with Children*, FB.
Neuschutz, K., *Children's Creative Play*, FB.
Paterson, J. and Bradley, P., *Beyond the Rainbow Bridge*, Michaelmas Press.
Pusch, R. (selected and edited by), *Waldorf Schools: Volume I, Kindergarten and Early Grades*, Mercury Press.
Pusch, R. (selected and edited by), *Waldorf Schools: Volume II, Upper Grades and High School*, Mercury Press.
Querido, R., *The Wonder of Childhood*, Rudolf Steiner College Bookstore.
Scott, A., *The Laughing Baby Remembering Nursery Rhymes and Reasons*, Rudolf Steiner College Bookstore.
Steiner, R., *The Poetry and Meaning of Fairy Tales*, Mercury Press.
Steiner, R., *Understanding Young Children. Excerpts from lectures by Rudolf Steiner Compiled for Kindergarten Teachers*, WECAN.
von Heydebrand, C., *Childhood, A Study of the Growing Child*, AP.
Willwerth, K., *Let's Dance and Sing Story Games for Children*, Mercury Press.
Zahlingen, B., *Plays for Puppets and Marionettes*, Rudolf Steiner College Bookstore.
zur Linden, W., *A Child is Born. Pregnancy, Birth: First Childhood*, RSP.

8. Teaching Resources

8.1 General

Mitchell, D., *Resource Material for Class Teachers – Grades K-8*, AWSNA.

8.2 Arts and Crafts

Auer, A., *Learning About the World Through Modelling*, AWSNA.
Collot d'Herbois, L., *Light, Darkness and Colour in Painting Therapy*.
Hart, F., *Art, the History of Painting, Sculpture, Architecture*, Rudolf Steiner Library
Howard, M., *Educating the Will*, AWSNA.
Loewe, H., *Basic Sculptural Modelling, Developing the will by working with pure forms in the first three grades*, AWSNA

Martin, M. (edited by), *Educating Through Arts and Crafts, An integrated approach to craft work in Steiner-Waldorf Schools*, SSF.

Müller, B., *Painting with Children*, FB.

Nobel, A., *Educating Through Art, The Steiner School Approach*, FB.

Petrash, C., *Earthwise/Earthways, Simple Environmental Activities for Young Children*, FB/Rudolf Steiner College Bookstore.

Strauss, M., *Understanding Children's Drawings, The Path to Manhood*, RSP.

Wildgruber, *Painting and Drawing in Waldorf Schools, Classes 1 to 8*, FB.

8.3 Drama

Bryer, E., *The Rainbow Puppet Theater Book*, WECAN.

Capel, E., *Collected Plays for Young and Old*, Temple Lodge Press.

Jaffke, C. (edited by), *Plays for the Lower and Middle School. Materials for Language Teaching at Rudolf Steiner (Waldorf) Schools*, Rudolf Steiner Library, Rudolf Steiner College Bookstore in US, available from Rudolf Steiner Bookshop, London.

Jaffke, C. (edited by), *More Plays for the Lower and Middle School. Materials for Language Teaching at Rudolf Steiner (Waldorf) Schools*, Rudolf Steiner Library, Rudolf Steiner College Bookstore in US, available from Rudolf Steiner Bookshop, London.

Ellersiek, W., *Nativity Plays for Children, Celebrating Christmas through Movement and Music*, FB.

Mitchell, D., *25 Plays, Inspired by Waldorf Teachers*, AWSNA.

Moore, R., *Five Plays for Waldorf Festivals*, SSF.

Pittis, A., *Pedagogical Theatre Dramaturgy and Performance Practice for the Lower and Middle School Grades*, AWSNA Publications, Rudolf Steiner College Bookstore.

Schwartz, E., *Plays for Children and Communities*, Rudolf Steiner College Bookstore.

Spence, R., *Clothing the Play, The Art and Craft of Stage Design*, AWSNA.

Wilkinson, R., *Plays for Puppets*, Rudolf Steiner College Bookstore.

8.4 English Language and Literature

See also: Poetry

Aiken, G., *Spotlight on Words*, Robinswood Press.

Harrer, D., *An English Manual for the Elementary School*, AWSNA.

Jaffke, C. (edited by), *Tongue Twisters and Speech Exercises. Materials for Language Teaching at Rudolf Steiner (Waldorf) Schools*. Rudolf Steiner College Bookstore for US, Rudolf Steiner Bookshop, London.

Jaffke, C. (edited by), *Rhythms, Rhymes, Games and Songs for the Lower School. Materials for Language Teaching at Rudolf Steiner (Waldorf) Schools*, Rudolf Steiner Library, Rudolf Steiner College Bookstore for US, Botton Bookshops for UK.

Jaffke, C. (edited by), *Poems for the Middle and Upper School. Materials for Language Teaching at Rudolf Steiner (Waldorf) Schools*, Rudolf Steiner Library, Rudolf Steiner College Bookstore for US, Rudolf Steiner Bookshop, London.

Jaffke, C. (edited by), *Riddles, Materials for Language Teaching at Rudolf Steiner (Waldorf) Schools*, Rudolf Steiner Library, Rudolf Steiner College Bookstore for US, Rudolf Steiner Bookshop, London.

Jaffke, C. (edited by), *Proverbs and Sayings. Materials for Language Teaching at Rudolf Steiner (Waldorf) Schools*, Rudolf Steiner Library, Rudolf Steiner College Bookstore for US, Rudolf Steiner Bookshop, London.

Kornberger, *The Power of Stories, Nurturing Children's Imagination and Consciousness*, FB.

Kovacs, C., *Parsifal*, FB.

MacKaye Barnes, C., *For the Love of Literature*, AWSNA.

Matthews, P., *Sing Me the Creation*, Hawthorn Press.

Meyer, R., *The Wisdom of Fairy Tales*, FB.

Nash-Wortham, M., *Phonic Rhyme Time*, Robinswood Press.

Schmid, R., *An English Grammar – The Language before Babel*, AWSNA Publications, Rudolf Steiner College Bookstore.

Schwartz, E., *Wish, Wonder, Surprise*, Rudolf Steiner College Bookstore.

Schwartz, E., *Why the Setting Sun Turns Red and Other Pedagogical Stories*, AWSNA.

Sloan, *Life Lessons, Reaching Teenagers Through Literature*, AWSNA.

Winter, D., *The Art and Science of Teaching Composition*, AWSNA.

Wyatt, I., *Hay for My Ox and other Stories*, FB.

8.5 Environmental Studies

Brierly, D. L., *In the Sea of Life Enisled*, Antropos Forlag.

Querido, R., *Geography and Man's Responsibility for the Earth*, Rudolf Steiner Library.

Querido, R., *On the Teaching of Geography: Excerpts from the Work of Rudolf Steiner*, Rudolf Steiner Library.

Schmutz, H-U., *Earth Science for Waldorf Schools*, AWSNA.

Wilkinson, R., *Plant Study*, Rudolf Steiner College Bookstore.

Wilkinson, R., *Teaching Geography*, Rudolf Steiner College Bookstore.

8.6 Eurythmy

Adams, F., *Eurythmy for the Elementary Grades*, AWSNA.
Down, R., *Leaving Room for the Angels – Eurythmy and The Art of Teaching*, AWSNA.
Lebret, E., *Allegro. Music for the Eurythmy Curriculum*, AWSNA.
Marquis, F., *Eurythmy for the Lower Grades*, ASWNA Publications.
Russell, L., *Kinesthetic Movement for Adolescents, Learning Through Movement and Eurythmy*, AWSNA.
Steiner, R., *Eurythmy as Visible Speech*, RSP (GA279).
Steiner, R., *An Introduction to Eurythmy*, AP.
Stoehr, S. and Oates, I., *Eurythmy An Art of Movement for Our Time*, Robinswood Press.
von Heider, W. M., *And Then Take Hands An Anthology of Rhymes, Poems, Stories, Legends and Plays for All Those Who Work With Children*, Rudolf Steiner College Bookstore.

8.7 Foreign Languages

Dahl, E., *Teaching Foreign Languages, A Practical Handbook for Steiner-Waldorf Teachers*, FB.
Forrer, E., *Andando Caminos, Teaching Spanish in Waldorf Schools*, AP
Jaffke, C., *Textes pour L'Enseignement des Langues Etrangères dans les Ecoles Waldorf, Recueil de Poèmes, Chants, Jeux et Comptines*, Rudolf Steiner College Bookstore in US, available from Rudolf Steiner Bookshop, London.
Jaffke, C., *Textes pour L'Enseignement des Langues Etrangères dans les Ecoles Waldorf, Poésies, Textes et Chansons*, Rudolf Steiner College Bookstore in US, available from Rudolf Steiner Bookshop, London.
Kiersch, J., *Language Teaching in Steiner-Waldorf Schools*, FB.
McCrary, K., *The Alpha Beta Book, An Introduction to Ancient Greek*, AWSNA.
Stott, M., *Foreign Language Teaching in Rudolf Steiner Schools, Guidelines for Class-Teachers and Language Teachers*, Hawthorn Press.
Stott, M., *Utopie, A Story from the 16th Century for the 7th Grade with Exercises*, Hawthorn Press.

8.8 Form Drawing and Writing

Dinklage, H., *Therapy Through Handwriting*, Mercury Press.
Gladich, J. and Sassi, P. A., *The "Write" Approach. Form Drawing for Better Handwriting*, Rudolf Steiner College Bookstore.
Kirchner, H., *Dynamic Drawing, Its Therapeutic Aspect*, Mercury Press.
Kutzli, R., *Creative Form Drawing, Workbooks 1, 2, & 3*, Hawthorn Press.
McAllen, A. E., *Teaching Children to Write; it's connection with the development of spatial consciousness in the child*, RSP.
Niederhauser, H. R. and Frohlich, M., *Form Drawing*, Mercury Press.

8.9 History and Mythology

Debusschere, E. B., *The Revelation of Evolutionary Events in Myths, Stories, and Legends*, AWSNA.
Harrar, D., *Chapters from Ancient History in Biographic Vein*, Mercury Press.
Harrar, D., *Roman Lives*, Mercury Press.
Kovacs, C., *Ancient Mythologies: India, Persia, Babylon, Egypt*, Wynstones Press.
Kovacs, C., *The Age of Discovery*, FB.
Kovacs, C., *The Age of Revolution*, FB.
Kovacs, C., *Ancient Greece*, FB.
Kovacs, C., *Ancient Rome*, FB.
Kovacs, C., *Norse Mythology*, FB.
Lindenberg, C., *Teaching History*, AWSNA.
Staley, B., *Hear the Voice of the Griot! Celebrating Africa in Geography, History and Culture*, AWSNA.
Veltman, W. F., *Hellas, Ancient Greek Culture in a New Perspective*, AWSNA.
Wilkinson, R., *Teaching History*, Rudolf Steiner College Bookstore.
Wyatt, I., *Homer's Odyssey*, FB.
Wyatt, I., *Norse Hero Tales*, FB.

8.10 Special Needs and Learning Support

Holtzapfel, W., *Children's Destinies*, Mercury Press.
Holtzapfel, W., *Human Organs*, FB.
Jantzen, C., *Dyslexia, Learning Disorder or Creative Gift?*, FB.
König, K., *Being Human: Diagnosis in Curative Education*, AP/Camphill Press.
Luxford, M., *Children with Special Needs*, FB.
McAllen, A. E., *The Extra Lesson*, Rudolf Steiner College Press.
McAllen, A. E., *The Listening Ear, The Development of Speech as a Creative Influence in Education*, Hawthorn Press.
Nash-Wortham, M. and Hunt, J., *Take Time*, Robinswood Press.
Steiner, R., *Education for Special Needs: The Curative Education Course*, RSP (GA317).
Uphoff, J. K., Gilmore, H. E. and Huber, R., *Summer Children*

Ready or Not for School, Rudolf Steiner College Bookstore.
Wilby, M. (Ed.), *Learning Difficulties, A Guide for Teachers*, Rudolf Steiner College Press.
Woodward, B. and Hogenboom, M., *Autism, A Holistic Approach*, FB.

8.11 Mathematics and Geometry

Anderson, H., *Active Arithmetic!*, AWNSA.
Allen, J., *Drawing Geometry, A Primer of Basic Forms*, FB.
Blackwood, J., *Mathematics in Nature, Space and Time*, FB.
Blackwood, *Geometry in Nature*, FB.
Edwards, L., *Projective Geometry*, FB.
Flansburg, S., *Math Magic*, Rudolf Steiner College Bookstore.
Franceschelli, A., *Algebra*, Mercury Press.
Franceschelli, A., *Mensuration*, Mercury Press.
Ghyka, M., *The Geometry of Art and Life*, Rudolf Steiner College Bookstore.
Harrer, D., *Math Lessons for Elementary Grades*, AWSNA.
Jarman, R., *Teaching Mathematics in Rudolf Steiner Schools. How to Become Holistic and Imaginative*, Hawthorn Press.
Keller-von Asten, H., *Encounters with the Infinite*, Walter Keller Press.
Pappas, T., *The Joy of Mathematics Discovering Mathematics Around You*, Rudolf Steiner College Bookstore.
Pappas, T., *More Joy of Mathematics Exploring Mathematics All Around You*, Rudolf Steiner College Bookstore.
Schuberth, E., *First Steps in Proven Geometry for the Upper Elementary Grades*, AWSNA.
Schuberth, E., *Geometry Lessons in the Waldorf School, Grades 4 and 5*, AWSNA.
Schuberth, E., *Mathematics Lessons for the Sixth Grade*, AWSNA.
Schuberth, E., *Teaching First Grade Math in Waldorf Schools*, Rudolf Steiner Library.
Schwaller de Lubicz, R. A., *A Study of Numbers A Guide to the Constant Creation of the Universe*, Rudolf Steiner College Bookstore.
Sheen, A. R., *Geometry and the Imagination*, AWSNA.
Sloan, D. (edited by), *The Computer Education: A Critical Perspective*, Rudolf Steiner Library.
Sloan, D., Fink, A. and Mitchell, D., *Computers and Waldorf Education*, AWSNA.
Swanson, H., *Geometry for the Waldorf High School*, AWSNA.
Ulin, B., *Finding the Path: Themes and Methods for the Teaching of Mathematics in a Waldorf School*, AWSNA.
van Bemelen, D. J., *A Drawing Lesson with Rudolf Steiner*, Mercury Press
von Baravalle, H., *Geometric Drawing and the Waldorf School Plan*, Rudolf Steiner College Bookstore.
von Baravalle, H., *The Geometry of Shadow Movements*, Mercury Press
von Baravalle, H., *The Teaching of Arithmetic and the Waldorf School Plan*, Rudolf Steiner College Bookstore.
von Baravalle, H., *The Waldorf Approach to Arithmetic Grades 1 – 8*, Rudolf Steiner College Bookstore.
Whicher, O., *Projective Geometry*, AP.

8.12 Movement

Brooking-Payne, K., *Games Children Play How Games and Sport Help Children Develop*, Hawthorn Press.
Bryer, E., *Movement for the Young Child, A Handbook for Eurythmists and Kindergarten Teachers*, WECAN
Cole, J., *Anna Banana 101 Jump Rope Rhymes*, Rudolf Steiner College Bookstore.
Ellersiek, W., *Gesture Games for Spring and Summer*, WECAN.
Ellersiek, W., *Gesture Games for Autumn and Winter*, WECAN.
Stark, D., *Coaching Team Sports in a Waldorf School*, AWSNA.
Taylor, M., *Finger Strings, A Book of Cat's Cradles and String Figures*, FB.
van Haren, W. and Kischnick, R., *Child's Play 1 & 2*, Hawthorn Press.
van Haren, W. and Kischnick, R., *Child's Play 3. Games for Life for Children and Teenagers*, Hawthorn Press.
von Heider, M., *Looking Forward. Games, Rhymes and Exercises to help Children develop their Learning Abilities*, Hawthorn Press.
Willwerth, K., *Let's Dance and Sing Story Games for Children*, Mercury Press.

8.13 Music

Foster, N., *The Mood of the Fifth, A Musical Approach to Childhood*, FB.
Frongillo, C., *The Importance of Being Musical*, AWSNA.
Jacobs, R., *Music for Young Children*, Hawthorn Press.
Jaffke C. and Maier, M., *Early One Morning. Folk Songs – Rounds – Ballads – Shanties – Spirituals and Plantation Songs – Madrigals*, Rudolf Steiner Library, Rudolf Steiner College Bookstore in US, Rudolf Steiner Bookshop, London.
Knierim, J., *Quintenlieder, Introduction to the Mood of the Fifth*, Rudolf Steiner College Bookstore.
Lebret, E., *Pentatonic Songs*, Rudolf Steiner College Bookstore.
Lebret, E., *Shepherd's Songbooks For Grades I, II and III of Waldorf Schools*, Rudolf Steiner College Bookstore.
Lebret, E., *Songs of Heaven and Earth*, Waldorf School

Association of Ontario.
Lewis, M., *When the Green Woods Laugh*, Association for Waldorf Education in London, Ontario.
Lindenberg, C-A., *The Child's Praise of the Seasons Festival Music to Sing*, Rudolf Steiner College Bookstore.
Lindenberg, C-A., *In Praise of the Seasons*, Rudolf Steiner College Bookstore.
Logan, A. (compiled and arranged by), *Building the Chorus*, Rose Harmony Association.
Logan, A., *One, Two, Three, for the Rose Lyre*, Rose Harmony Association.
Masters, B., *A Round of Rounds for the 52 Weeks of the Year*, Temple Lodge Press.
Masters, B. (ed.), *The Waldorf Song Book*, Floris Books.
Oram, P. and Forder, P., *A Change in the Year*, Starborn Books.
Willwerth, I., *Merrily We Sing, Original Songs in the Mood of the Fifth*, WECAN.
Society of Brothers, *Sing through the Day Ninety Songs for Younger Children*, Rudolf Steiner College Bookstore.
Society of Brothers, *Sing through the Seasons Ninety-9 Songs for Children*, Rudolf Steiner College Bookstore.

8.14 Poetry

Harrar, D., *Verses and Poems and Stories to Tell*, Mercury Press.
Kennedy, D., *The Waldorf Book of Poetry*, Living Arts.
Kennedy, D., *The Waldorf Book of Animal Poetry*, Living Arts.
Jaffke, C. (edited by), *Six Romantic Poets. Materials for Language Teaching at Rudolf Steiner (Waldorf) Schools*, Rudolf Steiner Library, Rudolf Steiner College Bookstore in US, Rudolf Steiner Bookshop, London.
Thomas, H., *A Journey Through Time in Verse and Rhyme*, FB.

8.15 Science

Bordear, S. P., *Volts to Hertz... the Rise of Electricity*, Rudolf Steiner College Bookstore.
Borjarsky, M., *A Demonstration Manual for Use in the Waldorf School Eighth Grade Chemistry Main Lesson*, Rudolf Steiner College Bookstore.
Davidson, N., *Sky Phenomena, A Guide to Naked-Eye Observation of the Stars*, Lindisfarne Books.
Edelglass, S. and D'Aleo, M., *Sensible Physics Teaching*, AWSNA.
Francis, K., *Rudolf Steiner and the Atom*, Adonis Press.
Graf, R. F., *Safe and Simple Electrical Experiments*, Rudolf Steiner Library.
Grohmann, G., *The Living World of Plants A Book for Children and Students of Nature*, AWSNA.
Grohmann, G., *The Plant, Vols. 1 & 2*, Bio-Dynamic Farming & Gardening Association.
Holdrege, C., *A Question of Genes*, AP.
Julius, F. H., *Fundamentals for a Phenomenological Study of Chemistry*, AWSNA.
Kennish, G., *Chemistry in Classes 7 and 8*, Wynstones School Publication.
Klocek, D., *Weather and Cosmos*, Rudolf Steiner College Bookstore.
Kolisko, E., M.D., *Zoology for Everybody, Volume 1: General*, Kolisko Archive Publications.
Kolisko, E., M.D., *Zoology for Everybody, Volume 2: Birds*, Kolisko Archive Publications.
Kolisko, E., M.D., *Zoology for Everybody, Volume 3: Mammals*, Kolisko Archive Publications.
Kolisko, E., M.D., *Zoology for Everybody, Volume 4: Protozoa*, Kolisko Archive Publications.
Kolisko, E., M.D., *Zoology for Everybody, Volume 5: Coelenterates, Echinoderms*, Kolisko Archive Publications.
Kolisko, E., M.D., *Zoology for Everybody, Volume 6: Tunicates, Molluscs*, Kolisko Archive Publications.
Kolisko, E., M.D., *Zoology for Everybody, Volume 7: Insects*, Kolisko Archive Publications.
Kolisko, E., M.D., *Zoology for Everybody, Volume 8: Amphibians, Reptiles*, Kolisko Archive Publications.
König, K., *Animals, An Imaginative Zoology*, FB.
Kovacs, C., *Botany*, FB.
Kovacs, C., *Geology and Astronomy*, FB.
Kovacs, C., *The Human Being and the Animal World*, FB.
Kovacs, C., *Muscles and Bones*, FB.
Kraul, W., *Astronomy for Young and Old, A Beginner's Guide to the Visible Sky*, FB.
Krupp, E. C., *Beyond the Blue Horizon Myths & Legends of the Sun, Moon, Stars, & Planets*, Rudolf Steiner College Bookstore.
Masters, B. (introduced and edited by), *Science in Education (Waldorf curriculum Studies Vol. 1)*, SSF/Lanthorn Press.
Mees, L. F. C., *Secrets of the Skeleton, Form in Metamorphosis*, AP.
Mirbt, C. R., *An Introduction to the Study of the Stars*, AWSNA.
Mitchell, D., *The Wonders of Waldorf Chemistry, Grades 7-9*, AWSNA.
Schultz, J., *Movement and Rhythms of the Stars A Guide to Naked-Eye Observation of Sun, Moon and Planets*, Floris Books/AP.
Trostli, R., *Physics is Fun!*, AWSNA.
von Baravalle, H., *Introduction to Astronomy in the Sixth Grade of the Waldorf Schools*, Rudolf Steiner College Bookstore.
von Baravalle, H., *Introduction to Physics and the Waldorf*

School Plan, Rudolf Steiner College Bookstore.

von Baravalle, H., *Introduction to Physics in Waldorf Schools The Balance Between Art and Science*, Rudolf Steiner College Bookstore.

von Baravalle, H., *On Teaching Physics and Mathematics*, Mercury Press.

von Mackenson, M., Dr., *A Phenomena-Based Physics Sound, Light, Heat Volume 1 for Grade 6* (edited by Mitchell, D. and translated by Petering, J.), AWSNA.

von Mackenson, M., Dr., *A Phenomena-Based Physics Sound, Light, Heat Volume 2 for Grade 7* (edited by Mitchell, D. and translated by Petering, J.), AWSNA.

von Mackenson, M., Dr., *A Phenomena-Based Physics Sound, Light, Heat Volume 3 for Grade 8* (edited by Mitchell, D. and translated by Petering, J.), AWSNA.

Wilkinson, R., *Teaching Physics*, Rudolf Steiner College Bookstore.

9. Organisation Development and School Community in Steiner-Waldorf Schools

Baldwin, S., *Nurturing Children and Families, One Model of a Parent/Child Program in a Waldorf School*, WECAN

Blanning, N., (ed.) *First Grade Readiness*, WECAN

Brüll, D., *The Waldorf School and Threefold Structure – The Embarrassing Mandate – About the Risk of Being an Anthroposophical Institution*, AWSNA.

Finser, T. M., *Finding Your Self, Supporting the Inner Life of the Teacher*, AWSNA.

Foster, N., (ed.) *Mentoring in Waldorf Early Childhood Education*, WECAN.

Gill, R. T., *School as a Living Entity*, AWSNA.

Gladstone, F., *Republican Academies*, SSF.

Koteen-Soule, H., (ed) *Professional Review and Evaluation in Waldorf Early Childhood Education*, WECAN.

Lehrs, E., *Republican, Not Democratic*, AWSNA.

Leist, M., *Parent Participation in the Life of a Waldorf School*, AWSNA.

McAlice, J., Engaged Community, *The Challenge of Self-Governance in Waldorf Schools*, AWSNA.

Mitchell, D. (edited by), *The Art of Administration*, AWSNA.

Mitchell, D. and Alsop D., *Economic Explorations*, AWSNA.

Muller, H., *Report Verses in Rudolf Steiner's Art of Education*, FB.

Murphy-Lang, C., *Developing the Observing Eye, Teacher Observation and Assessment in Early Childhood Education*, AWSNA.

Pietzner, C., *Handling Public Relations*, Rudolf Steiner College Bookstore.

Schaefer, C., *Partnerships of Hope, Building Waldorf School Communities*, AWSNA.

Spence, M., *A Context for a Renewed Economics*, AWSNA.

Spence, M., *Freeing the Human Spirit. The Threefold Social Order, Money and the Waldorf School*, AWSNA.

Zimmerman, H., *Speaking, Listening, Understanding*, Lindisfarne Press.

Steiner, R., *Awakening to Community*, RSP.

Lievegoed, B., *Developing Communities*, Hawthorn Press.

10. Journals

Economic Extracts The Economic Basis for Waldorf Education, AWSNA.

Multiculturalism in Waldorf Education, AWSNA.

Paideia, SSF.

Renewal: A Journal for Waldorf Education, AWSNA.

Research Bulletin, Waldorf Education Research Institute, Sunbridge College.

Waldorf Science Newsletter, AWSNA.

Index

Towards Creative Teaching

Notes to an Evolving Curriculum for Steiner Waldorf Class Teachers

Edited by Martyn Rawson and Kevin Avison

This wonderful resource book for Steiner-Waldorf class teachers offers ideas for planning, shaping and developing lessons for Classes 1 to 8.

Taking the Waldorf curriculum as its basis, and without being restrictive or prescriptive, this book comes out of a teachers' working group and provides helpful suggestions to both class teachers and subject specialists, adding to the richness and imagination of each teacher's own work.

The book is a truly comprehensive overview of all main-lesson and accompanying subjects, offering a wealth of guidance, knowledge and inspiration for Waldorf class teachers.

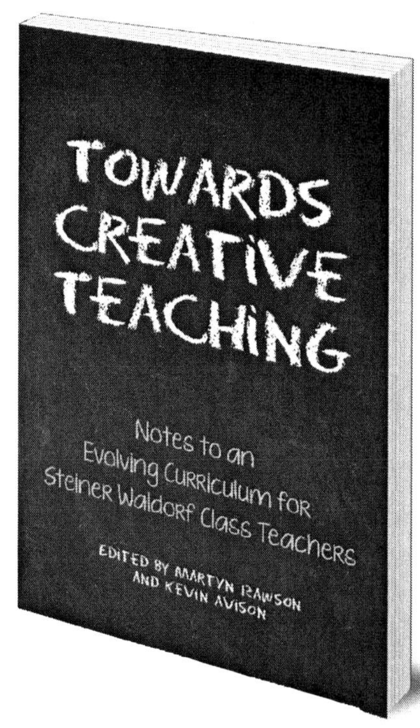